READING MODERN FICTION

THIRD EDITION

READING MODERN FICTION

THIRD EDITION

31 STORIES WITH CRITICAL AIDS

EDITED BY

WINIFRED LYNSKEY

PROFESSOR OF ENGLISH
PURDUE UNIVERSITY

CHARLES SCRIBNER'S SONS

NEW YORK

TO MY MOTHER AND FATHER

PREFACE

THE AIM of this book is threefold: to assemble a group of stories varying widely in theme and in form; to present the best modern writers of short fiction, both American and foreign; to give students stories they can enjoy. If we wish students to read good fiction outside the classroom, it seems witless to choose for their introduction to fiction stories which merely repel or bewilder them. The principle of enjoyment has been active, therefore, in this selection.

In the organization of this book, schematization has been avoided. Schematization is essentially artificial; it erects a barrier between the students and the story; and, it works harm to the stories it rigidly classifies. Henry James protested long ago against setting up artificial frontiers in the technique of fiction. Any good passage of fiction, he remarked, is narrative in its intention, and any good passage of dialogue is descriptive. Does not character determine action or incident? Does not action or incident illustrate character?

James asked these questions about the novel, but his comments have value for all fiction. They are especially pertinent today because of the many existing schemes for classifying short stories. How, indeed, does one separate character, action, symbol, and theme in a short story in order to classify? James contended that the only classification he could understand was the division of stories into those which had life and those which had not. It is hoped that the stories in this book can be classified as living.

The comments, questions, and analyses which accompany the book are not to be regarded as dogmatic interpretations of the stories. They are intended primarily to serve the student by directing his attention to details whose significance he might otherwise miss. When a student has learned, in Browning's phrase, that in good fiction a detail "means intensely," he is on his way to becoming a good reader. Aside from the formal analyses, the critical aids combine comment and question, as in a natural classroom discussion, and are specifically designed not to give the story away in advance of the reading. The book contains two formal analyses: a short analysis of a problem in Hemingway's "The Snows of Kilimanjaro," and a long, philosophical analysis of Mann's moral implications in "Mario and the Magician." For six other difficult stories, partial analyses have been included. Each "partial" analysis is intentionally so in order that the student may solve problems for himself. A partial analysis presents, in some detail, the approaches to a discussion of a story or of a story's chief problems. But it stops short of analyzing so completely that there is nothing left for a student to do.

The third edition of this anthology has sought to preserve the spirit and purpose of the original edition. The simplicity of the organization, retained in the third edition, gives the teacher freedom. It permits him to group the stories according to the purposes and abilities of a given class. He may wish to present first the function of plot through "The Outstation" and "The Hands of Mr. Ottermole." He may then undertake to show how the theme of a story is revealed through character in "The Valiant Woman," "Paul's Case," "A Good Man Is Hard to Find," and "First Confession;" through symbol in "First Love" and "The Man Who Missed the Bus." He may wish to group "Mario and the Magician," "The Secret Sharer," "The Bench of Desolation," and "The Second Tree from the Corner," and teach these stories as modern allegories. Or he may prefer to teach "Mario and the Magician" as an indictment of dictatorship when he presents some of the stories dealing with social problems: "Dry September," "Paul's Case," "The New Villa," and "The Passion of Lance Corporal Hawkins." He may wish to illustrate the function and power of irony through "They Weren't Going to Die" and "The Blue Hotel" or compare "The Snows of Kilimanjaro" and "The Second Death" as naturalistic and mystical studies of death. The teacher may thus organize his course according to his own plan.

I have received a good deal of counsel and assistance in the preparation of this book. I am indebted to many people: to Professor Joe Lee Davis of the University of Michigan for his criticism and advice; to many members of the Department of English of Purdue University for their suggestions, encouragement, and wisdom; to the Purdue Library staff: John Moriarty, director, and his assistants: Esther Schlundt, Margaret Sullivan, Eleanore Cammack, Mrs. Richard Crowder, and others; to Mrs. Ethel M. Hancock and Mrs. Jennie Bishop, who prepared the manuscript; to Mrs. Virgil Lokke, Mrs. Harold H. Watts, and Mrs. Bessie Mason, who read proof; and to the editorial staff of Charles Scribner's Sons for their unfailing kindliness and assistance.

My thanks are due also to the authors and publishers who generously gave me permission to reproduce copyrighted stories. Individual acknowledgments are made in the footnotes accompanying each story.

PURDUE UNIVERSITY   W. L.

CONTENTS

READING MODERN FICTION

THIRD EDITION

A TOOTH FOR PAUL REVERE

BY STEPHEN VINCENT BENÉT

STEPHEN VINCENT BENÉT (1898–1943), a distinguished novelist, poet, and writer of short stories, was born in Pennsylvania. He graduated from Yale in 1919 and received a Guggenheim award in 1926. *John Brown's Body*, a long narrative poem, won the Pulitzer Prize in 1929. Many of his short stories are contained in *Selected Works*, published in 1942.

Some say it all happened because of Hancock and Adams (said the old man, pulling at his pipe), and some put it back to the Stamp Act and before. Then there's some hold out for Paul Revere and his little silver box. But the way I heard it, it broke loose because of Lige Butterwick and his tooth.

What's that? Why, the American Revolution, of course. What else would I be talking about? Well, your story about the land down South that they had to plough with alligators reminded me.

No, this is a true story—or at least that's how I heard it told. My great-aunt was a Butterwick and I heard it from her. And, every now and then, she'd write it out and want to get it put in the history books. But they'd always put her off with some trifling sort of excuse. Till, finally, she got her dander up and wrote direct to the President of the United States. Well, no, he didn't answer himself exactly—the President's apt to be a pretty busy man. But the letter said he'd received her interesting communication and thanked her for it, so that shows you. We've got it framed, in the trailer—the ink's a little faded, but you can make out the man's name who signed it. It's either Bowers or Thorpe and he wrote a very nice hand.

A TOOTH FOR PAUL REVERE From *Selected Works of Stephen Vincent Benét*, published by Rinehart & Company, Inc. Copyright, 1937, by Stephen Vincent Benét.

You see, my great-aunt, she wasn't very respectful to the kind of history that does get into the books. What she liked was the queer corners of it and the tales that get handed down in families. Take Paul Revere, for instance—all most folks think about, with him, is his riding a horse. But when she talked about Paul Revere—why, you could just see him in his shop, brewing the American Revolution in a silver teapot and waiting for it to settle. Oh yes, he was a silversmith by trade—but she claimed he was something more. She claimed there was a kind of magic in that quick, skillful hand of his—and that he was one of the kind of folks that can see just a little bit farther into a millstone than most. But it was when she got to Lige Butterwick that she really turned herself loose.

For she claimed that it took all sorts to make a country—and that meant the dumb ones, too. I don't mean ijits or nincompoops—just the ordinary folks that live along from day to day. And that day may be a notable day in history—but it's just Tuesday to them, till they read all about it in the papers. Oh, the heroes and the great men—they can plan and contrive and see ahead. But it isn't till the Lige Butterwicks get stirred up that things really start to happen. Or so she claimed. And the way that they do get stirred up is often curious, as she'd tell this story to prove.

For, now you take Lige Butterwick—and, before his tooth started aching, he was just like you and me. He lived on a farm about eight miles from Lexington, Massachusetts, and he was a peaceable man. It was troubled times in the American colonies, what with British warships in Boston Harbor and British soldiers in Boston and Sons of Liberty hooting the British soldiers—not to speak of Boston tea parties and such. But Lige Butterwick, he worked his farm and didn't pay much attention. There's lots of people like that, even in troubled times.

When he went into town, to be sure, there was high talk at the tavern. But he bought his goods and came home again—he had ideas about politics, but he didn't talk about them much. He had a good farm and it kept him busy—he had a wife and five children and they kept him humping. The young folks could argue about King George and Sam Adams—he wondered how the corn was going to stand that year. Now and then, if somebody said that this and that was a burning shame, he'd allow as how it might be, just to be neighborly. But, inside, he was wondering whether next year he mightn't make an experiment and plant the west field in rye.

Well, everything went along for him the way that it does for most folks with good years and bad years, till one April morning, in 1775, he woke up with a toothache. Being the kind of man he was, he didn't pay much attention to it at first. But he mentioned it that evening, at supper, and his wife got a bag of hot salt for him. He held it to his face and it seemed to ease him, but he couldn't hold it there all night, and, next morning, the tooth hurt worse than ever.

Well, he stood it the next day and the next, but it didn't improve any.

He tried tansy tea and other remedies—he tried tying a string to it and having his wife slam the door. But, when it came to the pinch, he couldn't quite do it. So, finally, he took the horse and rode into Lexington town to have it seen to. Mrs. Butterwick made him—she said it might be an expense, but anything was better than having him act as if he wanted to kick the cat across the room every time she put her feet down hard.

When he got into Lexington, he noticed that folks there seemed kind of excited. There was a lot of talk about muskets and powder and a couple of men called Hancock and Adams who were staying at Parson Clarke's. But Lige Butterwick had his own business to attend to—and, besides, his tooth was jumping so he wasn't in any mood for conversation. He set off for the local barber's, as being the likeliest man he knew to pull a tooth.

The barber took one look at it and shook his head.

"I can pull her, Lige," he said. "Oh, I can pull her, all right. But she's got long roots and strong roots and she's going to leave an awful gap when she's gone. Now, what you really need," he said, kind of excited, for he was one of those perky little men who's always interested in the latest notion, "what you really need—though it's taking away my business —is one of these-here artificial teeth to go in the hole."

"Artificial teeth!" said Lige. "It's flying in the face of Nature!"

The barber shook his head. "No, Lige," he said, "that's where you're wrong. Artificial teeth is all the go these days, and Lexington ought to keep up with the times. It would do me good to see you with an artificial tooth—it would so."

"Well, it might do *you* good," said Lige, rather crossly, for his tooth was jumping, "but, supposing I did want one—how in tunket will I get one in Lexington?"

"Now you just leave that to me," said the barber, all excited, and he started to rummage around. "You'll have to go to Boston for it, but I know just the man." He was one of those men who can always tell you where to go and it's usually wrong. "See here," he went on. "There's a fellow called Revere in Boston that fixes them and they say he's a boss workman. Just take a look at this prospectus"—and he started to read from a paper:

" 'Whereas many persons are so unfortunate as to lose their fore-teeth'— that's you, Lige—'to their great detriment, not only in looks but in speaking, both in public and private, this is to inform all such that they may have them replaced by artificial ones'—see?—'that look as well as the natural and answer the end of speaking to all intents'—and then he's got his name—Paul Revere, goldsmith, near the head of Dr. Clarke's wharf, Boston."

"Sounds well enough," said Lige, "but what's it going to cost?"

"Oh, I know Revere," said the barber, swelling up like a robin. "Comes through here pretty often, as a matter of fact. And he's a decent fellow, if he is a pretty big bug in the Sons of Liberty. You just mention my name."

"Well, it's something I hadn't thought of," said Lige, as his tooth gave another red-hot jounce, "but in for a penny, in for a pound. I've missed a day's work already and that tooth's got to come out before I go stark, staring mad. But what sort of man is this Revere, anyway?"

"Oh, he's a regular wizard!" said the barber. "A regular wizard with his tools."

"Wizard!" said Lige. "Well, I don't know about wizards. But if he can fix my tooth I'll call him one."

"You'll never regret it," said the barber—and that's the way folks always talk when they're sending someone else to the dentist. So Lige Butterwick got on his horse again and started out for Boston. A couple of people shouted at him as he rode down the street, but he didn't pay any attention. And, going by Parson Clarke's, he caught a glimpse of two men talking in the Parson's front room. One was a tallish, handsomish man in pretty fine clothes and the other was shorter and untidy, with a kind of bulldog face. But they were strangers to him and he didn't really notice them—just rode ahead.

II

But as soon as he got into Boston he started to feel queer—and it wasn't only his tooth. He hadn't been there in four years and he'd expected to find it changed, but it wasn't that. It was a clear enough day and yet he kept feeling there was thunder in the air. There'd be knots of people, talking and arguing, on street corners, and then, when you got closer to them, they'd kind of melt away. Or, if they stayed, they'd look at you, out of the corners of their eyes. And there, in the Port of Boston, were the British warships, black and grim. He'd known they'd be there, of course, but it was different, seeing them. It made him feel queer to see their guns pointed at the town. He'd known there was trouble and dispute, in Boston, but the knowledge had passed over him like rain and hail. But now here he was in the middle of it—and it smelt like earthquake weather. He couldn't make head or tail of it, but he wanted to be home.

All the same, he'd come to get his tooth fixed, and, being New England, he was bound to do it. But first he stopped at a tavern for a bite and a sup, for it was long past his dinnertime. And there, it seemed to him, things got even more curious.

"Nice weather we're having, these days," he said, in a friendly way, to the barkeep.

"It's bitter weather for Boston," said the barkeep, in an unfriendly voice, and a sort of low growl went up from the boys at the back of the room and every eye fixed on Lige.

Well, that didn't help the toothache any, but, being a sociable person, Lige kept on.

"May be, for Boston," he said, "but out in the country we'd call it good planting weather."

The barkeep stared at him hard.

"I guess I was mistaken in you," he said. "It *is* good planting weather—for some kinds of trees."

"And what kind of trees were you thinking of?" said a sharp-faced man at Lige's left and squeezed his shoulder.

"There's trees and trees, you know," said a red-faced man at Lige's right, and gave him a dig in the ribs.

"Well, now that you ask me—" said Lige, but he couldn't even finish before the red-faced man dug him hard in the ribs again.

"The liberty tree!" said the red-faced man. "And may it soon be watered in the blood of tyrants!"

"The royal oak of England!" said the sharp-faced man. "And God save King George and loyalty!"

Well, with that it seemed to Lige Butterwick as if the whole tavern kind of riz up at him. He was kicked and pummeled and mauled and thrown into a corner and yanked out of it again, with the red-faced man and the sharp-faced man and all the rest of them dancing quadrilles over his prostrate form. Till, finally, he found himself out in the street with half his coat gone galley-west.

"Well," said Lige to himself, "I always heard city folks were crazy. But politics must be getting serious in these American colonies when they start fighting about trees!"

Then he saw the sharp-faced man was beside him, trying to shake his hand. He noticed with some pleasure that the sharp-faced man had the beginnings of a beautiful black eye.

"Nobly done, friend," said the sharp-faced man, "and I'm glad to find another true-hearted loyalist in this pestilent, rebellious city."

"Well, I don't know as I quite agree with you about that," said Lige. "But I came here to get my tooth fixed, not to talk politics. And as long as you've spoken so pleasant, I wonder if you could help me out. You see, I'm from Lexington way—and I'm looking for a fellow named Paul Revere—"

"Paul Revere!" said the sharp-faced man, as if the name hit him like a bullet. Then he began to smile again—not a pleasant smile.

"Oh, it's Paul Revere you want, my worthy and ingenuous friend from the country," he said. "Well, I'll tell you how to find him. You go up to the first British soldier you see and ask the way. But you better give the password first."

"Password?" said Lige Butterwick, scratching his ear.

"Yes," said the sharp-faced man, and his smile got wider. "You say to that British soldier, 'Any lobsters for sale today?' Then you ask about Revere."

"But why do I talk about lobsters first?" said Lige Butterwick, kind of stubborn.

"Well, you see," said the sharp-faced man, "the British soldiers wear red coats. So they like being asked about lobsters. Try it and see." And he went away, with his shoulders shaking.

Well, that seemed queer to Lige Butterwick, but no queerer than the other things that had happened that day. All the same, he didn't quite trust the sharp-faced man, so he took care not to come too close to the British patrol when he asked them about the lobsters. And it was lucky he did, for no sooner were the words out of his mouth than the British soldiers took after him and chased him clear down to the wharves before he could get away. At that, he only managed it by hiding in an empty tar-barrel, and when he got out he was certainly a sight for sore eyes.

"Well, I guess that couldn't have been the right password," he said to himself, kind of grimly, as he tried to rub off some of the tar. "All the same, I don't think soldiers ought to act like that when you ask them a civil question. But, city folks or soldiers, they can't make a fool out of me. I came here to get my tooth fixed and get it fixed I will, if I have to surprise the whole British Empire to do it."

And just then he saw a sign on a shop at the end of the wharf. And, according to my great-aunt, this was what was on the sign. It said "PAUL REVERE, SILVERSMITH" at the top, and then, under it, in smaller letters, "Large and small bells cast to order, engraving and printing done in job lots, artificial teeth sculptured and copper boilers mended, all branches of goldsmith and silversmith work and revolutions put up to take out. Express Service, Tuesdays and Fridays, to Lexington, Concord and Points West."

"Well," said Lige Butterwick, "kind of a Jack-of-all-trades. Now maybe I can get my tooth fixed." And he marched up to the door.

III

Paul Revere was behind the counter when Lige came in, turning a silver bowl over and over in his hands. A man of forty-odd he was, with a quick, keen face and snapping eyes. He was wearing Boston clothes, but there was a French look about him—for his father was Apollos Rivoire from the island of Guernsey, and good French Huguenot stock. They'd changed the name to Revere when they crossed the water.

It wasn't such a big shop, but it had silver pieces in it that people have paid thousands for, since. And the silver pieces weren't all. There were prints and engravings of the Port of Boston and caricatures of the British and all sorts of goldsmith work, more than you could put a name to. It was a crowded place, but shipshape. And Paul Revere moved about it, quick and keen, with his eyes full of life and hot temper—the kind of man who knows what he wants to do and does it the next minute.

There were quite a few customers there when Lige Butterwick first came in—so he sort of scrooged back in a corner and waited his chance. For one thing, after the queer sign and the barber's calling him a wizard, he wanted to be sure about this fellow, Revere, and see what kind of customers came to his shop.

Well, there was a woman who wanted a christening mug for a baby and a man who wanted a print of the Boston Massacre. And then there was a fellow who passed Revere some sort of message, under cover—Lige caught the whisper, "powder" and "Sons of Liberty," though he couldn't make out the rest. And, finally, there was a very fine silk-dressed lady who seemed to be giving Revere considerable trouble. Lige peeked at her round the corner of his chair, and, somehow or other, she reminded him of a turkey-gobbler, especially the strut.

She was complaining about some silver that Paul Revere had made for her—expensive silver it must have been. And "Oh, Master Revere, I'm so disappointed!" she was saying. "When I took the things from the box, I could just have cried!"

Revere drew himself up a little at that, Lige noticed, but his voice was pleasant.

"It is I who am disappointed, madam," he said, with a little bow. "But what was the trouble? It must have been carelessly packed. Was it badly dented? I'll speak to my boy."

"Oh no, it wasn't dented," said the turkey-gobbler lady. "But I wanted a really impressive silver service—something I can use when the Governor comes to dinner with us. I certainly *paid* for the best. And what have you given me?"

Lige waited to hear what Paul Revere would say. When he spoke, his voice was stiff.

"I have given you the best work of which I am capable, madam," he said. "It was in my hands for six months—and I think they are skillful hands."

"Oh," said the woman, and rustled her skirts. "I know you're a competent artisan, Master Revere—"

"Silversmith, if you please—" said Paul Revere, and the woman rustled again.

"Well, I don't care what you call it," she said, and then you could see her fine accent was put on like her fine clothes. "But I know I wanted a real service—something I could show my friends. And what have you given me? Oh, it's silver, if you choose. But it's just as plain and simple as a picket fence!"

Revere looked at her for a moment and Lige Butterwick thought he'd explode.

"Simple?" he said. "And plain? You pay me high compliments, madam!"

"Compliments indeed!" said the woman, and now she was getting furious. "I'm sending it back tomorrow! Why, there isn't as much as a lion or a unicorn on the cream jug. And I told you I wanted the sugar bowl covered with silver grapes! But you've given me something as bare as the hills of New England! And I won't stand it, I tell you! I'll send to England instead."

Revere puffed his cheeks and blew, but his eyes were dangerous.

"Send away, madam," he said. "We're making new things in this country—new men—new silver—perhaps, who knows, a new nation. Plain, simple, bare as the hills and rocks of New England—graceful as the boughs of her elm trees—if my silver were only like that indeed! But that is what I wish to make it. And, as for you, madam,"—he stepped toward her like a cat,—"with your lions and unicorns and grape leaves and your nonsense of bad ornament done by bad silversmiths—your imported bad taste and your imported British manners—puff!" And he blew at her, just the way you blow at a turkey-gobbler, till she fairly picked up her fine silk skirts and ran. Revere watched her out of the door and turned back, shaking his head.

"William!" he called to the boy who helped him in the shop. "Put up the shutters—we're closing for the day. And William—no word yet from Dr. Warren?"

"Not yet, sir," said the boy, and started to put up the shutters. Then Lige Butterwick thought it was about time to make his presence known.

So he coughed, and Paul Revere whirled and Lige Butterwick felt those quick, keen eyes boring into his. He wasn't exactly afraid of them, for he was stubborn himself, but he knew this was an unexpected kind of man.

"Well, my friend," said Revere, impatiently, "and who in the world are you?"

"Well, Mr. Revere," said Lige Butterwick. "It is Mr. Revere, isn't it? It's kind of a long story. But, closing or not, you've got to listen to me. The barber told me so."

"The barber!" said Revere, kind of dumbfounded.

"Uh-huh," said Lige, and opened his mouth. "You see, it's my tooth."

"Tooth!" said Revere, and stared at him as if they were both crazy. "You'd better begin at the beginning. But wait a minute. You don't talk like a Boston man. Where do you come from?"

"Oh, around Lexington way," said Lige. "And, you see—"

But the mention of Lexington seemed to throw Revere into a regular excitement. He fairly shook Lige by the shoulders.

"Lexington!" he said. "Were you there this morning?"

"Of course I was," said Lige. "That's where the barber I told you about—"

"Never mind the barber!" said Revere. "Were Mr. Hancock and Mr. Adams still at Parson Clarke's?"

"Well, they might have been, for all I know," said Lige. "But I couldn't say."

"Great heaven!" said Revere. "Is there a man in the American colonies who doesn't know Mr. Hancock and Mr. Adams?"

"There seems to be me," said Lige. "But, speaking of strangers—there *was* two of them staying at the parsonage, when I rode past. One was a handsomish man and the other looked more like a bulldog—"

"Hancock and Adams!" said Revere. "So they are still there." He took a turn or two up and down the room. "And the British ready to march!" he muttered to himself. "Did you see many soldiers as you came to my shop, Mr. Butterwick?"

"See them?" said Lige. "They chased me into a tar-barrel. And there was a whole passel of them up by the Common with guns and flags. Looked as if they meant business."

Revere took his hand and pumped it up and down.

"Thank you, Mr. Butterwick," he said. "You're a shrewd observer. And you have done me—and the colonies—an invaluable service."

"Well, that's nice to know," said Lige. "But, speaking about this tooth of mine—"

Revere looked at him and laughed, while his eyes crinkled.

"You're a stubborn man, Mr. Butterwick," he said. "All the better. I like stubborn men. I wish we had more of them. Well, one good turn deserves another—you've helped me and I'll do my best to help you. I've made artificial teeth—but drawing them is hardly my trade. All the same, I'll do what I can for you."

So Lige sat down in a chair and opened his mouth.

"Whew!" said Revere, with his eyes dancing. His voice grew solemn. "Mr. Butterwick," he said, "it seems to be a compound, agglutinated infraction of the upper molar. I'm afraid I can't do anything about it tonight."

"But—" said Lige.

"But here's a draught—that will ease the pain for a while," said Revere, and poured some medicine into a cup. "Drink!" he said, and Lige drank. The draught was red and spicy, with a queer, sleepy taste, but pungent. It wasn't like anything Lige had ever tasted before, but he noticed it eased the pain.

"There," said Revere. "And now you go to a tavern and get a good night's rest. Come back to see me in the morning—I'll find a tooth-drawer for you, if I'm here. And—oh yes—you'd better have some liniment."

He started to rummage in a big cupboard at the back of the shop. It was dark now, with the end of day and the shutters up, and whether it was the tooth, or the tiredness, or the draught Paul Revere had given him, Lige began to feel a little queer. There was a humming in his head and a lightness in his feet. He got up and stood looking over Paul Revere's shoulder, and it seemed to him that things moved and scampered in that cupboard in a curious way, as Revere's quick fingers took down this box and that. And the shop was full of shadows and murmurings.

"It's a queer kind of shop you've got here, Mr. Revere," he said, glad to hear the sound of his own voice.

"Well, some people think so," said Revere—and that time Lige was almost sure he saw something move in the cupboard. He coughed. "Say— what's in that little bottle?" he said, to keep his mind steady.

"That?" said Paul Revere, with a smile, and held the bottle up. "Oh, that's a little chemical experiment of mine. I call it Essence of Boston. But there's a good deal of East Wind in it."

"Essence of Boston," said Lige, with his eyes bulging. "Well, they did say you was a wizard. It's gen-u-wine magic, I suppose?"

"Genuine magic, of course," said Revere, with a chuckle. "And here's the box with your liniment. And here—"

He took down two little boxes—a silver and a pewter one—and placed them on the counter. But Lige's eyes went to the silver one—they were drawn to it, though he couldn't have told you why.

"Pick it up," said Paul Revere, and Lige did so and turned it in his hands. It was a handsome box. He could make out a growing tree and an eagle fighting a lion. "It's mighty pretty work," he said.

"It's my own design," said Paul Revere. "See the stars around the edge— thirteen of them? You could make a very pretty design with stars—for a new country, say—if you wanted to—I've sometimes thought of it."

"But what's in it?" said Lige.

"What's in it?" said Paul Revere, and his voice was light but steely. "Why, what's in the air around us? Gunpowder and war and the making of a new nation. But the time isn't quite ripe yet—not quite ripe."

"You mean," said Lige, and he looked at the box very respectful, "that this-here revolution folks keep talking about—"

"Yes," said Paul Revere, and he was about to go on. But just then his boy ran in, with a letter in his hand.

"Master!" he said. "A message from Dr. Warren!"

IV

Well, with that Revere started moving, and, when he started to move, he moved fast. He was calling for his riding boots in one breath and telling Lige Butterwick to come back tomorrow in another—and, what with all the bustle and confusion, Lige Butterwick nearly went off without his liniment after all. But he grabbed up a box from the counter, just as Revere was practically shoving him out of the door—and it wasn't till he'd got to his tavern and gone to bed for the night that he found out he'd taken the wrong box.

He found it out then because, when he went to bed, he couldn't get to sleep. It wasn't his tooth that bothered him—that had settled to a kind of dull ache and he could have slept through that. But his mind kept going over all the events of the day—the two folks he'd seen at Parson Clarke's and being chased by the British and what Revere had said to the turkey-gobbler woman—till he couldn't get any peace. He could feel something stirring in him, though he didn't know what it was.

" 'Tain't right to have soldiers chase a fellow down the street," he said to himself. "And 'tain't right to have people like that woman run down New England. No, it ain't. Oh me—I better look for that liniment of Mr. Revere's."

So he got up from his bed and went over and found his coat. Then he reached his hand in the pocket and pulled out the silver box.

Well, at first he was so flustrated that he didn't know rightly what to do. For here, as well as he could remember it, was gunpowder and war and the makings of a new nation—the revolution itself, shut up in a silver box by Paul Revere. He mightn't have believed there could be such things before he came to Boston. But now he did.

The draught was still humming in his head, and his legs felt a mite wobbly. But, being human, he was curious. "Now, I wonder what *is* inside that box," he said.

He shook the box and handled it, but that seemed to make it warmer, as if there was something alive inside it, so he stopped that mighty quick. Then he looked all over it for a keyhole, but here wasn't any keyhole, and, if there had been, he didn't have a key.

Then he put his ear to the box and listened hard. And it seemed to him that he heard, very tiny and far away, inside the box, the rolling fire of thousands of tiny muskets and the tiny, far-away cheers of many men. "Hold your fire!" he heard a voice say. "Don't fire till you're fired on—but, if they want a war, let it begin here!" And then there was a rolling of drums and a squeal of fifes. It was small, still, and far away, but it made him shake all over, for he knew he was listening to something in the future—and something that he didn't have a right to hear. He sat down on the edge of his bed, with the box in his hands.

"Now, what am I going to do with this?" he said. "It's too big a job for one man."

Well, he thought, kind of scared, of going down to the river and throwing the box in, but, when he thought of doing it, he knew he couldn't. Then he thought of his farm near Lexington and the peaceful days. Once the revolution was out of the box, there'd be an end to that. But then he remembered what Revere had said when he was talking with the woman about the silver—the thing about building a new country and

building it clean and plain. "Why, I'm not a Britisher," he thought.
"I'm a New Englander. And maybe there's something beyond that—
something people like Hancock and Adams know about. And, if it has to
come with a revolution—well, I guess it has to come. We can't stay
Britishers forever, here in this country."

He listened to the box again, and now there wasn't any shooting in it—
just a queer tune played on a fife. He didn't know the name of the tune,
but it lifted his heart.

He got up, sort of slow and heavy. "I guess I'll have to take this back
to Paul Revere," he said.

Well, the first place he went was Dr. Warren's, having heard Revere
mention it, but he didn't get much satisfaction there. It took quite a while
to convince them that he wasn't a spy, and, when he did, all they'd tell
him was that Revere had gone over the river to Charlestown. So he went
down to the water front to look for a boat. And the first person he met
was a very angry woman.

"No," she said, "you don't get any boats from me. There was a crazy
man along here an hour ago and he wanted a boat, too, and my husband
was crazy enough to take him. And then, do you know what he did?"

"No, mam," said Lige Butterwick.

"He made my husband take my best petticoat to muffle the oars so
they wouldn't make a splash when they went past that Britisher ship,"
she said, pointing out where the man-of-war *Somerset* lay at anchor. "My
best petticoat, I tell you! And when my husband comes back he'll get a
piece of my mind!"

"Was his name Revere?" said Lige Butterwick. "Was he a man of forty-
odd, keen-looking and kind of Frenchy?"

"I don't know what his right name is," said the woman, "but his name's
mud with me. My best petticoat tore in strips and swimming in that
nasty river!" And that was all he could get out of her.

All the same, he managed to get a boat at last—the story doesn't say
how—and row across the river. The tide was at young flood and the
moonlight bright on the water, and he passed under the shadow of the
Somerset, right where Revere had passed. When he got to the Charlestown side, he could see the lanterns in North Church, though he didn't
know what they signified. Then he told the folks at Charlestown he had
news for Revere and they got him a horse and so he started to ride. And,
all the while, the silver box was burning his pocket.

Well, he lost his way more or less, as you well might in the darkness,
and it was dawn when he came into Lexington by a side road. The dawn
in that country's pretty, with the dew still on the grass. But he wasn't
looking at the dawn. He was feeling the box burn his pocket and thinking hard.

Then, all of a sudden, he reined up his tired horse. For there, on the side road, were two men carrying a trunk—and one of them was Paul Revere.

They looked at each other and Lige began to grin. For Revere was just as dirty and mud-splashed as he was—he'd warned Hancock and Adams all right, but then, on his way to Concord, he'd got caught by the British and turned loose again. So he'd gone back to Lexington to see how things were there—and now he and the other fellow were saving a trunk of papers that Hancock had left behind, so they wouldn't fall into the hands of the British.

Lige swung off his horse. "Well, Mr. Revere," he said, "you see, I'm on time for that little appointment about my tooth. And, by the way, I've got something for you." He took the box from his pocket. And then he looked over toward Lexington Green and caught his breath. For, on the Green, there was a little line of Minute Men—neighbors of his, as he knew—and, in front of them, the British regulars. And, even as he looked, there was the sound of a gunshot, and, suddenly, smoke wrapped the front of the British line and he heard them shout as they ran forward.

Lige Butterwick took the silver box and stamped on it with his heel. And with that the box broke open—and there was a dazzle in his eyes for a moment and a noise of men shouting—and then it was gone.

"Do you know what you've done?" said Revere. "You've let out the American Revolution!"

"Well," said Lige Butterwick, "I guess it was about time. And I guess I'd better be going home, now. I've got a gun on the wall there. And I'll need it."

"But what about your tooth?" said Paul Revere.

"Oh, a tooth's a tooth," said Lige Butterwick. "But a country's a country. And, anyhow, it's stopped aching."

All the same, they say Paul Revere made a silver tooth for him, after the war. But my great-aunt wasn't quite sure of it, so I won't vouch for that.

COMMENT AND QUESTION

1. "A Tooth for Paul Revere" is part history, part folk tale, part fantasy. But its theme is unified. The theme is expressed in the sentence: "But it isn't till the Lige Butterwicks get stirred up that things really start to happen." In other words, how does a farmer become an embattled farmer?

2. The background of the American Revolution is laid before the reader. What well-known arguments are expressed in the following episodes?

    a. The fight in the tavern
    b. The encounter with the redcoats
    c. The customers in Revere's shop

3. Paul Revere is given a fairly complete biography in this story. He is accented, however, in his rôle as a revolutionary. Nevertheless, Lige will perform a service for the Revolution better than Revere can. But Revere is aware of the separate rôles.

a. How does Lige become a revolutionary in his first few words with Revere?

b. What is the medicine called Essence of Boston?

c. What is the meaning of the "shadows and murmurings" in Revere's shop?

4. By altering the normal perspective, fantasy gives a sharper meaning to an idea. The silver box is part of the fantasy here. That Revere would leave the box behind seems incredible at first. But what does the box contain? Why must Lige take it *to* Revere?

Why is it significant that Lige follows the precise route taken by Revere on his historic ride? When Lige reaches Charlestown, he announces that he has news for Revere. Since Revere already knows that the British are coming, what can the news be?

What is important about the way in which Lige finally opens the box?

THE MAN WHO MISSED
THE BUS

BY STELLA BENSON

STELLA BENSON (1892–1933) was born in
England but travelled widely in France,
Germany, Switzerland, and America. For a
number of years she lived in China, where
her husband, Mr. O'Gorman Anderson, was
an officer in the Chinese Customs Service. She
has written essays, novels, and poetry. The
best of her short stories may be found in *Collected Short Stories* (1936).

M R. ROBINSON's temper was quite sore by the time he reached St.
Pierre. The two irritations that most surely found the weak places in his
nervous defenses were noise and light in his eyes. And, as he told Monsieur Dupont, the proprietor of Les Trois Moineaux at St. Pierre, "If
there is one thing, monsieur, that is offensive—essentially offensive—that
is to say, a danger in itself—I mean to say noise doesn't have to have a
meaning. . . . What I mean is, monsieur, that noise—"

"*Numéro trente,*" said Monsieur Dupont to the chasseur.

Mr. Robinson always had to explain things very thoroughly in order
to make people really appreciate the force of what he had to say; and
even then it was a hard task to get them to acknowledge receipt, so to
speak, of his message. But he was a humble man, and he accounted for
the atmosphere of unanswered and unfinished remarks in which he lived
by admitting that his words were unfortunately always inadequate to
convey to a fellow-mortal the intense interest to be found in the curiosities
of behavior and sensation. His mind was overstocked with by-products of

THE MAN WHO MISSED THE BUS   From *Collected Short Stories* by Stella Benson.
Published by Macmillan & Co., Ltd. of London, 1936. Used with the permission
of Mrs. Georgina Berkeley and Curtis Brown Ltd. of London.

the business of life. He felt that every moment disclosed a new thing worth thinking of among the phenomena that his senses presented to him. Other people, he saw, let these phenomenal moments slip by unanalyzed; but if he had had the words and the courage, he felt, he could have awakened those of his fellow-creatures whom he met from their trance of shallow living. As it was, the relation of his explorations and wonderings sounded, even to his own ears, flat as the telling at breakfast of an ecstatic dream.

What he had meant to say about noise, for instance, had been that noise was *in itself* terrifying and horrible—not as a warning of danger but as a physical assault. Vulgar people treat noise only as a language that *means* something, he would have said, but really noise could not be translated, any more than rape could be translated. There was no such thing as an ugly harmless noise. The noise of an express train approaching and shrieking through a quiet station; the noise of heavy rain sweeping towards one through a forest; the noise of loud concerted laughter at an unheard joke—all benevolent noises if translated into concrete terms, were *in themselves* calamities. All this Mr. Robinson would have thought worth saying to Monsieur Dupont—worth continuing to say until Monsieur Dupont should have confessed to an understanding of his meaning; but as usual the words collapsed as soon as they left Mr. Robinson's lips.

Monsieur Dupont stood in the doorway of Les Trois Moineaux with his back to the light. Mr. Robinson could see the shape of his head set on stooping shoulders, with a little frail fluff of hair beaming round a baldness. He could see the rather crumpled ears with outleaning lobes bulging sharply against the light. But between ear and ear, between bald brow and breast he could see nothing but a black blank against the glare. Mr. Robinson had extremely acute sight—perhaps too acute, as he often wanted to tell people, since this was perhaps why the light in his eyes affected him so painfully.

"If my sight were less acute," he would have said, "I should not mind a glare so much—I mean to say, my eyes are so extremely receptive that they receive too much, or in other words the same cause that makes my eyes so very sensitive is . . ."

But nobody ever leaned forward eagerly and said, "I understand you perfectly, Mr. Robinson, and what you say is most interesting. Your sight includes so much that it cannot exclude excessive light, and this very naturally irritates your nerves, though the same peculiarity accounts for your intense powers of observation." Nobody ever said anything like that, but then, people are so self-engrossed.

Mr. Robinson was not self-engrossed—he was simply extravagantly interested in *things*, not people. For instance, he looked round now, as the chasseur sought in the shadows for his suitcase, and saw the terrace striped by long beams of light—broad flat beams that were strung like yellow sheets from every window and door in the hotel to the trees, tall urns, and tables of the terrace. A murmur of voices enlivened the air, but there were no human creatures in any beam—only blocked dark figures in the shadows—and, in every patch of light, a sleeping dog or cat or two. Dogs and cats lay extended or curled comfortably on the warm uneven paving stones, and Mr. Robinson's perfect sight absorbed the shape of every brown, tortoise-shell, or black marking on their bodies, as a geographer might accept the continents on a new unheard-of globe.

"It's just like geography—the markings on animals," Mr. Robinson had once said to an American who couldn't get away. "What I mean to say is that the markings on a dog or a rabbit have just as much sense as the markings on this world of ours—or in other words the archipelagoes of spots on this pointer puppy are just as importantly isolated from one another as they could be in any Adriatic sea."

But the American had only replied, "Why, no, Mr. Robinson, not half so important; I am taking my wife, with the aid of the American Express Company, to visit the Greek islands this summer; and we shall be sick on the sea and robbed on the land—whereas nobody but a flea ever visits the spots on that puppy, and the flea don't know and don't care a damn what color he bites into." Showing that nobody except Mr. Robinson ever really studied things impersonally.

Mr. Robinson, a very ingenious-minded and sensitive man with plenty of money, was always seeking new places to go to, where he might be a success—or rather, where his unaccountable failures elsewhere might not be known. St. Pierre, he thought, was an excellent venture, although the approach to it had been so trying. As soon as he had heard of it—through reading a short thoughtless sketch by a popular novelist in the *Daily Call*—he had felt hopeful about it. A little Provençal walled town on a hill, looking out over vineyards to the blue Mediterranean; a perfect little hotel—clean and with a wonderful cook—frequented by an interesting few. . . .

"By the time I get downstairs," thought Mr. Robinson as he carefully laid his trousers under the mattress in his room and donned another pair, "the lights will be lighted on the terrace, and I shall be able to see my future friends. I must tell some one about that curious broken reflection in the river Rhone."

He went downstairs and out onto the terrace, where the tinkle of glasses and plates made him feel hungry. He could hear, as he stood in the doorway looking out, one man's voice making a series of jokes in quick succession, each excited pause in his voice being filled by a gust and scrape of general laughter—like waves breaking on a beach with a clatter and then recoiling with a thin, hopeful, lonely sound. "Probably all his jokes are personalities," thought Mr. Robinson, "and, therefore, not essentially funny. No doubt they are slightly pornographic, at that. When will people learn how interesting and exciting *things* are? . . ."

A waiter behind him drew out a chair from a table in one of the squares of light thrown from a window. Mr. Robinson, after sitting down abstractedly, was just going to call the waiter back to tell him that his eyes were ultra-sensitive to light and that he could see nothing in that glare, when a large dog, with the bleached, patched, innocent face of a circus clown, came and laid its head on his knee. Mr. Robinson could never bear to disappoint an animal. He attributed to animals all the hot and cold variations of feeling that he himself habitually experienced, identifying the complacent fur of the brute with his own thin human skin. So that when the waiter, coming quietly behind him, put the wine list into his hand, Mr. Robinson merely said, "Thank you, garçon, but I never touch alcohol in any form—or, for the matter of that, tobacco either. In my opinion—" and did not call the rapidly escaping waiter back to ask him to move his table. The dog's chin was now comfortably pressed against his knee, and the dog's paw hooked in a pathetically prehensile way about his ankle.

Mr. Robinson made the best of his position in the dazzle and tried to look about him. The Trois Moineaux was built just outside the encircling wall of the tightly corseted little town of St. Pierre and, since St. Pierre clung to the apex of a conical hill, it followed that the inn terrace jutted boldly out over a steep, stepped fall of vineyards overhanging the plain. The plain was very dim now, overlaid by starlit darkness, yet at the edge of the terrace there was a sense of *view*, and all the occupied tables stood in a row against the low wall, diluting the food and drink they bore with starlight and space. The men and women sitting at these tables all had their faces to the world and their backs to Mr. Robinson. He could not see a single human face. He had come down too late to secure one of the outlooking tables, and his place was imprisoned in a web of light under an olive tree. In the middle of the table, peaches and green grapes were heaped on a one-legged dish. And on the edge of the dish a caterpillar waved five-sixths of its length drearily in the air, unable to believe that its world could really end at this abrupt slippery rim. Mr. Robinson, shading his eyes from the light, could see every detail of the caterpillar's figure, and it seemed to him worth many minutes of absorbed attention. Its color was a pale greenish-fawn, and it had two dark bumps on its brow by way of eyes.

"How unbearably difficult and lonely its life would seem to us," thought Mr. Robinson, leaning intensely over it. "How frightful if by mistake the merest spark of self-consciousness should get into an insect's body (an accidental short-circuit in the life current, perhaps), and it should know itself absolutely alone—appallingly free." He put his finger in the range of its persistent wavings and watched it crawl with a looping haste down his fingernail, accepting without question a quite fortuitous salvation from its dilemma. He laid his finger against a leaf, and the caterpillar disembarked briskly after its journey across alien elements. When it was gone, Mr. Robinson looked about him, dazed. "My goodness," he thought, "that caterpillar's face is the only one I have seen tonight!"

The noise of chatter and laughter went up like a kind of smoke from the flickering creatures at the tables near the edge of the terrace. At each table the heads and shoulders of men and women leaned together—were sucked together like flames in a common upward draft. "My dear, she looked like a . . . Oh, well, if you want to. . . . He's the kind of man who . . . *No*, my dear, not in my *bedroom*. . . . A rattling good yarn. . . . Stop me if I've told you this one before. . . ." One man, standing up a little unsteadily facing the table nearest to Mr. Robinson, made a speech: ". . . the last time . . . delightful company . . . fair sex . . . happiest hours of my life . . . mustn't waste your time . . . us mere men . . . as the Irishman said to the Scotchman when . . . happiest moments of all my life . . . one minute and I shall be done . . . always remember the happiest days of all my . . . well, I mustn't keep you . . . I heard a little story the other day. . . ." And all the time his audience leaned together round their table, embarrassed, looking away over the dark plain or murmuring together with bent heads.

The only woman whose face Mr. Robinson might have seen was shielding her face with her hands and shaking with silent laughter. The speaker was wavering on his feet very much as the caterpillar had wavered on its tail, and his wide gestures, clawing the air in search of the attention of his friends, suggested to Mr. Robinson the caterpillar's wild gropings for foothold where no foothold was. "Yes," thought Mr. Robinson, "the caterpillar was *my* host. No other face is turned to me."

However, as he thought this, a man came from a farther table and stood quite close, under the olive tree, between Mr. Robinson and the lighted doorway, looking down on him. The man stretched out his hand to the tree and leaned upon it. A freak of light caught the broad short hand, walnut-knuckled and brown, crooked over the bough. Mr. Robinson could not see the man's face at all, but he felt that the visit was friendly. To conciliate this sympathetic stranger, he would even have talked about the weather, or made a joke about pretty girls or beer; but he could not think of anything of that kind to say to a man whose hand, grasping an olive bough, was all that could be known of him. All that Mr. Robinson could do for the moment was to wonder what could have sent the man here. "It could not have been," thought Mr. Robinson humbly, "that he was attracted by my face, because nobody ever is." And then he began thinking how one man's loss is nearly always another man's gain, if considered broadly enough. For one to be forsaken, really, means that another has a new friend.

"This young man," thought Mr. Robinson, gazing at the black outline of the stranger's head, "has probably come here blindly, because of some sudden hurt, some stab, some insult, inflicted by his friends at that table over there—probably by a woman. Perhaps he thinks he has a broken heart (for he has young shoulders). Nothing short of a wound that temporarily robbed him of his social balance could make him do so strange a thing as suddenly to leave his friends and come here to stand silent by me in the shade. Yet if he only could—as some day, I am convinced, we all shall—know that the sum remains the same—that some other lover is the happier for this loss of his—and that if he had gained a smile from her, the pain he now feels would simply have been shifted to another heart—not dispelled . . . We only have to think impersonally enough, and even death—well, we are all either nearly dead or just born, more or less, and the balance of birth and death never appreciably alters. Personal thinking is the curse of existence. Why are we all crushed under the weight of this strangling *me*—this snake in our garden . . . ?"

So he said to the young man, "Isn't it a curious thing, looking round at young people and old people, that it doesn't really matter if they are born or dead—I mean to say, it's all the same whatever happens, if you follow me, and so many people mind when they needn't, if people would only realize—" At this moment there was a burst of clapping from the far table and the young man bounded from Mr. Robinson's side back to his friends, shouting, "Good egg—have you thought of a word already? Animal, vegetable, or mineral—and remember to speak up because I'm rather hard of hearing."

Mr. Robinson suddenly felt like Herbert Robinson, personally affronted. The sum of happiness (which of course remained unaltered by his setback) for a moment did not matter in the least. He pushed back his chair and walked away, leaving his cheese uneaten and the clown-faced dog without support. He went to his bedroom and sat down opposite his mirror, facing the reflection of his outward *me*. There sat the figure in the mirror, smooth, plump, pale, with small pouched eyes and thick, straight, wet-looking hair.

"What is this?" asked Mr. Robinson, studying the reflection of his disappointed face—the only human face he had seen that evening. "Look at me—I *am* alive—I am indeed very acutely alive—more alive, perhaps, than all these men and women half-blind—half-dead in their limitations of greed and sex. . . . It is true I have no personal claim on life; I am a virgin and I have no friends—yet I live intensely—and there are—there *are—there are* other forms of life than personal life. The eagle and the artichoke are equally alive; and perhaps my way of life is nearer to the eagle's than the artichoke's. And must I be alone—must I live behind cold shoulders because I see *out* instead of *in*—the most vivid form of life conceivable, if only it could be lived perfectly?"

He tried to see himself in the mirror, as was his habit, as a mere pliable pillar of life, a turret of flesh with a prisoner called *life* inside it. He stared himself out of countenance, trying, as it were, to dissolve his poor body by understanding it—poor white, sweating, rubbery thing that was called Herbert Robinson and had no friends. But tonight the prisoner called *life* clung to his prison—tonight his body tingled with egotism—tonight the oblivion that he called wisdom would not come, and he could not become conscious, as he longed to, of the live sky above the roof, the long winds streaming about the valleys, the billions of contented, wary, or terrified creatures moving about the living dust, weeds, and waters of the world. He remained just Herbert Robinson who had not seen any human face while in the midst of his fellow men.

He began to feel an immediate craving—an almost revengeful lust—to be alone, far from men, books, mirrors, and lights, watching, all his life long, the bodiless, mindless movements of animals—ecstatic living things possessing no *me*. "I should scarcely know I was alive, then, and perhaps never even notice when I died. . . ." He decided he would go away next day, and give no group again the chance to excommunicate him.

He remembered that he had seen a notice at the door of the hotel giving the rare times at which an auto-bus left and arrived at St. Pierre. "I will leave by the early bus, before any one is awake to turn his back on me."

He could not sleep, but lay uneasily on his bed reading the advertisements in a magazine he had brought with him. Advertisements always comforted him a good deal, because advertisers really, he thought, took a broad view; they wrote of—and to—their fellow men cynically and subtly, taking advantage of the vulgar passion for personal address, and yet treating humanity as one intricate mass—an instrument to be played upon. This seemed the ideal standpoint to Mr. Robinson, and yet he was insulted by the isolation such an ideal involved.

He dressed himself early, replaced in his suitcase the few clothes he had taken out, put some notes in an envelope addressed to Monsieur Dupont, and leaned out of the window to watch for the bus. St. Pierre, a sheaf of white-and-pink plaster houses, was woven together on a hill, like a haycock. The town, though compact and crowned by a sharp white bell-tower, seemed to have melted a little, like a thick candle; the centuries and the sun had softened its fortress outlines. The other hills, untopped by towns, seemed much more definitely constructed; they were austerely built of yellow and green blocks of vineyard, cemented by the dusty green of olive trees. Gleaming, white fluffy clouds peeped over the hills—"like kittens," thought Mr. Robinson, who had a fancy for trying to make cosmic comparisons between the small and the big. On the terrace of the inn half a dozen dogs sprawled in the early sun. Over the valley a hawk balanced and swung in the air, so hungry after its night's fast that it swooped rashly and at random several times, and was caught up irritably into the air again after each dash, as though dangling on a plucked thread. Mr. Robinson leaned long on his sill looking at it, until his elbows felt sore from his weight, and he began to wonder where the bus was that was going to take him away to loneliness. He went down to the terrace, carrying his suitcase, and stood in the archway. There was no sound of a coming bus—no sound at all, in fact, except a splashing and a flapping and a murmuring to the left and right of him. A forward step or two showed him that there were two long washing troughs, one on each side of the archway, each trough shaded by a stone gallery and further enclosed in a sort of trellis of leaning kneading women.

Mr. Robinson noticed uneasily that he could not see one woman's face; all were so deeply bent and absorbed. After a moment, however, a woman's voice from the row behind him asked him if he was waiting for the bus. He turned to reply, hoping to break the spell by finding an ingenuous rustic face lifted to look at him. But all the faces were bent once more, and it was another woman behind him again who told him that the bus had left ten minutes before. Once more the speaker bent over her work before Mr. Robinson had time to turn and see her face. "What a curious protracted accident," he thought, and had time to curse his strange isolation before he realized the irritation of being unable to leave St. Pierre for another half dozen hours. He flung his suitcase into the hall of the inn and walked off up a path that led through the vineyards. As if the whole affair had been prearranged, all the dogs on the terrace rose up and followed him, yawning and stretching surreptitiously, like workers reluctantly leaving their homes at the sound of a factory whistle.

Mr. Robinson, true to his habit, concentrated his attention on—or rather diffused it to embrace—the colors about him. The leaves of the vines especially held his eye; they wore the same frosty bloom that grapes themselves often wear—a sky-blue dew on the green leaf. Two magpies, with a bottle-green sheen on their wings, gave their police-rattle cry as he came near and then flew off, flaunting their long tails clumsily. A hundred feet higher, where the ground became too steep even for vines, Mr. Robinson found a grove of gnarled old olive trees, edging a thick wood of Spanish chestnuts. Here he sat down and looked between the tree-trunks and over the distorted shadows at the uneven yellow land and the thin blade of mat-blue sea stabbing the farthest hills. The dogs stood round him, expecting him to rise in a minute and lead them on again. Seeing that he still sat where he was, they wagged their tails tolerantly but invitingly. Finally they resigned themselves to the inevitable and began philosophically walking about the grove, sniffing gently at various points in search of a makeshift stationary amusement.

Mr. Robinson watched them with a growing sense of comfort. "Here," he thought, "are the good undeliberate beasts again; I knew they would save me. They don't shut themselves away from life in their little individualities, or account uniquely for their lusts on the silly ground of personality. Their bodies aren't prisons—they're just dormitories. . . ." He delighted in watching the dogs busily engrossed in being alive without self-consciousness. After all, he thought, he did not really depend on men. (For he had been doubting his prized detachment most painfully.)

One of the dogs discovered a mouse-hole and, after thrusting his nose violently into it to verify the immediacy of the smell, began digging, but not very cleverly because he was too large a dog for such petty sports. The other dogs hurried to the spot and, having verified the smell for themselves, stood restively round the first discoverer, wearing the irritable look we all wear when watching some one else bungle over something we feel (erroneously) that we could do very much better ourselves. Finally they pushed the original dog aside and began trying to dig, all in the same spot, but, finding this impossible, they tapped different veins of the same lode-smell. Soon a space of some ten feet square was filled with a perfect tornado of flying dust, clods, grass, and piston-like forepaws. Hind legs remained rooted while forelegs did all the work, but whenever the accumulation of earth to the rear of each dog became inconveniently deep, hindlegs, with a few impatient strong strokes, would dash the heap away to some distance—even as far as Mr. Robinson's boots. Quite suddenly all the dogs, with one impulse, admitted themselves beaten; they concluded without rancor that the area was unmistakably mouseless. They signified their contempt for the place in the usual canine manner, and walked away, sniffing, panting, sniffing again for some new excitement.

Mr. Robinson, who had been, for the duration of the affair, a dog in spirit, expecting at every second that a horrified mouse would emerge from this cyclone of attack, imitated his leaders and quieted down with an insouciance equal to theirs. But he had escaped from the menace of humanity; he was eased—he was sleepy. . . .

He slept for a great many hours, and when he awoke the sunlight was slanting down at the same angle as the hill, throwing immense shadows across the vineyards. The dogs had gone home. And there, on a space of flattened earth between two spreading tree-roots, was a mouse and its family. Mr. Robinson, all mouse now, with no memory of his canine past, lay quite still on his side. The mother mouse moved in spasms, stopping to quiver her nose over invisible interests in the dust. Her brood were like little curled feathers, specks of down blown about by a fitful wind. There seemed to be only one license to move shared by this whole mouse family; when mother stopped, one infant mouse would puff forward, and as soon as its impulse expired, another thistledown brother would glide erratically an inch or two. In this leisurely way the family moved across the space of earth and into the grass, appearing again and again between the green blades. Mr. Robinson lay still, sycophantically reverent.

Between two blades of grass the senior mouse came out onto a little plateau, about eighteen inches away from Mr. Robinson's unwinking eye. At that range Mr. Robinson could see its face as clearly as one sees the face of a wife over a breakfast table. It was a dignified but greedy face; its eyes, in so far as they had any expression at all, expressed a cold heart; its attraction lay in its texture, a delicious velvet—and that the mouse would never allow a human finger, however friendly, to enjoy. It would have guarded its person as a classical virgin guarded her honor. As soon as Mr. Robinson saw the mouse's remote expression he felt as a lost sailor on a sinking ship might feel, who throws his last rope—and no saving hands grasp it.

He heard the sound of human footsteps behind him. There was a tiny explosion of flight beside him—and the mouse family was not there. Through the little grove marched a line of men in single file, going home from their work in the vineyards over the hill. Mr. Robinson sat up and noticed, with a cold heart, that all the men wore the rush hats of the country pulled down against the low last light of the sun, and that not one face was visible.

Mr. Robinson sat for some time with his face in his hands. He felt his eyes with his finger, and the shape of his nose and cheekbone; he bit his finger with his strong teeth. Here was a face—the only human face in the world. Suddenly craving for the sight of that friend behind the mirror, he got up and walked back to the Trois Moineaux. He found himself very hungry, having starved all day; but his isolation gave him a so much deeper sense of lack than did his empty stomach that, although dinner was in progress among the bands of light and shade on the terrace, his first act was to run to his room and stand before the mirror. There was a mistiness in the mirror. He rubbed it with his hand. The mistiness persisted—a compact haze of blankness that exactly covered the reflection of his face. He moved to a different angle—he moved the mirror—he saw clearly the reflection of the room, of his tweed-clad figure, of his tie, of his suitcase in the middle of the floor; but his face remained erased, like an unsatisfactory charcoal sketch. Filled with an extraordinary fear, he stood facing the mirror for some minutes, feeling with tremulous fingers for his eyes, his lips, his forehead. There seemed to him to be the same sensation of haze in his sense of touch as in his eyesight—a nervelessness—a feeling of nauseating contact with a dead thing. It was like touching with an unsuspecting hand one's own limb numbed by cold or by an accident of position.

Mr. Robinson walked downstairs, dazed, and out onto the terrace. As before, the shadowed tables looking out over the edge of the terrace were already surrounded by laughing, chattering parties. Mr. Robinson took his seat, as before, under the olive tree. "Bring me a bottle of . . . Sauterne," he said to the waiter (for he remembered that his late unmarried sister used to sustain upon this wine a reputation for wit in the boarding house in which she had lived). "And, waiter, isn't there a table free looking out at the view? I can't see anything here." It was not the view he craved, of course, but only a point of vantage from which to see the faces of his mysterious noisy neighbors. His need for seeing faces was more immediate than ever, now that his one friend had failed him.

"There will be tables free there in a moment," said the waiter. "They are all going to dance soon. They're only waiting for the moon." And the waiter nodded his shadowed face towards a distant hill, behind which—looking at this moment like a great far red fire—the moon was coming up. "Look, the moon, the moon, the moon, look . . ." every one on the terrace was saying. And a few moments later, the moon—now completely round but cut in half by a neat bar of cloud, took flight lightly from the top of the hill.

There was a scraping of chairs, the scraping of a gramophone, and half a dozen couples of young men and women began dancing between the tall Italian urns and the olive trees on the terrace. Mr. Robinson poured himself out a large tumbler of Sauterne. "Waiter, I don't want a table at the edge now—I want one near the dancers—I want to see their faces."

"There are no tables free in the center of the terrace now. Several are vacant at the edge."

"I can see a table there, near the dancers, with only two chairs occupied. Surely I could sit with them."

"That table is taken by a large party, but most of them are dancing. They will come back there in a moment."

Mr. Robinson, disregarding the waiter and clutching his tumbler in one hand and his bottle in the other, strode to the table he had chosen. "I'm *too* lonely—I must sit here."

"So lonely, poo-oo-oor man," said the woman at the table, a stout middle-aged woman with high shoulders and a high bosom clad in saxe-blue sequins. She turned her face towards him in the pink light of the moon. Mr. Robinson, though desperate, was not surprised. Her face was the same blank—the same terrible disc of nothingness that he had seen in his mirror. Mr. Robinson looked at her companion in dreadful certainty. A twin blank faced him.

"Sh-lonely, eh?" came a thick young voice out of nothingness. "Well, m'lad, you'll be damn sight lonelier yet in minute 'f y' come buttin' in on—"

"Ow, Ronnie," expostulated his frightful friend—but at that moment the gramophone fell silent and the dancers came back to their table. Mr. Robinson scanned the spaces that should have been their faces one by one; they were like discs of dazzle seen after unwisely meeting the eye of the sun.

"'This old feller sayzzz—lonely—pinched your chair, Belle—'"

"Never mind, duckie," said Belle—and threw herself across Mr. Robinson's knee. "Plenty of room for little me."

The white emptiness of her face that was no face blocked out Mr. Robinson's view of the world.

"Oh, my God!" she cried, jumping up sudddenly. "I know why he's lonely—why—the man's not alive. Look at his face!"

"I am—I am—I am—" shouted Mr. Robinson in terror. "I'll show you I am . . ." He lurched after her and dragged her among the dancers as the music began again. He shut his eyes. He could hear her wild animal shrieks of laughter and feel her thin struggling body under his hands.

Mr. Robinson sat, quite still but racked by confusion, excitement, and disgust, beside the road on the wall of a vineyard, watching the last star slip down into the haze that enhaloed the hills. The moon had gone long ago. All Mr. Robinson's heart was set on catching the bus this morning; to him the dawn that was even now imperceptibly replacing the starlight was only a herald of the bus and of escape. He had no thoughts and no plans beyond catching the bus. He knew that he was cold, but flight would warm him; that he was hungry and thirsty, but flight would nourish him; that he was exhausted and broken-hearted, but flight would ease and comfort him.

A white glow crowned a hill, behind which the sky had long been pearly, and in a minute an unbearably bright ray shot from the hill into Mr. Robinson's eyes. The dazzling domed brow of the sun rose between a tree and a crag, and a lily-white light rushed into the valley.

The bus, crackling and crunching, waddled round the bend. Mr. Robinson hailed it with a distraught cry and gesture.

"*Enfin . . . très peu de places, m'sieu—n'y a qu'un tout p'tit coin par ici . . .*"

Mr. Robinson had no need now to look at the face of the driver, or at the rows of senseless sunlit ghosts that filled the bus. He knew his curse by now. He climbed into the narrow place indicated beside the driver. The bus lurched on down the narrow winding road that overhung the steep vineyards of the valley. Far below—so far below that one could not see the movement of the water—a yellow stream enmeshed its rocks in a net of plaited strands.

Mr. Robinson sat beside the driver, not looking at that phantom faceless face—so insulting to the comfortable sun—but looking only at the road that was leading him to escape. How far to flee he did not know, but all the hope there was, he felt, lay beyond the farthest turn of the road. After one spellbound look at the sun-blinded face of St. Pierre, clinging to its hivelike hill, he looked forward only, at the winding perilous road.

And his acute eyes saw, in the middle of the way, half a dozen specks of live fur, blowing about a shallow rut. . . . The bus's heavy approach had already caused a certain panic in the mouse family. One atom blew one way, one another; there was a sort of little muddled maze of running mice in the road.

Mr. Robinson's heart seemed to burst. Before he was aware, he had sprung to his feet and seized the wheel of the bus from the driver. He had about twenty seconds in which to watch the mice scuttling into the grass—to watch the low loose wall of the outer edge of the road crumble beneath the plunging weight of the bus. He saw, leaning crazily towards him, the face—the *face*—rolling eyes, tight grinning lips—of the driver, looking down at death. There, far down, was the yellow net of the river, spread to catch them all.

COMMENT AND QUESTION

1. Is Mr. Robinson, who hated "this strangling *me*," self-engrossed?

2. Two key questions are: Why does Mr. Robinson see no faces? Why does he finally see the driver's face?

3. Two lines of interest develop simultaneously in this story and produce a single revelation. One is the failure to see faces, the other, Mr. Robinson's interest in animals.

    a. Begin with the proprietor who stands with his back against the light and trace all the people who are faceless, ending with the episode of the mirror on p. 24.

    b. Begin with the dog who lays his head on Mr. Robinson's knee and notice all the animals through the mouse on p. 23. Why do animals console Mr. Robinson? Does he see their faces?

4. Why does Mr. Robinson feel like a lost sailor on a sinking ship when he observes the mouse on p. 24? Why does this incident occur almost simultaneously with the incident of the mirror on p. 24?

5. How does the woman at the dance merely confirm what the reader already knows?

6. The final incident contains all the threads of the story, faceless people, animals, Mr. Robinson's acute sight, a bus.

Why does Mr. Robinson try to rescue the mouse? What reward does he receive? What price does he pay?

THE HAPPY AUTUMN FIELDS

BY ELIZABETH BOWEN

ELIZABETH BOWEN (1899–   ) was born in
Ireland and lives in Bowen's Court, County
Cork, Ireland. Her book of short stories, *Ivy
Gripped the Steps* (1946), reflects the emo-
tional tension of life in England during the
Second World War. Other collections of her
short stories include *Joining Charles* (1929),
Look at All Those Roses (1941), *The Cat
Jumps* (1949), and *Early Stories* (1951). She
has written a number of novels: *The House
in Paris* (1936), *The Death of the Heart*
(1939), *The Heat of the Day* (1949), *The
Hotel* and *To the North* (1950), *Friends and
Relations* (1951), *The Last September*
(1952), and *A World of Love* (1955).

T HE family walking party, though it comprised so many, did not deploy
or straggle over the stubble but kept in a procession of threes and twos.
Papa, who carried his Alpine stick, led, flanked by Constance and little
Arthur. Robert and Cousin Theodore, locked in studious talk, had Emily
attached but not quite abreast. Next came Digby and Lucius, taking, to
left and right, imaginary aim at rooks. Henrietta and Sarah brought up
the rear.

It was Sarah who saw the others ahead on the blond stubble, who
knew them, knew what they were to each other, knew their names and
knew her own. It was she who felt the stubble under her feet, and who
heard it give beneath the tread of the others a continuous different more
distant soft stiff scrunch. The field and all these outlying fields in view
knew as Sarah knew that they were Papa's. The harvest had been good
and was now in: he was satisfied—for this afternoon he had made the

---

THE HAPPY AUTUMN FIELDS   Reprinted from *Ivy Gripped the Steps* by Elizabeth
Bowen, by permission of Alfred A. Knopf, Inc. and Messrs. Jonathan Cape Ltd.
Copyright 1941, 1946 by Elizabeth Bowen.

28

instinctive choice of his most womanly daughter, most nearly infant son. Arthur, whose hand Papa was holding, took an anxious hop, a skip and a jump to every stride of the great man's. As for Constance—Sarah could often see the flash of her hat-feather as she turned her head, the curve of her close bodice as she turned her torso. Constance gave Papa her attention but not her thoughts, for she had already been sought in marriage.

The landowners' daughters, from Constance down, walked with their beetle-green, mole or maroon skirts gathered up and carried clear of the ground, but for Henrietta, who was still ankle-free. They walked inside a continuous stuffy sound, but left silence behind them. Behind them, rooks that had risen and circled, sun striking blue from their blue-black wings, planed one by one to the earth and settled to peck again. Papa and the boys were dark-clad as the rooks but with no sheen, but for their white collars.

It was Sarah who located the thoughts of Constance, knew what a twisting prisoner was Arthur's hand, felt to the depths of Emily's pique at Cousin Theodore's inattention, rejoiced with Digby and Lucius at the imaginary fall of so many rooks. She felt back, however, as from a rocky range, from the converse of Robert and Cousin Theodore. Most she knew that she swam with love at the nearness of Henrietta's young and alert face and eyes which shone with the sky and queried the afternoon.

She recognized the colour of valediction, tasted sweet sadness, while from the cottage inside the screen of trees wood-smoke rose melting pungent and blue. This was the eve of the brothers' return to school. It was like a Sunday; Papa had kept the late afternoon free; all (all but one) encircling Robert, Digby and Lucius, they walked the estate the brothers would not see again for so long. Robert, it could be felt, was not unwilling to return to his books; next year he would go to college like Theodore; besides, to all this they saw he was not the heir. But in Digby and Lucius aiming and popping hid a bodily grief, the repugnance of victims, though these two were further from being heirs than Robert.

Sarah said to Henrietta: "To think they will not be here to-morrow!"

"*Is* that what you are thinking about?" Henrietta asked, with her subtle taste for the truth.

"More, I was thinking that you and I will be back again by one another at table. . . ."

"You know we are always sad when the boys are going, but we are never sad when the boys have gone." The sweet reciprocal guilty smile that started on Henrietta's lips finished on those of Sarah. "Also," the young sister said, "we know this is only something happening again. It happened last year, and it will happen next. But oh how should I feel, and how should you feel, if it were something that had not happened before?"

"For instance, when Constance goes to be married?"

"Oh, I don't mean *Constance!*" said Henrietta.

"So long," said Sarah, considering, "as, whatever it is, it happens to both of us?" She must never have to wake in the early morning except to the birdlike stirrings of Henrietta, or have her cheek brushed in the dark by the frill of another pillow in whose hollow did not repose Henrietta's cheek. Rather than they should cease to lie in the same bed she prayed they might lie in the same grave. "You and I will stay as we are," she said, "then nothing can touch one without touching the other."

"So you say; so I hear you say!" exclaimed Henrietta, who then, lips apart, sent Sarah her most tormenting look. "But I cannot forget that you chose to be born without me; that you would not wait—" But here she broke off, laughed outright and said: "Oh, *see!*"

Ahead of them there had been a dislocation. Emily took advantage of having gained the ridge to kneel down to tie her bootlace so abruptly that Digby all but fell over her, with an exclamation. Cousin Theodore had been civil enough to pause beside Emily, but Robert, lost to all but what he was saying, strode on, head down, only just not colliding into Papa and Constance, who had turned to look back. Papa, astounded, let go of Arthur's hand, whereupon Arthur fell flat on the stubble.

"Dear me," said the affronted Constance to Robert.

Papa said: "What is the matter there? May I ask, Robert, where you are going, sir? Digby, remember that is your sister Emily."

"Cousin Emily is in trouble," said Cousin Theodore.

Poor Emily, telescoped in her skirts and by now scarlet under her hat-brim, said in a muffled voice: "It is just my bootlace, Papa."

"Your bootlace, Emily?"

"I was just tying it."

"Then you had better tie it.— Am I to think," said Papa, looking round them all, "that you must all go down like a pack of ninepins because Emily has occasion to stoop?"

At this Henrietta uttered a little whoop, flung her arms round Sarah, buried her face in her sister and fairly suffered with laughter. She could contain this no longer; she shook all over. Papa, who found Henrietta so hopelessly out of order that he took no notice of her except at table, took no notice, simply giving the signal for the others to collect themselves and move on. Cousin Theodore, helping Emily to her feet, could be seen to see how her heightened colour became her, but she dispensed with his hand chillily, looked elsewhere, touched the brooch at her throat and said: "Thank you, I have not sustained an accident." Digby apologized to Emily, Robert to Papa and Constance. Constance righted Arthur, flicking his breeches over with her handkerchief. All fell into their different steps and resumed their way.

Sarah, with no idea how to console laughter, coaxed, "Come, come,

come," into Henrietta's ear. Between the girls and the others the distance widened; it began to seem that they would be left alone.

"And why not?" said Henrietta, lifting her head in answer to Sarah's thought.

They looked around them with the same eyes. The shorn uplands seemed to float on the distance, which extended dazzling to tiny blue glassy hills. There was no end to the afternoon, whose light went on ripening now they had scythed the corn. Light filled the silence which, now Papa and the others were out of hearing, was complete. Only screens of trees intersected and knolls made islands in the vast fields. The mansion and the home farm had sunk for ever below them in the expanse of woods, so that hardly a ripple showed where the girls dwelled.

The shadow of the same rook circling passed over Sarah then over Henrietta, who in their turn cast one shadow across the stubble. "But, Henrietta, we cannot stay here for ever."

Henrietta immediately turned her eyes to the only lonely plume of smoke, from the cottage. "Then let us go and visit the poor old man. He is dying and the others are happy. One day we shall pass and see no more smoke; then soon his roof will fall in, and we shall always be sorry we did not go to-day."

"But he no longer remembers us any longer."

"All the same, he will feel us there in the door."

"But can we forget this is Robert's and Digby's and Lucius's good-bye walk? It would be heartless of both of us to neglect them."

"Then how heartless Fitzgeorge is!" smiled Henrietta.

"Fitzgeorge is himself, the eldest and in the Army. Fitzgeorge I'm afraid is not an excuse for us."

A resigned sigh, or perhaps the pretence of one, heaved up Henrietta's still narrow bosom. To delay matters for just a moment more she shaded her eyes with one hand, to search the distance like a sailor looking for a sail. She gazed with hope and zeal in every direction but that in which she and Sarah were bound to go. Then— "Oh, but Sarah, here *they* are, coming—they are!" she cried. She brought out her handkerchief and began to fly it, drawing it to and fro through the windless air.

In the glass of the distance, two horsemen came into view, cantering on a grass track between the fields. When the track dropped into a hollow they dropped with it, but by now the drumming of hoofs was heard. The reverberation filled the land, the silence and Sarah's being; not watching for the riders to reappear she instead fixed her eyes on her sister's handkerchief which, let hang limp while its owner intently waited, showed a bitten corner as well as a damson stain. Again it became a flag, in furious motion.— "Wave too, Sarah, wave too! Make your bracelet flash!"

"They must have seen us if they will ever see us," said Sarah, standing still as a stone.

Henrietta's waving at once ceased. Facing her sister she crunched up her handkerchief, as though to stop it acting a lie. "I can see you are shy," she said in a dead voice. "So shy you won't even wave to *Fitzgeorge?*"

Her way of not speaking the *other* name had a hundred meanings; she drove them all in by the way she did not look at Sarah's face. The impulsive breath she had caught stole silently out again, while her eyes—till now at their brightest, their most speaking—dulled with uncomprehending solitary alarm. The ordeal of awaiting Eugene's approach thus became for Sarah, from moment to moment, torture.

Fitzgeorge, Papa's heir, and his friend Eugene, the young neighbouring squire, struck off the track and rode up at a trot with their hats doffed. Sun striking low turned Fitzgeorge's flesh to coral and made Eugene blink his dark eyes. The young men reined in; the girls looked up the horses. "And my father, Constance, the others?" Fitzgeorge demanded, as though the stubble had swallowed them.

"Ahead, on the way to the quarry, the other side of the hill."

"We heard you were all walking together," Fitzgeorge said, seeming dissatisfied.

"We are following."

"What, alone?" said Eugene, speaking for the first time.

"Forlorn!" glittered Henrietta, raising two mocking hands.

Fitzgeorge considered, said "Good" severely, and signified to Eugene that they would ride on. But too late: Eugene had dismounted. Fitzgeorge saw, shrugged and flicked his horse to a trot; but Eugene led his slowly between the sisters. Or rather, Sarah walked on his left hand, the horse on his right and Henrietta the other side of the horse. Henrietta, acting like somebody quite alone, looked up at the sky, idly holding one of the empty stirrups. Sarah, however, looked at the ground, with Eugene inclined as though to speak but not speaking. Enfolded, dizzied, blinded as though inside a wave, she could feel his features carved in brightness above her. Alongside the slender stepping of his horse, Eugene matched his naturally long free step to hers. His elbow was through the reins; with his fingers he brushed back the lock that his bending to her had sent falling over his forehead. She recorded the sublime act and knew what smile shaped his lips. So each without looking trembled before an image, while slow colour burned up the curves of her cheeks. The consummation would be when their eyes met.

At the other side of the horse, Henrietta began to sing. At once her pain, like a scientific ray, passed through the horse and Eugene to penetrate Sarah's heart.

We surmount the skyline: the family come into our view, we into theirs. They are halted, waiting, on the decline to the quarry. The handsome statufied group in strong yellow sunshine, aligned by Papa and crowned by Fitzgeorge, turn their judging eyes on the laggards, waiting to close their ranks round Henrietta and Sarah and Eugene. One more moment and it will be too late; no further communication will be possible. Stop oh stop Henrietta's heartbreaking singing! Embrace her close again! Speak the only possible word! Say—oh, say what? Oh, the word is lost!

"Henrietta . . ."

A shock of striking pain in the knuckles of the outflung hand—Sarah's? The eyes, opening, saw that the hand had struck, not been struck: there was a corner of a table. Dust, whitish and gritty, lay on the top of the table and on the telephone. Dull but piercing white light filled the room and what was left of the ceiling; her first thought was that it must have snowed. If so, it was winter now.

Through the calico stretched and tacked over the window came the sound of a piano: someone was playing Tchaikovsky badly in a room without windows or doors. From somewhere else in the hollowness came a cascade of hammering. Close up, a voice: "Oh, *awake,* Mary?" It came from the other side of the open door, which jutted out between herself and the speaker—he on the threshold, she lying on the uncovered mattress of a bed. The speaker added: "I had been going away."

Summoning words from somewhere she said: "Why? I didn't know you were here."

"Evidently—Say, who is 'Henrietta'?"

Despairing tears filled her eyes. She drew back her hurt hand, began to suck at the knuckle and whimpered, "I've hurt myself."

A man she knew to be "Travis," but failed to focus, came round the door saying: Really I don't wonder." Sitting down on the edge of the mattress he drew her hand away from her lips and held it: the act, in itself gentle, was accompanied by an almost hostile stare of concern. "Do listen, Mary," he said. "While you've slept I've been all over the house again, and I'm less than ever satisfied that it's safe. In your normal senses you'd never attempt to stay here. There've been alerts, and more than alerts, all day; one more bang anywhere near, which may happen at any moment, could bring the rest of this down. You keep telling me that you have things to see to—but do you know what chaos the rooms are in? Till they've gone ahead with more clearing, where can you hope to start? And if there *were* anything you could do, you couldn't do it. Your own nerves know that, if you don't: it was almost frightening, when I looked in just now, to see the way you were sleeping—you've shut up shop."

She lay staring over his shoulder at the calico window. He went on: "You don't like it here. Your self doesn't like it. Your will keeps driving your self, but it can't be driven the whole way—it makes its own get-out: sleep. Well, I want you to sleep as much as you (really) do. But *not* here. So I've taken a room for you in a hotel; I'm going now for a taxi, you can practically make the move without waking up."

"No, I can't get into a taxi without waking."

"Do you realize you're the last soul left in the terrace?"

"Then who is that playing the piano?"

"Oh, one of the furniture-movers in Number Six. I didn't count the jaquerie; of course *they're* in possession—unsupervised, teeming, having a high old time. While I looked in on you in here ten minutes ago they were smashing out that conservatory at the other end. Glass being done in in cold blood—it was brutalizing. You never batted an eyelid; in fact, I thought you smiled." He listened. "Yes, the piano—they are highbrow all right. You know there's a workman downstairs lying on your blue sofa looking for pictures in one of your French books?"

"No," she said, "I've no idea who is there."

"Obviously. With the lock blown off your front door anyone who likes can get in and out."

"Including you."

"Yes. I've had a word with a chap about getting that lock back before to-night. As for you, you don't know what is happening."

"I did," she said, locking her fingers before her eyes.

The unreality of this room and of Travis's presence preyed on her as figments of dreams that one knows to be dreams can do. This environment's being in semi-ruin struck her less than its being some sort of device or trap; and she rejoiced, if anything, in its decrepitude. As for Travis, he had his own part in the conspiracy to keep her from the beloved two. She felt he began to feel he was now unmeaning. She was struggling not to contemn him, scorn him for his ignorance of Henrietta, Eugene, her loss. His possessive angry fondness was part, of course, of the story of him and Mary, which like a book once read she remembered clearly but with indifference. Frantic at being delayed here, while the moment awaited her in the cornfield, she all but afforded a smile at the grotesquerie of being saddled with Mary's body and lover. Rearing up her head from the bare pillow, she looked, as far as the crossed feet, along the form inside which she found herself trapped: the irrelevant body of Mary, weighted down to the bed, wore a short black modern dress, flaked with plaster. The toes of the black suède shoes by their sickly whiteness showed Mary must have climbed over fallen ceilings; dirt engraved the fate-lines in Mary's palms.

This inspired her to say: "But I've made a start; I've been pulling out things of value or things I want."

For answer Travis turned to look down, expressively, at some object out of her sight, on the floor close by the bed. "*I* see," he said, "a musty old leather box gaping open with God knows what—junk, illegible letters, diaries, yellow photographs, chiefly plaster and dust. Of all things, Mary! —after a missing will?"

"Everything one unburies seems the same age."

"Then what are these, where do they come from—family stuff?"

"No idea," she yawned into Mary's hand. "They may not even be mine.

Having a house like this that had empty rooms must have made me store more than I knew, for years. I came on these, so I wondered. Look if you like."

He bent and began to go through the box—it seemed to her, not unsuspiciously. While he blew grit off packets and fumbled with tapes she lay staring at the exposed laths of the ceiling, calculating. She then said: "Sorry if I've been cranky, about the hotel and all. Go away just for two hours, then come back with a taxi, and I'll go quiet. Will that do?"

"Fine—except why not now?"

"*Travis . . .*"

"Sorry. It shall be as you say . . . You've got some good morbid stuff in this box, Mary—so far as I can see at a glance. The photographs seem more your sort of thing. Comic but lyrical. All of one set of people—a beard, a gun and a pot hat, a schoolboy with a moustache, a phaeton drawn up in front of mansion, a group on steps, a *carte de visite* of two young ladies hand-in-hand in front of a painted field—"

"*Give that to me!*"

She instinctively tried, and failed, to unbutton the bosom of Mary's dress: it offered no hospitality to the photograph. So she could only fling herself over on the mattress, away from Travis, covering the two faces with her body. Racked by that oblique look of Henrietta's she recorded, too, a sort of personal shock at having seen Sarah for the first time.

Travis's hand came over her, and she shuddered. Wounded, he said: "Mary . . ."

"Can't you leave *me* alone?"

She did not move or look till he had gone out saying: "Then, in two hours." She did not therefore see him pick up the dangerous box, which he took away under his arm, out of her reach.

They were back. Now the sun was setting behind the trees, but its rays passed dazzling between the branches into the beautiful warm red room. The tips of the ferns in the jardiniere curled gold, and Sarah, standing by the jardiniere, pinched at a leaf of scented geranium. The carpet had a great centre wreath of pomegranates, on which no tables or chairs stood, and its whole circle was between herself and the others.

No fire was lit yet, but where they were grouped was a hearth. Henrietta sat on a low stool, resting her elbow above her head on the arm of Mamma's chair, looking away intently as though into a fire, idle. Mamma embroidered, her needle slowed down by her thoughts; the length of tatting with roses she had already done overflowed stiffly over her supple skirts. Stretched on the rug at Mamma's feet, Arthur looked through an album of Swiss views, not liking them but vowed to be very quiet. Sarah, from where she stood, saw fuming cateracts and null eternal snows as poor Arthur kept turning over the pages, which had tissue paper between.

Against the white marble mantlepiece stood Eugene. The dark red shadows gathering in the drawing-room as the trees drowned more and more of the sun would reach him last, perhaps never: it seemed to Sarah that a lamp was lighted behind his face. He was the only gentleman with the ladies: Fitzgeorge had gone to the stables, Papa to give an order; Cousin Theodore was consulting a dictionary; in the gunroom Robert, Lucius and Digby went through the sad rites, putting away their guns. All this was known to go on but none of it could be heard.

This particular hour of subtle light—not to be fixed by the clock, for it was early in winter and late in summer and in spring and autumn now, about Arthur's bedtime—had always, for Sarah, been Henrietta's. To be with her indoors or out, upstairs or down, was to share the same crepitation. Her spirit ran on past yours with a laughing shiver into an element of its own. Leaves and branches and mirrors in empty rooms became animate. The sisters rustled and scampered and concealed themselves where nobody else was in play that was full of fear, fear that was full of play. Till, by dint of making each other's hearts beat violently, Henrietta so wholly and Sarah so nearly lost all human reason that Mama had been known look at them searchingly as she sat instated for evening among the calm amber lamps.

But now Henrietta had locked the hour inside her breast. By spending it seated beside mamma, in young imitation of Constance the Society daughter, she disclaimed for ever anything else. It had always been she who with one fierce act destroyed any toy that might be outgrown. She sat with straight back, poising her cheek remotely against her finger. Only by never looking at Sarah did she admit their eternal loss.

Eugene, not long returned from a foreign tour, spoke of travel, addressing himself to Mamma, who thought but did not speak of her wedding journey. But every now and then she had to ask Henrietta to pass the scissors or tray of carded wools, and Eugene seized every such moment to look at Sarah. Into eyes always brilliant with melancholy he dared begin to allow no other expression. But this in itself declared the conspiracy of still undeclared love. For her part she looked at him as though he, transfigured by the strange light, were indeed a picture, a picture who could not see her. The wallpaper now flamed scarlet behind his shoulder. Mamma, Henrietta, even unknowing Arthur were in no hurry to raise their heads.

Henrietta said: "If I were a man I should take my bride to Italy."

"There are mules in Switzerland," said Arthur.

"Sarah," said Mamma, who turned in her chair mildly, "where are you, my love; do you never mean to sit down?"

"To Naples," said Henrietta.

"Are you not thinking of Venice?" said Eugene.

"No," returned Henrietta, "why should I be? I should like to climb the volcano. But then I am not a man, and am still less likely ever to be a bride."

"Arthur . . ." Mamma said.

"Mamma?"

"Look at the clock."

Arthur sighed politely, got up and replaced the album on the circular table, balanced upon the rest. He offered his hand to Eugene, his cheek to Henrietta and to Mamma; then he started towards Sarah, who came to meet him. "Tell me, Arthur," she said, embracing him, "what did you do to-day?"

Arthur only stared with his button blue eyes. "You were there too; we went for a walk in the cornfield, with Fitzgeorge on his horse, and I fell down." He pulled out of her arms and said: "I must go back to my beetle." He had difficulty, as always, in turning the handle of the mahogany door. Mamma waited till he had left the room, then said: "Arthur is quite a man now; he no longer comes running to me when he has hurt himself. Why, I did not even know he had fallen down. Before we know, he will be going away to school too." She sighed and lifted her eyes to Eugene. "To-morrow is to be a sad day."

Eugene with a gesture signified his own sorrow. The sentiments of Mamma could have been uttered only here in the drawing-room, which for all its size and formality was lyrical and almost exotic. There was a look like velvet in darker parts of the air; sombre window draperies let out gushes of lace; the music on the pianoforte bore tender titles, and the harp though unplayed gleamed in a corner, beyond sofas, whatnots, arm-chairs, occasional tables that all stood on tottering little feet. At any moment a tinkle might have been struck from the lustres' drops of the brighter day, a vibration from the musical instruments, or a quiver from the fringes and ferns. But the towering vases upon the consoles, the albums piled on the tables, the shells and figurines on the flights of brackets, all had, like the alabaster Leaning Tower of Pisa, an equilibrium of their own. Nothing would fall or change. And everything in the drawing-room was muted, weighted, pivoted by Mamma. When she added: "We shall not feel quite the same," it was to be understood that she would not have spoken thus from her place at the opposite end of Papa's table.

"Sarah," said Henrietta curiously, "what made you ask Arthur what he had been doing? Surely you have not forgotten to-day?"

The sisters were seldom known to address or question one another in public; it was taken that they knew each other's minds. Mamma, though untroubled, looked from one to the other. Henrietta continued: "No day, least of all to-day, is like any other— Surely that must be true?" she said to Eugene. "You will never forget my waving my handkerchief?"

Before Eugene had composed an answer, she turned to Sarah: "Or *you*, them riding across the fields?"

Eugene also slowly turned his eyes on Sarah, as though awaiting with something like dread her answer to the question he had not asked. She drew a light little gold chair into the middle of the wreath of the carpet, where no one ever sat, and sat down. She said: "But since then I think I have been asleep."

"Charles the First walked and talked half an hour after his head was cut off," said Henrietta mockingly. Sarah in anguish pressed the palms of her hands together upon a shred of geranium leaf.

"How else," she said, "could I have had such a bad dream?"

"That must be the explanation!" said Henrietta.

"A trifle fanciful," said Mamma.

However rash it might be to speak at all, Sarah wished she knew how to speak more clearly. The obscurity and loneliness of her trouble was not to be borne. How could she put into words the feeling of dislocation, the formless dread that had been with her since she found herself in the drawing-room? The source of both had been what she must call her dream. How could she tell the others with what vehemence she tried to attach her being to each second, not because each was singular in itself, each a drop condensed from the mist of love in the room, but because she apprehended that the seconds were numbered? Her hope was that the others at least half knew. Were Henrietta and Eugene able to understand how completely, how nearly for ever, she had been swept from them, would they not without fail each grasp one of her hands?— She went so far as to throw her hands out, as though alarmed by a wasp. The shred of geranium fell to the carpet.

Mamma, tracing this behaviour of Sarah's to only one cause, could not but think reproachfully of Eugene. Delightful as his conversation had been, he would have done better had he paid this call with the object of interviewing Papa. Turning to Henrietta she asked her to ring for the lamps, as the sun had set.

Eugene, no longer where he had stood, was able to make no gesture towards the bell-rope. His dark head was under the tide of dusk; for, down on one knee on the edge of the wreath, he was feeling over the carpet for what had fallen from Sarah's hand. In the inevitable silence rooks on the return from the fields could be heard streaming over the house; their sound filled the sky and even the room, and it appeared so useless to ring the bell that Henrietta stayed quivering by Mama's chair. Eugene rose, brought out his fine white handkerchief and, while they watched, enfolded carefully in it what he had just found, then returned the handkerchief to his breast pocket. This was done so deep in the reverie that accompanies any final act that Mamma instinctively murmured to Henrietta: "But you will be my child when Arthur has gone."

The door opened for Constance to appear on the threshold. Behind her queenly figure globes approached, swimming in their own light: these were the lamps for which Henrietta had not rung, but these first were put on the hall tables. "Why, Mamma," exclaimed Constance, "I cannot see who is with you!"

"Eugene is with us," said Henrietta, "but on the point of asking if he may send for his horse."

"Indeed?" said Constance to Eugene. "Fitzgeorge has been asking for you, but I cannot tell where he is now."

The figures of Emily, Lucius and Cousin Theodore crisscrossed the lamplight there in the hall, to mass behind Constance's in the drawing-room door. Emily, over her sister's shoulder, said: "Mama, Lucius wishes to ask you whether for once he may take his guitar to school."—"One objection, however," said Cousin Theodore, "is that Lucius's trunk is already locked and strapped." "Since Robert is taking his box of inks," said Lucius, "I do not see why I should not take my guitar."— "But Robert," said Constance, "will soon be going to college."

Lucius squeezed past the others into the drawing-room in order to look anxiously at Mamma, who said: "You have thought of this late; we must go and see." The others parted to let Mamma, followed by Lucius, out. Then Constance, Emily and Cousin Theodore deployed and sat down in different parts of the drawing-room, to await the lamps.

"I am glad the rooks have done passing over," said Emily, "they make me nervous."—"Why," yawned Constance haughtily, "what do you think could happen?" Robert and Digby silently came in.

Eugene said to Sarah: "I shall be back to-morrow."

"But, oh—" she began. She turned to cry: "Henrietta!"

"Why, what is the matter?" said Henrietta, unseen at the back of the gold chair. "What could be sooner than to-morrow?"

"But something terrible may be going to happen."

"There cannot fail to be to-morrow," said Eugene gravely.

"*I* will see that there is to-morrow," said Henrietta.

"You will never let me out of your sight?"

Eugene, addressing himself to Henrietta, said: "Yes, promise her what she asks."

Henrietta cried: "She *is* never out of my sight. Who are you to ask me that, you Eugene? Whatever tries to come between me and Sarah becomes nothing. Yes, come to-morrow, come sooner, come—when you like, but no one will ever be quite alone with Sarah. You do not even know what you are trying to do. It is *you* who are making something terrible happen.— Sarah, tell him that that is true! Sarah—"

The others, in the dark on the chairs and sofas, could be felt to turn their judging eyes upon Sarah, who, as once before, could not speak—

—The house rocked; simultaneously the calico window split and more ceiling fell, though not on the bed. The enormous dull sound of the explosion died, leaving a minor trickle of dissolution still to be heard in parts of the house. Until the choking stinging plaster dust had had time to settle, she lay with lips pressed close, nostrils not breathing and eyes shut. Remembering the box, Mary wondered if it had been again buried. No, she found, looking over the edge of the bed: that had been unable to happen because the box was missing. Travis, who must have taken it, would when he came back no doubt explain why. She looked at her watch, which had stopped, which was not surprising; she did not remember winding it for the last two days, but then she could not remember much. Through the torn window appeared the timelessness of an impermeably clouded late summer afternoon.

There being nothing left, she wished he would come to take her to the hotel. The one way back to the fields was barred by Mary's surviving the fall of ceiling. Sarah was right in doubting that there would be tomorrow: Eugene, Henrietta were lost in time to the woman weeping there on the bed, no longer reckoning who she was.

At last she heard the taxi, then Travis hurrying up the littered stairs. "Mary, you're all right, Mary—*another?*" Such a helpless white face came round the door that she could only hold out her arms and say: "Yes, but where have *you* been?"

"You said two hours. But I wish—"

"I have missed you."

"Have you? Do you know you are crying?"

"Yes. How are we to live without natures? We only know inconvenience now, not sorrow. Everything pulverizes so easily because it is rot-dry; one can only wonder that it makes so much noise. The source, the sap must have dried up, or the pulse must have stopped, before you and I were conceived. So much flowed through people; so little flows through us. All we can do is imitate love or sorrow.— Why did you take away my box?"

He only said: "It is in my office."

She continued: "What has happened is cruel: I am left with a fragment torn out of a day, a day I don't even know where or when; and now how am I to help laying that like a pattern against the poor stuff of everything else?— Alternatively, I am a person drained by a dream. I cannot forget the climate of those hours. Or life at that pitch, eventful— not happy, no, but strung like a harp. I have had a sister called Henrietta."

"And I have been looking inside your box. What else can you expect?— I have had to write off this day, from the work point of view, thanks to you. So could I sit and do nothing for the last two hours? I just glanced through this and that—still, I know the family."

"You said it was morbid stuff."

"Did I? I still say it gives off something."

She said: "And then there was Eugene."

"Probably. I don't think I came on much of his except some notes he must have made for Fitzgeorge from some book on scientific farming. Well, there it is: I have sorted everything out and put it back again, all but a lock of hair that tumbled out of a letter I could not trace. So I've got the hair in my pocket."

"What colour is it?"

"Ash-brown. Of course, it is a bit—desiccated. Do you want it?"

"No," she said with a shudder. "Really, Travis, what revenges you take!"

"I didn't look at it that way," he said puzzled.

"Is the taxi waiting?" Mary got off the bed and, picking her way across the room, began to look about for things she ought to take with her, now and then stopping to brush her dress. She took the mirror out of her bag to see how dirty her face was. "Travis—" she said suddenly.

"Mary?"

"Only, I—"

"That's all right. Don't let us imitate anything just at present."

In the taxi, looking out of the window, she said: "I suppose, then, that I am descended from Sarah?"

"No," he said, "that would be impossible. There must be some reason why you should have those papers, but that is not the one. From all negative evidence Sarah, like Henrietta, remained unmarried. I found no mention of either, after a certain date, in the letters of Constance, Robert or Emily, which makes it seem likely both died young. Fitzgeorge refers, in a letter to Robert written in his old age, to some friend of their youth who was thrown from his horse and killed, riding back after a visit to their home. The young man, whose name doesn't appear, was alone; and the evening, which was in autumn, was fine though late. Fitzgeorge wonders, and says he will always wonder, what made the horse shy in those empty fields."

COMMENT AND QUESTION

1. *Chronology.* Half of this story takes place in World War Two, during the day and night bombing of London. The other half takes place about 1850.

2. *The impression of Victorian life.* In this story the reader will find a contrast drawn between the calm, well-ordered, traditional life of Victorian England and the chaos of life in World War Two. The author makes a significant point about Victorian life. She shows that under the Victorian surface, under the equanimity and propriety, lay repressed tension and passion. The solidity of Victorian life is best seen in the description of the drawing room in the third section. But what is hap-

pening beneath the surface? Awakened love and the violence of death
are in the room.

3. *Sarah and Henrietta.* At least three times we are given clues which
indicate that Henrietta is irrepressible, unstable, and ungovernable, all
of which help to explain her final act. Clearly Henrietta waved her
handkerchief once more as Eugene rode home across the darkening
autumn fields. Do you know what a sister fixation is? The final paragraph
of this story is frightening in its Freudian implications.

4. *Symbols.*

a. In the scene in the drawing room when Constance brings the
lamps, she exclaims to her mother, "I cannot see who is with you." The
principals, of course, are there: Eugene, Sarah, and Henrietta. Henrietta's
answer contains the symbolic implications. Love and death are in the
room. Henrietta's statement, "Eugene is with us," carries the promise of
love. The second half of Henrietta's statement carries the threat of death.

b. Notice that the drawing room carpet has a center wreath of
pomegranates. Pomegranates are forever associated with the mythological
tale of Ceres and her daughter, Proserpine. Seized by Pluto and carried
off to the underworld, Proserpine refused to eat until she could be
restored to light. But one day she ate six seeds of a pomegranate. As a
result, when she was finally restored to the light of day, it was for six
months only. The other six months she was forced to spend underground.

Sarah, too, is torn by divided emotions. When she is asked the veiled
question, "Do you love Eugene?", she places her chair in the middle of
the wreath of pomegranates in the carpet and answers evasively.

c. Notice how the bomb that awakens Mary comes at the climax
of the Victorian story.

5. *The purpose of the author.* The experience of Mary in "The Happy
Autumn Fields," is a kind of resistance against a wartime life which had
robbed her of personal identity and personal emotion. A serious student
will want to read Miss Bowen's preface to her collection of stories, *Ivy
Gripped the Steps,* from which "The Happy Autumn Fields," is taken.
The stories in this collection reveal in their consecutive arrangement "a
rising tide of hallucination" as Miss Bowen states in her preface, which
also tells how and why she came to write this particular story.

THEY WEREN'T GOING TO DIE

BY KAY BOYLE

KAY BOYLE (1903–   ) was born in St. Paul,
Minnesota, but during most of her adult life
she has lived in Europe. She has published
several volumes of short stories, a number of
novels, and a collection of poems. She has won
the O. Henry Memorial Award twice, in 1935
with "White Horses of Vienna," and in 1941
with "Defeat." In the ten years between 1940
and 1950 she was represented four times in
the *O. Henry Memorial Award Prize Stories*
collection. These four stories, "Monsieur Pan-
alitus," "Their Name Is Macaroni," "The
Canals of Mars," and "Summer Evening," reflect both the upheaval and the aftermath of
the Second World War.

THEY were most of them rather tall men, tall, lanky black men with
their heads carried high and with dignity on their smooth straight necks.
If you walked behind a group of them wandering idly and with almost
girl-like flippancy of gesture down the road, you could hear their shy,
giddy laughter and speech, and you saw at once that the uniform they
wore had nothing to do with their bones or their gait. The tunics and
trousers and boots had all been made for somebody else, for some other
race of men who knew when they came to a town what they wanted:
bistrot, or a *tabac*, or paper and ink to write to somebody at home. They
were never made for the softly hee-heeing, melodiously murmuring Senegalese, who went plucking the heads off daisies and nudging each other
like schoolgirls as they ambled through the springtime evening toward the
river and fields, out of the direction of and the setting for war. Their necks

rose rounded and smooth from the khaki cloth, with a little spring in the arch of them just before the hair began growing high on their pates, and from the back like this you could see the ears lying close to the small, elegantly fashioned skulls.

There was a general term for them, for the Senegalese: one that covered the whole foolish, aimless-seeming catastrophe of them, the long, loose-hanging hands and the narrow hips and the quickly lipped and unlipped smiles. In cinema theaters they were recognized as this, where they might be seen in the actualities of the week marching half indolently in military formation across the screen toward what nobody had taken the trouble to show them a picture of or told them how loud the noise was going to be. And Frenchmen, marking with colored pins on the wall map the drastic sweeping line of the German descent through France, would put their fingers down south of Lyon and speak the name for them again and again. They would say: "Here's where we're pushing the *chair de canon* up," and if the black men had heard it they would not have known what it meant or, anyway, that it was meant for them. But they wouldn't have heard it because they would have been wandering off toward the river, the incongruous army boots heavy and dusty on their feet, and daisies or the flowers of other weeds broken off and brushing switchlike in their hands. They knew they were going to kill people, maybe a lot of people, smiling big softlipped smiles and looking sideways in the evening at each other, but they hadn't come all the way out here just to die. They hadn't walked down the hills of home, descending the paths with their hands in their fathers' or their uncles' or their male cousins' or their older brothers' hands toward the colonial towns and military service, for absolutely nothing. They had taken a long time learning which was the right and which was the left, and how to count up to forty-six or -seven, and what the foreign orders meant. In a little while they knew they were going to start singing again, and do the belly dance to the tom-toms that summer, but one thing they weren't going to do: they certainly weren't going to die.

Twenty or more of them had been billeted in the Count's stable on his property south of the city, and the first evening the Count left them alone. But in the morning he put on his gray tweed jacket and smoothed his oiled, thinning hair back in his hands and stepped down the driveway to look them over in the sun: a big, well-manicured gentleman of fifty maybe, with heavy shoulders and a sveltely corseted *tour de taille,* and his pince-nez hanging on a ribbon. He had been an Anglophile so long that it showed by this time in the way his eyelids fell halfway over his sight and hung there, and the way his chin returned to his throat and vanished whenever he opened his mouth to speak. He stood in the stable door with the light behind him, the height and the weight exaggerated so, and the baby lieutenant whose family kept a good hotel on the water front at

Cannes stood before him in the darkness of the stable, not quite certain how to address him or exactly what to say. But the Count said at once:

"I gathered there was someone too young for it in command," and he snapped the pince-nez on the high hard arch of the nose his ancestors had handed down from one generation to the next. There it hung between the hard, well-shaven jowls, as outmoded as the battle-ax tacked up among the relics of another time and the armorial bearings in the dining hall. "There's one of them got into the house," the Count said. "I saw the back of him making down the corridor as I came out," and the little lieutenant straightened up like a flash and settled his leather belt in a military way.

"I'll have it taken care of at once, Monsieur," he said, but the Count wasn't finished with him yet. He took off his pince-nez and with the rim of one glass he tapped the lieutenant sharply on the khaki breast where the decorations hadn't yet been pinned.

"I don't know what the army's composed of this time or what kind of war you're running, young man," he said, and the lieutenant's color ran up under his delicate skin to his black silk brows, and he bit his lip. "As far as I can see there's no discipline, no order, not an ounce of stamina in the superiors." He drew up his heavy, stooping shoulders in the London-cut tweed and sucked his waist in, as if for military bearing, and looked down on the young officer with his bleak, withering eye.

"I feel certain it won't happen again, Monsieur," the little officer said, but for all of that it happened three times again that day.

It seemed there was nothing to be done with the tall, black, grinning fool who went sidling out of the loft no matter whom the lieutenant set to guard him, and went ambling back through the château's ancient, imported trees and in through the window or the door and down the ground-floor corridor to the place he liked so well. There they found him the first time when they searched the house, and there he was the second, and the third, not even taking the trouble to lock the door as other people did when they entered this particular place. He was sitting on the window sill above the porcelain receptacle, his puttees unwound and his breeches drawn up high, and his bare black feet hung down in the water that was there for another use entirely. The servants said they could hear him laughing out loud all the way in the kitchen whenever he pulled the chain and the water flushed up across his shins. Even the third time the lieutenant opened the door, the black man was sitting there, smiling right across his face, and reaching up to pull the chain again.

"What in the name of God do you think you're in France for?" the Count exploded before the lieutenant could clear his own throat of the youthful hesitation in it and snap the orders out.

"Kill Boche," said the Senegalese, with his feet dabbling in the water still. "Come kill Boche," he said, and he was reaching up to pull the por-

celain handle when the lieutenant took him by the neck of his tunic and
jerked him off the sill.

The weather held six weeks for war that time as it never did for
pleasure, and the Count told the lieutenant that afternoon to get the blacks
busy on the soil. His gardeners had been mobilized and he had been
making out with a boy as best as he could, but now he had had quite
enough of this military horseplay. The potato plants were waiting for the
earth to be hoed up compactly around them, so a half dozen of the
Senegalese were set to that, stripped to the waist and bent like oarsmen
under the sun. Others were put to work the length of the strawberry beds,
weeding and raking out between the clumps of low glossy leaves and the
just-shedding strawberry flowers beneath the southern wall. The pear trees
had been trained to spread out like vines across the hot stones of the
wall, and on the other side the main road from Lyon led on around the
curve and dropped down the hill to the village. Whenever the Senegalese
turned their heads that way they could see over the top of the wall,
through the pear leaves, whatever happened to be passing by.

They could see the trees and the fields and the waters of the river
moving off beyond, and they leaned on the rake handles and the spade
handles, talking among themselves. They would strike at the ground a
little, and then the Senegalese melody rose sweetly on their tongues and
they would pause again, giggling like women at each other. It was not
from indolence that they ceased to turn the earth or pluck the weeds out
of the Count's rich soil, nor out of what might have been native languor
that they leaned on their implements and looked off through the leaves.
They might have been merely waiting there, waiting for the name and the
look of the thing that was to come, and work was not in them, for this was
not the promise that had been made. The Count came out after tea and
he saw them leaning in these long, loose attitudes of ease, their big hands
hanging from their idle wrists, or clasped at rest on the rake handles and
the spade handles and the hoes. There they had paused, like children
halted on the edge of Christmas Eve, the blood humming with it, the
babble of credulity tittering from lip to ear to eye.

"What are you canaille waiting for?" the little lieutenant called out as
he hurried across the drive. He was beginning to play his part quite well,
although in a panicky, puerile way. The Senegalese shifted the instruments in their hands, and moved their feet, and looked out toward the
river. "What are you waiting for to get on with the job?" he shouted out,
and one of the black men lifted his hand like a black lily drooping from
the wrist and moved it toward the sky.

"Kill Boche," he said. "Waiting for the sun to go."

The Count seemed to have set the worldly manner aside for the moment, and he opened his arms in his gray tweed jacket and looked around
in mock bewilderment.

"But where is the Boche? There's no Boche here as far as I can see," he said. It was he, by his own cunning, who was to establish himself the unmistakable master of the situation as he was the master of the château and the lawn. "Everything's very peaceful and quiet here," he went on saying, and as he spoke to the blacks he put an innocent look on his long, outmoded face. He was going to get the better of them in their own way now, steal their blue-black thunder from them by his utter guilelessness and charm. "No Boche, no kill," he said, and his chin collapsed into his neck as he smiled around the vegetable garden at them. "Work," he said, and he made the gestures of spading, hoeing, raking before them on the air.

"Boche tomorrow, maybe Boche tonight," said the black man, and he lifted his hand again and moved it in casual indication from place to place. "Kill Boche there—there—there—there," he said, letting it fall from the wrist once toward the trees and once toward the wall and twice beyond it, and the Senegalese music of talk rose on their tongues again, then waned and died.

It was just before six that evening that the first motorcycle was heard coming down the road. The three Senegalese near the pear trees straightened up from the strawberry beds and their vision came level with the top of the wall and sought beyond it. They saw first the trees on the other side and then the surface of the road and at last the color of the solitary rider's jacket as he came leaning to the handle bars. They spoke the word or gave the sign in silence, and then their feet raced naked and wild back across the garden and the drive to where the guns were stacked in the stable yard, their legs reaching, their mouths splitting wide. They went so fast they were back in time for the second one: he dropped from his machine just where the brass studs began marking the curve of the turn and the motorcycle ran of itself a little way down the hill before it hit the tree. The third had a sidecar with a machine gunner riding in it, but neither the driver on the leather saddle nor the gunner behind his curved glass shield had time to see the khaki drape of the turbans or the guns along the wall. It did not make the turn this time but ran with the two dead men on its seats into the ditch and sputtered out there, and the others coming along behind were thirty seconds too late to see. There they came hastening down the road from Lyon, sidecar after sidecar of them driving fast, and as they came the black men picked them off over the garden wall and jumped up and down on the strawberry plants on their naked feet in glee.

The seventh or eighth was a single rider again, and this time the warning was there, splattered out on the road before him. He lifted his head to the pear leaves on top of the wall and braked so that the tires cried aloud, and swung the machine on its haunches, rearing and pawing the air. When he poured into speed and streamed back up the road, crouched flat to the bars, the black men's hearts stood still in pain. They waited there for a moment, and then they looked at each other and they could no longer find the sounds of laughter or speech. It might have been just after six on Christmas Day, and the stockings emptied, the presents all opened, the candles on the tree put out. They hadn't quite got over it when the nimble little tank came down the road, its eyes, like those of a snail, fingering them out, nor when the second tank came down behind it and the piece of the garden wall suddenly blew in.

The look of disappointment was on their faces still when the Count came out to have a look at them lying there. The machine gunners who had finished them off were removing their smoked goggles just inside the gate, and the German officer was chatting amiably with the Count as he walked with him out through the rose garden which shielded the vegetable beds from the drive. There were the black men, foolish-looking and rather giddy even in death, lying among the strawberry flowers and the potato plants.

"The staff will be along almost at once," the German officer was saying in a rather heavy but easy French. "I'd like to get this cleaned up without delay. It's a charming place, really charming. Regrettable that it was necessary to touch the wall."

The Count put his pince-nez on with a hand that did not tremble, and as the thought struck him with singular force, *Gentlemen, actually well-bred men this time, he said aloud:*

"The bodies removed?" and he felt himself sickening and turned the other way.

"Buried," said the German officer pleasantly. He had a kid glove, as scrupulously clean as if just lifted from the haberdasher's counter, on the hand with which he touched the Count's tweed. "I'm sorry to give you all this trouble," he said. "The staff will require most of the bedrooms for the moment at least." Then he turned toward the black men again and gave his orders. "Right where they are," he said shortly. "Snipers' burial." "Right there—there, you mean?" said the Count. He was thinking confusedly of the potato plants and the strawberry flowers, but he could not bring himself to turn and look at them again.

COMMENT AND QUESTION

1. The title of this story is made to apply obviously to the Senegalese. But it applies with most force to some other people in the story. Who are they?

2. When Hitler invaded France in 1940, France had a supposedly impregnable Maginot line and a fine army. But she collapsed swiftly. This story holds a clue to the shattering fall of France in the second World War.

3. Between 1870 and 1940, Germany invaded France three times. What details in the story reflect this history?

4. This story was published first in *The New Yorker* and reflects the understatement so characteristic of the style of the magazine. But unlike many *New Yorker* stories, "They Weren't Going to Die" develops emotion, here a warm sympathy for the Senegalese. Miss Boyle arouses also a feeling of injustice and pain because of the dishonor done to the Senegalese. In all fairness, were the Senegalese really snipers?

5. "What in the name of God do you think you're in France for?" Like the title, this question of the Count's is ironical and holds the theme of the story.

6. At the end of the story the Count is confused. What conflicting ideas and emotions seem to be possessing him?

7. Notice the recurring metaphor concerning Christmas. How does this metaphor help to explain the actions of the Senegalese?

THE HANDS OF
MR. OTTERMOLE

BY THOMAS BURKE

THOMAS BURKE (1887–1945) was born in
London. He established his reputation with
his stories about the East End of London.
His collections of short stories include *Limehouse Nights* (1919), *More Limehouse Nights*
(1921), and *A Tea-Shop in Limehouse*
(1931).

MURDER (said old Quong)—oblige me by passing my pipe—murder is
one of the simplest things in the world to do. Killing a man is a much
simpler matter than killing a duck. Not always so safe, perhaps, but
simpler. But to certain gifted people it is both simple and entirely safe.
Many minds of finer complexion than my own have discoloured themselves
in seeking to name the identity of the author of those wholesale murders
which took place last year. Who that man or woman really was, I know no
more than you do, but I have a theory of the person it could have been;
and if you are not pressed for time I will elaborate that theory into a
little tale.

As I had the rest of that evening and the whole of the next day for
dalliance in my ivory tower, I desired that he would tell me the story; and,
having reckoned up his cash register and closed the ivory gate, he told me
—between then and the dawn—his story of the Mallon End murders. Para-
phrased and condensed, it came out something like this.

At six o'clock of a January evening Mr. Whybrow was walking home
through the cobweb alleys of London's East End. He had left the golden
clamour of the great High Street to which the tram had brought him from

THE HANDS OF MR. OTTERMOLE From *A Tea-Shop in Limehouse*. Copyright
1927, 1929, 1930, 1931 by Thomas Burke. Reprinted by permission of Paul R.
Reynolds & Son.

the river and his daily work, and was now in the chess-board of byways that is called Mallon End. None of the rush and gleam of the High Street trickled into these byways. A few paces south—a flood-tide of life, foaming and beating. Here—only slow shuffling figures and muffled pulses. He was in the sink of London, the last refuge of European vagrants.

As though in tune with the street's spirit, he too walked slowly, with head down. It seemed that he was pondering some pressing trouble, but he was not. He had no trouble. He was walking slowly because he had been on his feet all day, and he was bent in abstraction because he was wondering whether the Missis would have herrings for his tea, or haddock; and he was trying to decide which would be the more tasty on a night like this. A wretched night it was, of damp and mist, and the mist wandered into his throat and his eyes, and the damp had settled on pavement and roadway, and where the sparse lamp-light fell it sent up a greasy sparkle that chilled one to look at. By contrast it made his speculations more agreeable, and made him ready for that tea—whether herring or haddock. His eye turned from the glum bricks that made his horizon, and went forward half a mile. He saw a gas-lit kitchen, a flamy fire and a spread tea-table. There was toast in the hearth and a singing kettle on the side and a piquant effusion of herrings, or maybe of haddock, or perhaps sausages. The vision gave his aching feet a throb of energy. He shook imperceptible damp from his shoulders, and hastened towards its reality.

But Mr. Whybrow wasn't going to get any tea that evening—or any other evening. Mr. Whybrow was going to die. Somewhere within a hundred yards of him another man was walking: a man much like Mr. Whybrow and much like any other man, but without the only quality that enables mankind to live peaceably together and not as madmen in a jungle. A man with a dead heart eating into itself and bringing forth the foul organisms that arise from death and corruption. And that thing in man's shape, or a whim or a settled idea—one cannot know—had said within himself that Mr. Whybrow should never taste another herring. Not that Mr. Whybrow had injured him. Not that he had any dislike of Mr. Whybrow. Indeed, he knew nothing of him save as a familiar figure about the streets. But, moved by a force that had taken possession of his empty cells, he had picked on Mr. Whybrow with that blind choice that makes us pick one restaurant table that has nothing to mark it from four or five other tables, or one apple from a dish of half-a-dozen equal apples; or that drives Nature to send a cyclone upon one corner of this planet, and destroy five hundred lives in that corner, and leave another five hundred in the same corner unharmed. So this man had picked on Mr. Whybrow, as he might have picked on you or me, had we been within his daily observation; and even now he was creeping through the blue-toned streets, nursing his large white hands, moving ever closer to Mr. Whybrow's tea-table, so closer to Mr. Whybrow himself.

He wasn't, this man, a bad man. Indeed, he had many of the social and amiable qualities, and passed as a respectable man, as most successful criminals do. But the thought had come into his mouldering mind that he would like to murder somebody, and, as he held no fear of God or man, he was going to do it, and would then go home to *his* tea. I don't say that flippantly, but as a statement of fact. Strange as it may seem to the humane, murderers must and do sit down to meals after a murder. There is no reason why they shouldn't, and many reasons why they should. For one thing, they need to keep their physical and mental vitality at full beat for the business of covering their crime. For another, the strain of their effort makes them hungry, and satisfaction at the accomplishment of a desired thing brings a feeling of relaxation towards human pleasures. It is accepted among non-murderers that the murderer is always overcome by fear for his safety and horror at his act; but this type is rare. His own safety is, of course, his immediate concern, but vanity is a marked quality of most murderers, and that, together with the thrill of conquest, makes him confident that he can secure it, and when he has restored his strength with food he goes about securing it as a young hostess goes about the arranging of her first big dinner—a little anxious, but no more. Criminologists and detectives tell us that *every* murderer, however intelligent or cunning, always makes one slip in his tactics—one little slip that brings the affair home to him. But that is only half-true. It is true only of the murderers who are caught. Scores of murderers are not caught: therefore scores of murderers do not make any mistake at all. This man didn't.

As for horror or remorse, prison chaplains, doctors and lawyers have told us that of murderers they have interviewed under condemnation and the shadow of death, only one here and there has expressed any contrition for his act, or shown any sign of mental misery. Most of them display only exasperation at having been caught when so many have gone undiscovered, or indignation at being condemned for a perfectly reasonable act. However normal and humane they may have been before the murder, they are utterly without conscience after it. For what is conscience? Simply a polite nickname for superstition, which is a polite nickname for fear. Those who associate remorse with murder are, no doubt, basing their ideas on the world-legend of the remorse of Cain, or are projecting their own frail minds into the mind of the murderer, and getting false reactions. Peaceable folk cannot hope to make contact with this mind, for they are not merely different in mental type from the murderer: they are different in their personal chemistry and construction. Some men can and do kill, not one man, but two or three, and go calmly about their daily affairs. Other men could not, under the most agonising provocation, bring themselves even to wound. It is men of this sort who imagine the murderer in torments of remorse and fear of the law, whereas he is actually sitting down to his tea.

The man with the large white hands was as ready for his tea as Mr. Whybrow was, but he had something to do before he went to it. When he had done that something, and made no mistake about it, he would be even more ready for it, and would go to it as comfortably as he went to it the day before, when his hands were stainless.

Walk on, then, Mr. Whybrow, walk on; and as you walk, look your last upon the familiar features of your nightly journey. Follow your jack-o'-lantern tea-table. Look well upon its warmth and colour and kindness; feed your eyes with it, and tease your nose with its gentle domestic odours; for you will never sit down to it. Within ten minutes' pacing of you a pursuing phantom has spoken in his heart, and you are doomed. There you go —you and phantom—two nebulous dabs of mortality, moving through green air along pavements of powder-blue, the one to kill, the other to be killed. Walk on. Don't annoy your burning feet by hurrying, for the more slowly you walk, the longer you will breathe the green air of this January dusk, and see the dreamy lamplight and the little shops, and hear the agreeable commerce of the London crowd and the haunting pathos of the street-organ. These things are dear to you, Mr. Whybrow. You don't know it now, but in fifteen minutes you will have two seconds in which to realise how inexpressibly dear they are.

Walk on, then, across this crazy chess-board. You are in Lagos Street now, among the tents of the wanderers of Eastern Europe. A minute or so, and you are in Loyal Lane, among the lodging-houses that shelter the useless and the beaten of London's camp-followers. The lane holds the smell of them, and its soft darkness seems heavy with the wail of the futile. But you are not sensitive to impalpable things, and you plod through it, unseeing, as you do every evening, and come to Blean Street, and plod through that. From basement to sky rise the tenements of an alien colony. Their windows slot the ebony of their walls with lemon. Behind those windows strange life is moving, dressed with forms that are not of London or of England, yet, in essence, the same agreeable life that you have been living, and to-night will live no more. From high above you comes a voice crooning *The Song of Katta*. Through a window you see a family keeping a religious rite. Through another you see a woman pouring out tea for her husband. You see a man mending a pair of boots; a mother bathing her baby. You have seen all these things before, and never noticed them. You do not notice them now, but if you knew that you were never going to see them again, you would notice them. You never *will* see them again, not because your life has run its natural course, but because a man whom you have often passed in the street has at his own solitary pleasure decided to usurp the awful authority of nature, and destroy you. So perhaps it's as well that you don't notice them, for your part in them is ended. No more for you these pretty moments of our earthly travail: only one moment of terror, and then a plunging darkness.

Closer to you this shadow of massacre moves, and now he is twenty yards behind you. You can hear his footfall, but you do not turn your head. You are familiar with footfalls. You are in London, in the easy security of your daily territory, and footfalls behind you, your instinct tells you, are no more than a message of human company.

But can't you hear something in those footfalls—something that goes with a widdershins beat? Something that says: *Look out, look out. Beware, beware.* Can't you hear the very syllables of *murd-er-er, murd-er-er?* No; there is nothing in footfalls. They are neutral. The foot of villainy falls with the same quiet note as the foot of honesty. But those footfalls, Mr. Whybrow, are bearing on to you a pair of hands, and there *is* something in hands. Behind you that pair of hands is even now stretching its muscles in preparation for your end. Every minute of your days you have been seeing human hands. Have you ever realised the sheer horror of hands— those appendages that are a symbol for our moments of trust and affection and salutation? Have you thought of the sickening potentialities that lie within the scope of that five-tentacled member? No, you never have; for all the human hands that you have seen have been stretched to you in kindness or fellowship. Yet, though the eyes can hate, and the lips can sting, it is only that dangling member that can gather the accumulated essence of evil, and electrify it into currents of destruction. Satan may enter into man by many doors, but in the hands alone can he find the servants of his will.

Another minute, Mr. Whybrow, and you will know all about the horror of human hands.

You are nearly home now. You have turned into your street—Caspar Street—and you are in the centre of the chess-board. You can see the front window of your little four-roomed house. The street is dark, and its three lamps give only a smut of light that is more confusing than darkness. It is dark—empty, too. Nobody about; no lights in the front parlours of the houses, for the families are at tea in their kitchens; and only a random glow in a few upper rooms occupied by lodgers. Nobody about but you and your following companion, and you don't notice him. You see him so often that he is never seen. Even if you turned your head and saw him, you would only say "Good-evening" to him, and walk on. A suggestion that he was a possible murderer would not even make you laugh. It would be too silly.

And now you are at your gate. And now you have found your door-key. And now you are in, and hanging up your hat and coat. The Missis has just called a greeting from the kitchen, whose smell is an echo of that greeting (herrings!) and you have answered it, when the door shakes under a sharp knock.

Go away, Mr. Whybrow. Go away from that door. Don't touch it. Get right away from it. Get out of the house. Run with the Missis to the back garden, and over the fence. Or call the neighbours. But don't touch that door. Don't, Mr. Whybrow, don't open . . .

Mr. Whybrow opened the door.

That was the beginning of what became known as London's Strangling Horrors. Horrors they were called because they were something more than murders: they were motiveless, and there was an air of black magic about them. Each murder was committed at a time when the street where the bodies were found was empty of any perceptible or possible murderer. There would be an empty alley. There would be a policeman at its end. He would turn his back on the empty alley for less than a minute. Then he would look round and run into the night with news of another strangling. And in any direction he looked nobody to be seen and no report to be had of anybody being seen. Or he would be on duty in a long quiet street, and suddenly be called to a house of dead people whom a few seconds earlier he had seen alive. And, again, whichever way he looked nobody to be seen; and although police whistles put an immediate cordon around the area, and searched all houses, no possible murderer to be found.

The first news of the murder of Mr. and Mrs. Whybrow was brought by the station sergeant. He had been walking through Caspar Street on his way to the station for duty, when he noticed the open door of No. 98. Glancing in, he saw by the gaslight of the passage a motionless body on the floor. After a second look he blew his whistle, and when the constables answered him he took one to join him in a search of the house, and sent others to watch all neighbouring streets, and make inquiries at adjoining houses. But neither in the house nor in the streets was anything found to indicate the murderer. Neighbours on either side, and opposite, were questioned, but they had seen nobody about, and had heard nothing. One had heard Mr. Whybrow come home—the scrape of his latch-key in the door was so regular an evening sound, he said, that you could set your watch by it for half-past six—but he had heard nothing more than the sound of the opening door until the sergeant's whistle. Nobody had been seen to enter the house or leave it, by front or back, and the necks of the dead people carried no fingerprints or other traces. A nephew was called in to go over the house, but he could find nothing missing; and anyway his uncle possessed nothing worth stealing. The little money in the house was untouched, and there were no signs of any disturbance of the property, or even of struggle. No signs of anything but brutal and wanton murder.

Mr. Whybrow was known to neighbours and work-mates as a quiet, likeable, home-loving man; such a man as could not have any enemies. But, then, murdered men seldom have. A relentless enemy who hates a man to the point of wanting to hurt him seldom wants to murder him, since to do that puts him beyond suffering. So the police were left with an impossible situation: no clue to the murderer and no motive for the murders; only the fact that they had been done.

The first news of the affair sent a tremor through London generally, and an electric thrill through all Mallon End. Here was a murder of two inoffensive people, not for gain and not for revenge; and the murderer, to whom, apparently, killing was a casual impulse, was at large. He had left no traces, and, provided he had no companions, there seemed no reason why he should not remain at large. Any clear-headed man who stands alone, and has no fear of God or man, can, if he chooses, hold a city, even a nation, in subjection; but your everyday criminal is seldom clear-headed, and dislikes being lonely. He needs, if not the support of confederates, at least somebody to talk to; his vanity needs the satisfaction of perceiving at first hand the effect of his work. For this he will frequent bars and coffee-shops and other public places. Then, sooner or later, in a glow of comradeship, he will utter the one word too much; and the nark, who is everywhere, has an easy job.

But though the doss-houses and saloons and other places were "combed" and set with watches, and it was made known by whispers that good money and protection were assured to those with information, nothing attaching to the Whybrow case could be found. The murderer clearly had no friends and kept no company. Known men of this type were called up and questioned, but each was able to give a good account of himself; and in a few days the police were at a dead end. Against the constant public gibe that the thing had been done almost under their noses, they became restive, and for four days each man of the force was working his daily beat under a strain. On the fifth day they became still more restive.

It was the season of annual teas and entertainments for the children of the Sunday Schools, and on an evening of fog, when London was a world of groping phantoms, a small girl, in the bravery of best Sunday frock and shoes, shining face and new-washed hair, set out from Logan Passage for St. Michael's Parish Hall. She never got there. She was not actually dead until half-past six, but she was as good as dead from the moment she left her mother's door. Somebody like a man, pacing the street from which the Passage led, saw her come out; and from that moment she was dead. Through the fog somebody's large white hands reached after her, and in fifteen minutes they were about her.

At half-past six a whistle screamed trouble, and those answering it found the body of little Nellie Brinoff in a warehouse entry in Minnow Street. The sergeant was first among them, and he posted his men to useful points, ordering them here and there in the tart tones of repressed rage, and berating the officer whose beat the street was. "I saw you, Magson, at the end of the lane. What were you up to there? You were there ten minutes before you turned." Magson began an explanation about keeping an eye on a suspicious-looking character at that end, but the sergeant cut him short: "Suspicious character be damned. You don't want to look for suspicious characters. You want to look for *murderers*. Messing about . . . and then this happens right where you ought to be. Now think what they'll say."

With the speed of ill news came the crowd, pale and perturbed; and on the story that the unknown monster had appeared again, and this time to a child, their faces streaked the fog with spots of hate and horror. But then came the ambulance and more police, and swiftly they broke up the crowd; and as it broke the sergeant's thought was thickened into words, and from all sides came low murmurs of "Right under their noses." Later inquiries showed that four people of the district, above suspicion, had passed that entry at intervals of seconds before the murder, and seen nothing and heard nothing. None of them had passed the child alive or seen her dead. None of them had seen anybody in the street except themselves. Again the police were left with no motive and with no clue.

And now the district, as you will remember, was given over, not to panic, for the London public never yields to that, but to apprehension and dismay. If these things were happening in their familiar streets, then anything might happen. Wherever people met—in the streets, the markets and the shops—they debated the one topic. Women took to bolting their windows and doors at the first fall of dusk. They kept their children closely under their eye. They did their shopping before dark, and watched anxiously, while pretending they weren't watching, for the return of their husbands from work. Under the Cockney's semi-humorous resignation to disaster, they hid an hourly foreboding. By the whim of one man with a pair of hands the structure and tenour of their daily life were shaken, as they always can be shaken by any man contemptuous of humanity and fearless of its laws. They began to realise that the pillars that supported the peaceable society in which they lived were mere straws that anybody could snap; that laws were powerful only so long as they were obeyed; that the police were potent only so long as they were feared. By the power of his hands this one man had made a whole community do something new: he had made it think, and left it gasping at the obvious.

And then, while it was yet gasping under his first two strokes, he made his third. Conscious of the horror that his hands had created, and hungry as an actor who has once tasted the thrill of the multitude, he made fresh advertisement of his presence; and on Wednesday morning, three days after the murder of the child, the papers carried to the breakfast-tables of England the story of a still more shocking outrage.

At 9:32 on Tuesday night a constable was on duty in Jarnigan Road, and at that time spoke to a fellow-officer named Petersen at the top of Clemming Street. He had seen this officer walk down that street. He could swear that the street was empty at that time, except for a lame boot-black whom he knew by sight, and who passed him and entered a tene-

ment on the side opposite that on which his fellow-officer was walking.
He had the habit, as all constables had just then, of looking constantly
behind him and around him, whichever way he was walking, and he was
certain that the street was empty. He passed his sergeant at 9:33, saluted
him, and answered his inquiry for anything seen. He reported that he had
seen nothing, and passed on. His beat ended at a short distance from
Clemming Street, and, having paced it, he turned and came again at 9:34
to the top of the street. He had scarcely reached it before he heard the
hoarse voice of the sergeant: "Gregory! You there? Quick. Here's another.
My God, it's Petersen! Garotted. Quick, call 'em up!"

That was the third of the Strangling Horrors, of which there were to be
a fourth and a fifth; and the five horrors were to pass into the unknown
and unknowable. That is, unknown as far as authority and the public were
concerned. The identity of the murderer *was* known, but to two men only.
One was the murderer himself; the other was a young journalist.

This young man, who was covering the affairs for his paper, the *Daily
Torch*, was no smarter than the other zealous newspaper men who were
hanging about these byways in the hope of a sudden story. But he was
patient, and he hung a little closer to the case than the other fellows, and
by continually staring at it he at last raised the figure of the murderer like
a genie from the stones on which he had stood to do his murders.

After the first few days the men had given up any attempt at exclusive
stories, for there was none to be had. They met regularly at the police-
station, and what little information there was they shared. The officials
were agreeable to them, but no more. The sergeant discussed with them
the details of each murder; suggested possible explanations of the man's
methods; recalled from the past those cases that had some similarity; and
on the matter of motive reminded them of the motiveless Neil Cream and
the wanton John Williams, and hinted that work was being done which
would soon bring the business to an end; but about that work he would
not say a word. The Inspector, too, was gracefully garrulous on the thesis
of Murder, but whenever one of the party edged the talk towards what
was being done in this immediate matter, he glided past it. Whatever the
officials knew, they were not giving it to newspaper men. The business
had fallen heavily upon them, and only by a capture made by their own
efforts could they rehabilitate themselves in official and public esteem.
Scotland Yard, of course, was at work, and had all the station's material;
but the station's hope was that they themselves would have the honour of
settling the affair; and however useful the co-operation of the Press might
be in other cases, they did not want to risk a defeat by a premature dis-
closure of their theories and plans.

So the sergeant talked at large, and propounded one interesting theory
after another, all of which the newspaper men had thought of themselves.

The young man soon gave up these morning lectures on the Philosophy of Crime, and took to wandering about the streets and making bright stories out of the effect of the murders on the normal life of the people. A melancholy job made more melancholy by the district. The littered roadways, the crestfallen houses, the bleared windows—all held the acid misery that evokes no sympathy: the misery of the frustrated poet. The misery was the creation of the aliens, who were living in this makeshift fashion because they had no settled homes, and would neither take the trouble to make a home where they *could* settle, nor get on with their wandering.

There was little to be picked up. All he saw and heard were indignant faces, and wild conjectures of the murderer's identity and of the secret of his trick of appearing and disappearing unseen. Since a policeman himself had fallen a victim, denunciations of the force had ceased, and the unknown was now invested with a cloak of legend. Men eyed other men, as though thinking: It might be *him.* It might be *him.* They were no longer looking for a man who had the air of a Madame Tussaud murderer; they were looking for a man, or perhaps some harridan woman, who had done these particular murders. Their thoughts ran mainly on the foreign set. Such ruffianism could scarcely belong to England, nor could the bewildering cleverness of the thing. So they turned to Roumanian gipsies and Turkish carpet-sellers. There, clearly, would be found the "warm" spot. These Eastern fellows—they knew all sorts of tricks, and they had no real religion—nothing to hold them within bounds. Sailors returning from those parts had told tales of conjurors who made themselves invisible; and there were tales of Egyptian and Arab potions that were used for abysmally queer purposes. Perhaps it *was* possible to them; you never knew. They were so slick and cunning, and they had such gliding movements; no Englishman could melt away as they could. Almost certainly the murderer would be found to be one of that sort—with some dark trick of his own—and just because they were sure that he *was* a magician, they felt that it was useless to look for him. He was a power, able to hold them in subjection and to hold himself untouchable. Superstition, which so easily cracks the frail shell of reason, had got into them. He could do anything he chose: he would never be discovered. These two points they settled, and they went about the streets in a mood of resentful fatalism.

They talked of their ideas to the journalist in half-tones, looking right and left, as though HE might overhear them and visit them. And though all the district was thinking of him and ready to pounce upon him, yet, so strongly had he worked upon them, that if any man in the street—say, a small man of commonplace features and form—had cried "*I* am the Monster!" would their stifled fury have broken into flood and have borne him down and engulfed him? Or would they not suddenly have seen something unearthly in that everyday face and figure, something unearthly in his everyday boots, something unearthly about his hat, something that marked him as one whom none of their weapons could alarm or pierce? And would they not momentarily have fallen back from this devil, as the devil fell back from the Cross made by the sword of Faust, and so have given him time to escape? I do not know; but so fixed was their belief in his invincibility that it is at least likely that they would have made this hesitation, had such an occasion arisen. But it never did. To-day this commonplace fellow, his murder lust glutted, is still seen and observed among them as he was seen and observed all the time; but because nobody then dreamt, or now dreams, that he was what he was, they observed him then, and observe him now, as people observe a lamp-post.

Almost was their belief in his invincibility justified; for, five days after the murder of the policeman Petersen, when the experience and inspiration of the whole detective force of London were turned towards his identification and capture, he made his fourth and fifth strokes.

At nine o'clock that evening, the young newspaper man, who hung about every night until his paper was away, was strolling along Richards Lane. Richards Lane is a narrow street, partly a stall-market, and partly residential. The young man was in the residential section, which carries on one side small working-class cottages, and on the other the wall of a railway goods-yard. The great wall hung a blanket of shadow over the lane, and the shadow and the cadaverous outline of the now deserted market stalls gave it the appearance of a living lane that had been turned to frost in the moment between breath and death. The very lamps, that elsewhere were nimbuses of gold, had here the rigidity of gems. The journalist, feeling this message of frozen eternity, was telling himself that he was tired of the whole thing, when in one stroke the frost was broken. In the moment between one pace and another silence and darkness were racked by a high scream and through the scream a voice: "Help! help! *He's here!*"

Before he could think what movement to make, the lane came to life. As though its invisible populace had been waiting on that cry, the door of every cottage was flung open, and from them and from the alleys poured shadowy figures bent in question-mark form. For a second or so they stood as rigid as the lamps; then a police whistle gave them direction, and the flock of shadows sloped up the street. The journalist followed them, and others followed him. From the main street and from surrounding streets they came, some risen from unfinished suppers, some disturbed in their ease of slippers and shirt-sleeves, some stumbling on infirm limbs, and some upright, and armed with pokers or the tools of their trade. Here and there above the wavering cloud of heads moved the bold helmets of policemen. In one dim mass they surged upon a cottage whose doorway was marked by the sergeant and two constables; and voices of those behind urged them on with "Get in! Find him! Run round the back! Over the wall!" and those in front cried: "Keep back! Keep back!"

And now the fury of a mob held in thrall by unknown peril broke loose. He was here—on the spot. Surely this time he *could not* escape. All minds were bent upon the cottage; all energies thrust towards its doors and windows and roof; all thought was turned upon one unknown man and his extermination. So that no one man saw any other man. No man saw the narrow, packed lane and the mass of struggling shadows, and all forgot to look among themselves for the monster who never lingered upon his victims. All forgot, indeed, that they, by their mass crusade of vengeance, were affording him the perfect hiding-place. They saw only the house, and they heard only the rending of woodwork and the smash of glass at back and front, and the police giving orders or crying with the chase; and they pressed on.

But they found no murderer. All they found was news of murder and a glimpse of the ambulance, and for their fury there was no other object than the police themselves, who fought against this hampering of their work.

The journalist managed to struggle through to the cottage door, and to get the story from the constable stationed there. The cottage was the home of a pensioned sailor and his wife and daughter. They had been at supper, and at first it appeared that some noxious gas had smitten all three in mid-action. The daughter lay dead on the hearth-rug, with a piece of bread-and-butter in her hand. The father had fallen sideways from his chair, leaving on his plate a filled spoon of rice-pudding. The mother lay half under the table, her lap filled with the pieces of a broken cup and splashes of cocoa. But in three seconds the idea of gas was dismissed. One glance at their necks showed that this was the Strangler again; and the police stood and looked at the room and momentarily shared the fatalism of the public. They were helpless.

This was his fourth visit, making seven murders in all. He was to do, as you know, one more—and to do it that night; and then he was to pass into history as the unknown London horror, and return to the decent life that he had always led, remembering little of what he had done, and worried not at all by the memory. Why did he stop? Impossible to say. Why did he begin? Impossible again. It just happened like that; and if he thinks at all of those days and nights, I surmise that he thinks of them as we think of foolish or dirty little sins that we committed in childhood. We say that they were not really sins, because we were not then consciously ourselves: we had not come to realisation; and we look back at that foolish little creature that we once were, and forgive him because he didn't know. So, I think, with this man.

There are plenty like him. Eugene Aram, after the murder of Daniel Clarke, lived a quiet, contented life for fourteen years, unhaunted by his crime and unshaken in his self-esteem. Dr. Crippen murdered his wife, and then lived pleasantly with his mistress in the house under whose floor he had buried the wife. Constance Kent, found Not Guilty of the murder of her young brother, led a peaceful life for five years before she confessed. George Joseph Smith and William Palmer lived amiably among their fellows untroubled by fear or by remorse for their poisonings and drownings. Charles Peace, at the time he made his one unfortunate essay, had settled down into a respectable citizen with an interest in antiques. It happened that, after a lapse of time, these men were discovered, but more murderers than we guess are living decent lives to-day, and will die in decency, undiscovered and unsuspected. As this man will.

But he had a narrow escape, and it was perhaps this narrow escape that brought him to a stop. The escape was due to an error of judgment on the part of the journalist.

As soon as he had the full story of the affair, which took some time, he spent fifteen minutes on the telephone, sending the story through, and at the end of the fifteen minutes, when the stimulus of the business had left him, he felt physically tired and mentally dishevelled. He was not yet free to go home; the paper would not go away for another hour; so he turned into a bar for a drink and some sandwiches.

It was then, when he had dismissed the whole business from his mind, and was looking about the bar and admiring the landlord's taste in watch-chains and his air of domination, and was thinking that the landlord of a well-conducted tavern had a more comfortable life than a newspaper man, that his mind received from nowhere a spark of light. He was not thinking about the Strangling Horrors; his mind was on his sandwich. As a public-house sandwich, it was a curiosity. The bread had been thinly cut, it was buttered, and the ham was not two months stale; it was ham as it should be. His mind turned to the inventor of this refreshment, the Earl of Sandwich, and then to George the Fourth, and then to the Georges, and to the legend of that George who was worried to know how the apple got into the apple-dumpling. He wondered whether George would have been equally puzzled to know how the ham got into the ham sandwich, and how long it would have been before it occurred to him that the ham could not have got there unless somebody had put it there. He got up to order another sandwich, and in that moment a little active corner of his mind settled the affair. If there was ham in his sandwich, somebody must have put it there. If seven people had been murdered, somebody must have been there to murder them. There was no aeroplane or automobile that would go into a man's pocket; therefore that somebody must have escaped either by running away or standing still; and again therefore—

He was visualising the front-page story that his paper would carry if his theory were correct, and if—a matter of conjecture—his editor had the necessary nerve to make a bold stroke, when a cry of "Time, gentlemen, please! All out!" reminded him of the hour. He got up and went out into a world of mist, broken by the ragged discs of roadside puddles and the streaming lightning of motor-buses. He was certain that he had *the* story, but, even if it were proved, he was doubtful whether the policy of his paper would permit him to print it. It had one great fault. It was truth, but it was impossible truth. It rocked the foundations of everything that newspaper readers believed and that newspaper editors helped them to believe. They might believe that Turkish carpet-sellers had the gift of making themselves invisible. They would not believe this.

As it happened, they were not asked to, for the story was never written. As his paper had by now gone away, and as he was nourished by his refreshment and stimulated by his theory, he thought he might put in an extra half-hour by testing that theory. So he began to look about for the man he had in mind—a man with white hair, and large white hands; otherwise an everyday figure whom nobody would look twice at. He wanted to spring his idea on this man without warning, and he was going to place himself within reach of a man armoured in legends of dreadfulness and grue. This might appear to be an act of supreme courage—that one man, with no hope of immediate outside support, should place himself at the mercy of one who was holding a whole parish in terror. But it wasn't. He didn't think about the risk. He didn't think about his duty to his employers or loyalty to his paper. He was moved simply by an instinct to follow a story to its end.

He walked slowly from the tavern and crossed into Fingal Street, making for Deever Market, where he had hope of finding his man. But his journey was shortened. At the corner of Lotus Street he saw him—or a man who looked like him. This street was poorly lit, and he could see little of the man: but he *could* see white hands. For some twenty paces he stalked him; then drew level with him; and at a point where the arch of a railway crossed the street, he saw that this was his man. He approached him with the current conversational phrase of the district: "Well, seen anything of the murderer?" The man stopped to look sharply at him; then, satisfied that the journalist was not the murderer, said:

"Eh? No, nor's anybody else, curse it. Doubt if they ever will."

"I don't know. I've been thinking about them, and I've got an idea."

"So?"

"Yes. Came to me all of a sudden. Quarter of an hour ago. And I'd felt that we'd all been blind. It's been staring us in the face."

The man turned again to look at him, and the look and the movement held suspicion of this man who seemed to know so much. "Oh? Has it? Well, if you're so sure, why not give us the benefit of it?"

"I'm going to." They walked level, and were nearly at the end of the little street where it meets Deever Market, when the journalist turned casually to the man. He put a finger on his arm. "Yes, it seems to me quite simple now. But there's still one point I don't understand. One little thing I'd like to clear up. I mean the motive. Now, as man to man, tell me, Sergeant Ottermole, just *why* did you kill all those inoffensive people?"

The sergeant stopped, and the journalist stopped. There was just enough light from the sky, which held the reflected light of the continent of London, to give his a sight of the sergeant's face, and the sergeant's face was turned to him with a wide smile of such urbanity and charm that the journalist's eyes were frozen as they met it. The smile stayed for some seconds. Then said the sergeant: "Well, to tell you the truth, Mister Newspaper Man, I don't know. I really don't know. In fact, I've been worried about it myself. But I've got an idea—just like you. Everybody knows that we can't control the workings of our minds. Don't they? Ideas come into our minds without asking. But everybody's supposed to be able to control his body. Why? Eh? We get our minds from lord-knows-where— from people who were dead hundreds of years before we were born. Mayn't we get our bodies in the same way? Our faces—our legs—our heads —they aren't completely ours. We don't make 'em. They come to us. And couldn't ideas come into our bodies like ideas come into our minds? Eh? Can't ideas live in nerve and muscle as well as in brain? Couldn't it be that parts of our bodies aren't really us, and couldn't ideas come into those parts all of a sudden, like ideas come into—into"—he shot his arms out, showing the great white-gloved hands and hairy wrists; shot them out so swiftly to the journalist's throat that his eyes never saw them—"into *my hands!*"

COMMENT AND QUESTION

Some of the details in this story seem to reflect the exploits of Jack the Ripper, who once terrorized the East End of London. Further comment cannot be made on this detective story without giving the plot away.

PAUL'S CASE

BY WILLA CATHER

WILLA CATHER (1876-1947) was born in Virginia but moved to Nebraska when still a child. Two of her best novels, *O Pioneers!* (1913) and *My Ántonia* (1918), are excellent studies of the Middle West. In 1923 she won the Pulitzer Prize with *One of Ours*, a novel of the First World War. *Death Comes for the Archbishop* (1927), a sympathetic portrayal of Catholic missionaries in New Mexico; *A Lost Lady* (1923), a pioneer novel of the Middle West; and *Shadows on the Rock* (1931), a picture of life in early Quebec—these three novels reveal Miss Cather as a versatile artist. Her books of short stories include *The Troll Garden* (1905), *Youth and the Bright Medusa* (1920), *Obscure Destinies* (1932), and *The Old Beauty and Others* (1948).

I⊤ WAS Paul's afternoon to appear before the faculty of the Pittsburgh High School to account for his various misdemeanours. He had been suspended a week ago, and his father had called at the Principal's office and confessed his perplexity about his son. Paul entered the faculty room suave and smiling. His clothes were a trifle outgrown, and the tan velvet on the collar of his open overcoat was frayed and worn; but for all that there was something of the dandy about him, and he wore an opal pin in his neatly knotted black four-in-hand, and a red carnation in his buttonhole. This latter adornment the faculty somehow felt was not properly significant of the contrite spirit befitting a boy under the ban of suspension.

Paul was tall for his age and very thin, with high, cramped shoulders

PAUL'S CASE Reprinted from *Youth and the Bright Medusa* by Willa Cather, by permission of Alfred A. Knopf, Inc. Copyright 1905, 1932 by Willa Cather.

and a narrow chest. His eyes were remarkable for a certain hysterical brilliancy, and he continually used them in a conscious, theatrical sort of way, peculiarly offensive in a boy. The pupils were abnormally large, as though he were addicted to belladonna, but there was a glassy glitter about them which that drug does not produce.

When questioned by the Principal as to why he was there, Paul stated, politely enough, that he wanted to come back to school. This was a lie, but Paul was quite accustomed to lying; found it, indeed, indispensable for overcoming friction. His teachers were asked to state their respective charges against him, which they did with such a rancour and aggrievedness as evinced that this was not a usual case. Disorder and impertinence were among the offences named, yet each of his instructors felt that it was scarcely possible to put into words the real cause of the trouble, which lay in a sort of hysterically defiant manner of the boy's; in the contempt which they all knew he felt for them, and which he seemingly made not the least effort to conceal. Once, when he had been making a synopsis of a paragraph at the blackboard, his English teacher had stepped to his side and attempted to guide his hand. Paul had started back with a shudder and thrust his hands violently behind him. The astonished woman could scarcely have been more hurt and embarrassed had he struck at her. The insult was so involuntary and definitely personal as to be unforgettable. In one way and another, he had made all his teachers, men and women alike, conscious of the same feeling of physical aversion. In one class he habitually sat with his hand shading his eyes; in another he always looked out of the window during the recitation; in another he made a running commentary on the lecture, with humorous intent.

His teachers felt this afternoon that his whole attitude was symbolized by his shrug and his flippantly red carnation flower, and they fell upon him without mercy, his English teacher leading the pack. He stood through it smiling, his pale lips parted over his white teeth. (His lips were continually twitching, and he had a habit of raising his eyebrows that was contemptuous and irritating to the last degree.) Older boys than Paul had broken down and shed tears under that ordeal, but his set smile did not once desert him, and his only sign of discomfort was the nervous trembling of the fingers that toyed with the buttons of his overcoat, and an occasional jerking of the other hand which held his hat. Paul was always smiling, always glancing about him, seeming to feel that people might be watching him and trying to detect something. This conscious expression, since it was as far as possible from boyish mirthfulness, was usually attributed to insolence or "smartness."

As the inquisition proceeded, one of his instructors repeated an impertinent remark of the boy's, and the Principal asked him whether he thought that a courteous speech to make to a woman. Paul shrugged his shoulders slightly and his eyebrows twitched.

"I don't know," he replied. "I didn't mean to be polite or impolite, either. I guess it's a sort of way I have, of saying things regardless."

The Principal asked him whether he didn't think that a way it would be well to get rid of. Paul grinned and said he guessed so. When he was told that he could go, he bowed gracefully and went out. His bow was like a repetition of the scandalous red carnation.

His teachers were in despair, and his drawing master voiced the feeling of them all when he declared there was something about the boy which none of them understood. He added: "I don't really believe that smile of his comes altogether from insolence; there's something sort of haunted about it. The boy is not strong, for one thing. There is something wrong about the fellow."

The drawing master had come to realize that, in looking at Paul, one saw only his white teeth and the forced animation of his eyes. One warm afternoon the boy had gone to sleep at his drawing-board, and his master had noted with amazement what a white, blue-veined face it was; drawn and wrinkled like an old man's about the eyes, the lips twitching even in his sleep.

His teachers left the building dissatisfied and unhappy; humiliated to have felt so vindictive toward a mere boy, to have uttered this feeling in cutting terms, and to have set each other on, as it were, in the gruesome game of intemperate reproach. One of them remembered having seen a miserable street cat set at bay by a ring of tormentors.

As for Paul, he ran down the hill whistling the Soldiers' Chorus from *Faust*, looking wildly behind him now and then to see whether some of his teachers were not there to witness his light-heartedness. As it was now late in the afternoon and Paul was on duty that evening as usher at Carnegie Hall, he decided that he would not go home to supper.

When he reached the concert hall the doors were not yet open. It was chilly outside, and he decided to go up into the picture gallery—always deserted at this hour—where there were some of Raffelli's gay studies of Paris streets and an airy blue Venetian scene or two that always exhilarated him. He was delighted to find no one in the gallery but the old guard, who sat in the corner, a newspaper on his knee, a black patch over one eye and the other closed. Paul possessed himself of the place and walked confidently up and down, whistling under his breath. After a while he sat down before a blue Rico and lost himself. When he bethought him to look at his watch, it was after seven o'clock, and he rose with a start and ran downstairs, making a face at Augustus Cæsar, peering out from the cast-room, and an evil gesture at the Venus of Milo as he passed her on the stairway.

When Paul reached the ushers' dressing-room half-a-dozen boys were there already, and he began excitedly to tumble into his uniform. It was one of the few that at all approached fitting, and Paul thought it very becoming—though he knew the tight, straight coat accentuated his narrow chest, about which he was exceedingly sensitive. He was always excited while he dressed, twanging all over to the tuning of the strings and the preliminary flourishes of the horns in the music-room; but tonight he seemed quite beside himself, and he teased and plagued the boys until, telling him that he was crazy, they put him down on the floor and sat on him.

Somewhat calmed by his suppression, Paul dashed out to the front of the house to seat the early comers. He was a model usher. Gracious and smiling he ran up and down the aisles. Nothing was too much trouble for him; he carried messages and brought programs as though it were his greatest pleasure in life, and all the people in his section thought him a charming boy, feeling that he remembered and admired them. As the house filled, he grew more and more vivacious and animated, and the colour came to his cheeks and lips. It was very much as though this were a great reception and Paul were the host. Just as the musicians came out to take their places, his English teacher arrived with checks for the seats which a prominent manufacturer had taken for the season. She betrayed some embarrassment when she handed Paul the tickets, and a *hauteur* which subsequently made her feel very foolish. Paul was startled for a moment, and had the feeling of wanting to put her out; what business had she here among all these fine people and gay colours? He looked her over and decided that she was not appropriately dressed and must be a fool to sit downstairs in such togs. The tickets had probably been sent her out of kindness, he reflected, as he put down a seat for her, and she had about as much right to sit there as he had.

When the symphony began Paul sank into one of the rear seats with a long sigh of relief, and lost himself as he had done before the Rico. It was not that symphonies, as such, meant anything in particular to Paul, but the first sigh of the instruments seemed to free some hilarious spirit within him; something that struggled there like the Genius in the bottle found by the Arab fisherman. He felt a sudden zest of life; the lights danced before his eyes and the concert hall blazed into unimaginable splendour. When the soprano soloist came on, Paul forgot even the nastiness of his teacher's being there, and gave himself up to the peculiar intoxication such personages always had for him. The soloist chanced to be a German woman, by no means in her first youth, and the mother of many children; but she wore a satin gown and a tiara, and she had that indefinable air of achievement, that world-shine upon her, which always blinded Paul to any possible defects.

After a concert was over, Paul was often irritable and wretched until he got to sleep,—and tonight he was even more than usually restless. He had the feeling of not being able to let down; of its being impossible to give up this delicious excitement which was the only thing that could be called living at all. During the last number he withdrew and, after hastily changing his clothes in the dressing-room, slipped out to the side door where the singer's carriage stood. Here he began pacing rapidly up and down the walk, waiting to see her come out.

Over yonder the Schenley, in its vacant stretch, loomed big and square through the fine rain, the windows of its twelve stories glowing like those of a lighted card-board house under a Christmas tree. All the actors and singers of any importance stayed there when they were in the city, and a number of the big manufacturers of the place lived there in the winter. Paul had often hung about the hotel, watching the people go in and out, longing to enter and leave school-masters and dull care behind him for ever.

At last the singer came out, accompanied by the conductor, who helped her into her carriage and closed the door with a cordial *auf wiedersehen,* —which set Paul to wondering whether she were not an old sweetheart of his. Paul followed the carriage over to the hotel, walking so rapidly as not to be far from the entrance when the singer alighted and disappeared behind the swinging glass doors which were opened by a negro in a tall hat and a long coat. In the moment that the door was ajar, it seemed to Paul that he, too, entered. He seemed to feel himself go after her up the steps, into the warm, lighted building, into an exotic, a tropical world of shiny, glistening surfaces and basking ease. He reflected upon the mysterious dishes that were brought into the dining-room, the green bottles in buckets of ice, as he had seen them in the supper party pictures of the Sunday supplement. A quick gust of wind brought the rain down with sudden vehemence, and Paul was startled to find that he was still outside in the slush of the gravel driveway; that his boots were letting in the water and his scanty overcoat was clinging wet about him; that the lights in front of the concert hall were out, and that the rain was driving in sheets between him and the orange glow of the windows above him. There it was, what he wanted—tangibly before him, like the fairy world of a Christmas pantomime; as the rain beat in his face, Paul wondered whether he were destined always to shiver in the black night outside, looking up at it.

He turned and walked reluctantly toward the car tracks. The end had to come sometime; his father in his nightclothes at the top of the stairs, explanations that did not explain, hastily improvised fictions that were forever tripping him up, his upstairs room and its horrible yellow wallpaper, the creaking bureau with the greasy plush collar-box, and over his painted wooden bed the pictures of George Washington and John Calvin, and the framed motto, "Feed my Lambs," which had been worked in red worsted by his mother, whom Paul could not remember.

Half an hour later, Paul alighted from the Negley Avenue car and went slowly down one of the side streets off the main thoroughfare. It was a highly respectable street, where all the houses were exactly alike, and where business men of moderate means begot and reared large families of children, all of whom went to Sabbath-school and learned the shorter catechism, and were interested in arithmetic; all of whom were as exactly alike as their homes, and of a piece with the monotony in which they lived. Paul never went up Cordelia Street without a shudder of loathing. His home was next the house of the Cumberland minister. He approached it tonight with the nerveless sense of defeat, the hopeless feeling of sinking back forever into ugliness and commonness that he had always had when he came home. The moment he turned into Cordelia Street he felt the waters close above his head. After each of these orgies of living, he experienced all the physical depression which follows a debauch; the loathing of respectable beds, of common food, of a house permeated by kitchen odours; a shuddering repulsion for the flavourless, colourless mass of every-day existence; a morbid desire for cool things and soft lights and fresh flowers.

The nearer he approached the house, the more absolutely unequal Paul felt to the sight of it all; his ugly sleeping chamber; the cold bath-room with the grimy zinc tub, the cracked mirror, the dripping spiggots; his father, at the top of the stairs, his hairy legs sticking out from his nightshirt, his feet thrust into carpet slippers. He was so much later than usual that there would certainly be inquiries and reproaches. Paul stopped short before the door. He felt that he could not be accosted by his father tonight; that he could not toss again on that miserable bed. He would not go in. He would tell his father that he had no car fare, and it was raining so hard he had gone home with one of the boys and stayed all night.

Meanwhile, he was wet and cold. He went around to the back of the house and tried one of the basement windows, found it open, raised it cautiously, and scrambled down the cellar wall to the floor. There he stood, holding his breath, terrified by the noise he had made; but the floor above him was silent, and there was no creak on the stairs. He found a soap-box, and carried it over to the soft ring of light that streamed from the furnace door, and sat down. He was horribly afraid of rats, so he did not try to sleep, but sat looking distrustfully at the dark, still terrified lest he might have awakened his father. In such reactions, after one of the experiences which made days and nights out of the dreary blanks of the calendar, when his senses were deadened, Paul's head was always singularly clear. Suppose his father had heard him getting in at the window and had come down and shot him for a burglar? Then, again, suppose his father had come down, pistol in hand, and he had cried out in time to save himself, and his father had been horrified to think how nearly he had killed him? Then, again, suppose a day should come when his father would remember that night, and wish there had been no warning cry to stay his hand? With this last supposition Paul entertained himself until daybreak.

The following Sunday was fine; the sodden November chill was broken by the last flash of autumnal summer. In the morning Paul had to go to church and Sabbath-school, as always. On seasonable Sunday afternoons the burghers of Cordelia Street usually sat out on their front "stoops," and talked to their neighbours on the next stoop, or called to those across the street in neighbourly fashion. The men sat placidly on gay cushions placed upon the steps that led down to the sidewalk, while the women, in their Sunday "waists," sat in rockers on the cramped porches, pretending to be greatly at their ease. The children played in the streets; there were so many of them that the place resembled the recreation grounds of a kindergarten. The men on the steps—all in their shirt sleeves, their vests unbuttoned—sat with their legs well apart, their stomachs comfortably protruding, and talked of the prices of things, or told anecdotes of the sagacity of their various chiefs and overlords. They occasionally looked over the multitude of squabbling children, listened affectionately to their high-pitched, nasal voices, smiling to see their own proclivities reproduced in their offspring, and interspersed their legends of the iron kings with remarks about their sons' progress at school, their grades in arithmetic, and the amounts they had saved in their toy banks.

On this last Sunday of November, Paul sat all the afternoon on the lowest step of his "stoop," staring into the street, while his sisters, in their rockers, were talking to the minister's daughters next door about how many shirt-waists they had made in the last week, and how many waffles some one had eaten at the last church supper. When the weather was warm, and his father was in a particularly jovial frame of mind, the girls made lemonade, which was always brought out in a red-glass pitcher, ornamented with forget-me-nots in blue enamel. This the girls thought very fine, and the neighbours joked about the suspicious colour of the pitcher.

Today Paul's father, on the top step, was talking to a young man who shifted a restless baby from knee to knee. He happened to be the young man who was daily held up to Paul as a model, and after whom it was his father's dearest hope that he would pattern. This young man was of a ruddy complexion, with a compressed, red mouth, and faded, near-sighted eyes, over which he wore thick spectacles, with gold bows that curved about his ears. He was clerk to one of the magnates of a great steel corporation, and was looked upon in Cordelia Street as a young man with a future. There was a story that, some five years ago—he was now barely twenty-six—he had been a trifle "dissipated," but in order to curb his appetites and save the loss of time and strength that a sowing of wild oats might have entailed, he had taken his chief's advice, oft reiterated to his employés, and at twenty-one had married the first woman whom **he** could persuade to share his fortunes. She happened to be an angular school-mistress, much older than he, who also wore thick glasses, and who had now borne him four children, all near-sighted, like herself.

The young man was relating how his chief, now cruising in the Mediterranean, kept in touch with all the details of the business, arranging his office hours on his yacht just as though he were at home, and "knocking off work enough to keep two stenographers busy." His father told, in turn, the plan his corporation was considering, of putting in an electric railway plant at Cairo. Paul snapped his teeth; he had an awful apprehension that they might spoil it all before he got there. Yet he rather liked to hear these legends of the iron kings, that were told and retold on Sundays and holidays; these stories of palaces in Venice, yachts on the Mediterranean, and high play at Monte Carlo appealed to his fancy, and he was interested in the triumphs of cash boys who had become famous, though he had no mind for the cash-boy stage.

After supper was over, and he had helped to dry the dishes, Paul nervously asked his father whether he could go to George's to get some help in his geometry, and still more nervously asked for car-fare. This latter request he had to repeat, as his father, on principle, did not like to hear requests for money, whether much or little. He asked Paul whether he could not go to some boy who lived nearer, and told him that he ought not to leave his school work until Sunday; but he gave him the dime. He was not a poor man, but he had a worthy ambition to come up in the world. His only reason for allowing Paul to usher was that he thought a boy ought to be earning a little.

Paul bounded upstairs, scrubbed the greasy odour of the dish-water from his hands with the ill-smelling soap he hated, and then shook over his fingers a few drops of violet water from the bottle he kept hidden in his drawer. He left the house with his geometry conspicuously under his arm, and the moment he got out of Cordelia Street and boarded a downtown car, he shook off the lethargy of two deadening days, and began to live again.

The leading juvenile of the permanent stock company which played at one of the downtown theatres was an acquaintance of Paul's, and the boy had been invited to drop in at the Sunday-night rehearsals whenever he could. For more than a year Paul had spent every available moment loitering about Charley Edwards's dressing-room. He had won a place among Edwards's following not only because the young actor, who could not afford to employ a dresser, often found him useful, but because he recognized in Paul something akin to what churchmen term "vocation."

It was at the theatre and at Carnegie Hall that Paul really lived; the rest was but a sleep and a forgetting. This was Paul's fairy tale, and it had for him all the allurement of a secret love. The moment he inhaled the gassy, painty, dusty odour behind the scenes, he breathed like a prisoner set free, and felt within him the possibility of doing or saying splendid, brilliant things. The moment the cracked orchestra beat out the overture from *Martha*, or jerked at the serenade from *Rigoletto*, all stupid and ugly things slid from him, and his senses were deliciously, yet delicately fired.

Perhaps it was because, in Paul's world, the natural nearly always wore the guise of ugliness, that a certain element of artificiality seemed to him necessary in beauty. Perhaps it was because his experience of life elsewhere was so full of Sabbath-school picnics, petty economies, wholesome advice as to how to succeed in life, and the unescapable odours of cooking, that he found this existence so alluring, these smartly-clad men and women so attractive, that he was so moved by these starry apple orchards that bloomed perennially under the lime-light.

It would be difficult to put it strongly enough how convincingly the stage entrance of that theatre was for Paul the actual portal of Romance. Certainly none of the company ever suspected it, least of all Charley Edwards. It was very like the old stories that used to float about London of fabulously rich Jews, who had subterranean halls, with palms, and fountains, and soft lamps and richly apparelled women who never saw the disenchanting light of London day. So, in the midst of that smoke-palled city, enamoured of figures and grimy toil, Paul had his secret temple, his wishing-carpet, this bit of blue-and-white Mediterranean shore bathed in perpetual sunshine.

Several of Paul's teachers had a theory that his imagination had been perverted by garish fiction; but the truth was, he scarcely ever read at all. The books at home were not such as would either tempt or corrupt a youthful mind, and as for reading the novels that some of his friends urged upon him—well, he got what he wanted much more quickly from music; any sort of music, from an orchestra to a barrel organ. He needed only the spark, the indescribable thrill that made his imagination master of his senses, and he could make plots and pictures enough of his own. It was equally true that he was not stagestruck—not, at any rate, in the usual acceptation of that expression. He had no desire to become an actor, any more than he had to become a musician. He felt no necessity to do any of these things; what he wanted was to see, to be in the atmosphere, float on the wave of it, to be carried out, blue league after blue league, away from everything.

After a night behind the scenes, Paul found the schoolroom more than ever repulsive; the bare floors and naked walls; the prosy men who never wore frock coats, or violets in their buttonholes; the women with their dull gowns, shrill voices, and pitiful seriousness about prepositions that govern the dative. He could not bear to have the other pupils think, for a moment, that he took these people seriously; he must convey to them that he considered it all trivial, and was there only by way of a joke, anyway. He had autograph pictures of all the members of the stock company which he showed his classmates, telling them the most incredible stories of his familiarity with these people, of his acquaintance with the soloists who came to Carnegie Hall, his suppers with them and the flowers he sent them. When these stories lost their effect, and his audience grew listless, he would bid all the boys good-bye, announcing that he was going to travel for awhile; going to Naples, to California, to Egypt. Then, next Monday, he would slip back, conscious and nervously smiling; his sister was ill, and he would have to defer his voyage until spring.

Matters went steadily worse with Paul at school. In the itch to let his instructors know how heartily he despised them, and how thoroughly he was appreciated elsewhere, he mentioned once or twice that he had no time to fool with theorems; adding—with a twitch of the eyebrows and a touch of that nervous bravado which so perplexed them—that he was helping the people down at the stock company; they were old friends of his.

The upshot of the matter was, that the Principal went to Paul's father, and Paul was taken out of school and put to work. The manager at Carnegie Hall was told to get another usher in his stead; the doorkeeper at the theatre was warned not to admit him to the house; and Charley Edwards remorsefully promised the boy's father not to see him again.

The members of the stock company were vastly amused when some of Paul's stories reached them—especially the women. They were hardworking women, most of them supporting indolent husbands or brothers, and they laughed rather bitterly at having stirred the boy to such fervid and florid inventions. They agreed with the faculty and with his father, that Paul's was a bad case.

The east-bound train was ploughing through a January snow-storm; the dull dawn was beginning to show grey when the engine whistled a mile out of Newark. Paul started up from the seat where he had lain curled in uneasy slumber, rubbed the breath-misted window glass with his hand, and peered out. The snow was whirling in curling eddies above the white bottom lands, and the drifts lay already deep in the fields and along the fences, while here and there the long dead grass and dried weed stalks protruded black above it. Lights shone from the scattered houses, and a gang of labourers who stood beside the track waved their lanterns.

Paul had slept very little, and he felt grimy and uncomfortable. He had made the all-night journey in a day coach because he was afraid if he took a Pullman he might be seen by some Pittsburgh business man who had noticed him in Denny & Carson's office. When the whistle woke him, he clutched quickly at his breast pocket, glancing about him with an uncertain smile. But the little, clay-bespattered Italians were still sleeping, the slatternly women across the aisle were in open-mouthed oblivion, and even the crumby, crying babies were for the nonce stilled. Paul settled back to struggle with his impatience as best he could.

When he arrived at the Jersey City station, he hurried through his breakfast, manifestly ill at ease and keeping a sharp eye about him. After he reached the Twenty-third Street station, he consulted a cabman, and had himself driven to a men's furnishing establishment which was just opening for the day. He spent upward of two hours there, buying with endless reconsidering and great care. His new street suit he put on in the fitting-room; the frock coat and dress clothes he had bundled into the cab with his new shirts. Then he drove to a hatter's and a shoe house. His next errand was at Tiffany's, where he selected silver mounted brushes and a scarf-pin. He would not wait to have his silver marked, he said. Lastly, he stopped at a trunk shop on Broadway, and had his purchases packed into various travelling bags.

It was a little after one o'clock when he drove up to the Waldorf, and, after settling with the cabman, went into the office. He registered from Washington; said his mother and father had been abroad, and that he had come down to await the arrival of their steamer. He told his story plausibly and had no trouble, since he offered to pay for them in advance, in engaging his rooms; a sleeping-room, sitting-room and bath.

Not once, but a hundred times Paul had planned this entry into New York. He had gone over every detail of it with Charley Edwards, and in his scrap book at home there were pages of description about New York hotels, cut from the Sunday papers.

When he was shown to his sitting-room on the eighth floor, he saw at a glance that everything was as it should be; there was but one detail in his mental picture that the place did not realize, so he rang for the bell boy and sent him down for flowers. He moved about nervously until the boy returned, putting away his new linen and fingering it delightedly as he did so. When the flowers came, he put them hastily into water, and then tumbled into a hot bath. Presently he came out of his white bath-room, resplendent in his new silk underwear, and playing with the tassels of his red robe. The snow was whirling so fiercely outside his windows that he could scarcely see across the street; but within, the air was deliciously soft and fragrant. He put the violets and jonquils on the tabouret beside the couch, and threw himself down with a long sigh, covering himself with a Roman blanket. He was thoroughly tired; he had been in such haste, he had stood up to such a strain, covered so much ground in the last twenty-four hours, that he wanted to think how it had all come about. Lulled by the sound of the wind, the warm air, and the cool fragrance of the flowers, he sank into deep, drowsy retrospection.

It had been wonderfully simple; when they had shut him out of the theatre and concert hall, when they had taken away his bone, the whole thing was virtually determined. The rest was a mere matter of opportunity. The only thing that at all surprised him was his own courage—for he realized well enough that he had always been tormented by fear, a sort of apprehensive dread that, of late years, as the meshes of the lies he had told closed about him, had been pulling the muscles of his body tighter and tighter. Until now, he could not remember a time when he had not been dreading something. Even when he was a little boy, it was always there—behind him, or before, or on either side. There had always been the shadowed corner, the dark place into which he dared not look, but from which something seemed always to be watching him—and Paul had done things that were not pretty to watch, he knew.

But now he had a curious sense of relief, as though he had at last thrown down the gauntlet to the thing in the corner.

Yet it was but a day since he had been sulking in the traces; but yesterday afternoon that he had been sent to the bank with Denny & Carson's deposit, as usual—but this time he was instructed to leave the book to be balanced. There was above two thousand dollars in checks, and nearly a thousand in the bank notes which he had taken from the book and quietly transferred to his pocket. At the bank he had made out a new deposit slip. His nerves had been steady enough to permit of his returning to the office, where he had finished his work and asked for a full day's holiday tomorrow, Saturday, giving a perfectly reasonable pretext. The bank book, he knew, would not be returned before Monday or Tuesday, and his father would be out of town for the next week. From the time he slipped the bank notes into his pocket until he boarded the night train for New York, he had not known a moment's hesitation.

How astonishingly easy it had all been; here he was, the thing done; and this time there would be no awakening, no figure at the top of the stairs. He watched the snow flakes whirling by his window until he fell asleep.

When he awoke, it was four o'clock in the afternoon. He bounded up with a start; one of his precious days gone already! He spent nearly an hour in dressing, watching every stage of his toilet carefully in the mirror. Everything was quite perfect; he was exactly the kind of boy he had always wanted to be.

When he went downstairs, Paul took a carriage and drove up Fifth avenue toward the Park. The snow had somewhat abated; carriages and tradesmen's wagons were hurrying soundlessly to and fro in the winter twilight; boys in woollen mufflers were shovelling off the doorsteps; the avenue stages made fine spots of colour against the white street. Here and there on the corners whole flower gardens blooming behind glass windows, against which the snow flakes stuck and melted; violets, roses, carnations, lilies of the valley—somehow vastly more lovely and alluring that they blossomed thus unnaturally in the snow. The Park itself was a wonderful stage winter-piece.

When he returned, the pause of the twilight had ceased, and the tune of the streets had changed. The snow was falling faster, lights streamed from the hotels that reared their many stories fearlessly up into the storm, defying the raging Atlantic winds. A long, black stream of carriages poured down the avenue, intersected here and there by other streams, tending horizontally. There were a score of cabs about the entrance of his hotel, and his driver had to wait. Boys in livery were running in and out of the awning stretched across the sidewalk, up and down the red velvet carpet laid from the door to the street. Above, about, within it all, was the rumble and roar, the hurry and toss of thousands of human beings as hot for pleasure as himself, and on every side of him towered the glaring affirmation of the omnipotence of wealth.

The boy set his teeth and drew his shoulders together in a spasm of realization; the plot of all dramas, the text of all romances, the nerve-stuff of all sensations was whirling about him like the snow flakes. He burnt like a faggot in a tempest.

When Paul came down to dinner, the music of the orchestra floated up the elevator shaft to greet him. As he stepped into the thronged corridor, he sank back into one of the chairs against the wall to get his breath. The lights, the chatter, the perfumes, the bewildering medley of colour— he had, for a moment, the feeling of not being able to stand it. But only for a moment; these were his own people, he told himself. He went slowly about the corridors, through the writing-rooms, smoking-rooms, reception-rooms, as though he were exploring the chambers of an enchanted palace, built and peopled for him alone.

When he reached the dining-room he sat down at a table near a window. The flowers, the white linen, the many-coloured wine glasses, the gay toilettes of the women, the low popping of corks, the undulating repetitions of the *Blue Danube* from the orchestra, all flooded Paul's dream with bewildering radiance. When the roseate tinge of his champagne was added—that cold, precious, bubbling stuff that creamed and foamed in his glass—Paul wondered that there were honest men in the world at all. This was what all the world was fighting for, he reflected; this was what all the struggle was about. He doubted the reality of his past. Had he ever known a place called Cordelia Street, a place where fagged looking business men boarded the early car? Mere rivets in a machine they seemed to Paul,— sickening men, with combings of children's hair always hanging to their coats, and the smell of cooking in their clothes. Cordelia Street—Ah, that belonged to another time and country! Had he not always been thus, had he not sat here night after night, from as far back as he could remember, looking pensively over just such shimmering textures, and slowly twirling the stem of a glass like this one between his thumb and middle finger? He rather thought he had.

He was not in the least abashed or lonely. He had no especial desire to meet or to know any of these people; all he demanded was the right to look on and conjecture, to watch the pageant. The mere stage properties

were all he contended for. Nor was he lonely later in the evening, in his
loge at the Opera. He was entirely rid of his nervous misgivings, of his
forced aggressiveness, of the imperative desire to show himself different
from his surroundings. He felt now that his surroundings explained him.
Nobody questioned the purple; he had only to wear it passively. He had
only to glance down at his dress coat to reassure himself that here it would
be impossible for anyone to humiliate him.

He found it hard to leave his beautiful sitting-room to go to bed that
night, and sat long watching the raging storm from his turret window.
When he went to sleep, it was with the lights turned on in his bedroom;
partly because of his old timidity, and partly so that, if he should wake
in the night, there would be no wretched moment of doubt, no horrible
suspicion of yellow wall-paper, or of Washington and Calvin above
his bed.

On Sunday morning the city was practically snowbound. Paul break-
fasted late, and in the afternoon he fell in with a wild San Francisco boy,
a freshman at Yale, who said he had run down for a "little flyer" over
Sunday. The young man offered to show Paul the night side of the town,
and the two boys went off together after dinner, not returning to the hotel
until seven o'clock the next morning. They had started out in the confiding
warmth of a champagne friendship, but their parting in the elevator was
singularly cool. The freshman pulled himself together to make his train,
and Paul went to bed. He awoke at two o'clock in the afternoon, very
thirsty and dizzy, and rang for ice-water, coffee, and the Pittsburgh
papers.

On the part of the hotel management, Paul excited no suspicion. There
was this to be said for him, that he wore his spoils with dignity and in no
way made himself conspicuous. His chief greediness lay in his ears and
eyes, and his excesses were not offensive ones. His dearest pleasures were
the grey winter twilights in his sitting-room; his quiet enjoyment of his
flowers, his clothes, his wide divan, his cigarette and his sense of power.
He could not remember a time when he had felt so at peace with himself.
The mere release from the necessity of petty lying, lying every day and
every day, restored his self-respect. He had never lied for pleasure, even
at school; but to make himself noticed and admired, to assert his difference from other Cordelia Street boys; and he felt a good deal more
manly, more honest, even, now that he had no need for boastful pretensions, now that he could, as his actor friends used to say, "dress the part."
It was characteristic that remorse did not occur to him. His golden days
went by without a shadow, and he made each as perfect as he could.

On the eighth day after his arrival in New York, he found the whole
affair exploited in the Pittsburgh papers, exploited with a wealth of detail
which indicated that local news of a sensational nature was at a low ebb.
The firm of Denny & Carson announced that the boy's father had re-

funded the full amount of his theft, and that they had no intention of prosecuting. The Cumberland minister had been interviewed, and expressed his hope of yet reclaiming the motherless lad, and Paul's Sabbath-school teacher declared that she would spare no effort to that end. The rumour had reached Pittsburgh that the boy had been seen in a New York hotel, and his father had gone East to find him and bring him home.

Paul had just come in to dress for dinner; he sank into a chair, weak in the knees, and clasped his head in his hands. It was to be worse than jail, even; the tepid waters of Cordelia Street were to close over him finally and forever. The grey monotony stretched before him in hopeless, unrelieved years; Sabbath-school, Young People's Meeting, the yellow-papered room, the damp dish-towels; it all rushed back upon him with sickening vividness. He had the old feeling that the orchestra had suddenly stopped, the sinking sensation that the play was over. The sweat broke out on his face, and he sprang to his feet, looking about him with his white, conscious smile, and winked at himself in the mirror. With something of the childish belief in miracles with which he had so often gone to class, all his lessons unlearned, Paul dressed and dashed whistling down the corridor to the elevator.

He had no sooner entered the dining-room and caught the measure of the music, than his remembrance was lightened by his old elastic power of claiming the moment, mounting with it, and finding it all sufficient. The glare and glitter about him, the mere scenic accessories had again, and for the last time, their old potency. He would show himself that he was game, he would finish the thing splendidly. He doubted, more than ever, the existence of Cordelia Street, and for the first time he drank his wine recklessly. Was he not, after all, one of these fortunate beings? Was he not still himself, and in his own place? He drummed a nervous accompaniment to the music and looked about him, telling himself over and over that it had paid.

He reflected drowsily, to the swell of the violin and the chill sweetness of his wine, that he might have done it more wisely. He might have caught an outbound steamer and been well out of their clutches before now. But the other side of the world had seemed too far away and too uncertain then; he could not have waited for it; his need had been too sharp. If he had to choose over again, he would do the same thing tomorrow. He looked affectionately about the dining-room, now gilded with a soft mist. Ah, it had paid indeed!

Paul was awakened next morning by a painful throbbing in his head and feet. He had thrown himself across the bed without undressing, and had slept with his shoes on. His limbs and hands were lead heavy, and his tongue and throat were parched. There came upon him one of those fateful attacks of clear-headedness that never occurred except when he was physically exhausted and his nerves hung loose. He lay still and closed his eyes and let the tide of realities wash over him.

His father was in New York; "stopping at some joint or other," he told himself. The memory of successive summers on the front stoop fell upon him like a weight of black water. He had not a hundred dollars left; and he knew now, more than ever, that money was everything, the wall that stood between all he loathed and all he wanted. The thing was winding itself up; he had thought of that on his first glorious day in New York, and had even provided a way to snap the thread. It lay on his dressing-table now; he had got it out last night when he came blindly up from dinner,— but the shiny metal hurt his eyes, and he disliked the look of it, anyway.

He rose and moved about with a painful effort, succumbing now and again to attacks of nausea. It was the old depression exaggerated; all the world had become Cordelia Street. Yet somehow he was not afraid of anything, was absolutely calm; perhaps because he had looked into the dark corner at last, and knew. It was bad enough, what he saw there; but somehow not so bad as his long fear of it had been. He saw everything clearly now. He had a feeling that he had made the best of it, that he had lived the sort of life he was meant to live, and for half an hour he sat staring at the revolver. But he told himself that was not the way, so he went downstairs and took a cab to the ferry.

When Paul arrived at Newark, he got off the train and took another cab, directing the driver to follow the Pennsylvania tracks out of the town. The snow lay heavy on the roadways and had drifted deep in the open fields. Only here and there the dead grass or dried weed stalks projected, singularly black, above it. Once well into the country, Paul dismissed the carriage and walked, floundering along the tracks, his mind a medley of irrelevant things. He seemed to hold in his brain an actual picture of everything he had seen that morning. He remembered every feature of both his drivers, the toothless old woman from whom he had bought the red flowers in his coat, the agent from whom he had got his ticket, and all of his fellow-passengers on the ferry. His mind, unable to cope with vital matters near at hand, worked feverishly and deftly at sorting and grouping these images. They made for him a part of the ugliness of the world, of the ache in his head, and the bitter burning on his tongue. He stooped and put a handful of snow into his mouth as he walked, but that, too, seemed hot. When he reached a little hillside, where the tracks ran through a cut some twenty feet below him, he stopped and sat down.

The carnations in his coat were drooping with the cold, he noticed; all their red glory over. It occurred to him that all the flowers he had seen in the show windows that first night must have gone the same way, long before this. It was only one splendid breath they had, in spite of their brave mockery at the winter outside the glass. It was a losing game in the end, it seemed, this revolt against the homilies by which the world is run. Paul took one of the blossoms carefully from his coat and scooped a little hole in the snow, where he covered it up. Then he dozed a while, from his weak condition, seeming insensible to the cold.

The sound of an approaching train woke him, and he started to his feet, remembering only his resolution, and afraid lest he should be too late. He stood watching the approaching locomotive, his teeth chattering, his lips drawn away from them in a frightened smile; once or twice he glanced nervously sidewise, as though he were being watched. When the right moment came, he jumped. As he fell, the folly of his haste occurred to him with merciless clearness, the vastness of what he had left undone. There flashed through his brain, clearer than ever before, the blue of Adriatic water, the yellow of Algerian sands.

He felt something strike his chest,—his body was being thrown swiftly through the air, on and on, immeasurably far and fast, while his limbs gently relaxed. Then, because the picture making mechanism was crushed, the disturbing visions flashed into black, and Paul dropped back into the immense design of things.

PARTIAL ANALYSIS

1. *The theme*. The theme of "Paul's Case" is a familiar one in the writing of Willa Cather. It is the conflict between the demands of art and the demands of a civilization hostile or alien to art. It is the conflict between the artist, who lives through his senses, and the drab citizen, who respects dullness and mediocrity. In such a conflict the great artist often survives because of his genius. "Paul's Case" is made human because Paul is not a great artist. He does not have even fifth-rate artistic ability. He seems to have no creative powers. He is simply a sensitive, romantic adolescent who wants to enjoy beauty.

2. *Paul's quest*. The major question in this story is: Could Paul have reconciled his desires with what his environment offered him? It is clear that he tried to adjust. In the first half of the story we see Paul seeking fulfillment. Where does he turn to satisfy his senses? Where is he happy? In the second half of the story Paul seeks fulfillment again. What drives him into this second attempt? At the end of the story, the problem still remains. Was Paul's problem insoluble? Could someone have helped Paul? If so, who?

3. *Paul's likes*. The reader who understands Paul, Paul's problem, and Paul's solution to his problem knows that he could have helped Paul. The reader of this story can play the rôle of a psychiatrist. He can begin his study of Paul's case by recalling a sound psychological observation: "Tell me what you like and I'll tell you what you are." Let the reader determine what Paul likes and he will know what Paul is.

It is not enough to say that Paul likes beauty. The specific quality of

Paul's "likes" holds the clue to Paul's mistakes, to his inability to adjust. For example, Paul likes flowers—not just flowers—but violets and roses behind the plate glass windows of a florist's shop in a snowstorm. He likes music—not just music—but a singer in a satin gown and tiara, emanating success. He likes stories of a king of finance on his yacht in the Mediterranean, but is not interested in the cash-boy stage of the rise to power. The list of what Paul likes must be both extensive and definite if the reader is to understand Paul. (What Paul dislikes is important, also. For example, Paul did not live in a slum. What, then, did he dislike in his home?)

4. *Paul's mistake.* The next step is the most difficult. What Paul likes must be translated into general terms. Thus the violets and roses in midwinter are *costly;* the singer is *successful* and *theatrical;* a king of finance is *romantic.* A list of five or six terms describing the inner quality of Paul's desires brings the reader face to face with the problem of Paul's maladjustment. Several passages are particularly significant at this point. Notice the following:

a. "Perhaps it was because, in Paul's world, the natural nearly always wore the guise of ugliness, that a certain amount of artificiality seemed to him necessary in beauty."

b. "He seemed to feel himself go after her up the steps, into the warm, lighted building, into an exotic, a tropical world of shiny, glistening surfaces and basking ease. He reflected upon the mysterious dishes that were brought into the dining-room, the green bottles in buckets of ice. . . ."

c. ". . . and on every side of him towered the glaring affirmation of the omnipotence of wealth."

5. *A solution for Paul.* What, then, was Paul's mistake in his search for beauty? To appreciate life through his senses was with him a psychological necessity and a truly legitimate necessity. But he could have found beauty, even in Pittsburgh. How? Could Paul have created beauty? What kind of work would have made him happy?

6. *Paul's character.* Not only Paul's problem but also Paul's character and personality play a part in Paul's final decision. Paul was adolescent. He had the nervous susceptibility, the sentimentality, the active imagination, the preoccupation with the ego, of the adolescent. Study the passage where the drawing master observes Paul asleep. Study the scene in the cellar.

What characteristics of Paul do the following passages illustrate?

a. "He had never lied for pleasure, even at school; but to make himself noticed and admired. . . ."

b. "He needed only the spark [music], the indescribable thrill that made his imagination master of his senses. . . ."

c. "The boy set his teeth and drew his shoulders together in a spasm of realization; the plot of all dramas, the text of all romance, the nerve-stuff of all sensations was whirling about him like the snow flakes. He burnt like a faggot in a tempest."

7. *The carnation.* The episode of the carnation at the end of the story is symbolic. It embodies Paul's life and Paul's problem. It explains why Paul will not go home to Cordelia Street. What is the relation between this episode and Paul's final act? One sentence from this passage is especially significant: "It was a losing game in the end, it seemed, this revolt against the homilies by which the world is run." This sentence, in fact, states the theme of the story.

8. *The structure.* For a story which has interested countless readers, the action is curiously static. The action does not really begin until the reader is three-fifths of the way through the story. Although the first four episodes are represented as a continuous plot, they are merely four habitual actions of Paul's. The author presents in these episodes a case history. We see Paul alternating between what he likes and dislikes, between school and a concert, home and the theater. The story begins when Paul is forced to choose between the alternatives, and he runs away to New York.

THE NEW VILLA

BY ANTON CHEKHOV

ANTON CHEKHOV (1860–1904) was born in Tagarog, South Russia. He came of a family of liberated serfs, was educated in his own town and at the University of Moscow, where he received a degree in medicine in 1884. He practiced little. Instead, between 1889 and 1900 he established his reputation in Russia as a master of the short story. After 1916, when he began to be translated into English, his reputation spread. A great many of his stories are now available in English. He was associated with the Moscow Art Theater, and his major plays are *The Sea Gull, Three Sisters, The Cherry Orchard,* and *Uncle Vanya.*

$\mathbf{T}$wo miles from the village of Obrutchanovo a huge bridge was being built. From the village, which stood up high on the steep river-bank, its trellis-like skeleton could be seen, and in foggy weather and on still winter days, when its delicate iron girders and all the scaffolding around was covered with hoar frost, it presented a picturesque and even fantastic spectacle. Kutcherov, the engineer who was building the bridge, a stout, broad-shouldered, bearded man in a soft crumpled cap drove through the village in his racing droshky or his open carriage. Now and then on holidays navvies working on the bridge would come to the village; they begged for alms, laughed at the women, and sometimes carried off something. But that was rare; as a rule the days passed quietly and peacefully as though no bridge-building were going on, and only in the evening,

THE NEW VILLA   By Anton Chekhov from *The Witch and Other Stories.* Reprinted by permission of The Macmillan Company and Chatto & Windus Ltd.

when camp fires gleamed near the bridge, the wind faintly wafted the
songs of the navvies. And by day there was sometimes the mournful clang
of metal, don-don-don.

It happened that the engineer's wife came to see him. She was pleased
with the river-banks and the gorgeous view over the green valley with
trees, churches, flocks, and she began begging her husband to buy a small
piece of ground and to build them a cottage on it. Her husband agreed.
They bought sixty acres of land, and on the high bank in a field, where
in earlier days the cows of Obrutchanovo used to wander, they built a
pretty house of two storeys with a terrace and a verandah, with a tower
and a flagstaff on which a flag fluttered on Sundays—they built it in about
three months, and then all the winter they were planting big trees, and
when spring came and everything began to be green there were already
avenues to the new house, a gardener and two labourers in white aprons
were digging near it, there was a little fountain, and a globe of looking-
glass flashed so brilliantly that it was painful to look at. The house had
already been named the New Villa.

On a bright, warm morning at the end of May two horses were brought
to Obrutchanovo to the village blacksmith, Rodion Petrov. They came
from the New Villa. The horses were sleek, graceful beasts, as white as
snow, and strikingly alike.

"Perfect swans!" said Rodion, gazing at them with reverent admiration.

His wife Stepanida, his children and grandchildren came out into the
street to look at them. By degrees a crowd collected. The Lytchkovs,
father and son, both men with swollen faces and entirely beardless, came
up bareheaded. Kozov, a tall, thin old man with a long, narrow beard,
came up leaning on a stick with a crook handle: he kept winking with
his crafty eyes and smiling ironically as though he knew something.

"It's only that they are white; what is there in them?" he said. "Put
mine on oats, and they will be just as sleek. They ought to be in a plough
and with a whip, too. . . ."

The coachman simply looked at him with disdain, but did not utter
a word. And afterwards, while they were blowing up the fire at the forge,
the coachman talked while he smoked cigarettes. The peasants learned
from him various details: his employers were wealthy people; his mistress,
Elena Ivanovna, had till her marriage lived in Moscow in a poor way as
a governess; she was kind-hearted, compassionate, and fond of helping
the poor. On the new estate, he told them, they were not going to plough
or to sow, but simply to live for their pleasure, live only to breathe the
fresh air. When he had finished and led the horses back a crowd of boys
followed him, the dogs barked, and Kozov, looking after him, winked
sarcastically.

"Landowners, too-oo!" he said. "They have built a house and set up
horses, but I bet they are nobodies—landowners, too-oo."

Kozov for some reason took a dislike from the first to the new house, to the white horses, and to the handsome, well-fed coachman. Kozov was a solitary man, a widower; he had a dreary life (he was prevented from working by a disease which he sometimes called a rupture and sometimes worms); he was maintained by his son, who worked at a confectioner's in Harkov and sent him money; and from early morning till evening he sauntered at leisure about the river or about the village; if he saw, for instance, a peasant carting a log, or fishing, he would say: "That log's dry wood—it is rotten," or, "They won't bite in weather like this." In times of drought he would declare that there would not be a drop of rain till the frost came; and when the rains came he would say that everything would rot in the fields, that everything was ruined. And as he said these things he would wink as though he knew something.

At the New Villa they burned Bengal lights and sent up fireworks in the evenings, and a sailing-boat with red lanterns floated by Obrutchanovo. One morning the engineer's wife, Elena Ivanovna, and her little daughter drove to the village in a carriage with yellow wheels and a pair of dark bay ponies; both mother and daughter were wearing broadbrimmed straw hats, bent down over their ears.

This was exactly at the time when they were carting manure, and the blacksmith Rodion, a tall, gaunt old man, bareheaded and barefooted, was standing near his dirty and repulsive-looking cart and, flustered, looked at the ponies, and it was evident by his face that he had never seen such little horses before.

"The Kutcherov lady has come!" was whispered around. "Look, the Kutcherov lady has come!"

Elena Ivanovna looked at the huts as though she were selecting one, and then stopped at the very poorest, at the windows of which there were so many children's heads—flaxen, red, and dark. Stepanida, Rodion's wife, a stout woman, came running out of the hut; her kerchief slipped off her grey head; she looked at the carriage facing the sun, and her face smiled and wrinkled up as though she were blind.

"This is for your children," said Elena Ivanovna, and she gave her three roubles.

Stepanida suddenly burst into tears and bowed down to the ground. Rodion, too, flopped to the ground, displaying his brownish bald head, and as he did so he almost caught his wife in the ribs with the fork. Elena Ivanovna was overcome with confusion and drove back.

II

The Lytchkovs, father and son, caught in their meadows two cart-horses, a pony, and a broad-faced Aalhaus bull-calf, and with the help of readheaded Volodka, son of the blacksmith Rodion, drove them to the village. They called the village elder, collected witnesses, and went to look at the damage.

"All right, let 'em!" said Kozov, winking, "le-et 'em! Let them get out of it if they can, the engineers! Do you think there is no such thing as law? All right! Send for the police inspector, draw up a statement! . . ."

"Draw up a statement," repeated Volodka.

"I don't want to let this pass!" shouted the younger Lytchkov. He shouted louder and louder, and his beardless face seemed to be more and more swollen. "They've set up a nice fashion! Leave them free, and they will ruin all the meadows! You've no sort of right to ill-treat people! We are not serfs now!"

"We are not serfs now!" repeated Volodka.

"We got on all right without a bridge," said the elder Lytchkov gloomily; "we did not ask for it. What do we want a bridge for? We don't want it!"

"Brothers, good Christians, we cannot leave it like this!"

"All right, let 'em!" said Kozov, winking. "Let them get out of it if they can! Landowners, indeed!"

They went back to the village, and as they walked the younger Lytchkov beat himself on the breast with his fist and shouted all the way, and Volodka shouted, too, repeating his words. And meanwhile quite a crowd had gathered in the village round the thoroughbred bull-calf and the horses. The bull-calf was embarrassed and looked up from under his brows, but suddenly lowered his muzzle to the ground and took to his heels, kicking up his hind legs; Kozov was frightened and waved his stick at him, and they all burst out laughing. Then they locked up the beasts and waited.

In the evening the engineer sent five roubles for the damage, and the two horses, the pony and the bull-calf, without being fed or given water, returned home, their heads hanging with a guilty air as though they were convicted criminals.

On getting the five roubles the Lytchkovs, father and son, the village elder and Volodka, punted over the river in a boat and went to a hamlet on the other side where there was a tavern, and there had a long carousal. Their singing and the shouting of the younger Lytchkov could be heard from the village. Their women were uneasy and did not sleep all night. Rodion did not sleep either.

"It's a bad business," he said, sighing and turning from side to side. "The gentleman will be angry, and then there will be trouble. . . . They have insulted the gentleman. . . . Oh, they've insulted him. It's a bad business. . . ."

It happened that the peasants, Rodion amongst them, went into their forest to divide the clearings for mowing, and as they were returning home they were met by the engineer. He was wearing a red cotton shirt and high boots; a setter dog with its long tongue hanging out, followed behind him.

"Good-day, brothers," he said.

The peasants stopped and took off their hats.

"I have long wanted to have a talk with you, friends," he went on. "This is what it is. Ever since the early spring your cattle have been in my copse and garden every day. Everything is trampled down; the pigs have rooted up the meadow, are ruining everything in the kitchen garden, and all the undergrowth in the copse is destroyed. There is no getting on with your herdsmen; one asks them civilly, and they are rude. Damage is done on my estate every day and I do nothing—I don't fine you or make a complaint; meanwhile you impounded my horses and my bull-calf and exacted five roubles. Was that right? Is that neighbourly?" he went on, and his face was so soft and persuasive, and his expression was not forbidding. "Is that the way decent people behave? A week ago one of your people cut down two oak saplings in my copse. You have dug up the road to Eresnevo, and now I have to go two miles round. Why do you injure me at every step? What harm have I done you? For God's sake, tell me! My wife and I do our utmost to live with you in peace and harmony; we help the peasants as we can. My wife is a kind, warm-hearted woman; she never refuses you help. That is her dream—to be of use to you and your children. You reward us with evil for our good. You are unjust, my friends. Think of that. I ask you earnestly to think it over. We treat you humanely; repay us in the same coin."

He turned and went away. The peasants stood a little longer, put on their caps and walked away. Rodion, who always understood everything that was said to him in some peculiar way of his own, heaved a sigh and said:

"We must pay. 'Repay in coin, my friends' . . . he said."

They walked to the village in silence. On reaching home Rodion said his prayer, took off his boots, and sat down on the bench beside his wife. Stepanida and he always sat side by side when they were at home, and always walked side by side in the street; they ate and they drank and they slept always together, and the older they grew the more they loved one another. It was hot and crowded in their hut, and there were children everywhere—on the floors, in the windows, on the stove. . . . In spite of her advanced years Stepanida was still bearing children, and now, looking at the crowd of children, it was hard to distinguish which were Rodion's and which were Volodka's. Volodka's wife, Lukerya, a plain young woman with prominent eyes and a nose like the beak of a bird, was kneading dough in a tub; Volodka was sitting on the stove with his legs hanging.

"On the road near Nikita's buckwheat . . . the engineer with his dog . . ." Rodion began, after a rest, scratching his ribs and his elbow.

"'You must pay,' says he . . . 'coin,' says he. . . . Coin or no coin, we shall have to collect ten kopecks from every hut. We've offended the gentleman very much. I am sorry for him. . . ."

"We've lived without a bridge," said Volodka, not looking at anyone, "and we don't want one."

"What next; the bridge is a government business."

"We don't want it."

"Your opinion is not asked. What is it to you?"

"'Your opinion is not asked,'" Volodka mimicked him. "We don't want to drive anywhere; what do we want with a bridge? If we have to, we can cross by the boat."

Someone from the yard outside knocked at the window so violently that it seemed to shake the whole hut.

"Is Volodka at home?" he heard the voice of the younger Lytchkov. "Volodka, come out, come along."

Volodka jumped down off the stove and began looking for his cap.

"Don't go, Volodka," said Rodion diffidently. "Don't go with them, son. You are foolish, like a little child; they will teach you no good; don't go!"

"Don't go, son," said Stepanida, and she blinked as thought about to shed tears. "I bet they are calling you to the tavern."

"'To the tavern,'" Volodka mimicked.

"You'll come back drunk again, you currish Herod," said Lukerya, looking at him angrily. "Go along, go along, and may you burn up with vodka, you tailless Satan!"

"You hold your tongue," shouted Volodka.

"They've married me to a fool, they've ruined me, a luckless orphan, you red-headed drunkard . . ." wailed Lukerya, wiping her face with a hand covered with dough. "I wish I had never set eyes on you."

Volodka gave her a blow on the ear and went off.

III

Elena Ivanovna and her little daughter visited the village on foot. They were out for a walk. It was a Sunday, and the peasant women and girls were walking up and down the street in their brightly-coloured dresses. Rodion and Stepanida, sitting side by side at their door, bowed and smiled to Elena Ivanovna and her little daughter as to acquaintances. From the windows more than a dozen children stared at them; their faces expressed amazement and curiosity, and they could be heard whispering:

"The Kutcherov lady had come! The Kutcherov lady!"

"Good-morning," said Elena Ivanovna, and she stopped; she paused, and then asked: "Well, how are you getting on?"

"We get along all right, thank God," answered Rodion, speaking rapidly. "To be sure we get along."

"The life we lead!" smiled Stepanida. "You can see our poverty your-self, dear lady! The family is fourteen souls in all, and only two bread-winners. We are supposed to be blacksmiths, but when they bring us a horse to shoe we have no coal, nothing to buy it with. We are worried to death, lady," she went on, and laughed. "Oh, oh, we are worried to death."

Elena Ivanovna sat down at the entrance and, putting her arm round her little girl, pondered something, and judging from the little girl's expression, melancholy thoughts were straying through her mind, too; as she brooded she played with the sumptuous lace on the parasol she had taken out of her mother's hands.

"Poverty," said Rodion, "a great deal of anxiety—you see no end to it. Here, God sends no rain . . . our life is not easy, there is no deny-ing it."

"You have a hard time in this life," said Elena Ivanovna, "but in the other world you will be happy."

Rodion did not understand her, and simply coughed into his clenched hand by way of reply. Stepanida said:

"Dear lady, the rich men will be all right in the next world, too. The rich put up candles, pay for services; the rich give to beggars, but what can the poor man do? He has no time to make the sign of the cross. He is the beggar of beggars himself; how can he think of his soul? And many sins come from poverty; from trouble we snarl at one another like dogs, we haven't a good word to say to one another, and all sorts of things happen, dear lady—God forbid! It seems we have no luck in this world nor the next. All the luck has fallen to the rich."

She spoke gaily; she was evidently used to talking of her hard life. And Rodion smiled, too; he was pleased that his old woman was so clever, so ready of speech.

"It is only on the surface that the rich seem to be happy," said Elena Ivanovna. "Every man has his sorrow. Here my husband and I do not live poorly, we have means, but are we happy? I am young, but I have had four children; my children are always being ill. I am ill, too, and con-stantly being doctored."

"And what is your illness?" asked Rodion.

"A woman's complaint. I get no sleep; a continual headache gives me no peace. Here I am sitting and talking, but my head is bad, I am weak all over, and I should prefer the hardest labour to such a condition. My soul, too, is troubled; I am in continual fear for my children, my husband. Every family has its own trouble of some sort; we have ours. I am not of noble birth. My grandfather was a simple peasant, my father was a trades-man in Moscow; he was a plain, uneducated man, too, while my husband's parents were wealthy and distinguished. They did not want him to marry me, but he disobeyed them, quarrelled with them, and they have not forgiven us to this day. That worries my husband; it troubles him and keeps him in constant agitation; he loves his mother, loves her dearly. So I am uneasy, too, my soul is in pain."

Peasants, men and women, were by now standing round Rodion's hut and listening. Kozov came up, too, and stood twitching his long, narrow beard. The Lytchkovs, father and son, drew near.

"And say what you like, one cannot be happy and satisfied if one does not feel in one's proper place." Elena Ivanovna went on. "Each of you has his strip of land, each of you works and knows what he is working for; my husband builds bridges—in short, everyone has his place, while I, I simply walk about. I have not my bit to work. I don't work, and feel as though I were an outsider. I am saying all this that you may not judge from outward appearances; if a man is expensively dressed and has means it does not prove that he is satisfied with his life."

She got up to go away and took her daughter by the hand.

"I like your place here very much," she said, and smiled, and from that faint, diffident smile one could tell how unwell she really was, how young and how pretty; she had a pale, thinnish face with dark eyebrows and fair hair. And the little girl was just such another as her mother: thin, fair, and slender. There was a fragrance of scent about them.

"I like the river and the forest and the village," Elena Ivanovna went on; "I could live here all my life, and I feel as though here I should get strong and find my place. I want to help you—I want to dreadfully—to be of use, to be a real friend to you. I know your need, and what I don't know I feel, my heart guesses. I am sick, feeble, and for me perhaps it is not possible to change my life as I would. But I have children. I will try to bring them up that they may be of use to you, may love you. I shall impress upon them continually that their life does not belong to them, but to you. Only I beg you earnestly, I beseech you, trust us, live in friendship with us. My husband is a kind, good man. Don't worry him, don't irritate him. He is sensitive to every trifle, and yesterday, for instance, your cattle were in our vegetable garden, and one of your people broke down the fence to the bee-hives, and such an attitude to us drives my husband to despair. I beg you," she went on in an imploring voice, and she clasped her hands on her bosom—"I beg you to treat us as good neighbours; let us live in peace! There is a saying, you know, that even a bad peace is better than a good quarrel, and, 'Don't buy property, but buy neighbours.' I repeat my husband is a kind man and good; if all goes well we promise to do everything in our power for you; we will mend the roads, we will build a school for your children. I promise you."

"Of course we thank you humbly, lady," said Lytchkov the father, looking at the ground; "you are educated people; it is for you to know best. Only, you see, Voronov, a rich peasant at Eresnevo, promised to build a school; he, too, said, 'I will do this for you,' 'I will do that for you,' and he only put up the framework and refused to go on. And then they made the peasants put the roof on and finish it; it cost them a thousand roubles. Voronov did not care; he only stroked his beard, but the peasants felt it a bit hard."

"That was a crow, but now there's a rook, too," said Kozov, and he winked.

There was the sound of laughter.

"We don't want a school," said Volodka sullenly. "Our children go to Petrovskoe, and they can go on going there; we don't want it."

Elena Ivanovna seemed suddenly intimidated; her face looked paler and thinner, she shrank into herself as though she had been touched with something coarse, and walked away without uttering another word. And she walked more and more quickly, without looking round.

"Lady," said Rodion, walking after her, "lady, wait a bit; hear what I would say to you."

He followed her without his cap, and spoke softly as though begging.

"Lady, wait and hear what I will say to you."

They had walked out of the village, and Elena Ivanovna stopped beside a cart in the shade of an old mountain ash.

"Don't be offended, lady," said Rodion. "What does it mean? Have patience. Have patience for a couple of years. You will live here, you will have patience, and it will all come round. Our folks are good and peaceable; there's no harm in them; it's God's truth I'm telling you. Don't mind Kozov and the Lytchkovs, and don't mind Volodka. He's a fool; he listens to the first that speaks. The others are quiet folks; they are silent. Some would be glad, you know, to say a word from the heart and to stand up for themselves, but cannot. They have a heart and a conscience, but no tongue. Don't be offended . . . have patience. . . . What does it matter?"

Elena Ivanovna looked at the broad, tranquil river, pondering, and tears flowed down her cheeks. And Rodion was troubled by those tears; he almost cried himself.

"Never mind . . ." he muttered. "Have patience for a couple of years. You can have the school, you can have the roads, only not all at once. If you went, let us say, to sow corn on that mound you would first have to weed it out, to pick out all the stones, and then to plough, and work and work . . . and with the people, you see, it is the same . . . you must work and work until you overcome them."

The crowd had moved away from Rodion's hut, and was coming along the street towards the mountain ash. They began singing songs and playing the concertina, and they kept coming closer and closer. . . .

"Mamma, let us go away from here," said the little girl, huddling up to her mother, pale and shaking all over; "let us go away, mamma!"

"Where?"

"To Moscow. . . . Let us go, mamma."

The child began crying.

Rodion was utterly overcome; his face broke into profuse perspiration; he took out of his pocket a little crooked cucumber, like a half-moon, covered with crumbs of rye bread, and began thrusting it into the little girl's hands.

"Come, come," he muttered, scowling severely; "take the little cucumber, eat it up. . . . You mustn't cry. Mamma will whip you. . . . She'll tell your father of you when you get home. Come, come. . . ."

They walked on, and he still followed behind them, wanting to say something friendly and persuasive to them. And seeing that they were both absorbed in their own thoughts and their own griefs, and not noticing him, he stopped and, shading his eyes from the sun, looked after them for a long time till they disappeared into their copse.

IV

The engineer seemed to grow irritable and petty, and in every trivial incident saw an act of robbery or outrage. His gate was kept bolted even by day, and at night two watchmen walked up and down the garden beating a board; and they gave up employing anyone from Obrutchanovo as a labourer. As ill-luck would have it someone (either a peasant or one of the workmen) took the new wheels off the cart and replaced them by old ones, then soon afterwards two bridles and a pair of pincers were carried off, and murmurs arose even in the village. People began to say that a search should be made at the Lytchkovs' and at Volodka's, and then the bridles and the pincers were found under the hedge in the engineer's garden; someone had thrown them down there.

It happened that the peasants were coming in a crowd out of the forest, and again they met the engineer on the road. He stopped, and without wishing them good-day he began, looking angrily first at one, then at another:

"I have begged you not to gather mushrooms in the park and near the yard, but to leave them for my wife and children, but your girls come before daybreak and there is not a mushroom left. . . . Whether one asks you or not it makes no difference. Entreaties, and friendliness, and persuasion I see are all useless."

He fixed his indignant eyes on Rodion and went on:

"My wife and I behaved to you as human beings, as to our equals, and you? But what's the use of talking! It will end by our looking down upon you. There is nothing left!"

And making an effort to restrain his anger, not to say too much, he turned and went on.

On getting home Rodion said his prayer, took off his boots, and sat down beside his wife.

"Yes . . ." he began with a sigh. "We were walking along just now, and Mr. Kutcherov met us. . . . Yes. . . . He saw the girls at daybreak. . . . 'Why don't they bring mushrooms,' he said . . . 'to my wife and children?' he said. . . . And then he looked at me and he said: 'I and my wife will look after you,' he said. I wanted to fall down at his feet, but I hadn't the courage. . . . God give him health. . . . God bless him! . . ."

Stephania crossed herself and sighed.

"They are kind, simple-hearted people," Rodion went on. " 'We shall look after you.' . . . He promised me that before everyone. In our old age . . . it wouldn't be a bad thing. . . . I should always pray for them. . . . Holy Mother, bless them. . . ."

The Feast of the Exaltation of the Cross, the fourteenth of September, was the festival of the village church. The Lytchkovs, father and son, went across the river early in the morning and returned to dinner drunk; they spent a long time going about the village, alternately singing and swearing; then they had a fight and went to the New Villa to complain. First Lytchkov the father went into the yard with a long ashen stick in his hands. He stopped irresolutely and took off his hat. Just at that moment the engineer and his family were sitting on the verandah, drinking tea.

"What do you want?" shouted the engineer.

"Your honour . . ." Lytchkov began, and burst into tears. "Show the Divine mercy, protect me . . . my son makes my life a misery . . . your honour. . . ."

Lytchkov the son walked up, too; he, too, was bareheaded and had a stick in his hand; he stopped and fixed his drunken senseless eyes on the verandah.

"It is not my business to settle your affairs," said the engineer. "Go to the rural captain or the police officer."

"I have been everywhere. . . . I have lodged a petition . . ." said Lytchkov the father, and he sobbed. "Where can I go now? He can kill me now, it seems. He can do anything. Is that the way to treat a father? A father?"

He raised his stick and hit his son on the head; the son raised his stick and struck his father just on his bald patch such a blow that the stick bounced back. The father did not even flinch, but hit his son again and again on the head. And so they stood and kept hitting one another on the head, and it looked not so much like a fight as some sort of a game. And peasants, men and women, stood in a crowd at the gate and looked into the garden, and the faces of all were grave. They were the peasants who had come to greet them for the holiday, but seeing the Lytchkovs, they were ashamed and did not go in.

The next morning Elena Ivanovna went with the children to Moscow. And there was a rumour that the engineer was selling his house. . . .

V

The peasants had long ago grown used to the sight of the bridge, and it was difficult to imagine the river at that place without a bridge. The heap of rubble left from the building of it had long been overgrown with grass, the navvies were forgotten, and instead of the strains of the "Dubinushka" that they used to sing, the peasants heard almost every hour the sounds of a passing train.

The New Villa has long ago been sold; now it belongs to a government clerk who comes here from the town for the holidays with his family, drinks tea on the terrace, and then goes back to the town again. He wears a cockade on his cap; he talks and clears his throat as though he were a very important official, though he is only of the rank of a collegiate secretary, and when the peasants bow he makes no response.

In Obrutchanovo everyone has grown older; Kozov is dead. In Rodion's hut there are even more children. Volodka has grown a long red beard. They are still as poor as ever.

In the early spring the Obrutchanovo peasants were sawing wood near the station. And after work they were going home; they walked without haste one after the other. Broad saws curved over their shoulders; the sun was reflected in them. The nightingales were singing in the bushes on the bank, larks were trilling in the heavens. It was quiet at the New Villa; there was not a soul there, and only golden pigeons—golden because the sunlight was streaming upon them—were flying over the house. All of them—Rodion, the two Lytchkovs, and Volodka—thought of the white horses, the little ponies, the fireworks, the boat with the lanterns; they remembered how the engineer's wife, so beautiful and so grandly dressed, had come into the village and talked to them in such a friendly way. And it seemed as though all that had never been; it was like a dream or a fairy-tale.

They trudged along, tired out, and mused as they went. . . . In their village, they mused, the people were good, quiet, sensible, fearing God, and Elena Ivanovna, too, was quiet, kind, and gentle; it made one sad to look at her, but why had they not got on together? Why had they parted like enemies? How was it that some mist had shrouded from their eyes what mattered most, and had let them see nothing but damage done by cattle, bridles, pincers, and all those trivial things which now, as they remembered them, seemed so nonsensical? How was it that with the new owner they lived in peace, and yet had been on bad terms with the engineer?

And not knowing what answer to make to these questions they were all silent except Volodka, who muttered something.

"What is it?" Rodion asked.

"We lived without a bridge . . ." said Volodka gloomily. "We lived without a bridge, and did not ask for one . . . and we don't want it. . . ."

No one answered him and they walked on in silence with drooping heads.

COMMENT AND QUESTION

1. The events in "The New Villa" occur about 1900 in the Russia of the Czars.

2. In many of his stories and plays Chekhov unmasks the idle and the ineffectual, the liar and the troublemaker, the self-deceived and the sentimental well-wisher. How many of these types appear in "The New Villa"?

3. Rodion is an important character. How does he differ from the other characters? Does he have great intelligence? What childlike errors does he make about the incident of the mushrooms and also about the engineer's phrase, "repay us in the same coin"?

4. Study Rodion's comments on work near the end of section III. Through Rodion Chekhov expresses one of the most important ideas not only of this story but also of his writing as a whole—the gospel of work. Chekhov felt that serious, earnest work would root out the laziness, the indifference, the boredom of the Russian society of his time and would engender a social revolution. In "The New Villa" Chekhov includes both gentry and peasants in his criticism.

5. In section III, study the conversation on poverty between Stepanida and Elena. Where is the irony? Is Elena self-deceived? Does she take a neurotic pleasure in her suffering? Is her charity self-conscious? Does she speak of work? Notice the parasol.

6. What is the ironical connection between the conversation on poverty and an early comment by the coachman: "On the new estate, he told them, they were not going to plough or sow, but simply to live for their pleasure, live only to breathe the fresh air"?

7. The bridge is clearly a symbol. Its purpose in the story is emphasized by the repeated comment: "We don't want a bridge."

8. Are the conflicts between the engineer and the peasants trivial? Why does the engineer become so angry about the mushrooms when he had been so tractable about the peasants' cutting down trees and digging up the road?

9. In section IV, what serious weakness does the engineer show in the incident where the Lytchkov son beats his father? As a peasant, Lytchkov was appealing to the engineer to assume what great responsibility?

10. The tone in this story is often comic. See the description of the impounded animals, the statements of Rodion, the picture of Lytchkov beating his father. What does this tone contribute?

The melancholy tone, set early by "the mournful clang of metal, don-don-don," is equally characteristic of Chekhov.

11. Chekhov often communicates through moods. What is the mood of the first paragraph? What is the mood of the last incident in section V? Are the questions the men ask themselves in this last incident answered by Volodka's last statement?

HOOK

BY WALTER VAN TILBURG CLARK

WALTER VAN TILBURG CLARK (1909–   )
was born in Maine but has spent most of his
life in Nevada. Much of his writing reflects
the history and culture of the West. He has
published a collection of short stories, *The
Watchful Gods* (1950). He has also published three novels, *The Ox-Bow Incident*
(1940), *The City of Trembling Leaves*
(1945), and *The Track of the Cat* (1949).

Hook, the hawks' child, was hatched in a dry spring among the oaks
beside the seasonal river, and was struck from the nest early. In the
drouth his single-willed parents had to extend their hunting ground by
more than twice, for the ground creatures upon which they fed died and
dried by the hundreds. The range became too great for them to wish to
return and feed Hook, and when they had lost interest in each other they
drove Hook down into the sand and brush and went back to solitary
courses over the bleaching hills.

Unable to fly yet, Hook crept over the ground, challenging all large
movements with recoiled head, erected, rudimentary wings, and the
small rasp of his clattering beak. It was during this time of abysmal
ignorance and continual fear that his eyes took on the first quality of a
hawk, that of being wide, alert and challenging. He dwelt, because of
his helplessness, among the rattling brush which grew between the oaks
and the river. Even in his thickets and near the water, the white sun was
the dominant presence. Except in the dawn, when the land wind stirred,
or in the late afternoon, when the sea wind became strong enough to

penetrate the half-mile inland to this turn in the river, the sun was the major force, and everything was dry and motionless under it. The brush, small plants and trees alike husbanded the little moisture at their hearts; the moving creatures waited for dark, when sometimes the sea fog came over and made a fine, soundless rain which relieved them.

The two spacious sounds of his life environed Hook at this time. One was the great rustle of the slopes of yellowed wild wheat, with over it the chattering rustle of the leaves of the California oaks, already as harsh and individually tremulous as in autumn. The other was the distant whisper of the foaming edge of the Pacific, punctuated by the hollow shoring of the waves. But these Hook did not yet hear, for he was attuned by fear and hunger to the small, spasmodic rustlings of live things. Dry, shrunken, and nearly starved, and with his plumage delayed, he snatched at beetles, dragging in the sand to catch them. When swifter and stronger birds and animals did not reach them first, which was seldom, he ate the small, silver fish left in the mud by the failing river. He watched, with nearly chattering beak, the quick, thin lizards pause, very alert, and raise and lower themselves, but could not catch them because he had to raise his wings to move rapidly, which startled them.

Only one sight and sound not of his world of microscopic necessity was forced upon Hook. That was the flight of the big gulls from the beaches, which sometimes, in quealing play, came spinning back over the foothills and the river bed. For some inherited reason, the big, ship-bodied birds did not frighten Hook, but angered him. Small and chewed-looking, with his wide, already yellowing eyes glaring up at them, he would stand in an open place on the sand in the sun and spread his shaping wings and clatter his bill like shaken dice. Hook was furious about the swift, easy passage of gulls.

His first opportunity to leave off living like a ground owl came accidentally. He was standing in the late afternoon in the red light under the thicket, his eyes half-filmed with drowse and the stupefaction of starvation, when suddenly something beside him moved, and he struck, and killed a field mouse driven out of the wheat by thirst. It was a poor mouse, shriveled and lice ridden, but in striking, Hook had tasted blood, which raised nest memories and restored his nature. With started neck plumage and shining eyes, he tore and fed. When the mouse was devoured, Hook had entered hoarse adolescence. He began to seek with a conscious appetite, and to move more readily out of shelter. Impelled by the blood appetite, so glorious after his long preservation upon the flaky and bitter stuff of bugs, he ventured even into the wheat in the open sun beyond the oaks, and discovered the small trails and holes among the roots. With his belly often partially filled with flesh, he grew rapidly in strength and will. His eyes were taking on their final change, their yellow growing deeper and more opaque, their stare more constant, their challenge less desperate. Once during this transformation, he surprised a ground squirrel, and although he was ripped and wing-bitten and could not hold his prey, he was not dismayed by the conflict, but exalted. Even while the wing was still drooping and the pinions not grown back, he was excited by other ground squirrels and pursued them futilely, and was angered by their dusty escapes. He realized that his world was a great arena for killing, and felt the magnificence of it.

The two major events of Hook's young life occurred in the same day. A little after dawn he made the customary essay and succeeded in flight. A little before sunset, he made his first sustained flight of over two hundred yards, and at its termination struck and slew a great buck squirrel whose thrashing and terrified gnawing and squealing gave him a wild delight. When he had gorged on the strong meat, Hook stood upright, and in his eyes was the stare of the hawk, never flagging in intensity but never swelling beyond containment. After that the stare had only to grow more deeply challenging and more sternly controlled as his range and deadliness increased. There was no change in kind. Hook had mastered the first of the three hungers which are fused into the single, flaming will of a hawk, and he had experienced the second.

The third and consummating hunger did not awaken in Hook until the following spring, when the exultation of space had grown slow and steady in him, so that he swept freely with the wind over the miles of coastal foothills, circling, and ever in sight of the sea, and used without struggle the warm currents lifting from the slopes, and no longer desired to scream at the range of his vision, but intently sailed above his shadow swiftly climbing to meet him on the hillsides, sinking away and rippling across the brush-grown canyons.

That spring the rains were long, and Hook sat for hours, hunched and angry under their pelting, glaring into the fogs of the river valley, and killed only small, drenched things flooded up from their tunnels. But when the rains had dissipated, and there were sun and sea wind again, the game ran plentiful, the hills were thick and shining green, and the new river flooded about the boulders where battered turtles climbed up to shrink and sleep. Hook then was scorched by the third hunger. Ranging farther, often forgetting to kill and eat, he sailed for days with growing rage, and woke at night clattering on his dead tree limb, and struck and struck and struck at the porous wood of the trunk, tearing it away. After days, in the draft of a coastal canyon miles below his own hills, he came upon the acrid taint he did not know but had expected, and sailing down it, felt his neck plumes rise and his wings quiver so that he swerved unsteadily. He saw the unmated female perched upon the tall and jagged stump of a tree that had been shorn by storm, and he stooped, as if upon game. But she was older than he, and wary of the gripe of his importunity, and banked off screaming, and he screamed also at the intolerable delay.

At the head of the canyon, the screaming pursuit was crossed by another male with a great wing-spread, and the light golden in the fringe of his plumage. But his more skillful opening played him false against the ferocity of the twice-balked Hook. His rising maneuver for position was cut short by Hook's wild, upward swoop, and at the blow he raked desperately and tumbled off to the side. Dropping, Hook struck him again, struggled to clutch, but only raked and could not hold, and, diving, struck once more in passage, and then beat up, yelling triumph, and saw the crippled antagonist side-slip away, half-tumble once, as the ripped wing failed to balance, then steady and glide obliquely into the cover of brush on the canyon side. Beating hard and stationary in the wind above the bush that covered his competitor, Hook waited an instant, but when the bush was still, screamed again, and let himself go off with the current, reseeking, infuriated by the burn of his own wounds, the thin choke-thread of the acrid taint.

On a hilltop projection of stone two miles inland, he struck her down, gripping her rustling body with his talons, beating her wings down with his wings, belting her head when she whimpered or thrashed, and at last clutching her neck with his hook and, when her coy struggles had given way to stillness, succeeded.

In the early summer, Hook drove the three young ones from their nest, and went back to lone circling above his own range. He was complete.

II

Throughout that summer and the cool, growthless weather of the winter, when the gales blew in the river canyon and the ocean piled upon the shore, Hook was master of the sky and the hills of his range. His flight became a lovely and certain thing, so that he played with the treacherous currents of the air with a delicate ease surpassing that of the gulls. He could sail for hours, searching the blanched grasses below him with telescopic eyes, gaining height against the wind, descending in mile-long, gently declining swoops when he curved and rode back, and never beating either wing. At the swift passage of his shadow within their vision, gophers, ground squirrels and rabbits froze, or plunged gibbering into their tunnels beneath matted turf. Now, when he struck, he killed easily in one hard-knuckled blow. Occasionally, in sport, he soared up over the river and drove the heavy and weaponless gulls downstream again, until they would no longer venture inland.

There was nothing which Hook feared now, and his spirit was wholly belligerent, swift and sharp, like his gaze. Only the mixed smells and incomprehensible activities of the people at the Japanese farmer's home, inland of the coastwise highway and south of the bridge across Hook's river, troubled him. The smells were strong, unsatisfactory and never clear, and the people, though they behaved foolishly, constantly running in and out of their built-up holes, were large, and appeared capable, with fearless eyes looking up at him, so that he instinctively swerved aside from them. He cruised over their yard, their gardens, and their bean fields, but he would not alight close to their buildings.

But this one area of doubt did not interfere with his life. He ignored it, save to look upon it curiously as he crossed, his afternoon shadow sliding in an instant over the chicken-and-crate-cluttered yard, up the side of the unpainted barn, and then out again smoothly, just faintly, liquidly rippling over the furrows and then over the stubble of the grazing slopes. When the season was dry, and the dead earth blew on the fields, he extended his range to satisfy his great hunger, and again narrowed it when the fields were once more alive with the minute movements he could not only see but anticipate.

Four times that year he was challenged by other hawks blowing up from behind the coastal hills to scud down his slopes, but two of these he slew in mid-air, and saw hurtle down to thump on the ground and lie still while he circled, and a third, whose wing he tore, he followed closely to earth and beat to death in the grass, making the crimson jet out from its breast and neck into the pale wheat. The fourth was a strong flier and experienced fighter, and theirs was a long, running battle, with brief, rising flurries of striking and screaming, from which down and plumage soared off.

Here, for the first time, Hook felt doubts, and at moments wanted to drop away from the scoring, burning talons and the twisted hammer strokes of the strong beak, drop away shrieking, and take cover and be still. In the end, when Hook, having outmaneuvered his enemy and come above him, wholly in control, and going with the wind, tilted and plunged for the death rap, the other, in desperation, threw over on his back and struck up. Talons locked, beaks raking, they dived earthward. The earth grew and spread under them amazingly, and they were not fifty feet above it when Hook, feeling himself turning toward the underside, tore free and beat up again on heavy, wrenched wings. The other, stroking swiftly, and so close to down that he lost wing plumes to a bush, righted himself and planed up, but flew on lumberingly between the hills and did not return. Hook screamed the triumph, and made a brief pretense of pursuit, but was glad to return, slow and victorious, to his dead tree.

In all these encounters Hook was injured, but experienced only the fighter's pride and exultation from the sting of wounds received in success-ful combat. And in each of them he learned new skill. Each time the wounds healed quickly, and left him a more dangerous bird.

In the next spring, when the rains and the night chants of the little frogs were past, the third hunger returned upon Hook with a new violence. In his quest, he came into the taint of a young hen. Others too were drawn by the unnerving perfume, but only one of them, the same with which Hook had fought his great battle, was a worthy competitor. This hunter drove off two, while two others, game but neophytes, were glad enough that Hook's impatience would not permit him to follow and kill. Then the battle between the two champions fled inland, and was a tactical marvel, but Hook lodged the neck-breaking blow, and struck again as they dropped past the treetops. The blood had already begun to pool on the gray, fallen foliage as Hook flapped up between branches, too spent to cry his victory. Yet his hunger would not let him rest until, late in the second day, he drove the female to ground, among the laurels of a strange river canyon.

When the two fledglings of this second brood had been driven from the nest, and Hook had returned to his own range, he was not only complete, but supreme. He slept without concealment on his bare limb, and did not open his eyes when, in the night, the heavy-billed cranes coughed in the shadows below him.

III

The turning point of Hook's career came that autumn, when the brush in the canyons rustled dryly and the hills, mowed close by the cattle, smoked under the wind as if burning. One midafternoon, when the black clouds were torn on the rim of the sea and the surf flowered white and high on the rocks, raining in over the low cliffs, Hook rode the wind diagonally across the river mouth. His great eyes, focused for small things stirring in the dust and leaves, overlooked so large and slow a movement as that of the Japanese farmer rising from the brush and lifting the two black eyes of his shotgun. Too late Hook saw and, startled, swerved, but wrongly. The surf muffled the reports, and nearly without sound, Hook felt the minute whips of the first shot, and the astounding, breath-breaking blow of the second.

Beating his good wing, tasting the blood that quickly swelled into his beak, he tumbled off with the wind and struck into the thickets on the far side of the river mouth. The branches tore him. Wild with rage, he thrust up and clattered his beak, challenging, but when he had fallen over twice, he knew that the trailing wing would not carry, and then heard the boots of the hunter among the stones in the river bed and, seeing him loom at the edge of the bushes, crept back among the thickest brush and was still. When he saw the boots stand before him, he reared back, lifting his good wing and cocking his head for the serpent-like blow, his beak open but soundless, his great eyes hard and very shining. The boots passed on. The Japanese farmer, who believed that he had lost chickens, and who had cunningly observed Hook's flight for many afternoons, until he could plot it, did not greatly want a dead hawk.

When Hook could hear nothing but the surf and the wind in the thicket, he let the sickness and shock overcome him. The fine film of the inner lid dropped over his big eyes. His heart beat frantically, so that it made the plumage of his shot-aching breast throb. His own blood throttled his breathing. But these things were nothing compared to the lightning of pain in his left shoulder, where the shot had bunched, shattering the airy bones so the pinions trailed on the ground and could not be lifted. Yet, when a sparrow lit in the bush over him, Hook's eyes flew open again, hard and challenging, his good wing was lifted and his beak strained open. The startled sparrow darted piping out over the river.

Throughout that night, while the long clouds blew across the stars and the wind shook the bushes about him, and throughout the next day, while the clouds still blew and massed until there was no gleam of sunlight on the sand bar, Hook remained stationary, enduring his sickness. In the second evening, the rains began. First there was a long, running patter of drops upon the beach and over the dry trees and bushes. At dusk there came a heavier squall, which did not die entirely, but slacked off to a continual, spaced splashing of big drops, and then returned with the front of the storm. In long, misty curtains, gust by gust, the rain swept over the sea, beating down its heaving, and coursed up the beach. The little jets of dust ceased to rise about the drops in the fields, and the mud began to gleam. Among the boulders of the river bed, darkling pools grew slowly.

Still Hook stood behind his tree from the wind, only gentle drops reaching him, falling from the upper branches and then again from the brush. His eyes remained closed, and he could still taste his own blood in his mouth, though it had ceased to come up freshly. Out beyond him, he heard the storm changing. As rain conquered the sea, the heave of the surf became a hushed sound, often lost in the crying of the wind. Then gradually, as the night turned toward morning, the wind also was broken by the rain. The crying became fainter, the rain settled toward steadiness, and the creep of the waves could be heard again, quiet and regular upon the beach.

At dawn there was no wind and no sun, but everywhere the roaring of the vertical, relentless rain. Hook then crept among the rapid drippings of the bushes, dragging his torn sail, seeking better shelter. He stopped often and stood with the shutters of film drawn over his eyes. At mid-morning he found a little cave under a ledge at the base of the sea cliff. Here, lost without branches and leaves about him, he settled to await improvement.

When, at midday of the third day, the rain stopped altogether, and the sky opened before a small, fresh wind, letting light through to glitter upon a tremulous sea, Hook was so weak that his good wing trailed also to prop him upright, and his open eyes were lusterless. But his wounds were hardened, and he felt the return of hunger. Beyond his shelter, he heard the gulls flying in great numbers and crying their joy at the cleared air. He could even hear, from the fringe of the river, the ecstatic and unstinted bubblings and chirpings of the small birds. The grassland, he felt, would be full of the stirring anew of the close-bound life, the un-drowned insects clicking as they dried out, the snakes slithering down, heads half erect, into the grasses where the mice, gophers and ground squirrels ran and stopped and chewed and licked themselves smoother and drier.

With the aid of this hunger, and on the crutches of his wings, Hook came down to stand in the sun beside his cave, whence he could watch the beach. Before him, in ellipses on tilting planes, the gulls flew. The surf was rearing again, and beginning to shelve and hiss on the sand. Through the white foam-writing it left, the long-billed pipers twinkled in bevies, escaping each wave, then racing down after it to plunge their fine drills into the minute double holes where the sand crabs bubbled. In the third row of breakers two seals lifted sleek, streaming heads and barked, and over them, trailing his spider legs, a great crane flew south. Among the stones at the foot of the cliff, small red and green crabs made a little, continuous rattling and knocking. The cliff swallows glittered and twanged on aerial forays.

The afternoon began auspiciously for Hook also. One of the two gulls which came squabbling above him dropped a freshly caught fish to the sand. Quickly Hook was upon it. Gripping it, he raised his good wing and cocked his head with open beak at the many gulls which had circled and come down at once toward the fall of the fish. The gulls sheered off, cursing raucously. Left alone on the sand, Hook devoured the fish and, after resting in the sun, withdrew again to his shelter.

IV

In the succeeding days, between rains, he foraged on the beach. He learned to kill and crack the small green crabs. Along the edge of the river mouth, he found the drowned bodies of mice and squirrels and even sparrows. Twice he managed to drive feeding gulls from their catch, charging upon them with buffeting wing and clattering beak. He grew stronger slowly, but the shot sail continued to drag. Often, at the choking thought of soaring and striking and the good, hot-blood kill, he strove to take off, but only the one wing came up, winnowing with a hiss, and drove him over onto his side in the sand. After these futile trials, he would rage and clatter. But gradually he learned to believe that he could not fly, that his life must now be that of the discharged nestling again. Denied the joy of space, without which the joy of loneliness was lost, the joy of battle and killing, the blood lust, became his whole concentration. It was his hope, as he charged feeding gulls, that they would turn and offer battle, but they never did. The sandpipers, at his approach, fled peeping, or, like a quiver of arrows shot together, streamed out over the surf in a long curve. Once, pent beyond bearing, he disgraced himself by shrieking challenge at the business-like heron which flew south every evening at the same time. The heron did not even turn his head, but flapped and glided on.

Hook's shame and anger became such that he stood awake at night. Hunger kept him awake also, for these little leavings of the gulls could not sustain his great body in its renewed violence. He became aware that the gulls slept at night in flocks on the sand, each with one leg tucked under him. He discovered also that the curlews and the pipers, often mingling, likewise slept, on the higher remnant of the bar. A sensation of evil delight filled him in the consideration of protracted striking among them.

There was only half of a sick moon in a sky of running but far-separated clouds on the night when he managed to stalk into the center of the sleeping gulls. This was light enough, but so great was his vengeful pleasure that there broke from him a shrill scream of challenge as he first struck. Without the power of flight behind it, the blow was not murderous, and this newly discovered impotence made Hook crazy, so that he screamed again and again as he struck and tore at the felled gull. He slew the one, but was twice knocked over by its heavy flounderings, and all the others rose above him, weaving and screaming, protesting in the thin moonlight. Wakened by their clamor, the wading birds also took wing, startled and plaintive. When the beach was quiet again, the flocks had settled elsewhere, beyond his pitiful range, and he was left alone beside the single kill. It was a disappointing victory. He fed with lowering spirit.

Thereafter, he stalked silently. At sunset he would watch where the gulls settled along the miles of beach, and after dark he would come like a sharp shadow among them, and drive with his hook on all sides of him, till the beatings of a poorly struck victim sent the flock up. Then he would turn vindictively upon the fallen and finish them. In his best night, he killed five from one flock. But he ate only a little from one, for the vigor resulting from occasional repletion strengthened only his ire, which became so great at such a time that food revolted him. It was not the joyous, swift, controlled hunting anger of a sane hawk, but something quite different, which made him dizzy if it continued too long, and left him unsatisfied with any kill.

Then one day, when he had very nearly struck a gull while driving it from a gasping yellowfin, the gull's wing rapped against him as it broke for its running start, and, the trailing wing failing to support him, he was knocked over. He flurried awkwardly in the sand to regain his feet, but his mastery of the beach was ended. Seeing him, in clear sunlight, struggling after the chance blow, the gulls returned about him in a flashing cloud, circling and pecking on the wing. Hook's plumage showed quick little jets of irregularity here and there. He reared back, clattering and erecting the good wing, spreading the great, rusty tail for balance. His eyes shone with a little of the old pleasure. But it died, for he could reach none of them. He was forced to turn and dance awkwardly on the sand, trying to clash bills with each tormentor. They banked up quealing and returned, weaving about him in concentric and overlapping circles. His scream was lost in their clamor, and he appeared merely to be hopping clumsily with his mouth open. Again he fell sideways. Before he could right himself, he was bowled over, and a second time, and lay on his side, twisting his neck to reach them and clappering in blind fury, and was struck three times by three successive gulls, shrieking their flock triumph.

Finally he managed to roll to his breast, and to crouch with his good wing spread wide and the other stretched nearly as far, so that he extended like a gigantic moth, only his snake head, with its now silent scimitar, erect. One great eye blazed under its level brow, but where the other had been was a shallow hole from which thin blood trickled to his russet gap.

In this crouch, by short stages, stopping repeatedly to turn and drive the gulls up, Hook dragged into the river canyon and under the stiff cover of the bitter-leafed laurel. There the gulls left him, soaring up with great clatter of their valor. Till nearly sunset Hook, broken spirited and enduring his hardening eye socket, heard them celebrating over the waves.

When his will was somewhat replenished, and his empty eye socket had stopped the twitching and vague aching which had forced him often to roll ignominiously to rub it in the dust, Hook ventured from the protective lacings of his thicket. He knew fear again, and the challenge of his remaining eye was once more strident, as in adolescence. He dared not return to the beaches, and with a new, weak hunger, the home hunger, enticing him, made his way by short hunting journeys back to the wild wheat slopes and the crisp oaks. There was in Hook an unwonted sensation now, that of the ever-neighboring possibility of death. This sensation was beginning, after his period as a mad bird on the beach, to solidify him into his last stage of life. When, during his slow homeward passage, the gulls wafted inland over him, watching the earth with curious, miserish eyes, he did not cower, but neither did he challenge, either by opened beak or by raised shoulder. He merely watched carefully, learning his first lessons in observing the world with one eye.

At first the familiar surroundings of the bend in the river and the tree with the dead limb to which he could not ascend, aggravated his humiliation, but in time, forced to live cunningly and half-starved, he lost much of his savage pride. At the first flight of a strange hawk over his realm, he was wild at his helplessness, and kept twisting his head like an owl, or spinning in the grass like a small and feathered dervish, to keep the hateful beauty of the wind-rider in sight. But in the succeeding weeks, as one after another coasted his beat, his resentment declined, and when one of the raiders, a haughty yearling, sighted his up-staring eye, and plunged and struck him dreadfully, and failed to kill him only because he dragged under a thicket in time, the second of his great hungers was gone. He had no longer the true lust to kill, no joy of battle, but only the poor desire to fill his belly.

Then truly he lived in the wheat and the brush like a ground owl, ridden with ground lice, dusty or muddy, ever half-starved, forced to sit for hours by small holes for petty and unsatisfying kills. Only once during the final months before his end did he make a kill where the breath of danger recalled his valor, and then the danger was such as a hawk with wings and eyes would scorn. Waiting beside a gopher hole, surrounded by the high, yellow grass, he saw the head emerge, and struck, and was amazed that there writhed in his clutch the neck and dusty coffin-skull of a rattlesnake. Holding his grip, Hook saw the great, thick body slither up after, the tip an erect, strident blur, and writhe on the dirt of the gopher's mound. The weight of the snake pushed Hook about, and once threw him down, and the rising and falling whine of the rattles made the moment terrible, but the vaulted mouth, gaping from the closeness of Hook's gripe, so that the pale, envenomed sabers stood out free, could not reach him. When Hook replaced the grip of his beak with the grip of his talons, and was free to strike again and again at the base of the head, the struggle was over. Hook tore and fed on the fine, watery flesh, and left the tattered armor and the long, jointed bone for the marching ants.

When the heavy rains returned, he ate well during the period of the first escapes from flooded burrows, and then well enough, in a vulture's way, on the drowned creatures. But as the rains lingered, and the burrows hung full of water, and there were no insects in the grass and no small birds sleeping in the thickets, he was constantly hungry, and finally unbearably hungry. His sodden and ground-broken plumage stood out raggedly about him, so that he looked fat, even bloated, but underneath it his skin clung to his bones. Save for his great talons and clappers, and the rain in his down, he would have been like a handful of air. He often stood for a long time under some bush or ledge, heedless of the drip, his one eye filmed over, his mind neither asleep or awake, but between. The gurgle and swirl of the brimming river, and the sound of chunks of the bank cut away to splash and dissolve in the already muddy flood, became familiar to him, and yet a torment, as if that great, ceaselessly working power of water ridiculed his frailty, within which only the faintest spark of valor still glimmered. The last two nights before the rain ended, he huddled under the floor of the bridge on the coastal highway, and heard the palpitant thunder of motors swell and roar over him. The trucks shook the bridge so that Hook, even in his famished lassitude, would sometimes open his one great eye wide and startled.

V

After the rains, when things became full again, bursting with growth and sound, the trees swelling, the thickets full of song and chatter, the fields, turning green in the sun, alive with rustling passages, and the moonlit nights strained with the song of the peepers all up and down the river and in the pools in the fields, Hook had to bear the return of the one hunger left him. At times this made him so wild that he forgot himself and screamed challenge from the open ground. The fretfulness of it spoiled his hunting, which was now entirely a matter of patience. Once he was in despair, and lashed himself through the grass and thickets, trying to rise when that virgin scent drifted for a few moments above the current of his own river. Then, breathless, his beak agape, he saw the strong suitor ride swiftly down on the wind over him, and heard afar the screaming fuss of the harsh wooing in the alders. For that moment even the battle heart beat in him again. The rim of his good eye was scarlet, and a little bead of new blood stood in the socket of the other. With beak and talon, he ripped at a fallen log, and made loam and leaves fly from about it.

But the season of love passed over to the nesting season, and Hook's love hunger, unused, shriveled in him with the others, and there remained in him only one stern quality befitting a hawk, and that the negative one, the remnant, the will to endure. He resumed his patient, plotted hunting, now along a field of the Japanese farmer, but ever within reach of the river thickets.

Growing tough and dry again as the summer advanced, inured to the family of the farmer, whom he saw daily, stooping and scraping with sticks in the ugly, open rows of their fields, where no lovely grass rustled and no life stirred save the shameless gulls, which walked at the heels of the workers, gobbling the worms and grubs as they turned up, Hook became nearly content with his shard of life. The only longing or resentment to pierce him was that which he suffered occasionally when forced to hide at the edge of the mile-long bean field from the wafted cruising and the restive, down-bent gaze of one of his own kind. For the rest, he was without flame, a snappish, dust-colored creature, fading into the grasses he trailed through, and suited to his petty ways.

At the end of that summer, for the second time in his four years, Hook underwent a drouth. The equinoctial period passed without a rain. The laurel and the rabbit-brush dropped dry leaves. The foliage of the oaks shriveled and curled. Even the night fogs in the river canyon failed. The farmer's red cattle on the hillside lowed constantly, and could not feed on the dusty stubble. Grass fires broke out along the highway, and ate fast in the wind, filling the hollows with the smell of smoke, and died in the dirt of the shorn hills. The river made no sound. Scum grew on its vestigial pools, and turtles died and stank among the rocks. The dust rode before the wind, and ascended and flowered to nothing between the hills, and every sunset was red with the dust in the air. The people in the farmer's house quarreled, and even struck one another. Birds were silent, and only the hawks flew much. The animals lay breathing hard for very long spells, and ran and crept jerkily. Their flanks were fallen in, and their eyes were red.

At first Hook gorged at the fringe of the grass fires on the multitudes of tiny things that came running and squeaking. But thereafter there were the blackened strips on the hills, and little more in the thin, crackling grass. He found mice and rats, gophers and ground-squirrels, and even rabbits, dead in the stubble and under the thickets, but so dry and flesh-less that only a faint smell rose from them, even on the sunny days. He starved on them. By early December he had wearily stalked the length of the eastern foothills, hunting at night to escape the voracity of his own kind, resting often upon his wings. The queer trail of his short steps and great horned toes zigzagged in the dust and was erased by the wind at dawn. He was nearly dead, and could make no sound through the horn funnels of his clappers.

Then one night the dry wind brought him, with the familiar, lifeless dust, another familiar scent, troublesome, mingled and unclear. In his vision-dominated brain he remembered the swift circle of his flight a year past, crossing in one segment, his shadow beneath him, a yard cluttered with crates and chickens, a gray barn and then again the plowed land and the stubble. Traveling faster than he had for days, impatient of his shrunken sweep, Hook came down to the farm. In the dark wisps of cloud blown among the stars over him, but no moon, he stood outside the wire of the chicken run. The scent of fat and blooded birds reached him from the shelter, and also within the enclosure was water. At the breath of the water, Hook's gorge contracted, and his tongue quivered and clove in its groove of horn. But there was the wire. He stalked its perimeter and found no opening. He beat it with his good wing, and felt it cut but not give. He wrenched at it with his beak in many places, but could not tear it. Finally, in a fury which drove the thin blood through him, he leaped repeatedly against it, beating and clawing. He was thrown back from the last leap as from the first, but in it he had risen so high as to clutch with his beak at the top wire. While he lay on his breast on the ground, the significance of this came upon him.

Again he leapt, clawed up the wire, and, as he would have fallen, made even the dead wing bear a little. He grasped the top and tumbled within. There again he rested flat, searching the dark with quick-turning head. There was no sound or motion but the throb of his own body. First he drank at the chill metal trough hung for the chickens. The water was cold, and loosened his tongue and his tight throat, but it also made him

drunk and dizzy, so that he had to rest again, his claws spread wide to
brace him. Then he walked stiffly, to stalk down the scent. He trailed it
up the runway. Then there was the stuffy, body-warm air, acrid with drop-
pings, full of soft rustlings as his talons clicked on the board floor. The
thick, white shapes showed faintly in the darkness. Hook struck quickly,
driving a hen to the floor with one blow, its neck broken and stretched out
stringily. He leaped the still pulsing body, and tore it. The rich, streaming
blood was overpowering to his dried senses, his starved, leathery body.
After a few swallows, the flesh choked him. In his rage, he struck down
another hen. The urge to kill took him again, as in those nights on the
beach. He could let nothing go. Balked of feeding, he was compelled to
slaughter. Clattering, he struck again and again. The henhouse was suddenly filled with the squawking and helpless rushing and buffeting of the
terrified, brainless fowls.

Hook reveled in mastery. Here was game big enough to offer weight
against a strike, and yet unable to soar away from his blows. Turning in
the midst of the turmoil, cannily, his fury caught at the perfect pitch, he
struck unceasingly. When the hens finally discovered the outlet, and
streamed into the yard, to run around the fence, beating and squawking,
Hook followed them, scraping down the incline, clumsy and joyous. In
the yard, the cock, a bird as large as he, and much heavier, found him out
and gave valiant battle. In the dark, and both earthbound, there was
little skill, but blow upon blow, and only chance parry. The still squawking hens pressed into one corner of the yard. While the duel went on, a
dog, excited by the sustained scuffling, began to bark. He continued to
bark, running back and forth along the fence on one side. A light flashed
on in an uncurtained window of the farmhouse, and streamed whitely
over the crates littering the ground.

Enthralled by his old battle joy, Hook knew only the burly cock before
him. Now, in the farthest reach of the window light, they could see each
other dimly. The Japanese farmer, with his gun and lantern, was already
at the gate when the finish came. The great cock leapt to jab with his
spurs and, toppling forward with extended neck as he fell, was struck and
extinguished. Blood had loosened Hook's throat. Shrilly he cried his
triumph. It was a thin and exhausted cry, but within him as good as when
he shrilled in mid-air over the plummeting descent of a fine foe in his
best spring.

The light from the lantern partially blinded Hook. He first turned and
ran directly from it, into the corner where the hens were huddled. They
fled apart before his charge. He essayed the fence, and on the second try,
in his desperation, was out. But in the open dust, the dog was on him,
circling, dashing in, snapping. The farmer, who at first had not fired because of the chickens, now did not fire because of the dog, and, when
he saw that the hawk was unable to fly, relinquished the sport to the dog,

holding the lantern up in order to see better. The light showed his own flat, broad, dark face as sunken also, the cheekbones very prominent, and showed the torn-off sleeves of his shirt and the holes in the knees of his overalls. His wife, in a stained wrapper, and barefooted, heavy black hair hanging around a young, passionless face, joined him hesitantly, but watched, fascinated and a little horrified. His son joined them too, encouraging the dog, but quickly grew silent. Courageous and cruel death, however it may afterward sicken the one who has watched it, is impossible to look away from.

In the circle of the light, Hook turned to keep the dog in front of him. His one eye gleamed with malevolence. The dog was an Airedale, and large. Each time he pounced, Hook stood ground, raising his good wing, the pinions newly torn by the fence, opening his beak soundlessly, and, at the closest approach, hissed furiously, and at once struck. Hit and ripped twice by the whetted horn, the dog recoiled more quickly from several subsequent jumps and, infuriated by his own cowardice, began to bark wildly. Hook maneuvered to watch him, keeping his head turned to avoid losing the foe on the blind side. When the dog paused, safely away, Hook watched him quietly, wing partially lowered, beak closed, but at the first move again lifted the wing and gaped. The dog whined, and the man spoke to him encouragingly. The awful sound of his voice made Hook for an instant twist his head to stare up at the immense figures behind the light. The dog again sallied, barking, and Hook's head spun back. His wing was bitten this time, and with a furious side-blow, he caught the dog's nose. The dog dropped him with a yelp, and then, smarting, came on more warily, as Hook propped himself up from the ground again between his wings. Hook's artificial strength was waning, but his heart still stood to the battle, sustained by a fear of such dimension as he had never known before, but only anticipated when the arrogant young hawk had driven him to cover. The dog, unable to find any point at which the merciless, unwinking eye was not watching him, the parted beak waiting, paused and whimpered again.

"Oh, kill the poor thing," the woman begged.

The man, though, encouraged the dog again, saying, "Sick him; sick him."

The dog rushed bodily. Unable to avoid him, Hook was bowled down, snapping and raking. He left long slashes, as from the blade of a knife, on the dog's flank, but before he could right himself and assume guard again, was caught by the good wing and dragged, clattering, and seeking to make a good stroke from his back. The man followed them to keep the light on them, and the boy went with him, wetting his lips with his tongue and keeping his fists closed tightly. The woman remained behind, but could not help watching the diminished conclusion.

In the little, palely shining arena, the dog repeated his successful maneuver three times, growling but not barking, and when Hook thrashed up from the third blow, both wings were trailing, and dark, shining streams crept on his black-fretted breast from the shoulders. The great eye flashed more furiously than it ever had in victorious battle, and the beak still gaped, but there was no more clatter. He faltered when turning to keep front; the broken wings played him false even as props. He could not rise to use his talons.

The man had tired of holding the lantern up, and put it down to rub his arm. In the low, horizontal light, the dog charged again, this time throwing the weight of his forepaws against Hook's shoulder, so that Hook was crushed as he struck. With his talons up, Hook raked at the dog's belly, but the dog conceived the finish, and furiously worried the feathered bulk. Hook's neck went limp, and between his gaping clappers came only a faint chittering, as from some small kill of his own in the grasses.

In this last conflict, however, there had been some minutes of the supreme fire of the hawk whose three hungers are perfectly fused in the one will; enough to burn off a year of shame.

Between the great sails the light body lay caved and perfectly still. The dog, smarting from his cuts, came to the master and was praised. The woman, joining them slowly, looked at the great wingspread, her husband raising the lantern that she might see it better.

"Oh, the brave bird," she said.

COMMENT AND QUESTION

1. The conflict here is the most universal of all conflicts. It is summed up in the third paragraph from the end: "In this last conflict, however, there had been some minutes of the supreme fire of the hawk whose three hungers are perfectly fused in the one will. . . ." What are the three hungers? What is the one will?

2. Explain the deep satisfaction produced in the reader by the last battle of Hook. Does this last battle arouse any other feelings in the reader?

3. What forces must Hook contend with? At what point is his supremacy complete?

4. What are Hook's fears?

5. What terms besides "barbaric" may be used to describe Hook?

6. This story tries to present life through sense impressions. The recording of sight and sound is especially keen. The student should note the most vivid passages.

7. Do we experience the life of Hook only through sense impressions? Are we given other insights? Is Hook given any "human" reactions? Does the story make ethical and moral judgments?

8. Show how the first three paragraphs establish most of the important motifs in the story, the drouth, the gulls, etc.

9. Notice that "Hook" is divided into five parts. If you will write a title for each part, you will see quite clearly the structural logic of the story.

THE SECRET SHARER

BY JOSEPH CONRAD

JOSEPH CONRAD (1857–1924), a Pole by birth, is one of the greatest of English novelists, and probably the greatest writer of sea stories in the English language. He was born Jósef Téodor Konrad Korzeniowski near Kiev, the Ukraine (Russian Poland). He went to sea as a young man in 1873 and followed the sea for twenty years. His voyages to Australia, South Africa, South America, and the Orient are reflected in his writing. When he was thirty-eight he published his first novel, *Almayer's Folly*. His better known novels are *Lord Jim* (1900), *Nostromo* (1904), and *Victory* (1915). His better known short stories and *novelle* are "The Lagoon," "Youth," "The Heart of Darkness," "The Secret Sharer," and "The Nigger of the Narcissus."

O N MY right hand there were lines of fishing-stakes resembling a mysterious system of half-submerged bamboo fences, incomprehensible in its division of the domain of tropical fishes, and crazy of aspect as if abandoned forever by some nomad tribe of fishermen now gone to the other end of the ocean; for there was no sign of human habitation as far as the eye could reach. To the left a group of barren islets, suggesting ruins of stone walls, towers, and blockhouses, had its foundations set in a blue sea that itself looked solid, so still and stable did it lie below my feet; even the track of light from the westering sun shone smoothly, without that animated glitter which tells of an imperceptible ripple. And when I turned my head to take a parting glance at the tug which had just left us anchored outside the bar, I saw the straight line of the flat shore joined to the stable sea, edge to edge, with a perfect and unmarked closeness, in one leveled floor half brown, half blue under the enormous dome of the sky. Corresponding in their insignificance to the islets of the sea, two small clumps of trees, one on each side of the only fault in the impeccable joint, marked the mouth of the river Meinam we had just left on the first preparatory stage of our homeward journey; and, far back on the inland level, a larger and loftier mass, the grove surrounding the great Paknam pagoda, was the only thing on which the eye could rest from the vain task of exploring the monotonous sweep of the horizon. Here and there gleams as of a few scattered pieces of silver marked the windings of the great river; and on the nearest of them, just within the bar, the tug steaming right into the land became lost to my sight, hull and funnel and masts, as though the impassive earth had swallowed her up without an effort, without a tremor. My eye followed the light cloud of her smoke, now here, now there, above the plain, according to the devious curves of the stream, but always fainter and farther away, till I lost it at last behind the miter-shaped hill of the great pagoda. And then I was left alone with my ship, anchored at the head of the Gulf of Siam.

She floated at the starting-point of a long journey, very still in an immense stillness, the shadows of her spars flung far to the eastward by the setting sun. At that moment I was alone on her decks. There was not a sound in her—and around us nothing moved, nothing lived, not a canoe on the water, not a bird in the air, not a cloud in the sky. In this breathless pause at the threshold of a long passage we seemed to be measuring our fitness for a long and arduous enterprise, the appointed task of both our existences to be carried out, far from all human eyes, with only sky and sea for spectators and for judges.

There must have been some glare in the air to interfere with one's sight, because it was only just before the sun left us that my roaming eyes made out beyond the highest ridge of the principal islet of the group something which did away with the solemnity of perfect solitude. The tide of darkness flowed on swiftly; and with tropical suddenness a swarm of stars came out above the shadowy earth, while I lingered yet, my hand resting lightly on my ship's rail as if on the shoulder of a trusted friend. But, with all that multitude of celestial bodies staring down at one, the comfort of quiet communion with her was gone for good. And there were also disturbing sounds by this time—voices, footsteps forward; the steward flitted along the main deck, a busily ministering spirit; a hand-bell tinkled urgently under the poop-deck. . . .

I found my two officers waiting for me near the supper table, in the lighted cuddy. We sat down at once, and as I helped the chief mate, I said:

"Are you aware that there is a ship anchored inside the islands? I saw her mastheads above the ridge as the sun went down."

He raised sharply his simple face, overcharged by a terrible growth of whisker, and emitted his usual ejaculations: "Bless my soul, sir! You don't say so!"

My second mate was a round-cheeked, silent young man, grave beyond his years, I thought; but as our eyes happened to meet I detected a slight quiver on his lips. I looked down at once. It was not my part to encourage sneering on board my ship. It must be said, too, that I knew very little of my officers. In consequence of certain events of no particular significance, except to myself, I had been appointed to the command only a fortnight before. Neither did I know much of the hands forward. All these people had been together for eighteen months or so, and my position was that of the only stranger on board. I mention this because it has some bearing on what is to follow. But what I felt most was my being a stranger to the ship; and if all the truth must be told, I was somewhat of a stranger to myself. The youngest man on board (barring the second mate), and untried as yet by a position of the fullest responsibilty, I was willing to take the adequacy of the others for granted. They had simply to be equal to their tasks; but I wondered how far I should turn out faithful to that ideal conception of one's own personality every man sets up for himself secretly.

Meantime the chief mate, with an almost visible effect of collaboration on the part of his round eyes and frightful whiskers, was trying to evolve a theory of the anchored ship. His dominant trait was to take all things into earnest consideration. He was of a painstaking turn of mind. As he used to say, he "liked to account to himself" for practically everything that came in his way, down to a miserable scorpion he had found in his cabin a week before. The why and the wherefore of that scorpion—how it got on board and came to select his room rather than the pantry (which was a dark place and more what a scorpion would be partial to), and how on earth it managed to drown itself in the inkwell of his writing-desk—had exercised him infinitely. The ship within the islands was much more easily accounted for; and just as we were about to rise from table he made his pronouncement. She was, he doubted not, a ship from home lately arrived. Probably she drew too much water to cross the bar except at the top of spring tides. Therefore she went into that natural harbor to wait for a few days in preference to remaining in an open roadstead.

"That's so," confirmed the second mate, suddenly, in his slightly hoarse voice. "She draws over twenty feet. She's the Liverpool ship *Sephora* with a cargo of coal. Hundred and twenty-three days from Cardiff."

We looked at him in surprise.

"The tugboat skipper told me when he came on board for your letters, sir," explained the young man. "He expects to take her up the river the day after tomorrow."

After thus overwhelming us with the extent of his information he slipped out of the cabin. The mate observed regretfully that he "could not account for that young fellow's whims." What prevented him telling us all about it at once, he wanted to know.

I detained him as he was making a move. For the last two days the crew had had plenty of hard work, and the night before they had very little sleep. I felt painfully that I—a stranger—was doing something unusual when I directed him to let all hands turn in without setting an anchor-watch. I proposed to keep on deck myself till one o'clock or thereabouts. I would get the second mate to relieve me at that hour.

"He will turn out the cook and the steward at four," I concluded, "and then give you a call. Of course at the slightest sign of any sort of wind we'll have the hands up and make a start at once."

He concealed his astonishment. "Very well, sir." Outside the cuddy he put his head in the second mate's door to inform him of my unheard-of caprice to take a five hours' anchor-watch on myself. I heard the other raise his voice incredulously—"What? The Captain himself?" Then a few more murmurs, a door closed, then another. A few moments later I went on deck.

My strangeness, which had made me sleepless, had prompted that unconventional arrangement, as if I had expected in those solitary hours of the night to get on terms with the ship of which I knew nothing, manned by men of whom I knew very little more. Fast alongside a wharf, littered like any ship in port with a tangle of unrelated things, invaded by unrelated shore people, I had hardly seen her yet properly. Now, as she lay cleared for sea, the stretch of her main-deck seemed to me very fine under the stars. Very fine, very roomy for her size, and very inviting. I descended the poop and paced the waist, my mind picturing to myself the coming passage through the Malay Archipelago, down the Indian Ocean, and up the Atlantic. All its phases were familiar enough to me, every characteristic, all the alternatives which were likely to face me on the high seas— everything! . . . except the novel responsibility of command. But I took heart from the reasonable thought that the ship was like other ships, the men like other men, and that the sea was not likely to keep any special surprises expressly for my discomfiture.

Arrived at that comforting conclusion, I bethought myself of a cigar and went below to get it. All was still down there. Everybody at the after end of the ship was sleeping profoundly. I came out again on the quarter-deck, agreeably at ease in my sleeping-suit on that warm breathless night, barefooted, a glowing cigar in my teeth, and, going forward, I was met by the profound silence of the fore end of the ship. Only as I passed the door of the forecastle I heard a deep, quiet, trustful sigh of some sleeper inside. And suddenly I rejoiced in the great security of the sea as compared with the unrest of the land, in my choice of that untempted life presenting no disquieting problems, invested with an elementary moral beauty by the absolute straightforwardness of its appeal and by the singleness of its purpose.

The riding-light in the fore-rigging burned with a clear, untroubled, as if symbolic, flame, confident and bright in the mysterious shades of the night. Passing on my way aft along the other side of the ship, I observed that the rope side-ladder, put over, no doubt, for the master of the tug when he came to fetch away our letters, had not been hauled in as it should have been. I became annoyed at this, for exactitude in small matters is the very soul of discipline. Then I reflected that I had myself peremptorily dismissed my officers from duty, and by my own act had prevented the anchor-watch being formally set and things properly attended to. I asked myself whether it was wise ever to interfere with the established routine of duties even from the kindest of motives. My action might have made me appear eccentric. Goodness only knew how that absurdly whiskered mate would "account" for my conduct, and what the whole ship thought of that informality of their new captain. I was vexed with myself.

Not from compunction certainly, but, as it were mechanically, I proceeded to get the ladder in myself. Now a side-ladder of that sort is a light affair and comes in easily, yet my vigorous tug, which should have brought it flying on board, merely recoiled upon my body in a totally unexpected jerk. What the devil! . . . I was so astounded by the immovableness of that ladder that I remained stock-still, trying to account for it to myself like that imbecile mate of mine. In the end, of course, I put my head over the rail.

The side of the ship made an opaque belt of shadow on the darkling glassy shimmer of the sea. But I saw at once something elongated and pale floating very close to the ladder. Before I could form a guess a faint flash of phosphorescent light, which seemed to issue suddenly from the naked body of a man, flickered in the sleeping water with the elusive, silent play of summer lightning in a night sky. With a gasp I saw revealed to my stare a pair of feet, the long legs, a broad livid back immersed right up to the neck in a greenish cadaverous glow. One hand, awash, clutched the bottom rung of the ladder. He was complete but for the head. A headless corpse! The cigar dropped out of my gaping mouth with a tiny plop and a short hiss quite audible in the absolute stillness of all things under heaven. At that I suppose he raised up his face, a dimly pale oval in the shadow of the ship's side. But even then I could only barely make out down there the shape of his black-haired head. However, it was enough for the horrid, frost-bound sensation which had gripped me about the chest to pass off. The moment of vain exclamations was past, too. I only climbed on the spare spar and leaned over the rail as far as I could, to bring my eyes nearer to that mystery floating alongside.

As he hung by the ladder, like a resting swimmer, the sea-lightning played about his limbs at every stir; and he appeared in it ghastly, silvery, fish-like. He remained as mute as a fish, too. He made no motion to get out of the water, either. It was inconceivable that he should not attempt to come on board, and strangely troubling to suspect that perhaps he did not want to. And my first words were prompted by just that troubled incertitude.

"What's the matter?" I asked in my ordinary tone, speaking down to the face upturned exactly under mine.

"Cramp," it answered, no louder. Then slightly anxious, "I say, no need to call anyone."

"I was not going to," I said.

"Are you alone on deck?"

"Yes."

I had somehow the impression that he was on the point of letting go the ladder to swim away beyond my ken—mysterious as he came. But, for the moment, this being appearing as if he had risen from the bottom of the sea (it was certainly the nearest land to the ship) wanted only to know the time. I told him. And he, down there, tentatively:

"I suppose your captain's turned in?"

"I am sure he isn't," I said.

He seemed to struggle with himself, for I heard something like the low, bitter murmur of doubt. "What's the good?" His next words came out with a hesitating effort.

"Look here, my man. Could you call him out quietly?"

I thought the time had come to declare myself.

"*I* am the captain."

I heard a "By Jove!" whispered at the level of the water. The phosphorescence flashed in the swirl of the water all about his limbs, his other hand seized the ladder.

"My name's Leggatt."

The voice was calm and resolute. A good voice. The self-possession of that man had somehow induced a corresponding state in myself. It was very quietly that I remarked:

"You must be a good swimmer."

"Yes. I've been in the water practically since nine o'clock. The question for me now is whether I am to let go this ladder and go on swimming till I sink from exhaustion, or—to come on board here."

I felt this was no mere formula of desperate speech, but a real alternative in the view of a strong soul. I should have gathered from this that he was young; indeed, it is only the young who are ever confronted by such clear issues. But at the time it was pure intuition on my part. A mysterious communication was established already between us two—in the face of that silent, darkened tropical sea. I was young, too; young enough to make no comment. The man in the water began suddenly to climb up the ladder, and I hastened away from the rail to fetch some clothes.

Before entering the cabin I stood still, listening in the lobby at the foot of the stairs. A faint snore came through the closed door of the chief mate's room. The second mate's door was on the hook, but the darkness in there was absolutely soundless. He, too, was young and could sleep like a stone. Remained the steward, but he was not likely to wake up before he was called. I got a sleeping-suit out of my room and, coming back on deck, saw the naked man from the sea sitting on the mainhatch, glimmering white in the darkness, his elbows on his knees and his head in his hands. In a moment he had concealed his damp body in a sleeping-suit of the same gray-stripe pattern as the one I was wearing and followed me like my double on the poop. Together we moved right aft, barefooted, silent.

"What is it?" I asked in a deadened voice, taking the lighted lamp out of the binnacle, and raising it to his face.

"An ugly business."

He had rather regular features: a good mouth; light eyes under somewhat heavy, dark eyebrows; a smooth, square forehead; no growth on his cheeks; a small, brown mustache, and a well-shaped, round chin. His expression was concentrated, meditative, under the inspecting light of the lamp I held up to his face; such as a man thinking hard in solitude might wear. My sleeping-suit was just right for his size. A well-knit young fellow of twenty-five at most. He caught his lower lip with the edge of white, even teeth.

"Yes," I said, replacing the lamp in the binnacle. The warm, heavy tropical night closed upon his head again.

"There's a ship over there," he murmured.

"Yes, I know. The *Sephora*. Did you know of us?"

"Hadn't the slightest idea. I am the mate of her—" He paused and corrected himself. "I should say I *was*."

"Aha! Something wrong?"

"Yes. Very wrong indeed. I've killed a man."

"What do you mean? Just now?"

"No, on the passage. Weeks ago. Thirty-nine south. When I say a man—"

"Fit of temper," I suggested, confidently.

The shadowy, dark head, like mine, seemed to nod imperceptibly above the ghostly gray of my sleeping-suit. It was, in the night, as though I had been faced by my own reflection in the depths of a somber and immense mirror.

"A pretty thing to have to own up to for a Conway boy," murmured my double, distinctly.

"You're a Conway boy?"

"I am," he said, as if startled. Then, slowly . . . "Perhaps you too—"

It was so; but being a couple of years older I had left before he joined. After a quick interchange of dates a silence fell; and I thought suddenly of my absurd mate with his terrific whiskers and the "Bless my soul—you don't say so" type of intellect. My double gave me an inkling of his thoughts by saying: "My father's a parson in Norfolk. Do you see me before a judge and jury on that charge? For myself I can't see the necessity. There are fellows that an angel from heaven— And I am not that. He was one of those creatures that are just simmering all the time with a silly sort of wickedness. Miserable devils that have no business to live at all. He wouldn't do his duty and wouldn't let anybody else do theirs. But what's the good of talking! You know well enough the sort of ill-conditioned snarling cur—"

He appealed to me as if our experiences had been as identical as our clothes. And I knew well enough the pestiferous danger of such a character where there are no means of legal repression. And I knew well enough also that my double there was no homicidal ruffian. I did not think of asking him for details, and he told me the story roughly in brusque, disconnected sentences. I needed no more. I saw it all going on as though I were myself inside that other sleeping-suit.

"It happened while we were setting a reefed foresail, at dusk. Reefed foresail! You understand the sort of weather. The only sail we had left to keep the ship running; so you may guess what it had been like for days. Anxious sort of job, that. He gave me some of his cursed insolence at the sheet. I tell you I was overdone with this terrific weather that seemed to have no end to it. Terrific, I tell you—and a deep ship. I believe the fellow himself was half crazed with funk. It was no time for gentlemanly reproof, so I turned round and felled him like an ox. He up and at me. We closed just as an awful sea made for the ship. All hands saw it coming and took to the rigging, but I had him by the throat, and went on shaking him like a rat, the men above us yelling, 'Look out! look out!' Then a crash as if the sky had fallen on my head. They say that for over ten minutes hardly anything was to be seen of the ship—just the three masts and a bit of the forecastle head and of the poop all awash driving along in a smother of foam. It was a miracle that they found us, jammed together behind the forebits. It's clear that I meant business, because I was holding him by the throat still when they picked us up. He was black in the face. It was too much for them. It seems they rushed us aft together, gripped as we were, screaming 'Murder!' like a lot of lunatics, and broke into the cuddy. And the ship running for her life, touch and go all the time, any minute her last in a sea fit to turn your hair gray only a-looking at it. I understand that the skipper, too, started raving like the rest of them. The man had been deprived of sleep for more than a week, and to have this sprung on him at the height of a furious gale nearly drove him out of his mind. I wonder they didn't fling me overboard after getting the carcass of their precious ship-mate out of my fingers. They had rather a job to separate us, I've been told. A sufficiently fierce story to make an old judge and a respectable jury sit up a bit. The first thing I heard when I came to myself was the maddening howling of that endless gale, and on that the voice of the old man. He was hanging on to my bunk, staring into my face out of his sou'wester.

" 'Mr. Leggatt, you have killed a man. You can act no longer as chief mate of this ship.' "

His care to subdue his voice made it sound monotonous. He rested a hand on the end of the skylight to steady himself with, and all that time did not stir a limb, so far as I could see. "Nice little tale for a quiet tea-party," he concluded in the same tone.

One of my hands, too, rested on the end of the skylight; neither did I stir a limb, so far as I knew. We stood less than a foot from each other. It occurred to me that if old "Bless my soul—you don't say so" were to put his head up the companion and catch sight of us, he would think he was seeing double, or imagine himself come upon a scene of weird witchcraft; the strange captain having a quiet confabulation by the wheel with his own gray ghost. I became very much concerned to prevent anything of the sort. I heard the other's soothing undertone.

"My father's a parson in Norfolk," it said. Evidently he had forgotten he had told me this important fact before. Truly a nice little tale.

"You had better slip down into my stateroom now," I said, moving off stealthily. My double followed my movements; our bare feet made no sound; I let him in, closed the door with care, and, after giving a call to the second mate, returned on deck for my relief.

"Not much sign of any wind yet," I remarked when he approached.

"No, sir. Not much," he assented, sleepily, in his hoarse voice, with just enough deference, no more, and barely suppressing a yawn.

"Well, that's all you have to look out for. You have got your orders."

"Yes, sir."

I paced a turn or two on the poop and saw him take up his position face forward with his elbow in the ratlines of the mizzen-rigging before I went below. The mate's faint snoring was still going on peacefully. The cuddy lamp was burning over the table on which stood a vase with flowers, a polite attention from the ship's provision merchant—the last flowers we should see for the next three months at the very least. Two bunches of bananas hung from the beam symmetrically, one on each side of the rudder-casing. Everything was as before in the ship—except that two of her captain's sleeping-suits were simultaneously in use, one motionless in the cuddy, the other keeping very still in the captain's stateroom.

It must be explained here that my cabin had the form of the capital letter L, the door being within the angle and opening into the short part of the letter. A couch was to the left, the bed-place to the right; my writing-desk and the chronometers' table faced the door. But anyone opening it, unless he stepped right inside, had no view of what I call the long (or vertical) part of the letter. It contained some lockers surmounted by a bookcase; and a few clothes, a thick jacket or two, caps, oilskin coat, and such like, hung on hooks. There was at the bottom of that part a door opening into my bath-room, which could be entered also directly from the saloon. But that way was never used.

The mysterious arrival had discovered the advantage of this particular shape. Entering my room, lighted strongly by a gift bulkhead lamp swung on gimbals above my writing-desk, I did not see him anywhere till he stepped out quietly from behind the coats hung in the recessed part.

"I heard somebody moving about, and went in there at once," he whispered.

I, too, spoke under my breath.

"Nobody is likely to come in here without knocking and getting permission."

He nodded. His face was thin and the sunburn faded, as though he had been ill. And no wonder. He had been, I heard presently, kept under arrest in his cabin for nearly seven weeks. But there was nothing sickly in his eyes or in his expression. He was not a bit like me, really; yet, as we stood leaning over my bed-place, whispering side by side, with our dark heads together and our backs to the door, anybody bold enough to open it stealthily would have been treated to the uncanny sight of a double captain busy talking in whispers with his other self.

"But all this doesn't tell me how you came to hang on to our side-ladder," I inquired, in the hardly audible murmurs we used, after he had told me something more of the proceedings on board the *Sephora* once the bad weather was over.

"When we sighted Java Head I had had time to think all those matters out several times over. I had six weeks of doing nothing else, and with only an hour or so every evening for a tramp on the quarter-deck."

He whispered, his arms folded on the side of my bed-place, staring through the open port. And I could imagine perfectly the manner of this thinking out—a stubborn if not a steadfast operation; something of which I should have been perfectly incapable.

"I reckoned it would be dark before we closed with the land," he continued, so low that I had to strain my hearing, near as we were to each other, shoulder touching shoulder almost. "So I asked to speak to the old man. He always seemed very sick when he came to see me—as if he could not look me in the face. You know, that foresail saved the ship. She was too deep to have run long under bare poles. And it was I that managed to set it for him. Anyway, he came. When I had him in my cabin—he stood by the door looking at me as if I had the halter round my neck already—I asked him right away to leave my cabin door unlocked at night while the ship was going through Sunda Straits. There would be the Java coast within two or three miles, off Angier Point. I wanted nothing more. I've had a prize for swimming my second year in the Conway."

"I can believe it," I breathed out.

"God only knows why they locked me in every night. To see some of their faces you'd have thought they were afraid I'd go about at night strangling people. Am I a murdering brute? Do I look it? By Jove! if I had been he wouldn't have trusted himself like that into my room. You'll say I might have chucked him aside and and bolted out, there and then— it was dark already. Well, no. And for the same reason I wouldn't think of trying to smash the door. There would have been a rush to stop me at the noise, and I did not mean to get into a confounded scrimmage. Somebody else might have got killed—for I would not have broken out only to get chucked back, and I did not want any more of that work. He refused, looking more sick than ever. He was afraid of the men, and also of that old second mate of his who had been sailing with him for years—a gray-headed old humbug; and his steward, too, had been with him devil knows how long—seventeen years or more—a dogmatic sort of loafer who hated me like poison, just because I was the chief mate. No chief mate ever made more than one voyage in the *Sephora*, you know. Those two old chaps ran the ship. Devil only knows what the skipper wasn't afraid of (all his nerve went to pieces altogether in that hellish spell of bad weather we had)— of what the law would do to him—of his wife, perhaps. Oh, yes! she's on board. Though I don't think she would have meddled. She would have been only too glad to have me out of the ship in any way. The 'brand of Cain' business, don't you see. That's all right. I was ready enough to go off wandering on the face of the earth—and that was price enough to pay for an Abel of that sort. Anyhow, he wouldn't listen to me. 'This thing must take its course. I represent the law here.' He was shaking like a leaf. 'So you won't?' 'No!' 'Then I hope you will be able to sleep on that,' I said, and turned my back on him. 'I wonder that *you* can,' cries he, and locks the door.

"Well, after that, I couldn't. Not very well. That was three weeks ago. We have had a slow passage through the Java Sea; drifted about Carimata for ten days. When we anchored here they thought, I suppose, it was all right. The nearest land (and that's five miles) is the ship's destination; the consul would soon set about catching me; and there would have been no object in bolting to these islets there. I don't suppose there's a drop of water on them. I don't know how it was, but tonight that steward, after bringing me my supper, went out to let me eat it, and left the door unlocked. And I ate it—all there was, too. After I had finished I strolled out on the quarter-deck. I don't know that I meant to do anything. A breath of fresh air was all I wanted, I believe. Then a sudden temptation came over me. I kicked off my slippers and was in the water before I had made up my mind fairly. Somebody heard the splash and they raised an awful hullabaloo. 'He's gone! Lower the boats! He's committed suicide! No, he's swimming.' Certainly I was swimming. It's not so easy for a swimmer like me to commit suicide by drowning. I landed on the nearest islet before the boat left the ship's side. I heard them pulling about in the dark, hailing, and so on, but after a bit they gave up. Everything quieted down and the anchorage became as still as death. I sat down on a stone and began to think. I felt certain they would start searching for me at daylight. There was no place to hide on those stony things—and if there had been, what would have been the good? But now I was clear of that ship, I was not going back. So after a while I took off all my clothes, tied them up in a bundle with a stone inside, and dropped them in the deep water on the outer side of that islet. That was suicide enough for me. Let them think what they liked, but I didn't mean to drown myself. I meant to swim till I sank—but that's not the same thing. I struck out for another of these little islands, and it was from that one that I first saw your riding-light. Something to swim for. I went on easily, and on the way I came upon a flat rock a foot or two above water. In the daytime, I dare say, you might make it out with a glass from your poop. I scrambled up on it and rested myself for a bit. Then I made another start. That last spell must have been over a mile."

His whisper was getting fainter and fainter, and all the time he stared straight out through the port-hole, in which there was not even a star to be seen. I had not interrupted him. There was something that made comment impossible in his narrative, or perhaps in himself; a sort of feeling, a quality, which I can't find a name for. And when he ceased, all I found was a futile whisper: "So you swam for our light?"

"Yes—straight for it. It was something to swim for. I couldn't see any stars low down because the coast was in the way, and I couldn't see the land, either. The water was like glass. One might have been swimming in a confounded thousand-feet deep cistern with no place for scrambling out anywhere; but what I didn't like was the notion of swimming round and round like a crazed bullock before I gave out; and as I didn't mean to go back . . . No. Do you see me being hauled back, stark naked, off one of these little islands by the scruff of the neck and fighting like a wild beast? Somebody would have got killed for certain, and I did not want any of that. So I went on. Then your ladder—"

"Why didn't you hail the ship?" I asked, a little louder.

He touched my shoulder lightly. Lazy footsteps came right over our heads and stopped. The second mate had crossed from the other side of the poop and might have been hanging over the rail, for all we knew.

"He couldn't hear us talking—could he?" My double breathed into my very ear, anxiously.

His anxiety was an answer, a sufficient answer, to the question I had put to him. An answer containing all the difficulty of that situation. I closed the port-hole quietly, to make sure. A louder word might have been overheard.

"Who's that?" he whispered then.

"My second mate. But I don't know much more of the fellow than you do."

And I told him a little about myself. I had been appointed to take charge while I least expected anything of the sort, not quite a fortnight ago. I didn't know either the ship or the people. Hadn't had the time in port to look about me or size anybody up. And as to the crew, all they knew was that I was appointed to take the ship home. For the rest, I was almost as much of a stranger on board as himself, I said. And at the moment I felt it most acutely. I felt that it would take very little to make me a suspect person in the eyes of the ship's company.

He had turned about meantime; and we, the two strangers in the ship, faced each other in identical attitudes.

"Your ladder—" he murmured, after a silence. "Who'd have thought of finding a ladder hanging over at night in a ship anchored out here! I felt just then a very unpleasant faintness. After the life I've been leading for nine weeks, anybody would have got out of condition. I wasn't capable of swimming round as far as your rudder-chains. And, lo and behold! there was a ladder to get hold of. After I gripped it I said to myself, 'What's the good?' When I saw a man's head looking over I thought I would swim away presently and leave him shouting—in whatever language it was. I didn't mind being looked at. I—I liked it. And then you speaking to me so quietly—as if you had expected me—made me hold on a little longer. It had been a confounded lonely time—I don't mean while swimming. I was glad to talk a little to somebody that didn't belong to the *Sephora*. As to asking for the captain, that was a mere impulse. It could have been no use, with all the ship knowing about me and the other people pretty certain to be round here in the morning. I don't know— I wanted to be seen, to talk with somebody, before I went on. I don't know what I would have said. . . . 'Fine night, isn't it?' or something of the sort."

"Do you think they will be round here presently?" I asked with some incredulity.

"Quite likely," he said, faintly.

He looked extremely haggard all of a sudden. His head rolled on his shoulders.

"H'm. We shall see then. Meantime get into that bed," I whispered. "Want help? There."

It was a rather high bed-place with a set of drawers underneath. This amazing swimmer really needed the lift I gave him by seizing his leg. He tumbled in, rolled over on his back, and flung one arm across his eyes. And then, with his face nearly hidden, he must have looked exactly as I used to look in that bed. I gazed upon my other self for a while before drawing across carefully the two green serge curtains which ran on a brass rod. I thought for a moment of pinning them together for greater safety, but I sat down on the couch, and once there I felt unwilling to rise and hunt for a pin. I would do it in a moment. I was extremely tired, in a peculiarly intimate way, by the strain of stealthiness, by the effort of whispering and the general secrecy of this excitement. It was three o'clock by now and I had been on my feet since nine, but I was not sleepy; I could not have gone to sleep. I sat there, fagged out, looking at the curtains, trying to clear my mind of the confused sensation of being in two places at once, and greatly bothered by an exasperating knocking in my head. It was a relief to discover suddenly that it was not in my head at all, but on the outside of the door. Before I could collect myself the words "Come in" were out of my mouth, and the steward entered with a tray, bringing in my morning coffee. I had slept, after all, and I was so frightened that I shouted, "This way! I am here, steward," as though he had been miles away. He put down the tray on the table next the couch and only then said, very quietly, "I can see you are here, sir." I felt him give me a keen look, but I dared not meet his eyes just then. He must have wondered why I had drawn the curtains of my bed before going to sleep on the couch. He went out, hooking the door open as usual.

I heard the crew washing decks above me. I knew I would have been told at once if there had been any wind. Calm, I thought, and I was doubly vexed. Indeed, I felt dual more than ever. The steward reappeared suddenly in the doorway. I jumped up from the couch so quickly that he gave a start.

"What do you want here?"

"Close your port, sir—they are washing decks."

"It is closed," I said, reddening.

"Very well, sir." But he did not move from the doorway and returned my stare in an extraordinary, equivocal manner for a time. Then his eyes wavered, all his expression changed, and in a voice unusually gentle, almost coaxingly:

"May I come in to take the empty cup away, sir?"

"Of course!" I turned my back on him while he popped in and out. Then I unhooked and closed the door and even pushed the bolt. This sort of thing could not go on very long. The cabin was as hot as an oven, too. I took a peep at my double, and discovered that he had not moved, his arm was still over his eyes; but his chest heaved; his hair was wet; his chin glistened with perspiration. I reached over him and opened the port.

"I must show myself on deck," I reflected.

Of course, theoretically, I could do what I liked, with no one to say nay to me within the whole circle of the horizon; but to lock my cabin door and take the key away I did not dare. Directly I put my head out of the companion I saw the group of my two officers, the second mate barefooted, the chief mate in long india-rubber boots, near the break of the poop, and the steward half-way down the poop-ladder talking to them eagerly. He happened to catch sight of me and dived, the second ran down on the main-deck shouting some order or other, and the chief mate came to meet me, touching his cap.

There was a sort of curiosity in his eye that I did not like. I don't know whether the steward had told them that I was "queer" only, or downright drunk, but I know the man meant to have a good look at me. I watched him coming with a smile which, as he got into point-blank range, took effect and froze his very whiskers. I did not give him time to open his lips.

"Square the yards by lifts and braces before the hands go to breakfast."

It was the first particular order I had given on board that ship; and I stayed on deck to see it executed, too. I had felt the need of asserting myself without loss of time. That sneering young cub got taken down a peg or two on that occasion, and I also seized the opportunity of having a good look at the face of every foremast man as they filed past me to go to the after braces. At breakfast time, eating nothing myself, I presided with such frigid dignity that the two mates were only too glad to escape from the cabin as soon as decency permitted; and all the time the dual working of my mind distracted me almost to the point of insanity. I was constantly watching myself, my secret self, as dependent on my actions as my own personality, sleeping in that bed, behind that door which faced me as I sat at the head of the table. It was very much like being mad, only it was worse because one was aware of it.

I had to shake him for a solid minute, but when at last he opened his eyes it was in the full possession of his senses, with an inquiring look.

"All's well so far," I whispered. "Now you must vanish into the bathroom."

He did so, as noiseless as a ghost, and then I rang for the steward, and facing him boldly, directed him to tidy up my stateroom while I was having my bath—"and be quick about it." As my tone admitted of no excuses, he said, "Yes, sir," and ran off to fetch his dust-pan and brushes. I took a bath and did most of my dressing, splashing, and whistling softly for the steward's edification, while the secret sharer of my life stood drawn up bolt upright in that little space, his face looking very sunken in day-light, his eyelids lowered under the stern, dark line of his eyebrows drawn together by a slight frown.

When I left him there to go back to my room the steward was finishing dusting. I sent for the mate and engaged him in some insignificant con-versation. It was, as it were, trifling with the terrific character of his whiskers; but my object was to give him an opportunity for a good look at my cabin. And then I could at last shut, with a clear conscience, the door of my stateroom and get my double back into the recessed part. There was nothing else for it. He had to sit still on a small folding stool, half smothered by the heavy coats hanging there. We listened to the steward going into the bath-room out of the saloon, filling the water-bottles there, scrubbing the bath, setting things to rights, whisk, bang, clatter—out again into the saloon—turn the key—click. Such was my scheme for keep-ing my second self invisible. Nothing better could be contrived under the circumstances. And there we sat; I at my writing-desk ready to appear busy with some papers, he behind me out of sight of the door. It would not have been prudent to talk in daytime; and I could not have stood the excitement of that queer sense of whispering to myself. Now and then, glancing over my shoulder, I saw him far back there, sitting rigidly on the low stool, his bare feet close together, his arms folded, his head hang-ing on his breast—and perfectly still. Anybody would have taken him for me.

I was fascinated by it myself. Every moment I had to glance over my shoulder. I was looking at him when a voice outside the door said:

"Beg pardon, sir."

"Well!" . . . I kept my eyes on him, and so when the voice outside the door announced, "There's a ship's boat coming our way, sir," I saw him give a start—the first movement he had made for hours. But he did not raise his bowed head.

"All right. Get the ladder over."

I hesitated. Should I whisper something to him? But what? His immo-bility seemed to have been never disturbed. What could I tell him he did not know already? . . . Finally I went on deck.

II

The skipper of the *Sephora* had a thin red whisker all round his face, and the sort of complexion that goes with hair of that color; also the par-ticular, rather smeary shade of blue in the eyes. He was not exactly a showy figure; his shoulders were high, his stature but middling—one leg slightly more bandy than the other. He shook hands, looking vaguely around. A spiritless tenacity was his main characteristic, I judged. I be-haved with a politeness which seemed to disconcert him. Perhaps he was shy. He mumbled to me as if he were ashamed of what he was saying;

gave his name (it was something like Archbold—but at this distance of years I hardly am sure), his ship's name, and a few other particulars of that sort, in the manner of a criminal making a reluctant and doleful confession. He had had terrible weather on the passage out—terrible—terrible —wife aboard, too.

By this time we were seated in the cabin and the steward brought in a tray with a bottle and glasses. "Thanks! No." Never took liquor. Would have some water, though. He drank two tumblerfuls. Terrible thirsty work. Ever since daylight had been exploring the islands round his ship.

"What was that for—fun?" I asked, with an appearance of polite interest.

"No!" He sighed. "Painful duty."

As he persisted in his mumbling and I wanted my double to hear every word, I hit upon the notion of informing him that I regretted to say I was hard of hearing.

"Such a young man, too!" he nodded, keeping his smeary blue, unintelligent eyes fastened upon me. "What was the cause of it—some disease?" he inquired, without the least sympathy and as if he thought that, if so, I'd got no more than I deserved.

"Yes; disease," I admitted in a cheerful tone which seemed to shock him. But my point was gained, because he had to raise his voice to give me his tale. It is not worth while to record that version. It was just over two months since all this had happened, and he had thought so much about it that he seemed completely muddled as to its bearings, but still immensely impressed.

"What would you think of such a thing happening on board your own ship? I've had the *Sephora* for these fifteen years. I am a well-known shipmaster."

He was densely distressed—and perhaps I should have sympathized with him if I had been able to detach my mental vision from the unsuspected sharer of my cabin as though he were my second self. There he was on the other side of the bulkhead, four or five feet from us, no more, as we sat in the saloon. I looked politely at Captain Archbold (if that was his name), but it was the other I saw, in a gray sleeping-suit, seated on a low stool, his bare feet close together, his arms folded, and every word said between us falling into the ears of his dark head bowed on his chest.

"I have been at sea now, man and boy, for seven-and-thirty years, and I've never heard of such a thing happening in an English ship. And that it should be my ship. Wife on board, too."

I was hardly listening to him.

"Don't you think," I said, "that the heavy sea which, you told me, came aboard just then might have killed the man? I have seen the sheer weight of a sea kill a man very neatly, by simply breaking his neck."

"Good God!" he uttered, impressively, fixing his smeary blue eyes on me. "The sea! No man killed by the sea ever looked like that." He seemed positively scandalized at my suggestion. And as I gazed at him, certainly not prepared for anything original on his part, he advanced his head close to mine and thrust his tongue out at me so suddenly that I couldn't help starting back.

After scoring over my calmness in this graphic way he nodded wisely. If I had seen the sight, he assured me, I would never forget it as long as I lived. The weather was too bad to give the corpse a proper sea burial. So next day at dawn they took it up on the poop, covering its face with a bit of bunting; he read a short prayer, and then, just as it was, in its oilskins and long boots, they launched it amongst those mountainous seas that seemed ready every moment to swallow up the ship herself and the terrified lives on board of her.

"That reefed foresail saved you," I threw in.

"Under God—it did," he exclaimed fervently. "It was by a special mercy, I firmly believe, that it stood some of those hurricane squalls."

"It was the setting of that sail which—" I began.

"God's own hand in it," he interrupted me. "Nothing less could have done it. I don't mind telling you that I hardly dared give the order. It seemed impossible that we could touch anything without losing it, and then our last hope would have been gone."

The terror of that gale was on him yet. I let him go on for a bit, then said, casually—as if returning to a minor subject:

"You were very anxious to give up your mate to the shore people, I believe?"

He was. To the law. His obscure tenacity on that point had in it something incomprehensible and a little awful; something, as it were, mystical, quite apart from his anxiety that he should not be suspected of "countenancing any doings of that sort." Seven-and-thirty virtuous years at sea, of which over twenty of immaculate command, and the last fifteen in the *Sephora*, seemed to have laid him under some pitiless obligation.

"And you know," he went on, groping shamefacedly amongst his feelings, "I did not engage that young fellow. His people had some interest with my owners. I was in a way forced to take him on. He looked very smart, very gentlemanly, and all that. But do you know—I never liked him, somehow. I am a plain man. You see, he wasn't exactly the sort for the chief mate of a ship like the *Sephora*."

I had become so connected in thoughts and impressions with the secret sharer of my cabin that I felt as if I, personally, were being given to understand that I, too, was not the sort that would have done for the chief mate of a ship like the *Sephora*. I had no doubt of it in my mind.

"Not at all the style of man. You understand," he insisted, superfluously, looking hard at me.

I smiled urbanely. He seemed at a loss for a while.

"I suppose I must report a suicide."

"Beg pardon?"

"Sui-cide! That's what I'll have to write to my owners directly I get in."

"Unless you manage to recover him before tomorrow," I assented, dispassionately. . . . "I mean, alive."

He mumbled something which I really did not catch, and I turned my ear to him in a puzzled manner. He fairly bawled:

"The land—I say, the mainland is at least seven miles off my anchorage."

"About that."

My lack of excitement, of curiosity, of surprise, of any sort of pronounced interest, began to arouse his distrust. But except for the felicitous pretense of deafness I had not tried to pretend anything. I had felt utterly incapable of playing the part of ignorance properly, and therefore was afraid to try. It is also certain that he had brought some ready-made suspicions with him, and that he viewed my politeness as a strange and unnatural phenomenon. And yet how else could I have received him? Not heartily! That was impossible for psychological reasons, which I need not state here. My only object was to keep off his inquiries. Surlily? Yes, but surliness might have provoked a point-blank question. From its novelty to him and from its nature, punctilious courtesy was the manner best calculated to restrain the man. But there was the danger of his breaking through my defense bluntly. I could not, I think, have met him by a direct lie, also for psychological (not moral) reasons. If he had only known how afraid I was of his putting my feeling of identity with the other to the test! But, strangely enough—(I thought of it only afterwards)—I believe that he was not a little disconcerted by the reverse side of that weird situation, by something in me that reminded him of the man he was seeking—suggested a mysterious similitude to the young fellow he had distrusted and disliked from the first.

However that might have been, the silence was not very prolonged. He took another oblique step.

"I reckon I had no more than a two-mile pull to your ship. Not a bit more."

"And quite enough, too, in this awful heat," I said.

Another pause full of mistrust followed. Necessity, they say, is mother of invention, but fear, too, is not barren of ingenious suggestions. And I was afraid he would ask me point-blank for news of my other self.

"Nice little saloon, isn't it?" I remarked, as if noticing for the first time the way his eyes roamed from one closed door to the other. "And very well fitted out, too. Here, for instance," I continued, reaching over the back of my seat negligently and flinging the door open, "is my bath-room."

He made an eager movement, but hardly gave it a glance. I got up, shut the door of the bath-room, and invited him to have a look round, as if I were very proud of my accommodation. He had to rise and be shown round, but he went through the business without any raptures whatever.

"And now we'll have a look at my stateroom," I declared, in a voice as loud as I dared to make it, crossing the cabin to the starboard side with purposely heavy steps.

He followed me in and gazed around. My intelligent double had vanished. I played my part.

"Very convenient—isn't it?"

"Very nice. Very comf . . ." He didn't finish and went out brusquely as if to escape from some unrighteous wiles of mine. But it was not to be. I had been too frightened not to feel vengeful; I felt I had him on the run, and I meant to keep him on the run. My polite insistence must have had something menacing in it, because he gave in suddenly. And I did not let him off a single item; mate's room, pantry, storerooms, the very sail-locker which was also under the poop—he had to look into them all. When at last I showed him out on the quarter-deck he drew a long, spiritless sigh, and mumbled dismally that he must really be going back to his ship now. I desired my mate, who had joined us, to see to the captain's boat.

The man of whiskers gave a blast on the whistle which he used to wear hanging round his neck, and yelled, "*Sephora's* away!" My double down there in my cabin must have heard, and certainly could not feel more relieved than I. Four fellows came running out from somewhere forward and went over the side, while my own men, appearing on deck too, lined the rail. I escorted my visitor to the gangway ceremoniously, and nearly overdid it. He was a tenacious beast. On the very ladder he lingered, and in that unique, guiltily conscientious manner of sticking to the point:

"I say . . . you . . . you don't think that—"

I covered his voice loudly:

"Certainly not. . . . I am delighted. Good-by."

I had an idea of what he meant to say, and just saved myself by the privilege of defective hearing. He was too shaken generally to insist, but my mate, close witness of that parting, looked mystified and his face took on a thoughtful cast. As I did not want to appear as if I wished to avoid all communication with my officers, he had the opportunity to address me.

"Seems a very nice man. His boat's crew told our chaps a very extraordinary story, if what I am told by the steward is true. I suppose you had it from the captain, sir?"

"Yes. I had a story from the captain."

"A very horrible affair—isn't it, sir?"

"It is."

"Beats all these tales we hear about murders in Yankee ships."

"I don't think it beats them. I don't think it resembles them in the least."

"Bless my soul—you don't say so! But of course I've no acquaintance whatever with American ships, not I, so I couldn't go against your knowledge. It's horrible enough for me. . . . But the queerest part is that those fellows seemed to have some idea the man was hidden aboard here. They had really. Did you ever hear of such a thing?"

"Preposterous—isn't it?"

We were walking to and fro athwart the quarter-deck. No one of the crew forward could be seen (the day was Sunday), and the mate pursued:

"There was some little dispute about it. Our chaps took offense. 'As if we would harbor a thing like that,' they said. 'Wouldn't you like to look for him in our coal-hole?' Quite a tiff. But they made it up in the end. I suppose he did drown himself. Don't you, sir?"

"I don't suppose anything."

"You have no doubt in the matter, sir?"

"None whatever."

I left him suddenly. I felt I was producing a bad impression, but with my double down there it was most trying to be on deck. And it was almost as trying to be below. Altogether a nerve-trying situation. But on the whole I felt less torn in two when I was with him. There was no one in the whole ship whom I dared take into my confidence. Since the hands had got to know his story, it would have been impossible to pass him off for anyone else, and an accidental discovery was to be dreaded now more than ever. . . .

The steward being engaged in laying the table for dinner, we could talk only with our eyes when I first went down. Later in the afternoon we had a cautious try at whispering. The Sunday quietness of the ship was against us; the stillness of air and water around her was against us; the elements, the men were against us—everything was against us in our secret partnership; time itself—for this could not go on forever. The very trust in Providence was, I suppose, denied to his guilt. Shall I confess that this thought cast me down very much? And as to the chapter of accidents which counts for so much in the book of success, I could only hope that it was closed. For what favorable accident could be expected?

"Did you hear everything?" were my first words as soon as we took up our position side by side, leaning over my bed-place.

He had. And the proof of it was his earnest whisper, "The man told you he hardly dared to give the order."

I understood the reference to be to that saving foresail.

"Yes. He was afraid of it being lost in the setting."

"I assure you he never gave the order. He may think he did, but he never gave it. He stood there with me on the break of the poop after the maintopsail blew away, and whimpered about our last hope—positively whimpered about it and nothing else—and the night coming on! To hear one's skipper go on like that in such weather was enough to drive any fellow out of his mind. It worked me up into a sort of desperation. I just took it into my own hands and went away from him, boiling, and— **But** what's the use telling you? *You* know! . . . Do you think that if I had not been pretty fierce with them I should have got the men to do anything? Not it! The bo's'n perhaps? Perhaps! It wasn't a heavy sea—it was a sea gone mad! I suppose the end of the world will be something like that; and a man may have the heart to see it coming once and be done with it—but to have to face it day after day— I don't blame anybody. I was precious little better than the rest. Only—I was an officer of that old coal-wagon, anyhow—"

"I quite understand," I conveyed that sincere assurance into his ear. He was out of breath with whispering; I could hear him pant slightly. It was all very simple. The same strung-up force which had given twenty-four men a chance, at least, for their lives, had, in a sort of recoil, crushed an unworthy mutinous existence.

But I had no leisure to weigh the merits of the matter—footsteps in the saloon, a heavy knock. "There's enough wind to get under way with, sir." Here was the call of a new claim upon my thoughts and even upon my feelings.

"Turn the hands up," I cried through the door. "I'll be on deck directly."

I was going out to make the acquaintance of my ship. Before I left the cabin our eyes met—the eyes of the only two strangers on board. I pointed to the recessed part where the little campstool awaited him and laid my finger on my lips. He made a gesture—somewhat vague—a little mysterious, accompanied by a faint smile, as if of regret.

This is not the place to enlarge upon the sensations of a man who feels for the first time a ship move under his feet to his own independent word. In my case they were not unalloyed. I was not wholly alone with my command; for there was that stranger in my cabin. Or rather, I was not completely and wholly with her. Part of me was absent. That mental feeling of being in two places at once affected me physically as if the mood of secrecy had penetrated my very soul. Before an hour had elapsed since the ship had begun to move, having occasion to ask the mate (he stood by my side) to take a compass bearing of the Pagoda, I caught myself reaching up to his ear in whispers. I say I caught myself, but enough had escaped to startle the man. I can't describe it otherwise than by saying that he shied. A grave, preoccupied manner, as though he were in possession of some perplexing intelligence, did not leave him henceforth. A little later I moved away from the rail to look at the compass with such a stealthy gait that the helmsman noticed it—and I could not help noticing the unusual roundness of his eyes. These are trifling instances, though it's to no commander's advantage to be suspected of ludicrous eccentricities. But I was also more seriously affected. There are to a seaman certain words, gestures, that should in given conditions come as naturally, as instinctively as the winking of a menaced eye. A certain order should spring on to his lips without thinking; a certain sign should get itself made, so to speak, without reflection. But all unconscious alertness had abandoned me. I had to make an effort of will to recall myself back (from the cabin) to the conditions of the moment. I felt that I was appearing an irresolute commander to those people who were watching me more or less critically.

And, besides, there were the scares. On the second day out, for instance, coming off the deck in the afternoon (I had straw slippers on my bare feet) I stopped at the open pantry door and spoke to the steward. He was doing something there with his back to me. At the sound of my voice he nearly jumped out of his skin, as the saying is, and incidentally broke a cup.

"What on earth's the matter with you?" I asked, astonished.

He was extremely confused. "Beg your pardon, sir. I made sure you were in your cabin."

"You see I wasn't."

"No, sir. I could have sworn I had heard you moving in there not a moment ago. It's most extraordinary . . . very sorry, sir."

I passed on with an inward shudder. I was so identified with my secret double that I did not even mention the fact in those scanty, fearful whispers we exchanged. I suppose he had made some slight noise of some kind or other. It would have been miraculous if he hadn't at one time or another. And yet, haggard as he appeared, he looked always perfectly self-controlled, more than calm—almost invulnerable. On my suggestion he remained almost entirely in the bath-room, which, upon the whole, was the safest place. There could be really no shadow of an excuse for anyone ever wanting to go in there, once the steward had done with it. It was a very tiny place. Sometimes he reclined on the floor, his legs bent, his head sustained on one elbow. At others I would find him on the camp-stool, sitting in his gray sleeping-suit and with his cropped dark hair like a patient, unmoved convict. At night I would smuggle him into my bed-place, and we would whisper together, with the regular footfalls of the officer of the watch passing and repassing over our heads. It was an infinitely miserable time. It was lucky that some tins of fine preserves were stowed in a locker in my stateroom; hard bread I could always get hold of; and so he lived on stewed chicken, paté de foie gras, asparagus, cooked oysters, sardines—on all sorts of abominable sham delicacies out of tins. My early morning coffee he always drank; and it was all I dared do for him in that respect.

Every day there was the horrible maneuvering to go through so that my room and then the bath-room should be done in the usual way. I came to hate the sight of the steward, to abhor the voice of that harmless man. I felt that it was he who would bring on the disaster of discovery. It hung like a sword over our heads.

The fourth day out, I think (we were then working down the east side of the Gulf of Siam, tack for tack, in light winds and smooth water)—the fourth day, I say, of this miserable juggling with the unavoidable, as we sat at our evening meal, that man, whose slightest movement I dreaded, after putting down the dishes ran up on deck busily. This could not be dangerous. Presently he came down again; and then it appeared that he had remembered a coat of mine which I had thrown over a rail to dry after having been wetted in a shower which had passed over the ship in the afternoon. Sitting stolidly at the head of the table I became terrified at the sight of the garment on his arm. Of course he made for my door. There was no time to lose.

"Steward," I thundered. My nerves were so shaken that I could not govern my voice and conceal my agitation. This was the sort of thing that made my terrifically whiskered mate tap his forehead with his fore-finger. I had detected him using that gesture while talking on deck with a confidential air to the carpenter. It was too far to hear a word, but I had no doubt that this pantomime could only refer to the strange new captain.

"Yes, sir," the pale-faced steward turned resignedly to me. It was this maddening course of being shouted at, checked without rhyme or reason, arbitrarily chased out of my cabin, suddenly called into it, sent flying out of his pantry on incomprehensible errands, that accounted for the growing wretchedness of his expression.

"Where are you going with that coat?"

"To your room, sir."

"Is there another shower coming?"

"I'm sure I don't know, sir. Shall I go up again and see, sir?"

"No! never mind."

My object was attained, as of course my other self in there would have heard everything that passed. During this interlude my two officers never raised their eyes off their respective plates; but the lip of that confounded cub, the second mate, quivered visibly.

I expected the steward to hook my coat on and come out at once. He was very slow about it; but I dominated my nervousness sufficiently not to shout after him. Suddenly I became aware (it could be heard plainly enough) that the fellow for some reason or other was opening the door of the bath-room. It was the end. The place was literally not big enough to swing a cat in. My voice died in my throat and I went stony all over. I expected to hear a yell of surprise and terror, and made a movement, but had not the strength to get on my legs. Everything remained still. Had my second self taken the poor wretch by the throat? I don't know what I could have done next moment if I had not seen the steward come out of my room, close the door, and then stand quietly by the sideboard.

"Saved," I thought. "But, no! Lost! Gone! He was gone!"

I laid my knife and fork down and leaned back in my chair. My head swam. After a while, when sufficiently recovered to speak in a steady voice, I instructed my mate to put the ship round at eight o'clock himself.

"I won't come on deck," I went on. "I think I'll turn in, and unless the wind shifts I don't want to be disturbed before midnight. I feel a bit seedy."

"You did look middling bad a little while ago," the chief mate remarked without showing any great concern.

They both went out, and I stared at the steward clearing the table. There was nothing to be read on that wretched man's face. But why did he avoid my eyes I asked myself. Then I thought I should like to hear the sound of his voice.

"Steward!"

"Sir!" Startled as usual.

"Where did you hang up that coat?"

"In the bath-room, sir." The usual anxious tone. "It's not quite dry yet, sir."

For some time longer I sat in the cuddy. Had my double vanished as he had come? But of his coming there was an explanation, whereas his disappearance would be inexplicable. . . . I went slowly into my dark room, shut the door, lighted the lamp, and for a time dared not turn round. When at last I did I saw him standing bolt-upright in the narrow recessed part. It would not be true to say I had a shock, but an irresistible doubt of his bodily existence flitted through my mind. Can it be, I asked myself, that he is not visible to other eyes than mine? It was like being haunted. Motionless, with a grave face, he raised his hands slightly at me in a gesture which meant clearly, "Heavens! what a narrow escape!" Narrow indeed. I think I had come creeping quietly as near insanity as any man who has not actually gone over the border. That gesture restrained me, so to speak.

The mate with the terrific whiskers was now putting the ship on the other tack. In the moment of profound silence which follows upon the hands going to their stations I heard on the poop his raised voice: "Hard alee!" and the distant shout of the order repeated on the maindeck. The sails, in that light breeze, made but a faint fluttering noise. It ceased. The ship was coming round slowly; I held my breath in the renewed stillness of expectation; one wouldn't have thought that there was a single living soul on her decks. A sudden brisk shout, "Mainsail haul!" broke the spell, and in the noisy cries and rush overhead of the men running away with the main-brace we two, down in my cabin, came together in our usual position by the bed-place.

He did not wait for my question. "I heard him fumbling here and just managed to squat myself down in the bath," he whispered to me. "The fellow only opened the door and put his arm in to hang the coat up. All the same——"

"I never thought of that," I whispered back, even more appalled than before at the closeness of the shave, and marveling at that something unyielding in his character which was carrying him through so finely. There was no agitation in his whisper. Whoever was being driven distracted, it was not he. He was sane. And the proof of his sanity was continued when he took up the whispering again.

"It would never do for me to come to life again."

It was something that a ghost might have said. But what he was alluding to was his old captain's reluctant admission of the theory of suicide. It would obviously serve his turn—if I had understood at all the view which seemed to govern the unalterable purpose of his action.

"You must maroon me as soon as ever you can get amongst these islands off the Cambodge shore," he went on.

"Maroon you! We are not living in a boy's adventure tale," I protested. His scornful whispering took me up.

"We aren't indeed! There's nothing of a boy's tale in this. But there's nothing else for it. I want no more. You don't suppose I am afraid of what can be done to me? Prison or gallows or whatever they may please. But you don't see me coming back to explain such things to an old fellow in a wig and twelve respectable tradesmen, do you? What can they know whether I am guilty or not—or of *what* I am guilty, either? That's my affair. What does the Bible say? 'Driven off the face of the earth.' Very well. I am off the face of the earth now. As I came at night so I shall go."

"Impossible!" I murmured. "You can't."

"Can't? . . . Not naked like a soul on the Day of Judgment. I shall freeze on to this sleeping-suit. The Last Day is not yet—and . . . you have understood thoroughly. Didn't you?"

I felt suddenly ashamed of myself. I may say truly that I understood—and my hesitation in letting that man swim away from my ship's side had been a mere sham sentiment, a sort of cowardice.

"It can't be done now till next night," I breathed out. "The ship is on the off-shore tack and the wind may fail us."

"As long as I know that you understand," he whispered. "But of course you do. It's a great satisfaction to have got somebody to understand. You seem to have been there on purpose." And in the same whisper, as if we two whenever we talked had to say things to each other which were not fit for the world to hear, he added, "It's very wonderful."

We remained side by side talking in our secret way—but sometimes silent or just exchanging a whispered word or two at long intervals. And as usual he stared through the port. A breath of wind came now and again into our faces. The ship might have been moored in dock, so gently and on an even keel she slipped through the water, that did not murmur even at our passage, shadowy and silent like a phantom sea.

At midnight I went on deck, and to my mate's great surprise put the ship round on the other tack. His terrible whiskers flitted round me in silent criticism. I certainly should not have done it if it had been only a

question of getting out of that sleepy gulf as quickly as possible. I believe
he told the second mate, who relieved him, that it was a great want of
judgment. The other only yawned. That intolerable cub shuffled about so
sleepily and lolled against the rails in such a slack, improper fashion that
I came down on him sharply.

"Aren't you properly awake yet?"

"Yes, sir! I am awake."

"Well, then, be good enough to hold yourself as if you were. And keep
a look-out. If there's any current we'll be closing with some islands before
daylight."

The east side of the gulf is fringed with islands, some solitary, others in
groups. On the blue background of the high coast they seem to float on
silvery patches of calm water, arid and gray, or dark green and rounded
like clumps of evergreen bushes, with the larger ones, a mile or two long,
showing the outlines of ridges, ribs of gray rock under the dank mantle of
matted leafage. Unknown to trade, to travel, almost to geography, the
manner of life they harbor is an unsolved secret. There must be villages—
settlements of fishermen at least—on the largest of them, and some communication with the world is probably kept up by native craft. But all that
forenoon, as we headed for them, fanned along by the faintest of breezes,
I saw no sign of man or canoe in the field of the telescope I kept on pointing at the scattered group.

At noon I gave no orders for a change of course, and the mate's whiskers
became much concerned and seemed to be offering themselves unduly
to my notice. At last I said:

"I am going to stand right in. Quite in—as far as I can take her."

The stare of extreme surprise imparted an air of ferocity also to his eyes,
and he looked truly terrific for a moment.

"We're not doing well in the middle of the gulf," I continued, casually.
"I am going to look for the land breezes tonight."

"Bless my soul! Do you mean, sir, in the dark amongst the lot of all
them islands and reefs and shoals?"

"Well—if there are any regular land breezes at all on this coast one must
get close inshore to find them, mustn't one?"

"Bless my soul!" he exclaimed again under his breath. All that afternoon
he wore a dreamy, contemplative appearance which in him was a mark of
perplexity. After dinner I went into my stateroom as if I meant to take
some rest. There we two bent our dark heads over a half-unrolled chart
lying on my bed.

"There," I said. "It's got to be Koh-ring. I've been looking at it ever
since sunrise. It has got two hills and a low point. It must be inhabited.
And on the coast opposite there is what looks like the mouth of a biggish
river—with some town, no doubt, not far up. It's the best chance for you
that I can see."

"Anything. Koh-ring let it be."

He looked thoughtfully at the chart as if surveying chances and distances from a lofty height—and following with his eyes his own figure
wandering on the blank land of Cochin-China, and then passing off that
piece of paper clean out of sight into uncharted regions. And it was as if
the ship had two captains to plan her course for her. I had been so
worried and restless running up and down that I had not had the patience
to dress that day. I had remained in my sleeping-suit, with straw slippers
and a soft floppy hat. The closeness of the heat in the gulf had been most
oppressive, and the crew were used to see me wandering in that airy
attire.

"She will clear the south point as she heads now," I whispered into his
ear. "Goodness only knows when, though, but certainly after dark. I'll
edge her in to half a mile, as far as I may be able to judge in the dark—"

"Be careful," he murmured, warningly—and I realized suddenly that all
my future, the only future for which I was fit, would perhaps go irretriev-
ably to pieces in any mishap to my first command.

I could not stop a moment longer in the room. I motioned him to get
out of sight and made my way on the poop. That unplayful cub had the
watch. I walked up and down for a while thinking things out, then beck-
oned him over.

"Send a couple of hands to open the two quarter-deck ports," I said,
mildly.

He actually had the impudence, or else so forgot himself in his wonder
at such an incomprehensible order, as to repeat:

"Open the quarter-deck ports! What for, sir?"

"The only reason you need concern yourself about is because I tell you
to do so. Have them opened wide and fastened properly."

He reddened and went off, but I believe made some jeering remark to
the carpenter as to the sensible practice of ventilating a ship's quarter-
deck. I know he popped into the mate's cabin to impart the fact to him
because the whiskers came on deck, as it were by chance, and stole
glances at me from below—for signs of lunacy or drunkenness, I suppose.

A little before supper, feeling more restless than ever, I rejoined, for a
moment, my second self. And to find him sitting so quietly was surprising,
like something against nature, inhuman.

I developed my plan in a hurried whisper.

"I shall stand in as close as I dare and then put her round. I will presently find means to smuggle you out of here into the sail-locker, which
communicates with the lobby. But there is an opening, a sort of square for
hauling the sails out, which gives straight on the quarter-deck and which
is never closed in fine weather, so as to give air to the sails. When the
ship's way is deadened in stays and all the hands are aft at the main-
braces you will have a clear road to slip out and get overboard through

the open quarter-deck port. I've had them both fastened up. Use a rope's end to lower yourself into the water so as to avoid a splash—you know. It could be heard and cause some beastly complication."

He kept silent for a while, then whispered, "I understand."

"I won't be there to see you go," I began with an effort. "The rest . . . I only hope I have understood, too."

"You have. From first to last"—and for the first time there seemed to be a faltering, something strained in his whisper. He caught hold of my arm, but the ringing of the supper bell made me start. He didn't, though; he only released his grip.

After supper I didn't come below again till well past eight o'clock. The faint, steady breeze was loaded with dew; and the wet, darkened sails held all there was of propelling power in it. The night, clear and starry, sparkled darkly, and the opaque, lightless patches shifting slowly against the low stars were the drifting islets. On the port bow there was a big one more distant and shadowily imposing by the great space of sky it eclipsed.

On opening the door I had a back view of my very own self looking at a chart. He had come out of the recess and was standing near the table.

"Quite dark enough," I whispered.

He stepped back and leaned against my bed with a level, quiet glance. I sat on the couch. We had nothing to say to each other. Over our heads the officer of the watch moved here and there. Then I heard him move quickly. I knew what that meant. He was making for the companion; and presently his voice was outside my door.

"We are drawing in pretty fast, sir. Land looks rather close."

"Very well," I answered. "I am coming on deck directly."

I waited till he was gone out of the cuddy, then rose. My double moved too. The time had come to exchange our last whispers, for neither of us was ever to hear each other's natural voice.

"Look here!" I opened a drawer and took out three sovereigns. "Take this anyhow. I've got six and I'd give you the lot, only I must keep a little money to buy some fruit and vegetables for the crew from native boats as we go through Sunda Straits."

He shook his head.

"Take it," I urged him, whispering desperately. "No one can tell what—"

He smiled and slapped meaningly the only pocket of the sleeping-jacket. It was not safe, certainly. But I produced a large old silk handkerchief of mine, and tying the three pieces of gold in a corner, pressed it on him. He was touched, I suppose, because he took it at last and tied it quickly round his waist under the jacket, on his bare skin.

Our eyes met; several seconds elapsed, till, our glances still mingled, I extended my hand and turned the lamp out. Then I passed through the cuddy, leaving the door of my room wide open. . . . "Steward!"

He was still lingering in the pantry in the greatness of his zeal, giving a rub-up to a plated cruet stand the last thing before going to bed. Being careful not to wake up the mate, whose room was opposite, I spoke in an undertone.

He looked round anxiously. "Sir!"

"Can you get me a little hot water from the galley?"

"I am afraid, sir, the galley fire's been out for some time now."

"Go and see."

He flew up the stairs.

"Now," I whispered, loudly, into the saloon—too loudly, perhaps, but I was afraid I couldn't make a sound. He was by my side in an instant—the double captain slipped past the stairs—through a tiny dark passage . . . a sliding door. We were in the sail-locker, scrambling on our knees over the sails. A sudden thought struck me. I saw myself wandering barefooted, bareheaded, the sun beating on my dark poll. I snatched off my floppy hat and tried hurriedly in the dark to ram it on my other self. He dodged and fended off silently. I wonder what he thought had come to me before he understood and suddenly desisted. Our hands met gropingly, lingered united in a steady, motionless clasp for a second. . . . No word was breathed by either of us when they separated.

I was standing quietly by the pantry door when the steward returned.

"Sorry, sir. Kettle barely warm. Shall I light the spirit-lamp?"

"Never mind."

I came out on deck slowly. It was now a matter of conscience to shave the land as close as possible—for now he must go overboard whenever the ship was put in stays. Must! There could be no going back for him. After a moment I walked over to leeward and my heart flew into my mouth at the nearness of the land on the bow. Under any other circumstances I would not have held on a minute longer. The second mate had followed me anxiously.

I looked on till I felt I could command my voice.

"She will weather," I said then in a quiet tone.

"Are you going to try that, sir?" he stammered out incredulously.

I took no notice of him and raised my tone just enough to be heard by the helmsman.

"Keep her good full."

"Good full, sir."

The wind fanned my cheek, the sails slept, the world was silent. The strain of watching the dark loom of the land grow bigger and denser was too much for me. I had shut my eyes—because the ship must go closer. She must! The stillness was intolerable. Were we standing still?

When I opened my eyes the second view started my heart with a thump. The black southern hill of Koh-ring seemed to hang right over the ship like a towering fragment of the everlasting night. On that enor-

mous mass of blackness there was not a gleam to be seen, not a sound to
be heard. It was gliding irresistibly towards us and yet seemed already
within reach of the hand. I saw the vague figures of the watch grouped
in the waist, gazing in awed silence.

"Are you going on, sir?" inquired an unsteady voice at my elbow.

I ignored it. I had to go on.

"Keep her full. Don't check her way. That won't do now," I said,
warningly.

"I can't see the sails very well," the helmsman answered me, in strange,
quavering tones.

Was she close enough? Already she was, I won't say in the shadow of
the land, but in the very blackness of it, already swallowed up as it were,
gone too close to be recalled, gone from me altogether.

"Give the mate a call," I said to the young man who stood at my elbow
as still as death. "And turn all hands up."

My tone had a borrowed loudness reverberated from the height of the
land. Several voices cried out together: "We are all on deck, sir."

Then stillness again, with the great shadow gliding closer, towering
higher, without a light, without a sound. Such a hush had fallen on the
ship that she might have been a bark of the dead floating in slowly under
the very gate of Erebus.

"My God! Where are we?"

It was the mate moaning at my elbow. He was thunderstruck, and as it
were deprived of the moral support of his whiskers. He clapped his hands
and absolutely cried out, "Lost!"

"Be quiet," I said, sternly.

He lowered his tone, but I saw the shadowy gesture of his despair.
"What are we doing here?"

"Looking for the land wind."

He made as if to tear his hair, and addressed me recklessly.

"She will never get out. You have done it, sir. I knew it'd end in something like this. She will never weather, and you are too close now to stay.
She'll drift ashore before she's round. O my God!"

I caught his arm as he was raising it to batter his poor devoted head,
and shook it violently.

"She's ashore already," he wailed, trying to tear himself away.

"Is she? . . . Keep good full there!"

"Good full, sir," cried the helmsman in a frightened, thin, child-like
voice.

I hadn't let go the mate's arm and went on shaking it. "Ready about,
do you hear? You go forward"—shake—"and stop there"—shake—"and hold
your noise"—shake—"and see these head-sheets properly overhauled"—
shake, shake—shake.

And all the time I dared not look towards the land lest my heart should fail me. I released my grip at last and he ran forward as if fleeing for dear life.

I wondered what my double there in the sail-locker thought of this commotion. He was able to hear everything—and perhaps he was able to understand why, on my conscience, it had to be thus close—no less. My first order "Hard alee!" re-echoed ominously under the towering shadow of Koh-ring as if I had shouted in a mountain gorge. And then I watched the land intently. In that smooth water and light wind it was impossible to feel the ship coming-to. No! I could not feel her. And my second self was making now ready to slip out and lower himself overboard. Perhaps he was gone already . . . ?

The great black mass brooding over our very mastheads began to pivot away from the ship's side silently. And now I forgot the secret stranger ready to depart, and remembered only that I was a total stranger to the ship. I did not know her. Would she do it? How was she to be handled?

I swung the mainyard and waited helplessly. She was perhaps stopped, and her very fate hung in the balance, with the black mass of Koh-ring like the gate of the everlasting night towering over her taffrail. What would she do now? Had she way on her yet? I stepped to the side swiftly, and on the shadowy water I could see nothing except a faint phosphorescent flash revealing the glassy smoothness of the sleeping surface. It was impossible to tell—and I had not learned yet the feel of my ship. Was she moving? What I needed was something easily seen, a piece of paper, which I could throw overboard and watch. I had nothing on me. To run down for it I didn't dare. There was no time. All at once my strained, yearning stare distinguished a white object floating within a yard of the ship's side. White on the black water. A phosphorescent flash passed under it. What was that thing? . . . I recognized my own floppy hat. It must have fallen off his head . . . and he didn't bother. Now I had what I wanted—the saving mark for my eyes. But I hardly thought of my other self, now gone from the ship, to be hidden forever from all friendly faces, to be a fugitive and a vagabond on the earth, with no brand of the curse on his sane forehead to stay a slaying hand . . . too proud to explain.

And I watched the hat—the expression of my sudden pity for his mere flesh. It had been meant to save his homeless head from the dangers of the sun. And now—behold—it was saving the ship, by serving me for a mark to help out the ignorance of my strangeness. Ha! It was drifting forward, warning me just in time that the ship had gathered sternway.

"Shift the helm," I said in a low voice to the seaman standing still like a statue.

The man's eyes glistened wildly in the binnacle light as he jumped round to the other side and spun round the wheel.

I walked to the break of the poop. On the overshadowed deck all hands stood by the forebraces waiting for my order. The stars ahead seemed to be gliding from right to left. And all was so still in the world that I heard the quiet remark, "She's round," passed in a tone of intense relief between two seamen.

"Let go and haul."

The foreyards ran round with a great noise, amidst cheery cries. And now the frightful whiskers made themselves heard giving various orders. Already the ship was drawing ahead. And I was alone with her. Nothing! no one in the world should stand now between us, throwing a shadow on the way of silent knowledge and mute affection, the perfect communion of a seaman with his first command.

Walking to the taffrail, I was in time to make out, on the very edge of a darkness thrown by a towering black mass like the very gateway of Erebus—yes, I was in time to catch an evanescent glimpse of my white hat left behind to mark the spot where the secret sharer of my cabin and of my thoughts, as though he were my second self, had lowered himself into the water to take his punishment: a free man, a proud swimmer striking out for a new destiny.

PARTIAL ANALYSIS

1. *The intention of Conrad.* The world of Conrad is both dark and bright, dark in its picture of evil, bright in its picture of the worth of a human being. To Conrad, as to Hardy, evil is a powerful constituent of the framework of the universe. And Conrad, like Hardy, is a master at describing evil, evil with the odds in its favor, evil ranging the world freely, with humanity as its natural prey.

Against this black background, Conrad's ideal characters glow very bright. Although they have human frailty, they are moved by an obscure sense of their moral destiny. Beset by the hostile forces of evil, they nevertheless achieve self-fulfillment and preserve their moral integrity. In their greatest moments they rise to defend their ideals against the dark power which seeks to conquer them. If they lose their lives, they still win, because they have been true to their own conscience.

"The Secret Sharer" dramatizes some of these ideas. It is not a somber story, except for one brief moment, when, at the close, the mass of Kohring seems instinct with evil. Rather, it is a hopeful story and reveals Conrad's conception of the moral worth and dignity of a human being.

The reader will find on p. 117 a sentence which states the theme of the story quite explicitly. In the second paragraph, also, Conrad describes his purpose in specific symbols.

2. *The sense of isolation.* Study the first two paragraphs for setting and mood. Consider, also, that on the ship the captain is utterly alone. Alone, except for what? Study the last two paragraphs. Is the captain still alone?

What part does the idea of solitude or isolation play in Conrad's conception of a human being? What part does it play in Conrad's idea that a man can betray only his own conscience?

3. *The symbolic level.* A story with symbolic intentions must be studied first for plot and for character motivation. The details of the plot and of character motivation are then translated into the symbolic meaning. In "The Secret Sharer" the symbolic meanings are rooted in the actions and motives of a captain who is taking command of his ship. The captain's first watch, the discussion with Captain Archbold about the reefed foresail, the maneuvering to catch a breeze—all these incidents on the plot level have a parallel significance on the symbolic level.

The following is a brief exercise in translating the details of the plot level into the symbolic level. Notice, here, that just as in "The Bench of Desolation," the initial impulse toward self-fulfillment must spring from the hero or protagonist, himself. The first halting efforts of the captain are seen in the episode on pages 119–120.

    a. *Plot level:* The captain's first act on his ship is to stand a five hours' anchor watch. What effect does this sudden and unusual order have upon the position of the rope side-ladder? What part does the rope side-ladder play in the appearance of Leggatt?

    Symbolic level: Almost indirectly, the captain's first assertion of his command brings to light his secret self. What does this incident mean in the progress of the story as a whole?

    b. *Plot level:* The captain is afraid that Leggatt won't come on board, is even more afraid that Leggatt doesn't want to come on board. In his uncertainty the capatin delays telling who he is. Then the captain firmly declares his identity. What happens?

    Symbolic level: Positive self-assertion results in an active response of the secret self. What does the captain's uncertainty mean? What does the sudden swirl of phosphorescence mean?

4. *The captain and Leggatt.*

    a. What physical qualities or accidents of background make the captain and Leggatt sharers of the same identity? But how do they differ in their personalities? Notice Leggatt's words, the expression on his face, his attitude toward the crew when he is a ship's officer, his conduct in a crisis on the *Sephora*, his attitude toward his own destiny. Compare Leggatt with the captain.

    b. What symbolic quality is embodied in Leggatt's ability as a swimmer? While telling of his escape, Leggatt says: "I meant to swim till I sank—but that's not the same thing [as suicide]." This moral ideal—this perseverance in a struggle against odds—is typical of Conrad and keynotes the character of Leggatt.

    c. Both Leggatt and the captain are "suspect." What actions of the captain arouse the apprehension of his crew? Could both the sentence stating the theme and the second paragraph of the story refer to Leggatt as well as to the captain?

d. Study the episode of Leggatt on board the *Sephora*. Who gave the order for setting the reefed foresail? Who should have given the order?

e. How does his conversation with Leggatt during the first night in the cabin affect the captain? What action does the captain perform the next morning?

5. *The captain of the Sephora.* Captain Archbold is part of the symbolism of this story. Study the description of him at the beginning of section II. Notice the tone he uses when he identifies himself.

What are Captain Archbold's relations with his officers and crew?

Remember that Captain Archbold has come looking for the secret self in order to shackle him. Is Captain Archbold then a threat, a warning, or an object lesson? Or all three? Explain the reflection of the protagonist on p. 133: "If he had only known how afraid I was of his putting my feeling of identity with the other to the test!"

6. *The test.*

a. *The odds.* The odds are heavy against the successful outcome of the test. This position is typical of Conrad. His human beings are the more remarkable because they valiantly face great odds. A paragraph on p. 135 lists some of the odds. During the test both Leggatt and the captain are dressed in sleeping-suits. Some critics have said that the sleeping-suit is a symbol of the unconscious. Could not the detail of the sleeping-suit also mean that both men are defenseless?

b. *The darkness.* The test occurs in darkness. Darkness has long been a symbol of what? The darkness is made blacker by the mass of Koh-ring. Explain the symbolic intention of: "Such a hush had fallen on the ship that she might have been a bark of the dead floating in slowly under the very gates of Erebus." What part does Koh-ring play on the plot level? On the symbolic level?

c. *The light in the darkness.* What does the captain see in the darkness? Why is this object important?

7. *Additional meanings.* In *The Art of Modern Fiction* Mr. Ray B. West, Jr., and Mr. Robert Wooster Stallman present a detailed analysis of "The Secret Sharer." They find three allegories in the story, a moral, a psychological, and an aesthetic. The present discussion has considered only the moral allegory.

The student might explore the possibilities of a psychological and an aesthetic allegory. For the psychological allegory, consider that Leggatt comes up out of darkness, naked. He goes back down into darkness, dressed like the captain. Leggatt and the captain never hear each other's natural voice. And the phosphorescence in black waters always reveals the presence of the secret self.

THE BLUE HOTEL

BY STEPHEN CRANE

STEPHEN CRANE (1871–1900) was born in
New Jersey. He served as a correspondent in
the Greco-Turkish War and in Cuba in the
Spanish-American War. He was only twenty-
nine when he died in England, but in his
short lifetime he wrote brilliantly and published a number of novels and many short
stories. His first novel, *Maggie* (1896), was
privately printed because no publisher would
print it. His next novel, *The Red Badge of
Courage* (1895), written before he had seen
a battlefield, made him famous. This novel
and two short stories, "The Open Boat" and
"The Blue Hotel" have become American
classics.

T HE PALACE HOTEL at Fort Romper was painted a light blue, a shade
that is on the legs of a kind of heron, causing the bird to declare its position against any background. The Palace Hotel, then, was always screaming and howling in a way that made the dazzling winter landscape of
Nebraska seem only a gray swampish hush. It stood alone on the prairie,
and when the snow was falling the town two hundred yards away was
not visible. But when the traveler alighted at the railway station he was
obliged to pass the Palace Hotel before he could come upon the company
of low clapboard houses which composed Fort Romper, and it was not
to be thought that any traveler could pass the Palace Hotel without looking at it. Pat Scully, the proprietor, had proved himself a master of
strategy when he chose his paints. It is true that on clear days, when

THE BLUE HOTEL   Reprinted from *Twenty Stories* by Stephen Crane, by permission of Alfred A. Knopf, Inc. Copyright 1899, 1926 by Alfred A. Knopf, Inc.

the great transcontinental expresses, long lines of swaying Pullmans, swept through Fort Romper, passengers were overcome at the sight, and the cult that knows the brown-reds and the subdivisions of the dark greens of the East expressed shame, pity, horror, in a laugh. But to the citizens of this prairie town and to the people who would naturally stop there, Pat Scully had performed a feat. With this opulence and splendor, these creeds, classes, egotisms, that streamed through Romper on the rails day after day, they had no color in common.

As if the displayed delights of such a blue hotel were not sufficiently enticing, it was Scully's habit to go every morning and evening to meet the leisurely trains that stopped at Romper and work his seductions upon any man that he might see wavering, gripsack in hand.

One morning, when a snow-crusted engine dragged its long string of freight cars and its one passenger coach to the station, Scully performed the marvel of catching three men. One was a shaky and quick-eyed Swede, with a great shining cheap valise; one was a tall bronzed cowboy, who was on his way to a ranch near the Dakota line; one was a little silent man from the East, who didn't look it, and didn't announce it. Scully practically made them prisoners. He was so nimble and merry and kindly that each probably felt it would be the height of brutality to try to escape. They trudged off over the creaking board sidewalks in the wake of the eager little Irishman. He wore a heavy fur cap squeezed tightly down on his head. It caused his two red ears to stick out stiffly, as if they were made of tin.

At last, Scully, elaborately, with boisterous hospitality, conducted them through the portals of the blue hotel. The room which they entered was small. It seemed to be merely a proper temple for an enormous stove, which, in the center, was humming with godlike violence. At various points on its surface the iron had become luminous and glowed yellow from the heat. Beside the stove Scully's son Johnnie was playing High-Five with an old farmer who had whiskers both gray and sandy. They were quarreling. Frequently the old farmer turned his face toward a box of sawdust—colored brown from tobacco juice—that was behind the stove, and spat with an air of great impatience and irritation. With a loud flourish of words Scully destroyed the game of cards, and bustled his son upstairs with part of the baggage of the new guests. He himself conducted them to three basins of the coldest water in the world. The cowboy and the Easterner burnished themselves fiery red with this water, until it seemed to be some kind of metal-polish. The Swede, however, merely dipped his fingers gingerly and with trepidation. It was notable that throughout this series of small ceremonies the three travelers were made to feel that Scully was very benevolent. He was conferring great favors upon them. He handed the towel from one to another with an air of philanthropic impulse.

Afterward they went to the first room, and, sitting about the stove, listened to Scully's officious clamor at his daughters, who were preparing the midday meal. They reflected in the silence of experienced men who tread carefully amid new people. Nevertheless, the old farmer, stationary, invincible in his chair near the warmest part of the stove, turned his face from the sawdust-box frequently and addressed a glowing commonplace to the strangers. Usually he was answered in short but adequate sentences by either the cowboy or the Easterner. The Swede said nothing. He seemed to be occupied in making furtive estimates of each man in the room. One might have thought that he had the sense of silly suspicion which comes to guilt. He resembled a badly frightened man.

Later, at dinner, he spoke a little, addressing his conversation entirely to Scully. He volunteered that he had come from New York, where for ten years he had worked as a tailor. These facts seemed to strike Scully as fascinating, and afterward he volunteered that he had lived at Romper for fourteen years. The Swede asked about the crops and the price of labor. He seemed barely to listen to Scully's extended replies. His eyes continued to rove from man to man.

Finally, with a laugh and a wink, he said that some of these Western communities were very dangerous; and after his statement he straightened his legs under the table, tilted his head, and laughed again, loudly. It was plain that the demonstration had no meaning to the others. They looked at him wondering and in silence.

II

As the men trooped heavily back into the front room, the two little windows presented views of a turmoiling sea of snow. The huge arms of the wind were making attempts—mighty, circular, futile—to embrace the flakes as they sped. A gate-post like a still man with a blanched face stood aghast amid this profligate fury. In a hearty voice Scully announced the presence of a blizzard. The guests of the blue hotel, lighting their pipes, assented with grunts of lazy masculine contentment. No island of the sea could be exempt in the degree of this little room with its humming stove. Johnnie, son of Scully, in a tone which defined his opinion of his ability as a card-player, challenged the old farmer of both gray and sandy whiskers to a game of High-Five. The farmer agreed with a contemptuous and bitter scoff. They sat close to the stove, and squared their knees under a wide board. The cowboy and the Easterner watched the game with interest. The Swede remained near the window, aloof, but with a countenance that showed signs of an inexplicable excitement.

The play of Johnnie and the gray-beard was suddenly ended by another quarrel. The old man arose while casting a look of heated scorn at his adversary. He slowly buttoned his coat, and then stalked with fabulous dignity from the room. In the discreet silence of all other men the Swede laughed. His laughter rang somehow childish. Men by this time had begun to look at him askance, as if they wished to inquire what ailed him.

A new game was formed jocosely. The cowboy volunteered to become the partner of Johnnie, and they all then turned to ask the Swede to throw in his lot with the little Easterner. He asked some questions about the game, and, learning that it wore many names, and that he had played it when it was under an alias, he accepted the invitation. He strode toward the men nervously, as if he expected to be assaulted. Finally, seated, he gazed from face to face and laughed shrilly. This laugh was so strange that the Easterner looked up quickly, the cowboy sat intent and with his mouth open, and Johnnie paused, holding the cards with still fingers.

Afterward there was a short silence. Then Johnnie said, "Well, let's get at it. Come on now!" They pulled their chairs forward until their knees were bunched under the board. They began to play, and their interest in the game caused the others to forget the manner of the Swede.

The cowboy was a board-whacker. Each time that he held superior cards he whanged them, one by one, with exceeding force, down upon the improvised table, and took the tricks with a glowing air of prowess and pride that sent thrills of indignation into the hearts of his opponents. A game with a board-whacker in it is sure to become intense. The countenances of the Easterner and the Swede were miserable whenever the cowboy thundered down his aces and kings, while Johnnie, his eyes gleaming with joy, chuckled and chuckled.

Because of the absorbing play none considered the strange ways of the Swede. They paid strict heed to the game. Finally, during a lull caused by a new deal, the Swede suddenly addressed Johnnie: "I suppose there have been a good many men killed in this room." The jaws of the others dropped and they looked at him.

"What in hell are you talking about?" said Johnnie.

The Swede laughed again his blatant laugh, full of a kind of false courage and defiance. "Oh, you know what I mean all right," he answered.

"I'm a liar if I do!" Johnnie protested. The card was halted, and the men stared at the Swede. Johnnie evidently felt that as the son of the proprietor, he should make a direct inquiry. "Now, what might you be drivin' at, mister?" he asked. The Swede winked at him. It was a wink full of cunning. His fingers shook on the edge of the board. "Oh, maybe you think I have been to nowheres. Maybe you think I'm a tenderfoot?"

"I don't know nothin' about you," answered Johnnie, "and I don't give a damn where you've been. All I got to say is that I don't know what you're driving at. There hain't never been nobody killed in this room."

The cowboy, who had been steadily gazing at the Swede, then spoke: "What's wrong with you, mister?"

Apparently it seemed to the Swede that he was formidably menaced. He shivered and turned white near the corners of his mouth. He sent an appealing glance in the direction of the little Easterner. During these moments he did not forget to wear his air of advanced pot-valor. "They say they don't know what I mean," he remarked mockingly to the Easterner.

The latter answered after prolonged and cautious reflection. "I don't understand you," he said, impassively.

The Swede made a movement then which announced that he thought he had encountered treachery from the only quarter where he had expected sympathy, if not help. "Oh, I see you are all against me, I see—"

The cowboy was in a state of deep stupefaction. "Say," he cried, as he tumbled the deck violently down upon the board, "say, what are you gittin' at, hey?"

The Swede sprang up with the celerity of a man escaping from a snake on the floor. "I don't want to fight!" he shouted. "I don't want to fight!"

The cowboy stretched his long legs indolently and deliberately. His hands were in his pockets. He spat into the sawdust-box. "Well, who the hell thought you did?" he inquired.

The Swede backed rapidly toward a corner of the room. His hands were out protectingly in front of his chest, but he was making an obvious struggle to control his fright. "Gentlemen," he quavered, "I suppose I am going to be killed before I can leave this house! I suppose I am going to be killed before I can leave this house!" In his eyes was the dying-swan look. Through the windows could be seen the snow turning blue in the shadow of dusk. The wind tore at the house, and some loose thing beat regularly against the clapboards like a spirit tapping.

A door opened, and Scully himself entered. He paused in surprise as he noted the tragic attitude of the Swede. Then he said, "What's the matter here?"

The Swede answered him swiftly and eagerly: "These men are going to kill me."

"Kill you!" ejaculated Scully. "Kill you! What are you talkin'?"

The Swede made the gesture of a martyr.

Scully wheeled sternly upon his son. "What is this, Johnnie?"

The lad had grown sullen. "Damned if I know," he answered. "I can't make no sense to it." He began to shuffle the cards, fluttering them together with an angry snap. "He says a good many men have been killed in this room, or something like that. And he says he's goin' to be killed here too. I don't know what ails him. He's crazy, I shouldn't wonder."

Scully then looked for explanation to the cowboy, but the cowboy simply shrugged his shoulders.

"Kill you?" said Scully again to the Swede. "Kill you? Man, you're off your nut."

"Oh, I know," burst out the Swede. "I know what will happen. Yes,

I'm crazy—yes. Yes, of course, I'm crazy—yes. But I know one thing—" There was a sort of sweat of misery and terror upon his face. "I know I won't get out of here alive."

The cowboy drew a deep breath, as if his mind was passing into the last stages of dissolution. "Well, I'm doggoned," he whispered to himself.

Scully wheeled suddenly and faced his son. "You've been troublin' this man!"

Johnnie's voice was loud with its burden of grievance. "Why, good Gawd, I ain't done nothin' to 'im."

The Swede broke in. "Gentlemen, do not disturb yourselves. I will leave this house. I will go away, because"—he accused them dramatically with his glance—"because I do not want to be killed."

Scully was furious with his son. "Will you tell me what is the matter, you young divil? What's the matter, anyhow? Speak out!"

"Blame it!" cried Johnnie in despair, "don't I tell you I don't know? He —he says we want to kill him, and that's all I know. I can't tell what ails him."

The Swede continued to repeat: "Never mind, Mr. Scully; never mind. I will leave this house. I will go away, because I do not wish to be killed. Yes, of course, I am crazy—yes. But I know one thing! I will go away. I will leave this house. Never mind, Mr. Scully; never mind. I will go away."

"You will not go 'way," said Scully. "You will not go 'way until I hear the reason of this business. If anybody has troubled you I will take care of him. This is my house. You are under my roof, and I will not allow any peaceable man to be troubled here." He cast a terrible eye upon Johnnie, the cowboy, and the Easterner.

"Never mind, Mr. Scully; never mind. I will go away. I do not wish to be killed." The Swede moved toward the door which opened upon the stairs. It was evidently his intention to go at once for his baggage.

"No, no," shouted Scully peremptorily; but the white-faced man slid by him and disappeared. "Now," said Scully severely, "what does this mane?"

Johnnie and the cowboy cried together: "Why, we didn't do nothin' to 'im!"

Scully's eyes were cold. "No," he said, "you didn't?"

Johnnie swore a deep oath. "Why, this is the wildest loon I ever see. We didn't do nothin' at all. We were jest sittin' here playin' cards, and he—"

The father suddenly spoke to the Easterner, "Mr. Blanc," he asked, "what has these boys been doin'?"

The Easterner reflected again. "I didn't see anything wrong at all," he said at last, slowly.

Scully began to howl. "But what does it mane?" He stared ferociously at his son. "I have a mind to lather you for this, me boy."

Johnnie was frantic. "Well, what have I done?" he bawled at his father.

III

"I think you are tongue-tied," said Scully finally to his son, the cowboy, and the Easterner; and at the end of this scornful sentence he left the room.

Upstairs the Swede was swiftly fastening the straps of his great valise. Once his back happened to be half turned toward the door, and, hearing a noise there, he wheeled and sprang up, uttering a loud cry. Scully's wrinkled visage showed grimly in the light of the small lamp he carried. This yellow effulgence, streaming upward, colored only his prominent features, and left his eyes, for instance, in mysterious shadow. He resembled a murderer.

"Man! man!" he exclaimed, "have you gone daffy?"

"Oh, no! Oh, no!" rejoined the other. "There are people in this world who know pretty nearly as much as you do—understand?"

For a moment they stood gazing at each other. Upon the Swede's deathly pale cheeks were two spots brightly crimson and sharply edged, as if they had been carefully painted. Scully placed the light on the table and sat himself on the edge of the bed. He spoke ruminatively. "By cracky, I never heard of such a thing in my life. It's a complete muddle. I can't, for the soul of me, think how you ever got this idea into your head." Presently he lifted his eyes and asked: "And did you sure think they were going to kill you?"

The Swede scanned the old man as if he wished to see into his mind. "I did," he said at last. He obviously suspected that this answer might precipitate an outbreak. As he pulled on a strap his whole arm shook, the elbow wavering like a bit of paper.

Scully banged his hand impressively on the footboard of the bed. "Why, man, we're goin' to have a line of ilictric street-cars in this town next spring."

"'A line of electric street-cars,'" repeated the Swede, stupidly.

"And," said Scully, "there's a new railroad goin' to be built down from Broken Arm to here. Not to mention the four churches and the smashin' big brick schoolhouse. Then there's the big factory, too. Why, in two years Romper'll be a met-tro-*pol*-is."

Having finished the preparation of his baggage, the Swede straightened himself. "Mr. Scully," he said, with sudden hardihood, "how much do I owe you?"

"You don't owe me anythin'," said the old man, angrily.

"Yes, I do," retorted the Swede. He took seventy-five cents from his pocket and tendered it to Scully; but the latter snapped his fingers in disdainful refusal. However, it happened that they both stood gazing in a strange fashion at three silver pieces on the Swede's open palm.

"I'll not take your money," said Scully at last. "Not after what's been goin' on here." Then a plan seemed to strike him. "Here," he cried, picking up his lamp and moving toward the door. "Here! Come with me a minute."

"No," said the Swede, in overwhelming alarm.

"Yes," urged the old man. "Come on! I want you to come and see a picter—just across the hall—in my room."

The Swede must have concluded that his hour was come. His jaw dropped and his teeth showed like a dead man's. He ultimately followed Scully across the corridor, but he had the step of one hung in chains.

Scully flashed the light high on the wall of his own chamber. There was revealed a ridiculous photograph of a little girl. She was leaning against a balustrade of gorgeous decoration, and the formidable bang to her hair was prominent. The figure was as graceful as an upright sled-stake, and, withal, it was of the hue of lead. "There," said Scully, tenderly, "that's the picter of my little girl that died. Her name was Carrie. She had the purtiest hair you ever saw! I was that fond of her, she—"

Turning then, he saw that the Swede was not contemplating the picture at all, but, instead, was keeping keen watch on the gloom in the rear.

"Look, man!" cried Scully, heartily. "That's the picter of my little gal that died. Her name was Carrie. And then here's the picter of my oldest boy, Michael. He's a lawyer in Lincoln, an' doin' well. I gave that boy a grand eddication, and I'm glad for it now. He's a fine boy. Look at 'im now. Ain't he bold as blazes, him there in Lincoln, an honored an' re-spicted gintleman! An honored and respicted gintleman," concluded Scully with a flourish. And, so saying, he smote the Swede jovially on the back.

The Swede faintly smiled.

"Now," said the old man, "there's only one more thing." He dropped suddenly to the floor and thrust his head beneath the bed. The Swede could hear his muffled voice. "I'd keep it under me piller if it wasn't for that boy Johnnie. Then there's the old woman— Where is it now? I never put it twice in the same place. Ah, now come out with you!"

Presently he backed clumsily from under the bed, dragging with him an old coat rolled into a bundle. "I've fetched him," he muttered. Kneel-ing on the floor, he unrolled the coat and extracted from its heart a large yellow-brown whisky-bottle.

His first maneuver was to hold the bottle up to the light. Reassured, apparently, that nobody had been tampering with it, he thrust it with a generous movement toward the Swede.

The weak-kneed Swede was about to eagerly clutch this element of strength, but he suddenly jerked his hand away and cast a look of horror upon Scully.

"Drink," said the old man affectionately. He had risen to his feet, and now stood facing the Swede.

There was a silence. Then again Scully said: "Drink!"

The Swede laughed wildly. He grabbed the bottle, put it to his mouth; and as his lips curled absurdly around the opening and his throat worked, he kept his glance, burning with hatred, upon the old man's face.

IV

After the departure of Scully the three men, with the cardboard still upon their knees, preserved for a long time an astounded silence. Then Johnnie said: "That's the doddangedest Swede I ever see."

"He ain't no Swede," said the cowboy, scornfully.

"Well, what is he then?" cried Johnnie. "What is he then?"

"It's my opinion," replied the cowboy deliberately, "he's some kind of a Dutchman." It was a venerable custom of the country to entitle as Swedes all light-haired men who spoke with a heavy tongue. In consequence the idea of the cowboy was not without its daring. "Yes, sir," he repeated, "It's my opinion this feller is some kind of a Dutchman."

"Well, he says he's a Swede, anyhow," muttered Johnnie, sulkily. He turned to the Easterner: "What do you think, Mr. Blanc?"

"Oh, I don't know," replied the Easterner.

"Well, what do you think makes him act that way?" asked the cowboy.

"Why, he's frightened." The Easterner knocked his pipe against a rim of the stove. "He's clear frightened out of his boots."

"What at?" cried Johnnie and the cowboy together.

The Easterner reflected over his answer.

"What at?" cried the others again.

"Oh, I don't know, but it seems to me this man has been reading dime novels, and he thinks he's right out in the middle of it—the shootin' and stabbin' and all."

"But," said the cowboy, deeply scandalized, "this ain't Wyoming, ner none of them places. This is Nebrasker."

"Yes," added Johnnie, "an' why don't he wait till he gits *out West*?"

The traveled Easterner laughed. "It isn't different there even—not in these days. But he thinks he's right in the middle of hell."

Johnnie and the cowboy mused long.

"It's awful funny," remarked Johnnie at last.

"Yes," said the cowboy. "This is a queer game. I hope we don't git snowed in, because then we'd have to stand this here man bein' around with us all the time. That wouldn't be no good."

"I wish pop would throw him out," said Johnnie.

Presently they heard a loud stamping on the stairs, accompanied by ringing jokes in the voice of old Scully, and laughter, evidently from the Swede. The men around the stove stared vacantly at each other. "Gosh!"

said the cowboy. The door flew open, and old Scully, flushed and anecdotal, came into the room. He was jabbering at the Swede, who followed him, laughing bravely. It was the entry of two roisterers from a banquet hall.

"Come now," said Scully sharply to the three seated men, "move up and give us a chance at the stove." The cowboy and the Easterner obediently sidled their chairs to make room for the new-comers. Johnnie, however, simply arranged himself in a more indolent attitude, and then remained motionless.

"Come! Git over, there," said Scully.

"Plenty of room on the other side of the stove," said Johnnie.

"Do you think we want to sit in the draught?" roared the father.

But the Swede here interposed with a grandeur of confidence. "No, no. Let the boy sit where he likes," he cried in a bullying voice to the father.

"All right! All right!" said Scully, deferentially. The cowboy and the Easterner exchanged glances of wonder.

The five chairs were formed in a cresent about one side of the stove. The Swede began to talk; he talked arrogantly, profanely, angrily. Johnnie, the cowboy, and the Easterner maintained a morose silence, while old Scully appeared to be receptive and eager, breaking in constantly with sympathetic ejaculations.

Finally the Swede announced that he was thirsty. He moved in his chair, and said that he would go for a drink of water.

"I'll git it for you," cried Scully at once.

"No," said the Swede, contemptuously. "I'll get it for myself." He arose and stalked with the air of an owner off into the executive parts of the hotel.

As soon as the Swede was out of hearing Scully sprang to his feet and whispered intensely to the others: "Upstairs he thought I was tryin' to poison 'im."

"Say," said Johnnie, "this makes me sick. Why don't you throw 'im out in the snow?"

"Why, he's all right now," declared Scully. "It was only that he was from the East, and he thought this was a tough place. That's all. He's all right now."

The cowboy looked with admiration upon the Easterner. "You were straight," he said. "You were on to that there Dutchman."

"Well," said Johnnie to his father, "he may be all right now, but I don't see it. Other time he was scared, but now he's too fresh."

Scully's speech was always a combination of Irish brogue and idiom, Western twang and idiom, and scraps of curiously formal diction taken from the story-books and newspapers. He now hurled a strange mass of language at the head of his son. "What do I keep? What do I keep? What do I keep?" he demanded, in a voice of thunder. He slapped his knee impressively, to indicate that he himself was going to make reply, and that all should heed. "I keep a hotel," he shouted. "A hotel, do you mind? A guest under my roof has sacred privileges. He is to be intimidated by none. Not one word shall he hear that would prijudice him in favor of goin' away. I'll not have it. There's no place in this here town where they can say they iver took in a guest of mine because he was afraid to stay here." He wheeled suddenly upon the cowboy and the Easterner. "Am I right?"

"Yes, Mr. Scully," said the cowboy, "I think you're right."

"Yes, Mr. Scully," said the Easterner, "I think you're right."

V

At six-o'clock supper, the Swede fizzed like a firewheel. He sometimes seemed on the point of bursting into riotous song, and in all his madness he was encouraged by old Scully. The Easterner was encased in reserve; the cowboy sat in wide-mouthed amazement, forgetting to eat, while Johnnie wrathily demolished great plates of food. The daughters of the house, when they were obliged to replenish the biscuits, approached as warily as Indians, and, having succeeded in their purpose, fled with ill-concealed trepidation. The Swede domineered the whole feast, and he gave it the appearance of a cruel bacchanal. He seemed to have grown suddenly taller; he gazed, brutally disdainful, into every face. His voice rang through the room. Once when he jabbed out harpoon-fashion with his fork to pinion a biscuit, the weapon nearly impaled the hand of the Easterner, which had been stretched quietly out for the same biscuit.

After supper, as the men filed toward the other room, the Swede smote Scully ruthlessly on the shoulder. "Well, old boy, that was a good, square meal." Johnnie looked hopefully at his father; he knew that shoulder was tender from an old fall; and, indeed, it appeared for a moment as if Scully was going to flame out over the matter, but in the end he smiled a sickly smile and remained silent. The others understood from his manner that he was admitting his responsibility for the Swede's new viewpoint.

Johnnie, however, addressed his parent in an aside. "Why don't you license somebody to kick you downstairs?" Scully scowled darkly by way of reply.

When they were gathered about the stove, the Swede insisted on another game of High-Five. Scully gently deprecated the plan at first, but the Swede turned a wolfish glare upon him. The old man subsided, and the Swede canvassed the others. In his tone there was always a great threat. The cowboy and the Easterner both remarked indifferently that they would play. Scully said that he would presently have to go to meet the 6:58 train, and so the Swede turned menacingly upon Johnnie. For a moment their glances crossed like blades, and then Johnnie smiled and said, "Yes, I'll play."

They formed a square, with the little board on their knees. The Easterner and the Swede were again partners. As the play went on, it was noticeable that the cowboy was not board-whacking as usual. Meanwhile, Scully, near the lamp, had put on his spectacles and, with an appearance curiously like an old priest, was reading a newspaper. In time he went out to meet the 6:58 train, and, despite his precautions, a gust of polar wind whirled into the room as he opened the door. Besides scattering the cards, it chilled the players to the marrow. The Swede cursed frightfully. When Scully returned, his entrance disturbed a cozy and friendly scene. The Swede again cursed. But presently they were once more intent, their heads bent forward and their hands moving swiftly. The Swede had adopted the fashion of board-whacking.

Scully took up his paper and for a long time remained immersed in matters which were extraordinarily remote from him. The lamp burned badly, and once he stopped to adjust the wick. The newspaper, as he turned from page to page, rustled with a slow and comfortable sound. Then suddenly he heard three terrible words: "You are cheatin'!"

Such scenes often prove that there can be little of dramatic import in environment. Any room can present a tragic front; any room can be comic. This little den was now hideous as a torture-chamber. The new faces of the men themselves had changed it upon the instant. The Swede held a huge fist in front of Johnnie's face, while the latter looked steadily over it into the blazing orbs of his accuser. The Easterner had grown pallid; the cowboy's jaw had dropped in that expression of bovine amazement which was one of his important mannerisms. After the three words, the first sound in the room was made by Scully's paper as it floated forgotten to his feet. His spectacles had also fallen from his nose, but by a clutch he had saved them in air. His hand, grasping the spectacles, now remained poised awkwardly and near his shoulder. He stared at the card-players.

Probably the silence was while a second elapsed. Then, if the floor had been suddenly twitched out from under the men they could not have moved quicker. The five had projected themselves headlong toward a common point. It happened that Johnnie, in rising to hurl himself upon the Swede, had stumbled slightly because of his curiously instinctive care for the cards and the board. The loss of the moment allowed time for the arrival of Scully, and also allowed the cowboy time to give the Swede a great push which sent him staggering back. The men found tongue together, and hoarse shouts of rage, appeal, or fear burst from every throat. The cowboy pushed and jostled feverishly at the Swede, and the Easterner and Scully clung wildly to Johnnie; but through the smoky air, above the swaying bodies of the peace-compellers, the eyes of the two warriors ever sought each other in glances of challenge that were at once hot and steely.

Of course the board had been overturned, and now the whole company of cards was scattered over the floor, where the boots of the men trampled the fat and painted kings and queens as they gazed with their silly eyes at the war that was waging above them.

Scully's voice was dominating the yells. "Stop now! Stop, I say! Stop, now—"

Johnnie, as he struggled to burst through the rank formed by Scully and the Easterner, was crying, "Well, he says I cheated! He says I cheated! I won't allow no man to say I cheated! If he says I cheated, he's a — —!"

The cowboy was telling the Swede, "Quit now! Quit, d'ye hear—"

The screams of the Swede never ceased: "He did cheat! I saw him! I saw him—"

As for the Easterner, he was importuning in a voice that was not heeded: "Wait a moment, can't you? Oh, wait a moment. What's the good of a fight over a game of cards? Wait a moment—"

In this tumult no complete sentences were clear. "Cheat"—"Quit"—"He says"—these fragments pierced the uproar and rang out sharply. It was remarkable that, whereas Scully undoubtedly made the most noise, he was the least heard of any of the riotous band.

Then suddenly there was a great cessation. It was as if each man had paused for breath; and although the room was still lighted with the anger of men, it could be seen that there was no danger of immediate conflict, and at once Johnnie, shouldering his way forward, almost succeeded in confronting the Swede. "What did you say I cheated for? What did you say I cheated for? I don't cheat, and I won't let any man say I do!"

The Swede said, "I saw you! I saw you!"

"Well," cried Johnnie, "I'll fight any man what says I cheat!"

"No, you won't," said the cowboy. "Not here."

"Ah, be still, can't you?" said Scully, coming between them.

The quiet was sufficient to allow the Easterner's voice to be heard. He was repeating, "Oh, wait a moment, can't you? What's the good of a fight over a game of cards? Wait a moment!"

Johnnie, his red face appearing above his father's shoulder, hailed the Swede again. "Did you say I cheated?"

The Swede showed his teeth. "Yes."

"Then," said Johnnie, "we must fight."

"Yes, fight," roared the Swede. He was like a demoniac. "Yes, fight! I'll show you what kind of a man I am! I'll show you who you want to fight! Maybe you think I can't fight! Maybe you think I can't! I'll show you, you skin, you card-sharp! Yes, you cheated! You cheated! You cheated!"

"Well, let's go at it, then, mister," said Johnnie, coolly.

The cowboy's brow was beaded with sweat from his efforts in intercepting all sorts of raids. He turned in despair to Scully. "What are you goin' to do now?"

A change had come over the Celtic visage of the old man. He now seemed all eagerness; his eyes glowed.

"We'll let them fight," he answered, stalwartly. "I can't put up with it any longer. I've stood this damned Swede till I'm sick. We'll let them fight."

VI

The men prepared to go out of doors. The Easterner was so nervous that he had great difficulty in getting his arms into the sleeves of his new leather coat. As the cowboy drew his fur cap down over his ears his hands trembled. In fact, Johnnie and old Scully were the only ones who displayed no agitation. These preliminaries were conducted without words.

Scully threw open the door. "Well, come on," he said. Instantly a terrific wind caused the flame of the lamp to struggle at its wick, while a puff of black smoke sprang from the chimney-top. The stove was in mid-current of the blast, and its voice swelled to equal the roar of the storm. Some of the scarred and bedabbled cards were caught up from the floor and dashed helplessly against the farther wall. The men lowered their heads and plunged into the tempest as into a sea.

No snow was falling, but great whirls and clouds of flakes, swept up from the ground by the frantic winds, were streaming southward with the speed of bullets. The covered land was blue with the sheen of an unearthly satin, and there was no other hue save where, at the low, black railway station—which seemed incredibly distant—one light gleamed like a tiny jewel. As the men floundered into a thigh-deep drift, it was known that the Swede was bawling out something. Scully went to him, put a hand on his shoulder, and projected an ear. "What's that you say?" he shouted.

"I say," bawled the Swede again, "I won't stand much show against this gang. I know you'll all pitch on me."

Scully smote him reproachfully on the arm. "Tut, man!" he yelled. The wind tore the words from Scully's lips and scattered them far alee.

"You are all a gang of—" boomed the Swede, but the storm also seized the remainder of this sentence.

Immediately turning their backs upon the wind, the men had swung around a corner to the sheltered side of the hotel. It was the function of the little house to preserve here, amid this great devastation of snow, an irregular V-shape of heavily encrusted grass, which crackled beneath the feet. One could imagine the great drifts piled against the windward side. When the party reached the comparative peace of this spot it was found that the Swede was still bellowing.

"Oh, I know what kind of a thing this is! I know you'll all pitch on me. I can't lick you all!"

Scully turned upon him panther-fashion. "You'll not have to whip all of us. You'll have to whip my son Johnnie. An' the man what troubles you durin' that time will have me to dale with."

The arrangements were swiftly made. The two men faced each other, obedient to the harsh commands of Scully, whose face, in the subtly luminous gloom, could be seen set in the austere impersonal lines that are pictured on the countenances of the Roman veterans. The Easterner's teeth were chattering, and he was hopping up and down like a mechanical toy. The cowboy stood rock-like.

The contestants had not stripped off any clothing. Each was in his ordinary attire. Their fists were up, and they eyed each other in a calm that had the elements of leonine cruelty in it.

During this pause, the Easterner's mind, like a film, took lasting impressions of three men—the iron-nerved master of the ceremony; the Swede, pale, motionless, terrible; and Johnnie, serene yet ferocious, brutish yet heroic. The entire prelude had in it a tragedy greater than the tragedy of action, and this aspect was accentuated by the long, mellow cry of the blizzard, as it sped the tumbling and wailing flakes into the black abyss of the south.

"Now!" said Scully.

The two combatants leaped forward and crashed together like bullocks. There was heard the cushioned sound of blows, and of a curse squeezing out from between the tight teeth of one.

As for the spectators, the Easterner's pent-up breath exploded from him with a pop of relief, absolute relief from the tension of the preliminaries. The cowboy bounded into the air with a yowl. Scully was immovable as from supreme amazement and fear at the fury of the fight which he himself had permitted and arranged.

For a time the encounter in the darkness was such a perplexity of flying arms that it presented no more detail than would a swiftly revolving wheel. Occasionally a face, as if illumined by a flash of light, would shine out, ghastly and marked with pink spots. A moment later, the men might have been known as shadows, if it were not for the involuntary utterance of oaths that came from them in whispers.

Suddenly a holocaust of warlike desire caught the cowboy, and he bolted forward with the speed of a broncho. "Go it, Johnnie! go it! Kill him! Kill him!"

Scully confronted him. "Kape back," he said; and by his glance the cowboy could tell that this man was Johnnie's father.

To the Easterner there was a monotony of unchangeable fighting that was an abomination. This confused mingling was eternal to his sense, which was concentrated in a longing for the end, the priceless end. Once the fighters lurched near him, and as he scrambled hastily backward he heard them breathe like men on the rack.

"Kill him, Johnnie! Kill him! Kill him! Kill him!" The cowboy's face was contorted like one of those agony masks in museums.

"Keep still," said Scully, icily.

Then there was a sudden loud grunt, incomplete, cut short, and Johnnie's body swung away from the Swede and fell with sickening heaviness to the grass. The cowboy was barely in time to prevent the mad Swede from flinging himself upon his prone adversary. "No, you don't," said the cowboy, interposing an arm. "Wait a second."

Scully was at his son's side. "Johnnie! Johnnie, me boy!" His voice had a quality of melancholy tenderness. "Johnnie! Can you go on with it?" He looked anxiously down into the bloody, pulpy face of his son.

There was a moment of silence, and then Johnnie answered in his ordinary voice, "Yes, I—it—yes."

Assisted by his father he struggled to his feet. "Wait a bit now till you git your wind," said the old man.

A few paces away the cowboy was lecturing the Swede. "No, you don't! Wait a second!"

The Easterner was plucking at Scully's sleeve. "Oh, this is enough," he pleaded. "This is enough! Let it go as it stands. This is enough!"

"Bill," said Scully, "git out of the road." The cowboy stepped aside. "Now." The combatants were actuated by a new caution as they advanced toward collision. They glared at each other, and then the Swede aimed a lightning blow that carried with it his entire weight. Johnnie was evidently half stupid from weakness, but he miraculously dodged, and his fist sent the over-balanced Swede sprawling.

The cowboy, Scully, and the Easterner burst into a cheer that was like a chorus of triumphant soldiery, but before its conclusion the Swede had scuffled agilely to his feet and come in berserk abandon at his foe. There was another perplexity of flying arms, and Johnnie's body again swung away and fell, even as a bundle might fall from a roof. The Swede instantly staggered to a little wind-waved tree and leaned upon it, breathing like an engine, while his savage and flame-lit eyes roamed from face to face as the men bent over Johnnie. There was a splendor of isolation in his situation at this time which the Easterner felt once when, lifting his eyes from the man on the ground, he beheld that mysterious and lonely figure, waiting.

"Are you any good yet, Johnnie?" asked Scully in a broken voice.

The son gasped and opened his eyes languidly. After a moment he answered, "No—I ain't—any good—any—more." Then, from shame and bodily ill, he began to weep, the tears furrowing down through the blood-stains on his face. "He was too—too—too heavy for me."

Scully straightened and addressed the waiting figure. "Stranger," he said, evenly, "it's all up with our side." Then his voice changed into that vibrant huskiness which is commonly the tone of the most simple and deadly announcements. "Johnnie is whipped."

Without replying, the victor moved off on the route to the front door of the hotel.

The cowboy was formulating new and unspellable blasphemies. The Easterner was startled to find that they were out in a wind that seemed to come direct from the shadowed arctic floes. He heard again the wail of the snow as it was flung to its grave in the south. He knew now that all this time the cold had been sinking into him deeper and deeper, and he wondered that he had not perished. He felt indifferent to the condition of the vanquished man.

"Johnnie, can you walk?" asked Scully.

"Did I hurt—hurt him any?" asked the son.

"Can you walk, boy? Can you walk?"

Johnnie's voice was suddenly strong. There was a robust impatience in it. "I asked you whether I hurt him any!"

"Yes, yes, Johnnie," answered the cowboy, consolingly; "he's hurt a good deal."

They raised him from the ground, and as soon as he was on his feet he went tottering off, rebuffing all attempts at assistance. When the party rounded the corner they were fairly blinded by the pelting of the snow. It burned their faces like fire. The cowboy carried Johnnie through the drift to the door. As they entered, some cards again rose from the floor and beat against the wall.

The Easterner rushed to the stove. He was so profoundly chilled that he almost dared to embrace the glowing iron. The Swede was not in the room. Johnnie sank into a chair and, folding his arms on his knees, buried his face in them. Scully, warming one foot and then the other at a rim of the stove, muttered to himself with Celtic mournfulness. The cowboy had removed his fur cap, and with a dazed and rueful air he was running one hand through his tousled locks. From overhead they could hear the creaking of boards, as the Swede tramped here and there in his room.

The sad quiet was broken by the sudden flinging open of a door that led toward the kitchen. It was instantly followed by an inrush of women. They precipitated themselves upon Johnnie amid a chorus of lamentation. Before they carried their prey off to the kitchen, there to be bathed and harangued with that mixture of sympathy and abuse which is a feat of their sex, the mother straightened herself and fixed old Scully with an eye of stern reproach. "Shame be upon you, Patrick Scully!" she cried. "Your own son, too. Shame be upon you!"

"There, now! Be quiet, now!" said the old man, weakly.

"Shame be upon you, Patrick Scully!" The girls, rallying to this slogan, sniffed disdainfully in the direction of those trembling accomplices, the cowboy and the Easterner. Presently they bore Johnnie away, and left the three men to dismal reflection.

VII

"I'd like to fight this here Dutchman myself," said the cowboy, breaking a long silence.

Scully wagged his head sadly. "No, that wouldn't do. It wouldn't be right. It wouldn't be right."

"Well, why wouldn't it?" argued the cowboy. "I don't see no harm in it."

"No," answered Scully, with mournful heroism. "It wouldn't be right. It was Johnnie's fight, and now we mustn't whip the man just because he whipped Johnnie."

"Yes, that's true enough," said the cowboy; "but—he better not get fresh with me, because I couldn't stand no more of it."

"You'll not say a word to him," commanded Scully, and even then they heard the tread of the Swede on the stairs. His entrance was made theatric. He swept the door back with a bang and swaggered to the middle of the room. No one looked at him. "Well," he cried, insolently, at Scully, "I s'pose you'll tell me now how much I owe you?"

The old man remained stolid. "You don't owe me nothin'."

"Huh!" said the Swede, "huh! Don't owe 'im nothin'."

The cowboy addressed the Swede. "Stranger, I don't see how you come to be so gay around here."

Old Scully was instantly alert. "Stop!" he shouted, holding his hand forth, fingers upward. "Bill, you shut up!"

The cowboy spat carelessly into the sawdust-box. "I didn't say a word, did I?" he asked.

"Mr. Scully," called the Swede, "how much do I owe you?" It was seen that he was attired for departure, and that he had his valise in his hand.

"You don't owe me nothin'," repeated Scully in the same imperturbable way.

"Huh!" said the Swede. "I guess you're right. I guess if it was any way at all, you'd owe me somethin'. That's what I guess." He turned to the cowboy. " 'Kill him! Kill him! Kill him!' " he mimicked, and then guffawed victoriously. " 'Kill him!' " He was convulsed with ironical humor.

But he might have been jeering the dead. The three men were immovable and silent, staring with glassy eyes at the stove.

The Swede opened the door and passed into the storm, giving one derisive glance backward at the still group.

As soon as the door was closed, Scully and the cowboy leaped to their feet and began to curse. They trampled to and fro, waving their arms and smashing into the air with their fists. "Oh, but that was a hard minute!"

wailed Scully. "That was a hard minute! Him there leerin' and scoffin'! One bang at his nose was worth forty dollars to me that minute! How did you stand it, Bill?"

"How did I stand it?" cried the cowboy in a quivering voice. "How did I stand it? Oh!"

The old man burst into sudden brogue. "I'd loike to take that Swade," he wailed, "and hould 'im down on a shtone flure and bate 'im to a jelly wid a shtick!"

The cowboy groaned in sympathy. "I'd like to git him by the neck and ha-ammer him"—he brought his hand down on a chair with a noise like a pistol-shot—"hammer that there Dutchman until he couldn't tell himself from a dead coyote!"

"I'd bate 'im until he—"

"I'd show *him* some things—"

And then together they raised a yearning, fanatic cry—"Oh-o-oh! if we only could—"

"Yes!"

"Yes!"

"And then I'd—"

"O-o-oh!"

VIII

The Swede, tightly gripping his valise, tacked across the face of the storm as if he carried sails. He was following a line of little naked, gasping trees which, he knew, must mark the way of the road. His face, fresh from the pounding of Johnnie's fists, felt more pleasure than pain in the wind and the driving snow. A number of square shapes loomed upon him finally, and he knew them as the houses of the main body of the town. He found a street and made travel along it, leaning heavily upon the wind whenever, at a corner, a terrific blast caught him.

He might have been in a deserted village. We picture the world as thick with conquering and elate humanity, but here, with the bugles of the tempest pealing, it was hard to imagine a peopled earth. One viewed the existence of man then as a marvel, and conceded a glamour of wonder to these lice which were caused to cling to a whirling, fire-smitten, ice-locked, disease-stricken, space-lost bulb. The conceit of man was explained by this storm to be the very engine of life. One was a coxcomb not to die in it. However, the Swede found a saloon.

In front of it an indomitable red light was burning, and the snowflakes were made blood-color as they flew through the circumscribed territory of the lamp's shining. The Swede pushed open the door of the saloon and entered. A sanded expanse was before him, and at the end of it four men sat about a table drinking. Down one side of the room extended a radiant bar, and its guardian was leaning upon his elbows listening to the talk of the men at the table. The Swede dropped his valise upon the floor and, smiling fraternally upon the barkeeper, said, "Gimme some whisky, will you?" The man placed a bottle, a whisky-glass, and a glass of ice-thick water upon the bar. The Swede poured himself an abnormal portion of whisky and drank it in three gulps. "Pretty bad night," remarked the bartender, indifferently. He was making the pretension of blindness which is usually a distinction of his class; but it could have been seen that he was furtively studying the half-erased blood-stains on the face of the Swede. "Bad night," he said again.

"Oh, it's good enough for me," replied the Swede, hardily, as he poured himself some more whiskey. The barkeeper took his coin and maneuvered it through its reception by the highly nickeled cash-machine. A bell rang; a card labeled "20 cts." had appeared.

"No," continued the Swede, "this isn't too bad weather. It's good enough for me."

"So?" murmured the barkeeper, languidly.

The copious drams made the Swede's eyes swim, and he breathed a trifle heavier. "Yes, I like this weather. I like it. It suits me." It was apparently his design to impart a deep significance to these words.

"So?" murmured the bartender again. He turned to gaze dreamily at the scroll-like birds and bird-like scrolls which had been drawn with soap upon the mirrors in back of the bar.

"Well, I guess I'll take another drink," said the Swede, presently. "Have something?"

"No, thanks; I'm not drinkin'," answered the bartender. Afterward he asked, "How did you hurt your face?"

The Swede immediately began to boast loudly. "Why, in a fight. I thumped the soul out of a man down here at Scully's hotel."

The interest of the four men at the table was at last aroused.

"Who was it?" said one.

"Johnnie Scully," blustered the Swede. "Son of the man what runs it. He will be pretty near dead for some weeks, I can tell you. I made a nice thing of him, I did. He couldn't get up. They carried him in the house. Have a drink?"

Instantly the men in some subtle way encased themselves in reserve. "No, thanks," said one. The group was of curious formation. Two were prominent local business men; one was the district attorney; and one was a professional gambler of the kind known as "square." But a scrutiny of the group would not have enabled an observer to pick the gambler from the men of more reputable pursuits. He was, in fact, a man so delicate in manner, when among people of fair class, and so judicious in his choice of victims, that in the strictly masculine part of the town's life he had come to be explicitly trusted and admired. People called him a thoroughbred. The fear and contempt with which his craft was regarded were undoubtedly the reason why his quiet dignity shone conspicuous above the quiet dignity of men who might be merely hatters, billiard-markers, or grocery clerks. Beyond an occasional unwary traveler who came by rail, this gambler was supposed to prey solely upon reckless and senile farmers, who, when flush with good crops, drove into town in all the pride and confidence of an absolutely invulnerable stupidity. Hearing at times in circuitous fashion of the despoilment of such a farmer, the important men of Romper invariably laughed in contempt of the victim, and if they thought of the wolf at all, it was with a kind of pride at the knowledge that he would never dare think of attacking their wisdom and courage. Besides, it was popular that this gambler had a real wife and two real children in a neat cottage in a suburb, where he led an exemplary home life; and when anyone even suggested a discrepancy in his character, the crowd immediately vociferated descriptions of this virtuous family circle. Then men who led exemplary home lives, and men who did not lead exemplary home lives, all subsided in a bunch, remarking that there was nothing more to be said.

However, when a restriction was placed upon him—as, for instance, when a strong clique of members of the new Pollywog Club refused to permit him, even as a spectator, to appear in the rooms of the organization—the candor and gentleness with which he accepted the judgment disarmed many of his foes and made his friends more desperately partisan. He invariably distinguished between himself and a respectable Romper man so quickly and frankly that his manner actually appeared to be a continual broadcast compliment.

And one must not forget to declare the fundamental fact of his entire position in Romper. It is irrefutable that in all affairs outside his business, in all matters that occur eternally and commonly between man and man, this thieving card-player was so generous, so just, so moral, that, in a contest, he could have put to flight the consciences of nine tenths of the citizens of Romper.

And so it happened that he was seated in this saloon with the two prominent local merchants and the district attorney.

The Swede continued to drink raw whisky, meanwhile babbling at the barkeeper and trying to induce him to indulge in potations. "Come on. Have a drink. Come on. What—no? Well, have a little one, then. By gawd, I've whipped a man tonight, and I want to celebrate. I whipped him good, too. Gentlemen," the Swede cried to the men at the table, "have a drink?"

"Ssh!" said the barkeeper.

The group at the table, although furtively attentive, had been pretending to be deep in talk, but now a man lifted his eyes toward the Swede and said, shortly, "Thanks. We don't want any more."

At this reply the Swede ruffled out his chest like a rooster. "Well," he exploded, "it seems I can't get anybody to drink with me in this town. Seems so, don't it? Well!"

"Ssh!" said the barkeeper.

"Say," snarled the Swede, "don't you try to shut me up. I won't have it. I'm a gentleman, and I want people to drink with me. And I want 'em to drink with me now. *Now*—do you understand?" He rapped the bar with his knuckles.

Years of experience had calloused the bartender. He merely grew sulky. "I hear you," he answered.

"Well," cried the Swede, "listen hard then. See those men over there? Well, they're going to drink with me, and don't you forget it. Now you watch."

"Hi!" yelled the barkeeper, "this won't do!"

"Why won't it?" demanded the Swede. He stalked over to the table, and by chance laid his hand upon the shoulder of the gambler. "How about this?" he asked wrathfully. "I asked you to drink with me."

The gambler simply twisted his head and spoke over his shoulder. "My friend, I don't know you."

"Oh, hell!" answered the Swede, "come and have a drink."

"Now, my boy," advised the gambler, kindly, "take your hand off my shoulder and go 'way and mind your own business." He was a little, slim man, and it seemed strange to hear him use this tone of heroic patronage to the burly Swede. The other men at the table said nothing.

"What! You won't drink with me, you little dude? I'll make you, then! I'll make you!" The Swede had grasped the gambler frenziedly at the throat, and was dragging him from his chair. The other men sprang up. The barkeeper dashed around the corner of his bar. There was a great tumult, and then was seen a long blade in the hand of the gambler. It shot forward, and a human body, this citadel of virtue, wisdom, power, was pierced as easily as if it had been a melon. The Swede fell with a cry of supreme astonishment.

The prominent merchants and the district attorney must have at once tumbled out of the place backward. The bartender found himself hanging limply to the arm of a chair and gazing into the eyes of a murderer.

"Henry," said the latter, as he wiped his knife on one of the towels that hung beneath the bar rail, "you tell 'em where to find me. I'll be home, waiting for 'em." Then he vanished. A moment afterward the barkeeper was in the street dinning through the storm for help and, moreover, companionship.

The corpse of the Swede, alone in the saloon, had its eyes fixed upon a dreadful legend that dwelt atop of the cash-machine: "This registers the amount of your purchase."

IX

Months later, the cowboy was frying pork over the stove of a little ranch near the Dakota line, when there was a quick thud of hoofs outside, and presently the Easterner entered with the letters and the papers.

"Well," said the Easterner at once, "the chap that killed the Swede has got three years. Wasn't much, was it?"

"He has? Three years?" The cowboy poised his pan of pork, while he ruminated upon the news. "Three years. That ain't much."

"No. It was a light sentence," replied the Easterner as he unbuckled his spurs. "Seems there was a good deal of sympathy for him in Romper."

"If the bartender had been any good," observed the cowboy, thoughtfully, "he would have gone in and cracked that there Dutchman on the head with a bottle in the beginnin' of it and stopped all this here murderin'."

"Yes, a thousand things might have happened," said the Easterner, tartly.

The cowboy returned his pan of pork to the fire, but his philosophy continued. "It's funny, ain't it? If he hadn't said Johnnie was cheatin' he'd be alive this minute. He was an awful fool. Game played for fun, too. Not for money. I believe he was crazy."

"I feel sorry for that gambler," said the Easterner.

"Oh, so do I," said the cowboy. "He don't deserve none of it for killin' who he did."

"The Swede might not have been killed if everything had been square."

"Might not have been killed?" exclaimed the cowboy. "Everythin' square? Why, when he said that Johnnie was cheatin' and acted like such a jackass? And then in the saloon he fairly walked up to git hurt?" With these arguments the cowboy browbeat the Easterner and reduced him to rage.

"You're a fool!" cried the Easterner, viciously. "You're a bigger jackass than the Swede by a million majority. Now let me tell you one thing. Let me tell you something. Listen! Johnnie *was* cheating!"

" 'Johnnie,' " said the cowboy, blankly. There was a minute of silence, and then he said, robustly, "Why, no. The game was only for fun."

"Fun or not," said the Easterner, "Johnnie was cheating. I saw him. I know it. I saw him. And I refused to stand up and be a man. I let the Swede fight it out alone. And you—you were simply puffing around the place and wanting to fight. And then old Scully himself! We are all in it! This poor gambler isn't even a noun. He is kind of an adverb. Every sin is the result of a collaboration. We, five of us, have collaborated in the murder of this Swede. Usually there are from a dozen to forty women really involved in every murder, but in this case it seems to be only five men—you, I, Johnnie, old Scully; and that fool of an unfortunate gambler came merely as a culmination, the apex of a human movement, and gets all the punishment."

The cowboy, injured and rebellious, cried out blindly into this fog of mysterious theory: "Well, I didn't do anythin', did I?"

PARTIAL ANALYSIS

1. *The power of chance.* In "The Blue Hotel," as in other stories by Crane, chance is a powerful force. It determines good and evil, rewards and punishment, life and death. But it seems to have a mysterious power. Chance circumstances in "The Blue Hotel" snowball into necessity, or fate. The Swede seems doomed from the start. In fact, the feeling of inescapable doom which hangs over the story, in spite of the play of chance events, has led critics to compare "The Blue Hotel" with Greek tragedy.

The casual events of the story seem to have a power greater than the power of acts intentionally performed by men. Like Hardy, Crane regards with sardonic amusement those actions which men call purposeful. In Hardy's *The Return of the Native*, whenever Diggory Venn tries to remedy a bad situation, he makes matters worse. With excellent motives, Venn prevents Wildeve from visiting Eustacia at night. Goaded into visiting Eustacia by day, Wildeve helps to set up the chain of events which lead to Mrs. Yeobright's death, a catastrophe unforeseen by Venn. A similar irony runs through "The Blue Hotel." The student reading "The Blue Hotel" should notice what men *do*. The motives of men have little effect on fate. Recording what men *do* is in itself a partial definition of naturalism. As a naturalistic writer, Crane has commanded attention.

2. *The background.* Some matters should be cleared up at the outset. This story is laid in a Western state, Nebraska, probably in the last decade of the nineteenth century. This fact must be understood before the reader can explain why the Swede is a frightened man at the beginning of the story. Why is the Swede afraid of card games? Why does he laugh repeatedly? Is it a laugh of nervous bravado? What frightens the Swede at the opening of section III? Why does Scully show the Swede the picture of his little girl and speak of churches and electric cars? How does the Easterner explain the Swede's actions?

3. *The five men.* Often, in this story, the reader feels that the Swede is willfully plotting his own downfall, willfully driving himself toward the end he fears the most. But the Swede is not alone. Others besides himself have helped to weave the web which entangles him. At the end of the story Crane concludes: "Every sin is the result of collaboration." The Easterner, Scully, Johnnie, the cowboy, and the gambler—these five men share the guilt of the particular sin in this story. Ironically, the gambler, who is least guilty, takes all the punishment.

The reader should trace the responsibility of these five men. By some action or by a series of actions, each one of the five confirms the fate of the Swede. Ironically, the men who think that they are helping the Swede the most are the men who are most guilty.

a. The Easterner, who is heavily responsible, is a quiet, intelligent man who is aware of the gathering forces from the beginning of the story. For example, after the first few blows he tries to stop the fight. What other actions or statements of his are conciliatory? But what is his share in the "sin"?

b. Scully also is heavily responsible from the moment the travellers leave the train. Much of the change in the Swede from the time in section II, where he cries, "I don't want to fight!" to his roar in section V, where he yells, "Yes, fight!" is due to Scully.

c. Johnnie is responsible through simple overt acts. What two acts of Johnnie influence the Swede's fate?

d. The cowboy is fairly minor. But his actions during the card games and the fight contribute also to the "sin."

e. The gambler, like Johnnie, commits an overt act but bears the least personal responsibility. The gambler "isn't even a noun," says Crane. "He is kind of an adverb." In the sentence, "A man is killed suddenly," the gambler plays the part of the "suddenly." The student should write a second sentence in which the gambler functions as a noun, and observe the difference in meaning.

4. *The Swede.* There remains the part played by the Swede himself, who walks into a saloon and straight into the conflict he had feared. The student should trace the change in the Swede from "the badly frightened man" who first enters the hotel to the man fighting in the snow. During the fight, the cowboy, Scully, and the Easterner burst into a spontaneous cheer when Johnnie sends the Swede sprawling. In the beginning of the story these men had regarded the Swede with indifference. Why do they now champion Johnnie? How far is the Swede responsible for this change?

There are four card games in the story. Study these carefully. Why was the farmer angry with Johnnie? Who are board-whackers? How far is the Swede responsible in the fourth card game?

The incident in the saloon is explained less by the character of the gambler than it is by the appearance, action, and personality of the Swede. What is the matter with the Swede's appearance? What is the bartender furtively studying? The Swede is "flown with insolence and wine," flushed with victory. How had he got into this state? Do the four men at the table realize his state? The answer to this question lies partly in the closing paragraphs of section VII. What mood had the Swede aroused in Scully and the cowboy at that point? What mood is the Swede arousing in the gambler? Is the Swede guilty of what the Greeks called *hybris*, the sin of "insolence toward the Gods"?

5. *The irony.* Some of the irony in this story has already been noted. But Crane's mocking tone hardly wavers throughout the story. The mockery is all-inclusive in the scene in the saloon, from the description of the Swede, "smiling fraternally," to the "moral" gambler and the "sulky" bartender. Even the apex of the action is treated with irony as the gambler's blade shoots forward, and the barkeeper goes "dinning through the storm for help and, moreover, companionship." The irony reaches its height at the end of section VIII, where Crane focuses our attention on the "dreadful legend" of the cash register: "This registers the amount of your purchase." Whose eyes are fixed on this sign? What is the symbolic interpretation? How does the "legend" of the cash register state the theme of the story?

The student should find other examples of irony. There is ironic humor, for example, in the repeated motif of the cards. During the fight in the hotel the cards had been scattered on the floor, "where the boots of the men trampled the fat and painted kings and queens as they gazed with their silly eyes at the war that was raging above them." The scattered cards are referred to twice more. What is Crane's purpose here?

DRY SEPTEMBER

BY WILLIAM FAULKNER

WILLIAM FAULKNER (1897–   ) has lived most of his life in Mississippi, where he was born. He served in the Canadian Air Force in the First World War. Since 1931 he has been one of the most prominent writers of fiction in America. His volumes of short stories include the following: *Idyll in the Desert* (1931), *These Thirteen* (1931), *Miss Zilphia Gant* (1932), *Doctor Martino and Other Stories* (1934), *Go Down Moses* (1942), *Knight's Gambit* (1949), and *Collected Stories of William Faulkner* (1950). He has also written a cycle of novels about a mythical locality in Mississippi. Among his best known novels are *The Sound and the Fury* (1929), *As I Lay Dying* (1930), *Light in August* (1932), *The Hamlet* (1940), *Requiem for a Nun* (1950), and *A Fable* (1954), which won the Pulitzer Prize. In 1950 he received the Nobel Prize for Literature.

Through the bloody September twilight, aftermath of sixty-two rainless days, it had gone like a fire in dry grass—the rumor, the story, whatever it was. Something about Miss Minnie Cooper and a Negro. Attacked, insulted, frightened: none of them, gathered in the barber shop on that Saturday evening where the ceiling fan stirred, without freshening it, the vitiated air, sending back upon them, in recurrent surges of stale pomade and lotion, their own stale breath and odors, knew exactly what had happened.

"Except it wasn't Will Mayes," a barber said. He was a man of middle age; a thin, sand-colored man with a mild face, who was shaving a client.

"I know Will Mayes. He's a good nigger. And I know Miss Minnie Cooper, too."

"What do you know about her?" a second barber said.

"Who is she?" the client said. "A young girl?"

"No," the barber said. "She's about forty, I reckon. She aint married. That's why I dont believe—"

"Believe, hell!" a hulking youth in a sweat-stained silk shirt said. "Wont you take a white woman's word before a nigger's?"

"I dont believe Will Mayes did it," the barber said. "I know Will Mayes."

"Maybe you know who did it, then. Maybe you already got him out of town, you damn niggerlover."

"I dont believe anybody did anything. I dont believe anything happened. I leave it to you fellows if them ladies that get old without getting married dont have notions that a man cant—"

"Then you are a hell of a white man," the client said. He moved under the cloth. The youth had sprung to his feet.

"You dont?" he said. "Do you accuse a white woman of lying?"

The barber held the razor poised above the half-risen client. He did not look around.

"It's this durn weather," another said. "It's enough to make a man do anything. Even to her."

Nobody laughed. The barber said in his mild, stubborn tone: "I aint accusing nobody of nothing. I just know and you fellows know how a woman that never—"

"You damn niggerlover!" the youth said.

"Shut up, Butch," another said. "We'll get the facts in plenty of time to act."

"Who is? Who's getting them?" the youth said. "Facts, hell! I—"

"You're a fine white man," the client said. "Aint you?" In his frothy beard he looked like a desert rat in the moving pictures. "You tell them, Jack," he said to the youth. "If there aint any white men in this town, you can count on me, even if I aint only a drummer and a stranger."

"That's right, boys," the barber said. "Find out the truth first. I know Will Mayes."

"Well, by God!" the youth shouted. "To think that a white man in this town—"

"Shut up, Butch," the second speaker said. "We got plenty of time."

The client sat up. He looked at the speaker. "Do you claim that anything excuses a nigger attacking a white woman? Do you mean to tell me you are a white man and you'll stand for it? You better go back North where you came from. The South dont want your kind here."

"North what?" the second said. "I was born and raised in this town."

"Well, by God!" the youth said. He looked about with a strained, baffled gaze, as if he was trying to remember what it was he wanted to say or to do. He drew his sleeve across his sweating face. "Damn if I'm going to let a white woman—"

"You tell them, Jack," the drummer said. "By God, if they—"

The screen door crashed open. A man stood in the floor, his feet apart and his heavy-set body poised easily. His white shirt was open at the throat; he wore a felt hat. His hot, bold glance swept the group. His name was McLendon. He had commanded troops at the front in France and had been decorated for valor.

"Well," he said, "are you going to sit there and let a black son rape a white woman on the streets of Jefferson?"

Butch sprang up again. The silk of his shirt clung flat to his heavy shoulders. At each armpit was a dark halfmoon. "That's what I been telling them! That's what I—"

"Did it really happen?" a third said. "This aint the first man scare she ever had, like Hawkshaw says. Wasn't there something about a man on the kitchen roof, watching her undress, about a year ago?"

"What?" the client said. "What's that?" The barber had been slowly forcing him back into the chair; he arrested himself reclining, his head lifted, the barber still pressing him down.

McLendon whirled on the third speaker. "Happen? What the hell difference does it make? Are you going to let the black sons get away with it until one really does it?"

"That's what I'm telling them!" Butch shouted. He cursed, long and steady, pointless.

"Here, here," a fourth said. "Not so loud. Dont talk so loud."

"Sure," McLendon said; "no talking necessary at all. I've done my talking. Who's with me?" He poised on the balls of his feet, roving his gaze.

The barber held the drummer's face down, the razor poised. "Find out the facts first, boys. I know Willy Mayes. It wasn't him. Let's get the sheriff and do this thing right."

McLendon whirled upon him his furious, rigid face. The barber did not look away. They looked like men of different races. The other barbers had ceased also above their prone clients. "You mean to tell me," McLendon said, "that you'd take a nigger's word before a white woman's? Why, you damn niggerloving—"

The third speaker rose and grasped McLendon's arm; he too had been a soldier. "Now, now. Let's figure this thing out. Who knows anything about what really happened?"

"Figure out hell!" McLendon jerked his arm free. "All that're with me get up from there. The ones that aint—" He roved his gaze, dragging his sleeve across his face.

Three men rose. The drummer in the chair sat up. "Here," he said, jerking at the cloth about his neck; "get this rag off me. I'm with him. I dont live here, but by God, if our mothers and wives and sisters—" He smeared the cloth over his face and flung it to the floor. McLendon stood in the floor and cursed the others. Another rose and moved toward him. The remainder sat uncomfortable, not looking at one another, then one by one they rose and joined him.

The barber picked the cloth from the floor. He began to fold it neatly. "Boys, dont do that. Will Mayes never done it. I know."

"Come on," McLendon said. He whirled. From his hip pocket protruded the butt of a heavy automatic pistol. They went out. The screen door crashed behind them reverberant in the dead air.

The barber wiped the razor carefully and swiftly, and put it away, and ran to the rear, and took his hat from the wall. "I'll be back as soon as I can," he said to the other barbers. "I cant let—" He went out, running. The two other barbers followed him to the door and caught it on the rebound, leaning out and looking up the street after him. The air was flat and dead. It had a metallic taste at the base of the tongue.

"What can he do?" the first said. The second one was saying "Jees Christ, Jees Christ" under his breath. "I'd just as lief be Will Mayes as Hawk, if he gets McLendon riled."

"Jees Christ, Jees Christ," the second whispered.

"You reckon he really done it to her?" the first said.

II

She was thirty-eight or thirty-nine. She lived in a small frame house with her invalid mother and a thin, sallow, unflagging aunt, where each morning between ten and eleven she would appear on the porch in a lace-trimmed boudoir cap, to sit swinging in the porch swing until noon. After dinner she lay down for a while, until the afternoon began to cool. Then, in one of the three or four new voile dresses which she had each summer, she would go downtown to spend the afternoon in the stores with the other ladies, where they would handle the goods and haggle over the prices in cold, immediate voices, without any intention of buying.

She was of comfortable people—not the best in Jefferson, but good people enough—and she was still on the slender side of ordinary looking, with a bright, faintly haggard manner and dress. When she was young she had had a slender, nervous body and a sort of hard vivacity which had enabled her for a time to ride upon the crest of the town's social life as exemplified by the high school party and church social period of her contemporaries while still children enough to be unclassconscious.

She was the last to realize that she was losing ground; that those among whom she had been a little brighter and louder flame than any other were beginning to learn the pleasure of snobbery—male—and retaliation—female. That was when her face began to wear that bright, haggard look. She still carried it to parties on shadowy porticoes and summer lawns, like a mask or a flag, with that bafflement of furious repudiation of truth in her eyes. One evening at a party she heard a boy and two girls, all schoolmates, talking. She never accepted another invitation.

She watched the girls with whom she had grown up as they married and got homes and children, but no man ever called on her steadily until the children of the other girls had been calling her "aunty" for several years, the while their mothers told them in bright voices about how popular Aunt Minnie had been as a girl. Then the town began to see her driving on Sunday afternoons with the cashier in the bank. He was a widower of about forty—a high-colored man, smelling always faintly of the barber shop or of whisky. He owned the first automobile in town, a red runabout; Minnie had the first motoring bonnet and veil the town ever saw. Then the town began to say: "Poor Minnie." "But she is old enough to take care of herself," others said. That was when she began to ask her old schoolmates that their children call her "cousin" instead of "aunty."

It was twelve years now since she had been relegated into adultery by public opinion, and eight years since the cashier had gone to a Memphis bank, returning for one day each Christmas, which he spent at an annual bachelors' party at a hunting club on the river. From behind their curtains the neighbors would see the party pass, and during the over-the-way Christmas day visiting they would tell her about him, about how well he looked, and how they heard that he was prospering in the city, watching with bright, secret eyes her haggard, bright face. Usually by that hour there would be the scent of whisky on her breath. It was supplied her by a youth, a clerk at the soda fountain: "Sure; I buy it for the old gal. I reckon she's entitled to a little fun."

Her mother kept to her room altogether now; the gaunt aunt ran the house. Against that background Minnie's bright dresses, her idle and empty days, had a quality of furious unreality. She went out in the evenings only with women now, neighbors, to the moving pictures. Each afternoon she dressed in one of the new dresses and went downtown alone, where her young "cousins" were already strolling in the late afternoons with their delicate, silken heads and thin, awkward arms and conscious hips, clinging to one another or shrieking and giggling with paired boys in the soda fountain when she passed and went on along the serried store fronts, in the doors of which the sitting and lounging men did not even follow her with their eyes any more.

III

The barber went swiftly up the street where the sparse lights, insect-swirled, glared in rigid and violent suspension in the lifeless air. The day had died in a pall of dust; above the darkened square, shrouded by the spent dust, the sky was as clear as the inside of a brass bell. Below the east was a rumor of the twice-waxed moon.

When he overtook them McLendon and three others were getting into a car parked in an alley. McLendon stooped his thick head, peering out beneath the top. "Changed your mind, did you?" he said. "Damn good thing; by God, tomorrow when this town hears about how you talked tonight—"

"Now, now," the other ex-soldier said. "Hawkshaw's all right. Come on, Hawk; jump in."

"Will Mayes never done it, boys," the barber said. "If anybody done it. Why, you all know well as I do there aint any town where they got better niggers than us. And you know how a lady will kind of think things about men when there aint any reason to, and Miss Minnie anyway—"

"Sure, sure," the soldier said. "We're just going to talk to him a little; that's all."

"Talk hell!" Butch said. "When we're through with the—"

"Shut up, for God's sake!" the soldier said. "Do you want everybody in town—"

"Tell them, by God!" McLendon said. "Tell every one of the sons that'll let a white woman—"

"Let's go; let's go: here's the other car." The second car slid squealing out of a cloud of dust at the alley mouth. McLendon started his car and took the lead. Dust lay like fog in the street. The street lights hung nimbused as in water. They drove on out of town.

A rutted lane turned at right angles. Dust hung above it too, and above all the land. The dark bulk of the ice plant, where the Negro Mayes was night watchman, rose against the sky. "Better stop here, hadn't we?" the soldier said. McLendon did not reply. He hurled the car up and slammed to a stop, the headlights glaring on the blank wall.

"Listen here, boys," the barber said; "if he's here, dont that prove he never done it? Dont it? If it was him, he would run. Dont you see he would?" The second car came up and stopped. McLendon got down; Butch sprang down beside him. "Listen, boys," the barber said.

"Cut the lights off!" McLendon said. The breathless dark rushed down. There was no sound in it save their lungs as they sought air in the parched dust in which for two months they had lived; then the diminishing crunch of McLendon's and Butch's feet, and a moment later McLendon's voice:

"Will! . . . Will!"

Below the east the wan hemorrhage of the moon increased. It heaved above the ridge, silvering the air, the dust, so that they seemed to breathe, live, in a bowl of molten lead. There was no sound of nightbird nor insect, no sound save their breathing and a faint ticking of contracting metal about the cars. Where their bodies touched one another they seemed to sweat dryly, for no more moisture came. "Christ!" a voice said; "let's get out of here."

But they didn't move until vague noises began to grow out of the darkness ahead; then they got out and waited tensely in the breathless dark. There was another sound: a blow, a hissing expulsion of breath and McLendon cursing in undertone. They stood a moment longer, then they ran forward. They ran in a stumbling clump, as though they were fleeing something. "Kill him, kill the son," a voice whispered. McLendon flung them back.

"Not here," he said. "Get him into the car." "Kill him, kill the black son!" the voice murmured. They dragged the Negro to the car. The barber had waited beside the car. He could feel himself sweating and he knew he was going to be sick at the stomach.

"What is it, captains?" the Negro said. "I aint done nothing. 'Fore God, Mr. John." Someone produced handcuffs. They worked busily about the Negro as though he were a post, quiet, intent, getting in one another's way. He submitted to the handcuffs, looking swiftly and constantly from dim face to dim face. "Who's here, captains?" he said, leaning to peer into the faces until they could feel his breath and smell his sweaty reek. He spoke a name or two. "What you all say I done, Mr. John?"

McLendon jerked the car door open. "Get in!" he said.

The Negro did not move. "What you all going to do with me, Mr. John? I aint done nothing. White folks, captains, I aint done nothing: I swear 'fore God." He called another name.

"Get in!" McLendon said. He struck the Negro. The others expelled their breath in a dry hissing and struck him with random blows and he whirled and cursed them, and swept his manacled hands across their faces and slashed the barber upon the mouth, and the barber struck him also. "Get him in there," McLendon said. They pushed at him. He ceased struggling and got in and sat quietly as the others took their places. He sat between the barber and the soldier, drawing his limbs in so as not to touch them, his eyes going swiftly and constantly from face to face. Butch clung to the running board. The car moved on. The barber nursed his mouth with his handkerchief.

"What's the matter, Hawk?" the soldier said.

"Nothing," the barber said. They regained the highroad and turned away from town. The second car dropped back out of the dust. They went on, gaining speed; the final fringe of houses dropped behind.

"Goddam, he stinks!" the soldier said.

"We'll fix that," the drummer in front beside McLendon said. On the running board Butch cursed into the hot rush of air. The barber leaned suddenly forward and touched McLendon's arm.

"Let me out, John," he said.

"Jump out, niggerlover," McLendon said without turning his head. He drove swiftly. Behind them the sourceless lights of the second car glared in the dust. Presently McLendon turned into a narrow road. It was rutted with disuse. It led back to an abandoned brick kiln—a series of reddish mounds and weed- and vine-choked vats without bottom. It had been used for pasture once, until one day the owner missed one of his mules. Although he prodded carefully in the vats with a long pole, he could not even find the bottom of them.

"John," the barber said.

"Jump out, then," McLendon said, hurling the car along the ruts. Beside the barber the Negro spoke:

"Mr. Henry."

The barber sat forward. The narrow tunnel of the road rushed up and past. Their motion was like an extinct furnace blast: cooler, but utterly dead. The car bounded from rut to rut.

"Mr. Henry," the Negro said.

The barber began to tug furiously at the door. "Look out, there!" the soldier said, but the barber had already kicked the door open and swung onto the running board. The soldier leaned across the Negro and grasped at him, but he had already jumped. The car went on without checking speed.

The impetus hurled him crashing through dust-sheathed weeds, into the ditch. Dust puffed about him, and in a thin, vicious crackling of sapless stems he lay choking and retching until the second car passed and died away. Then he rose and limped on until he reached the highroad and turned toward town, brushing at his clothes with his hands. The moon was higher, riding high and clear of the dust at last, and after a while the town began to glare beneath the dust. He went on, limping. Presently he heard cars and the glow of them grew in the dust behind him and he left the road and crouched again in the weeds until they passed. McLendon's car came last now. There were four people in it and Butch was not on the running board.

They went on; the dust swallowed them; the glare and the sound died away. The dust of them hung for a while, but soon the eternal dust absorbed it again. The barber climbed back onto the road and limped on toward town.

IV

As she dressed for supper on that Saturday evening, her own flesh felt like fever. Her hands trembled among the hooks and eyes, and her eyes had a feverish look, and her hair swirled crisp and crackling under the comb. While she was still dressing the friends called for her and sat while she donned her sheerest underthings and stockings and a new voile dress.

"Do you feel strong enough to go out?" they said, their eyes bright too, with a dark glitter. "When you have had time to get over the shock, you must tell us what happened. What he said and did; everything."

In the leafed darkness, as they walked toward the square, she began to breathe deeply, something like a swimmer preparing to dive, until she ceased trembling, the four of them walking slowly because of the terrible heat and out of solicitude for her. But as they neared the square she began to tremble again, walking with her head up, her hands clenched at her sides, their voices about her murmurous, also with that feverish, glittering quality of their eyes.

They entered the square, she in the center of the group, fragile in her fresh dress. She was trembling worse. She walked slower and slower, as children eat ice cream, her head up and her eyes bright in the haggard banner of her face, passing the hotel and the coatless drummers in chairs along the curb looking around at her: "That's the one: see? The one in pink in the middle." "Is that her? What did they do with nigger? Did they—?" "Sure. He's all right." "All right, is he?" "Sure. He went on a little trip." Then the drug store, where even the young men lounging in the doorway tipped their hats and followed with their eyes the motion of her hips and legs when she passed.

They went on, passing the lifted hats of the gentlemen, the suddenly ceased voices, deferent, protective. "Do you see?" the friends said. Their voices sounded like long, hovering sighs of hissing exultation. "There's not a Negro on the square. Not one."

They reached the picture show. It was like a miniature fairyland with its lighted lobby and colored lithographs of life caught in its terrible and beautiful mutations. Her lips began to tingle. In the dark, when the picture began, it would be all right; she could hold back the laughing so it would not waste away so fast and so soon. So she hurried on before the turning faces, the undertones of low astonishment, and they took their accustomed places where she could see the aisle against the silver glare and the young men and girls coming in two and two against it.

The lights flicked away; the screen glowed silver, and soon life began to unfold, beautiful and passionate and sad, while still the young men and girls entered, scented and sibilant in the half dark, their paired backs in silhouette delicate and sleek, their slim, quick bodies awkward, divinely young, while beyond them the silver dream accumulated, inevitably on and on. She began to laugh. In trying to suppress it, it made more noise than ever; heads began to turn. Still laughing, her friends raised her and led her out, and she stood at the curb, laughing on a high, sustained note, until the taxi came up and they helped her in.

They removed the pink voile and the sheer underthings and the stockings, and put her to bed, and cracked ice for her temples, and sent for the doctor. He was hard to locate, so they ministered to her with hushed ejaculations, renewing the ice and fanning her. While the ice was fresh and cold she stopped laughing and lay still for a time, moaning only a little. But soon the laughing welled again and her voice rose screaming.

"Shhhhhhhhhhh! Shhhhhhhhhhhhhh!" they said, freshening the ice-pack, smoothing her hair, examining it for gray; "poor girl!" Then to one another: "Do you suppose anything really happened?" their eyes darkly aglitter, secret and passionate. "Shhhhhhhhhh! Poor girl! Poor Minnie!"

V

It was midnight when McLendon drove up to his neat new house. It was trim and fresh as a birdcage and almost as small, with its clean, green-and-white paint. He locked the car and mounted the porch and entered. His wife rose from a chair beside the reading lamp. McLendon stopped in the floor and stared at her until she looked down.

"Look at that clock," he said, lifting his arm, pointing. She stood before him, her face lowered, a magazine in her hands. Her face was pale, strained, and weary-looking. "Haven't I told you about sitting up like this, waiting to see when I come in?"

"John," she said. She laid the magazine down. Poised on the balls of his feet, he glared at her with his hot eyes, his sweating face.

"Didn't I tell you?" He went toward her. She looked up then. He caught her shoulder. She stood passive, looking at him.

"Don't, John. I couldn't sleep . . . The heat; something. Please, John. You're hurting me."

"Didn't I tell you?" He released her and half struck, half flung her across the chair, and she lay there and watched him quietly as he left the room.

He went on through the house, ripping off his shirt, and on the dark, screened porch at the rear he stood and mopped his head and shoulders with the shirt and flung it away. He took the pistol from his hip and laid it on the table beside the bed, and sat on the bed and removed his shoes, and rose and slipped his trousers off. He was sweating again already, and he stooped and hunted furiously for the shirt. At last he found it and wiped his body again, and, with his body pressed against the dusty screen, he stood panting. There was no movement, no sound, not even an insect. The dark world seemed to lie stricken beneath the cold moon and the lidless stars.

COMMENT AND QUESTION

1. The title has both a literal and a symbolic meaning. Show how the title describes the two causes of the main event in the story.

2. Do the men in the barbershop seem on the defensive? If so, why should they be?

3. How does section II clinch the arguments of the barber?

4. Notice the closing passages of sections I and IV. What insight do they give into the psychology of the townspeople?

5. "Dry September" is notable for its restraint. In a story of violence, restraint will increase the tension. Study the struggle on p. 182. Study the scene in the car where Will Mayes says only, "Mr. Henry." Find other incidents where much is left unsaid.

6. Can you give a psychological explanation of the following?

    a. The barber's striking Will Mayes.

    b. Miss Minnie's hysteria.

    c. McClendon's striking his wife.

7. Where is the irony in McClendon's decoration for valor? In Miss Minnie's attending the movie with her "girl friends"?

8. Notice the opening paragraph, which both sets the tone and establishes the plot. How does this paragraph contain explicitly or implicitly the main elements of the story? What words suggest the violence to come?

Study the effect gained by the order of "attacked, insulted, frightened." Reverse the order to "frightened, insulted, attacked," and observe the difference in meaning.

THE LAST OF THE BELLES

BY F. SCOTT FITZGERALD

F. SCOTT FITZGERALD (1896–1940) was born
in Minnesota. He studied at Princeton and
served briefly in the army in the First World
War. His work reflects the climate of the jazz
age in America and of the expatriates of the
same age in Europe. He lived for a short time
in Hollywood and wrote for the motion pictures. His best novels are *The Great Gatsby*
(1925), *Tender Is the Night* (1934, revised
author's version 1951), and the unfinished *The
Last Tycoon* (1941). His short stories appear
in the following collections: *Tales of the Jazz
Age* (1922), *All the Sad Young Men* (1926),
Taps at Reveille (1935), and *The Stories of
F. Scott Fitzgerald* (1951) edited with an introduction by Malcolm Cowley.

AFTER Atlanta's elaborate and theatrical rendition of Southern charm,
we all underestimated Tarleton. It was a little hotter than anywhere we'd
been—a dozen rookies collapsed the first day in that Georgia sun—and
when you saw herds of cows drifting through the business streets, hi-yaed
by colored drovers, a trance stole down over you out of the hot light: you
wanted to move a hand or foot to be sure you were alive.

So I stayed out at camp and let Lieutenant Warren tell me about the
girls. This was fifteen years ago, and I've forgotten how I felt, except that
the days went along, one after another, better than they do now, and I
was empty-hearted, because up North she whose legend I had loved for
three years was getting married. I saw the clippings and newspaper photo-

graphs. It was "a romantic wartime wedding," all very rich and sad. I felt vividly the dark radiance of the sky under which it took place and, as a young snob, was more envious than sorry.

A day came when I went into Tarleton for a haircut and ran into a nice fellow named Bill Knowles, who was in my time at Harvard. He'd been in the National Guard division that preceded us in camp; at the last moment he had transferred to aviation and had been left behind.

"I'm glad I met you, Andy," he said with undue seriousness. "I'll hand you on all my information before I start for Texas. You see, there're really only three girls here—"

I was interested; there was something mystical about there being three girls.

"—and here's one of them now."

We were in front of a drug store and he marched me in and introduced me to a lady I promptly detested.

"The other two are Ailie Calhoun and Sally Carrol Happer."

I guessed from the way he pronounced her name that he was interested in Ailie Calhoun. It was on his mind what she would be doing while he was gone; he wanted her to have a quiet, uninteresting time.

At my age I don't even hesitate to confess that entirely unchivalrous images of Ailie Calhoun—that lovely name—rushed into my mind. At twenty-three there is no such thing as a preëmpted beauty; though, had Bill asked me, I would doubtless have sworn in all sincerity to care for her like a sister. He didn't; he was just fretting out loud at having to go. Three days later he telephoned me that he was leaving next morning and he'd take me to her house that night.

We met at the hotel and walked uptown through the flowery, hot twilight. The four white pillars of the Calhoun house faced the street, and behind them the veranda was dark as a cave with hanging, weaving, climbing vines.

When we came up the walk a girl in a white dress tumbled out of the front door, crying, "I'm so sorry I'm late!" and seeing us, added: "Why, I thought I heard you come ten minutes——"

She broke off as a chair creaked and another man, an aviator from Camp Harry Lee, emerged from the obscurity of the veranda.

"Why, Canby!" she cried. "How are you?"

He and Bill Knowles waited with the tenseness of open litigants.

"Canby, I want to whisper to you, honey," she said, after just a second. "You'll excuse us, Bill."

They went aside. Presently Lieutenant Canby, immensely displeased, said in a grim voice, "Then we'll make it Thursday, but that means sure." Scarcely nodding to us, he went down the walk, the spurs with which he presumably urged on his aeroplane gleaming in the lamplight.

"Come in—I don't just know your name——"

There she was—the Southern type in all its purity. I would have recognized Ailie Calhoun if I'd never heard Ruth Draper or read Marse Chan. She had the adroitness sugar-coated with sweet, voluble simplicity, the suggested background of devoted fathers, brothers and admirers stretching back into the South's heroic age, the unfailing coolness acquired in the endless struggle with the heat. There were notes in her voice that ordered slaves around, that withered up Yankee captains, and then soft, wheedling notes that mingled in unfamiliar loveliness with the night.

I could scarcely see her in the darkness, but when I rose to go—it was plain that I was not to linger—she stood in the orange light from the doorway. She was small and very blond; there was too much fever-colored rouge on her face, accentuated by a nose dabbed clownish white, but she shone through that like a star.

"After Bill goes I'll be sitting here all alone night after night. Maybe you'll take me to the country-club dances." The pathetic prophecy brought a laugh from Bill. "Wait a minute," Ailie murmured. "Your guns are all crooked."

She straightened my collar pin, looking up at me for a second with something more than curiosity. It was a seeking look, as if she asked, "Could it be you?" Like Lieutenant Canby, I marched off unwillingly into the suddenly insufficient night.

Two weeks later I sat with her on the same veranda, or rather she half lay in my arms and yet scarcely touched me—how she managed that I don't remember. I was trying unsuccessfully to kiss her, and had been trying for the best part of an hour. We had a sort of joke about my not being sincere. My theory was that if she'd let me kiss her I'd fall in love with her. Her argument was that I was obviously insincere.

In a lull between two of these struggles she told me about her brother who had died in his senior year at Yale. She showed me his picture—it was a handsome, earnest face with a Leyendecker forelock—and told me that when she met someone who measured up to him she'd marry. I found this family idealism discouraging; even my brash confidence couldn't compete with the dead.

The evening and other evenings passed like that, and ended with my going back to camp with the remembered smell of magnolia flowers and a mood of vague dissatisfaction. I never kissed her. We went to the vaudeville and to the country club on Saturday nights, where she seldom took ten consecutive steps with one man, and she took me to barbecues and rowdy watermelon parties, and never thought it was worth while to change what I felt for her into love. I see now that it wouldn't have been hard, but she was a wise nineteen and she must have seen that we were emotionally incompatible. So I became her confidant instead.

We talked about Bill Knowles. She was considering Bill; for, though she wouldn't admit it, a winter at school in New York and a prom at Yale had turned her eyes North. She said she didn't think she'd marry a Southern man. And by degrees I saw that she was consciously and voluntarily different from these other girls who sang nigger songs and shot craps in the country-club bar. That's why Bill and I and others were drawn to her. We recognized her.

June and July, while the rumors reached us faintly, ineffectually, of battle and terror overseas, Ailie's eyes roved here and there about the country-club floor, seeking for something among the tall young officers. She attached several, choosing them with unfailing perspicacity—save in the case of Lieutenant Canby, whom she claimed to despise, but, nevertheless, gave dates to "because he was so sincere"—and we apportioned her evenings among us all summer.

One day she broke all her dates—Bill Knowles had leave and was coming. We talked of the event with scientific impersonality—would he move her to a decision? Lieutenant Canby, on the contrary, wasn't impersonal at all; made a nuisance of himself. He told her that if she married Knowles he was going to climb up six thousand feet in his aeroplane, shut off the motor and let go. He frightened her—I had to yield him my last date before Bill came.

On Saturday night she and Bill Knowles came to the country club. They were very handsome together and once more I felt envious and sad. As they danced out on the floor the three-piece orchestra was playing *After You've Gone*, in a poignant incomplete way that I can hear yet, as if each bar were trickling off a precious minute of that time. I knew then that I had grown to love Tarleton, and I glanced about half in panic to see if some face wouldn't come in for me out of that warm, singing, outer darkness that yielded up couple after couple in organdie and olive drab. It was a time of youth and war, and there was never so much love around.

When I danced with Ailie she suddenly suggested that we go outside to a car. She wanted to know why didn't people cut in on her tonight? Did they think she was already married?

"Are you going to be?"

"I don't know, Andy. Sometimes, when he treats me as if I were sacred, it thrills me." Her voice was hushed and far away. "And then——"

She laughed. Her body, so frail and tender, was touching mine, her face was turned up to me, and there, suddenly, with Bill Knowles ten yards off, I could have kissed her at last. Our lips just touched experimentally; then an aviation officer turned a corner of the veranda near us, peered into our darkness and hesitated.

"Ailie."

"Yes."

"You heard about this afternoon?"

"What?" She leaned forward, tenseness already in her voice.

"Horace Canby crashed. He was instantly killed."

She got up slowly and stepped out of the car.

"You mean he was killed?" she said.

"Yes. They don't know what the trouble was. His motor——"

"Oh-h-h!" Her rasping whisper came through the hands suddenly covering her face. We watched her helplessly as she put her head on the side of the car, gagging dry tears. After a minute I went for Bill, who was standing in the stag line, searching anxiously about for her, and told him she wanted to go home.

I sat on the steps outside. I had disliked Canby, but his terrible, pointless death was more real to me then than the day's toll of thousands in France. In a few minutes Ailie and Bill came out. Ailie was whimpering a little, but when she saw me her eyes flexed and she came over swiftly.

"Andy"—she spoke in a quick, low voice—"of course you must never tell anybody what I told you about Canby yesterday. What he said, I mean."

"Of course not."

She looked at me a second longer as if to be quite sure. Finally she was sure. Then she sighed in such a quaint little way that I could hardly believe my ears, and her brow went up in what can only be described as mock despair.

"An-dy!"

I looked uncomfortably at the ground, aware that she was calling my attention to her involuntarily disastrous effect on men.

"Good night, Andy!" called Bill as they got into a taxi.

"Good night," I said, and almost added: "You poor fool."

II

Of course I should have made one of those fine moral decisions that people make in books, and despised her. On the contrary, I don't doubt that she could still have had me by raising her hand.

A few days later she made it all right by saying wistfully, "I know you think it was terrible of me to think of myself at a time like that, but it was such a shocking coincidence."

At twenty-three I was entirely unconvinced about anything, except that some people were strong and attractive and could do what they wanted, and others were caught and disgraced. I hoped I was of the former. I was sure Ailie was.

I had to revise other ideas about her. In the course of a long discussion with some girl about kissing—in those days people still talked about kissing more than they kissed—I mentioned the fact that Ailie had only kissed two or three men, and only when she thought she was in love. To my considerable disconcertion the girl figuratively just lay on the floor and howled.

"But it's true," I assured her, suddenly knowing it wasn't. "She told me herself."

"Ailie Calhoun! Oh, my heavens! Why, last year at the Tech spring house party——"

This was in September. We were going overseas any week now, and to bring us up to full strength a last batch of officers from the fourth training camp arrived. The fourth camp wasn't like the first three—the candidates were from the ranks; even from the drafted divisions. They had queer names without vowels in them, and save for a few young militiamen, you couldn't take it for granted that they came out of any background at all. The addition to our company was Lieutenant Earl Schoen from New Bedford, Massachusetts; as fine a physical specimen as I have ever seen. He was six-foot-three, with black hair, high color and glossy dark-brown eyes. He wasn't very smart and he was definitely illiterate, yet he was a good officer, high-tempered and commanding, and with that becoming touch of vanity that sits well on the military. I had an idea that New Bedford was a country town, and set down his bumptious qualities to that.

We were doubled up in living quarters and he came into my hut. Inside of a week there was a cabinet photograph of some Tarleton girl nailed brutally to the shack wall.

"She's no jane or anything like that. She's a society girl; goes with all the best people here."

The following Sunday afternoon I met the lady at a semi-private swimming pool in the country. When Ailie and I arrived, there was Schoen's muscular body rippling out of a bathing suit at the far end of the pool.

"Hey, lieutenant!"

When I waved back at him he grinned and winked, jerking his head toward the girl at his side. Then, digging her in the ribs, he jerked his head at me. It was a form of introduction.

"Who's that with Kitty Preston?" Ailie asked, and when I told her she said he looked like a street-car conductor, and pretended to look for her transfer.

A moment later he crawled powerfully and gracefully down the pool and pulled himself up at our side. I introduced him to Ailie.

"How do you like my girl, lieutenant?" he demanded, "I told you she was all right, didn't I?" He jerked his head toward Ailie; this time to indicate that his girl and Ailie moved in the same circles. "How about us all having dinner together down at the hotel some night?"

I left them in a moment, amused as I saw Ailie visibly making up her mind that here, anyhow, was not the ideal. But Lieutenant Earl Schoen was not to be dismissed so lightly. He ran his eyes cheerfully and inoffensively over her cute, slight figure, and decided that she would do even better than the other. Then minutes later I saw them in the water together, Ailie swimming away with a grim little stroke she had, and Schoen wallowing riotously around her and ahead of her, sometimes pausing and staring at her, fascinated, as a boy might look at a nautical doll.

While the afternoon passed he remained at her side. Finally Ailie came over to me and whispered, with a laugh: "He's a following me around. He thinks I haven't paid my carfare."

She turned quickly. Miss Kitty Preston, her face curiously flustered, stood facing us.

"Ailie Calhoun, I didn't think it of you to go out and delib'ately try to take a man away from another girl."—An expression of distress at the impending scene flitted over Ailie's face—"I thought you considered yourself above anything like that."

Miss Preston's voice was low, but it held that tensity that can be felt farther than it can be heard, and I saw Ailie's clear lovely eyes glance about in panic. Luckily, Earl himself was ambling cheerfully and innocently toward us.

"If you care for him you certainly oughtn't to belittle yourself in front of him," said Ailie in a flash, her head high.

It was her acquaintance with the traditional way of behaving against Kitty Preston's naïve and fierce possessiveness; or if you prefer it, Ailie's "breeding" against the other's "commonness." She turned away.

"Wait a minute, kid!" cried Earl Schoen. "How about your address? Maybe I'd like to give you a ring on the phone."

She looked at him in a way that should have indicated to Kitty her entire lack of interest.

"I'm very busy at the Red Cross this month," she said, her voice as cool as her slicked-back blond hair. "Good-by."

On the way home she laughed. Her air of having been unwittingly involved in a contemptible business vanished.

"She'll never hold that young man," she said. "He wants somebody new."

"Apparently he wants Ailie Calhoun."

The idea amused her.

"He could give me his ticket punch to wear, like a fraternity pin. What fun! If mother ever saw anybody like that come in the house, she'd just lie down and die."

And to give Ailie credit, it was fully a fortnight before he did come to her house, although he rushed her until she pretended to be annoyed at the next country-club dance.

"He's the biggest tough, Andy," she whispered to me. "But he's so sincere."

She used the word "tough" without the conviction it would have carried had he been a Southern boy. She only knew it with her mind; her ear couldn't distinguish between one Yankee voice and another. And somehow

Mrs. Calhoun didn't expire at his appearance on the threshold. The supposedly ineradicable prejudices of Ailie's parents were a convenient phenomenon that disappeared at her wish. It was her friends who were astonished. Ailie, always a little above Tarleton, whose beaus had been very carefully the "nicest" men of the camp—Ailie and Lieutenant Schoen! I grew tired of assuring people that she was merely distracting herself—and indeed every week or so there was someone new—an ensign from Pensacola, an old friend from New Orleans—but always, in between times, there was Earl Schoen.

Orders arrived for an advance party of officers and sergeants to proceed to the port of embarkation and take ship to France. My name was on the list. I had been on the range for a week and when I got back to camp, Earl Schoen buttonholed me immediately.

"We're giving a little farewell party in the mess. Just you and I and Captain Craker and three girls."

Earl and I were to call for the girls. We picked up Sally Carrol Happer and Nancy Lamar, and went on to Ailie's house; to be met at the door by the butler with the announcement that she wasn't home.

"Isn't home?" Earl repeated blankly. "Where is she?"

"Didn't leave no information about that; just said she wasn't home."

"But this is a darn funny thing!" he exclaimed. He walked around the familiar dusky veranda while the butler waited at the door. Something occurred to him. "Say," he informed me—"say, I think she's sore."

I waited. He said sternly to the butler, "You tell her I've got to speak to her a minute."

"How'm I goin' tell her that when she ain't home?"

Again Earl walked musingly around the porch. Then he nodded several times and said:

"She's sore at something that happened downtown."

In a few words he sketched out the matter to me.

"Look here; you wait in the car," I said. "Maybe I can fix this." And when he reluctantly retreated: "Oliver, you tell Miss Ailie I want to see her alone."

After some argument he bore this message and in a moment returned with a reply:

"Miss Ailie say she don't want to see that other gentleman about nothing never. She say come in if you like."

She was in the library. I had expected to see a picture of cool, outraged dignity, but her face was distraught, tumultuous, despairing. Her eyes were red-rimmed, as though she had been crying slowly and painfully, for hours.

"Oh, hello, Andy," she said brokenly. "I haven't seen you for so long. Has he gone?"

"Now, Ailie——"

"Now, Ailie!" she cried. "Now, Ailie! He spoke to me, you see. He lifted his hat. He stood there ten feet from me with that horrible—that horrible woman—holding her arm and talking to her, and then when he saw me he raised his hat. Andy, I didn't know what to do. I had to go in the drug store and ask for a glass of water, and I was so afraid he'd follow in after me that I asked Mr. Rich to let me go out the back way. I never want to see him or hear of him again."

I talked. I said what one says in such cases. I said it for half an hour. I could not move her. Several times she answered by murmuring something about his not being "sincere," and for the fourth time I wondered what the word meant to her. Certainly not constancy; it was, I half suspected, some special way she wanted to be regarded.

I got up to go. And then, unbelievably, the automobile horn sounded three times impatiently outside. It was stupefying. It said as plainly as if Earl were in the room, "All right; go to the devil then! I'm not going to wait here all night."

Ailie looked at me aghast. And suddenly a peculiar look came into her face, spread, flickered, broke into a teary, hysterical smile.

"Isn't he awful?" she cried in helpless despair. "Isn't he terrible?"

"Hurry up," I said quickly. "Get your cape. This is our last night."

And I can still feel that last night vividly, the candlelight that flickered over the rough boards of the mess shack, over the frayed paper decorations left from the supply company's party, the sad mandolin down a company street that kept picking *My Indiana Home* out of the universal nostalgia of the departing summer. The three girls lost in this mysterious men's city felt something, too—a bewitched impermanence as though they were on a magic carpet that had lighted on the Southern countryside, and any moment the wind would lift it and waft it away. We toasted ourselves and the South. Then we left our napkins and empty glasses and a little of the past on the table, and hand in hand went out into the moonlight itself. Taps had been played; there was no sound but the far-away whinny of a horse, and a loud persistent snore at which we laughed, and the leathery snap of a sentry coming to port over by the guardhouse. Craker was on duty; we others got into a waiting car, motored into Tarleton and left Craker's girl.

Then Ailie and Earl, Sally and I, two and two in the wide back seat, each couple turned from the other, absorbed and whispering, drove away into the wide, flat darkness.

We drove through pine woods heavy with lichen and Spanish moss, and between the fallow cotton fields along a road white as the rim of the world. We parked under the broken shadow of a mill where there was the sound of running water and restive squawky birds and over everything a brightness that tried to filter in anywhere—into the lost nigger cabins, the automobile, the fastnesses of the heart. The South sang to us—I wonder if they remember. I remember—the cool pale faces, the somnolent amorous eyes and the voices:

"Are you comfortable?"

"Yes; are you?"

"Are you sure you are?"

"Yes."

Suddenly we knew it was late and there was nothing more. We turned home.

Our detachment started for Camp Mills next day, but I didn't go to France after all. We passed a cold month on Long Island, marched aboard a transport with steel helmets slung at our sides and then marched off again. There wasn't any more war. I had missed the war. When I came back to Tarleton I tried to get out of the Army, but I had a regular commission and it took most of the winter. But Earl Schoen was one of the first to be demobilized. He wanted to find a good job "while the picking was good." Ailie was noncommittal, but there was an understanding between them that he'd be back.

By January the camps, which for two years had dominated the little city, were already fading. There was only the persistent incinerator smell to remind one of all that activity and bustle. What life remained centred bitterly about divisional headquarters building with the disgruntled regular officers who had also missed the war.

And now the young men of Tarleton began drifting back from the ends of the earth—some with Canadian uniforms, some with crutches or empty sleeves. A returned battalion of the National Guard paraded through the streets with open ranks for their dead, and then stepped down out of romance forever and sold you things over the counters of local stores. Only a few uniforms mingled with the dinner coats at the country-club dance.

Just before Christmas, Bill Knowles arrived unexpectedly one day and left the next—either he gave Ailie an ultimatum or she had made up her mind at last. I saw her sometimes when she wasn't busy with returned heroes from Savannah and Augusta, but I felt like an outmoded survival— and I was. She was waiting for Earl Schoen with such a vast uncertainty that she didn't like to talk about it. Three days before I got my final discharge he came.

I first happened upon them walking down Market Street together, and I don't think I've ever been so sorry for a couple in my life; though I suppose the same situation was repeating itself in every city where there had been camps. Exteriorly Earl had about everything wrong with him that could be imagined. His hat was green, with a radical feather; his suit was slashed and braided in a grotesque fashion that national advertising and the movies have put an end to. Evidently he had been to his old barber, for his hair bloused neatly on his pink, shaved neck. It wasn't as though he had been shiny and poor, but the background of mill-town dance halls and outing clubs flamed out at you—or rather flamed out at Ailie. For she had never quite imagined the reality; in these clothes even the natural grace of that magnificent body had departed. At first he boasted of his fine job; it would get them along all right until he could "see some easy money." But from the moment he came back into her world on its own terms he must have known it was hopeless. I don't know what Ailie said or how much her grief weighed against her stupefaction. She acted quickly—three days after his arrival, Earl and I went North together on the train.

"Well, that's the end of that," he said moodily. "She's a wonderful girl, but too much of a highbrow for me. I guess she's got to marry some rich guy that'll give her a great social position. I can't see that stuck-up sort of thing." And then, later: "She said to come back and see her in a year, but I'll never go back. This aristocrat stuff is all right if you got the money for it, but——"

"But it wasn't real," he meant to finish. The provincial society in which he had moved with so much satisfaction for six months already appeared to him as affected, "dudish" and artificial.

"Say, did you see what I saw getting on the train?" he asked me after a while. "Two wonderful janes, all alone. What do you say we mosey into the next car and ask them to lunch? I'll take the one in blue." Halfway down the car he turned around suddenly. "Say, Andy," he demanded, frowning; "one thing—how do you suppose she knew I used to command a street car? I never told her that."

"Search me."

III

This narrative arrives now at one of the big gaps that stared me in the face when I began. For six years, while I finished at Harvard Law and built commercial aeroplanes and backed a pavement block that went gritty under trucks, Ailie Calhoun was scarcely more than a name on a Christmas card; something that blew a little in my mind on warm nights when I remembered the magnolia flowers. Occasionally an acquaintance of Army days would ask me, "What became of that blond girl who was so popular?" but I didn't know. I ran into Nancy Lamar at the Montmartre in New York one evening and learned that Ailie had become engaged to a man in Cincinnati, had gone North to visit his family and then broken it off. She was lovely as ever and there was always a heavy beau or two. But neither Bill Knowles nor Earl Schoen had ever come back.

And somewhere about that time I heard that Bill Knowles had married a girl he met on a boat. There you are—not much of a patch to mend six years with.

Oddly enough, a girl seen at twilight in a small Indiana station started me thinking about going South. The girl, in stiff pink organdie, threw her arms about a man who got off our train and hurried him to a waiting car, and I felt a sort of pang. It seemed to me that she was bearing him off into the lost midsummer world of my early twenties, where time had stood still and charming girls, dimly seen like the past itself, still loitered along the dusky streets. I suppose that poetry is a Northern man's dream of the South. But it was months later that I sent off a wire to Ailie, and immediately followed it to Tarleton.

It was July. The Jefferson Hotel seemed strangely shabby and stuffy—a boosters' club burst into intermittent song in the dining room that my memory had long dedicated to officers and girls. I recognized the taxi driver who took me up to Ailie's house, but his "Sure, I do, lieutenant," was unconvincing. I was only one of twenty thousand.

It was a curious three days. I suppose some of Ailie's first young lustre must have gone the way of such mortal shining, but I can't bear witness to it. She was still so physically appealing that you wanted to touch the personality that trembled on her lips. No—the change was more profound than that.

At once I saw she had a different line. The modulations of pride, the vocal hints that she knew the secrets of a brighter, finer antebellum day, were gone from her voice; there was no time for them now as it rambled on in the half-laughing, half-desperate banter of the newer South. And everything was swept into this banter in order to make it go on and leave no time for thinking—the present, the future, herself, me. We went to a rowdy party at the house of some young married people, and she was the nervous, glowing centre of it. After all, she wasn't eighteen, and she was as attractive in her role of reckless clown as she had ever been in her life.

"Have you heard anything from Earl Schoen?" I asked her the second night, on our way to the country-club dance.

"No." She was serious for a moment. "I often think of him. He was the——" She hesistated.

"Go on."

"I was going to say the man I loved most, but that wouldn't be true. I never exactly loved him, or I'd have married him any old how, wouldn't I?" She looked at me questioningly. "At least I wouldn't have treated him like that."

"It was impossible."

"Of course," she agreed uncertainly. Her mood changed; she became flippant: "How the Yankees did deceive us poor little Southern girls. Ah, me!"

When we reached the country club she melted like a chameleon into the—to me—unfamiliar crowd. There was a new generation upon the floor, with less dignity than the ones I had known, but none of them were more a part of its lazy, feverish essence than Ailie. Possibly she had perceived that in her initial longing to escape from Tarleton's provincialism she had been walking alone, following a generation which was doomed to have no successors. Just where she lost the battle, waged behind the white pillars of her veranda, I don't know. But she had guessed wrong, missed out somewhere. Her wild animation, which even now called enough men around her to rival the entourage of the youngest and freshest, was an admission of defeat.

I left her house, as I had so often left it that vanished June, in a mood of vague dissatisfaction. It was hours later, tossing about my bed in the hotel, that I realized what was the matter, what had always been the matter—I was deeply and incurably in love with her. In spite of every incompatibility, she was still, she would always be to me, the most attractive girl I had ever known. I told her so next afternoon. It was one of those hot days I knew so well, and Ailie sat beside me on a couch in the darkened library.

"Oh, no, I couldn't marry you," she said, almost frightened; "I don't love you that way at all. . . . I never did. And you don't love me. I didn't mean to tell you now, but next month I'm going to marry another man. We're not even announcing it, because I've done that twice before." Suddenly it occurred to her that I might be hurt: "Andy, you just had a silly idea, didn't you? You know I couldn't ever marry a Northern man."

"Who is he?" I demanded.

"A man from Savannah."

"Are you in love with him?"

"Of course I am." We both smiled. "Of course I am! What are you trying to make me say?"

There were no doubts, as there had been with other men. She couldn't afford to let herself have doubts. I knew this because she had long ago stopped making any pretensions with me. This very naturalness, I realized, was because she didn't consider me as a suitor. Beneath her mask of an instinctive thoroughbred she had always been on to herself, and she couldn't believe that anyone not taken in to the point of uncritical worship could really love her. That was what she called being "sincere"; she felt most security with men like Canby and Earl Schoen, who were incapable of passing judgments on the ostensibly aristocratic heart.

"All right," I said, as if she had asked my permission to marry. "Now, would you do something for me?"

"Anything."

"Ride out to camp."

"But there's nothing left there, honey."

"I don't care."

We walked downtown. The taxi driver in front of the hotel repeated her objection: "Nothing there now, cap."

"Never mind. Go there anyhow."

Twenty minutes later he stopped on a wide unfamiliar plain powdered with new cotton fields and marked with isolated clumps of pine.

"Like to drive over yonder where you see the smoke?" asked the driver. "That's the new state prison."

"No. Just drive along this road. I want to find where I used to live."

An old race course, inconspicuous in the camp's day of glory, had reared its dilapidated grandstand in the desolation. I tried in vain to orient myself.

"Go along this road past that clump of trees, and then turn right—no, turn left."

He obeyed, with professional disgust.

"You won't find a single thing, darling," said Ailie. "The contractors took it all down."

We rode slowly along the margin of the fields. It might have been here——

"All right. I want to get out," I said suddenly.

I left Ailie sitting in the car, looking very beautiful with the warm breeze stirring her long, curly bob.

It might have been here. That would make the company streets down there and the mess shack, where we dined that night, just over the way.

The taxi driver regarded me indulgently while I stumbled here and there in the knee-deep underbrush, looking for my youth in a clapboard or a strip of roofing or a rusty tomato can. I tried to sight on a vaguely familiar clump of trees, but it was growing darker now and I couldn't be quite sure they were the right trees.

"They're going to fix up the old race course," Ailie called from the car. "Tarleton's getting quite doggy in its old age."

No. Upon consideration they didn't look like the right trees. All I could be sure of was this place that had once been so full of life and effort was gone, as if it had never existed, and that in another month Ailie would be gone, and the South would be empty for me forever.

COMMENT AND QUESTION

1. Ailie Calhoun is a complex character. The reader will discover this truth when he tries to reconcile some of her less attractive qualities with the fact that Andy, who is mature and perceptive, remains hopelessly in love with her throughout the story.

   a. Does Ailie symbolize for Andy the lost midsummer world of his early twenties, "where time had stood still and charming girls, dimly seen like the past itself, still loitered along the dusky streets"? If so, this romantic conception must be reconciled with the following:

(1) Andy's semi-satiric portrait of Ailie in the paragraph in section I, beginning, "There she was—the Southern type in all its purity."

(2) The episode of Canby.

(3) Andy's final reflection upon Ailie in the paragraph in section III, beginning, "Beneath her mask of an instinctive thoroughbred. . . ."

b. This story was first published in 1929, when fiction writers were handling the subject of sex in what has come to be known as the "hard-boiled" manner. But "The Last of the Belles" is not a hard-boiled story; in fact, the portrait of Ailie is touched with sympathy rather than with scorn. The observations in this story, nevertheless, are acute.

What did Ailie want from love? Is a belle a coquette? What are the connotations of the two terms? What did Ailie mean by sincerity?

Is Ailie afraid of sex? If so, why is she attracted to Earl Schoen?

Consider the episode where Ailie meets Earl Schoen on the street. Ailie objects not so much to the woman with Earl as she does to an action of Earl's. What does this whole episode reveal about Ailie?

2. It has recently been recognized that a longing for wealth and social position motivated the life of Fitzgerald. But does not the author have a clear-sighted attitude toward snobbishness in this story?

In the story, "The Snows of Kilimanjaro," you will find (on p. 262) a reference to Fitzgerald in "poor Julian," and a reference to one of the stories of Fitzgerald, a story entitled "The Rich Boy." Do these references help in the interpretation of "The Last of the Belles"?

3. For a young man, Andy is unusual in his wisdom, his sensitivity, and his melancholy. He is superior to all the other characters. For example, is he not aware of his own snobbishness? Is his nostalgia ever completely explained?

4. "I suppose that poetry is a Northern man's dream of the South." This statement is a clue to the main theme of this story. This theme is seen in the title; in the phrase, "the South's heroic age"; in the significant sentence in section I, "We recognized her"; and most of all in the paragraph in section II, beginning "We drove through pine woods heavy with lichen. . . ."

Is the nostalgia in this story connected with this theme?

In one episode Earl Schoen displays a "photograph of some Tarleton girl nailed brutally to the shack wall." Does this episode merely indicate the social abyss where Earl Schoen dwells or is it related to a larger theme, the passing of "the South's heroic age"?

5. The defects in Fitzgerald's short stories are usually balanced by flashes of perception. Find the following statements and study them in their context for implications which give a depth of meaning to the story and to issues beyond the story.

a. ". . . and there was never so much love around."

b. ". . . then stepped down out of romance forever and sold you things over the counters of local stores."

c. ". . . looking for my youth in a clapboard or a strip of roofing or a rusty tomato can."

THE OTHER SIDE OF
THE HEDGE

BY EDWARD MORGAN FORSTER

EDWARD MORGAN FORSTER (1879–) has
written essays, novels, and short stories. He
was born in London and has lived in England
most of his life, but has travelled in Italy,
Greece, Egypt, and India. His best novel, *A
Passage to India* (1927), is a revelation of
the British and Indian character. His other
novels include *Where Angels Fear to Tread*
(1905), *The Longest Journey* (1907), *A
Room with a View* (1908), and *Howard's
End* (1910). His short stories appear in *The
Collected Tales of E. M. Forster* (1947). One
of his best known short stories, "The Machine
Stops," was a protest against the mechanical
Utopia of H. G. Wells. He has written a vol-
ume of criticism, *Aspects of the Novel* (1927).

M Y PEDOMETER told me that I was twenty-five; and, though it is a
shocking thing to stop walking, I was so tired that I sat down on a milestone to rest. People outstripped me, jeering as they did so, but I was too
apathetic to feel resentful, and even when Miss Eliza Dimbleby, the great
educationist, swept past, exhorting me to persevere, I only smiled and
raised my hat.

At first I thought I was going to be like my brother, whom I had had
to leave by the roadside a year or two round the corner. He had wasted
his breath on singing, and his strength on helping others. But I had

THE OTHER SIDE OF THE HEDGE Reprinted from *The Celestial Omnibus* by
E. M. Forster, by permission of Alfred A. Knopf, Inc. Copyright 1947 by Alfred
A. Knopf, Inc.

travelled more wisely, and now it was only the monotony of the highway that oppressed me—dust under foot and brown crackling hedges on either side, ever since I could remember.

And I had already dropped several things—indeed, the road behind was strewn with the things we all had dropped; and the white dust was settling down on them, so that already they looked no better than stones. My muscles were so weary that I could not even bear the weight of those things I still carried. I slid off the milestone into the road, and lay there prostrate, with my face to the great parched hedge, praying that I might give up.

A little puff of air revived me. It seemed to come from the hedge; and, when I opened my eyes, there was a glint of light through the tangle of boughs and dead leaves. The hedge could not be as thick as usual. In my weak, morbid state, I longed to force my way in, and see what was on the other side. No one was in sight, or I should not have dared to try. For we of the road do not admit in conversation that there is another side at all.

I yielded to the temptation, saying to myself that I would come back in a minute. The thorns scratched my face, and I had to use my arms as a shield, depending on my feet alone to push me forward. Halfway through I would have gone back, for in the passage all the things I was carrying were scraped off me, and my clothes were torn. But I was so wedged that return was impossible, and I had to wriggle blindly forward, expecting every moment that my strength would fail me, and that I should perish in the undergrowth.

Suddenly cold water closed round my head, and I seemed sinking down for ever. I had fallen out of the hedge into a deep pool. I rose to the surface at last, crying for help, and I heard someone on the opposite bank laugh and say: "Another!" And then I was twitched out and laid panting on the dry ground.

Even when the water was out of my eyes, I was still dazed, for I had never been in so large a space, nor seen such grass and sunshine. The blue sky was no longer a strip, and beneath it the earth had risen grandly into hills—clean, bare buttresses, with beech trees in their folds, and meadows and clear pools at their feet. But the hills were not high, and there was in the landscape a sense of human occupation—so that one might have called it a park or garden, if the words did not imply a certain triviality and constraint.

As soon as I got my breath, I turned to my rescuer and said:

"Where does this place lead to?"

"Nowhere, thank the Lord!" said he, and laughed. He was a man of fifty or sixty—just the kind of age we mistrust on the road—but there was no anxiety in his manner, and his voice was that of a boy of eighteen.

"But it must lead somewhere!" I cried, too much surprised at his answer to thank him for saving my life.

"He wants to know where it leads!" he shouted to some men on the hill side, and they laughed back, and waved their caps.

I noticed then that the pool into which I had fallen was really a moat which bent round to the left and to the right, and that the hedge followed it continually. The hedge was green on this side—its roots showed through the clear water, and fish swam about in them—and it was wreathed over with dog-roses and Traveller's Joy. But it was a barrier, and in a moment I lost all pleasure in the grass, the sky, the trees, the happy men and women, and realized that the place was but a prison, for all its beauty and extent.

We moved away from the boundary, and then followed a path almost parallel to it, across the meadows. I found it difficult walking, for I was always trying to out-distance my companion, and there was no advantage in doing this if the place led nowhere. I had never kept step with anyone since I left my brother.

I amused him by stopping suddenly and saying disconsolately, "This is perfectly terrible. One cannot advance: one cannot progress. Now we of the road——"

"Yes. I know."

"I was going to say, we advance continually."

"I know."

"We are always learning, expanding, developing. Why, even in my short life I have seen a great deal of advance—the Transvaal War, the Fiscal Question, Christian Science, Radium. Here for example—"

I took out my pedometer, but it still marked twenty-five, not a degree more.

"Oh, it's stopped! I meant to show you. It should have registered all the time I was walking with you. But it makes me only twenty-five."

"Many things don't work in here," he said. "One day a man brought in a Lee-Metford, and that wouldn't work."

"The laws of science are universal in their application. It must be the water in the moat that has injured the machinery. In normal conditions everything works. Science and the spirit of emulation—those are the forces that have made us what we are."

I had to break off and acknowledge the pleasant greetings of people whom we passed. Some of them were singing, some talking, some engaged in gardening, hay-making, or other rudimentary industries. They all seemed happy; and I might have been happy too, if I could have forgotten that the place led nowhere.

I was startled by a young man who came sprinting across our path, took a little fence in fine style, and went tearing over a ploughed field till he plunged into a lake, across which he began to swim. Here was true energy, and I exclaimed: "A cross-country race! Where are the others?"

"There are no others," my companion replied; and, later on, when we passed some long grass from which came the voice of a girl singing exquisitely to herself, he said again: "There are no others." I was bewildered at the waste in production, and murmured to myself, "What does it all mean?"

He said: "It means nothing but itself"—and he repeated the words slowly, as if I were a child.

"I understand," I said quietly, "but I do not agree. Every achievement is worthless unless it is a link in the chain of development. And I must not trespass on your kindness any longer. I must get back somehow to the road, and have my pedometer mended."

"First, you must see the gates," he replied, "for we have gates, though we never use them."

I yielded politely, and before long we reached the moat again, at a point where it was spanned by a bridge. Over the bridge was a big gate, as white as ivory, which was fitted into a gap in the boundary hedge. The gate opened outwards, and I exclaimed in amazement, for from it ran a road—just such a road as I had left—dusty under foot, with brown crackling hedges on either side as far as the eye could reach.

"That's my road!" I cried.

He shut the gate and said: "But not your part of the road. It is through this gate that humanity went out countless ages ago, when it was first seized with the desire to walk."

I denied this, observing that the part of the road I myself had left was not more than two miles off. But with the obstinacy of his years he repeated: "It is the same road. This is the beginning, and though it seems to run straight away from us, it doubles so often, that it is never far from our boundary and sometimes touches it." He stooped down by the moat, and traced on its moist margin an absurd figure like a maze. As we walked back through the meadows, I tried to convince him of his mistake.

"The road sometimes doubles, to be sure, but that is part of our discipline. Who can doubt that its general tendency is onward? To what goal we know not—it may be to some mountain where we shall touch the sky, it may be over precipices into the sea. But that it goes forward—who can doubt that? It is the thought of that that makes us strive to excel, each in his own way, and gives us an impetus which is lacking with you. Now that man who passed us—it's true that he ran well, and jumped well, and swam well; but we have men who can run better, and men who can jump better, and who can swim better. Specialization has produced results which would surprise you. Similarly, that girl——"

Here I interrupted myself to exclaim: "Good gracious me! I could have sworn it was Miss Eliza Dimbleby over there, with her feet in the fountain!"

He believed that it was.

"Impossible! I left her on the road, and she is due to lecture this evening at Tunbridge Wells. Why, her train leaves Cannon Street in—of course my watch has stopped like everything else. She is the last person to be here."

"People always are astonished at meeting each other. All kinds come through the hedge, and come at all times—when they are drawing ahead in the race, when they are lagging behind, when they are left for dead. I often stand near the boundary listening to the sounds of the road—you know what they are—and wonder if anyone will turn aside. It is my great happiness to help someone out of the moat, as I helped you. For our country fills up slowly, though it was meant for all mankind."

"Mankind have other aims," I said gently, for I thought him well-meaning; "and I must join them." I bade him good evening, for the sun was declining, and I wished to be on the road by nightfall. To my alarm, he caught hold of me, crying: "You are not to go yet!" I tried to shake him off, for we had no interests in common, and his civility was becoming irksome to me. But for all my struggles the tiresome old man would not let go; and, as wrestling is not my specialty, I was obliged to follow him.

It was true that I could have never found alone the place where I came in, and I hoped that, when I had seen the other sights about which he was worrying, he would take me back to it. But I was determined not to sleep in the country, for I mistrusted it, and the people too, for all their friendliness. Hungry though I was, I would not join them in their evening meals of milk and fruit, and, when they gave me flowers, I flung them away as soon as I could do so unobserved. Already they were lying down for the night like cattle—some out on the bare hillside, others in groups under the beeches. In the light of an orange sunset I hurried on with my unwelcome guide, dead tired, faint for want of food, but murmuring indomitably: "Give me life, with its struggles and victories, with its failures and hatreds, with its deep moral meaning and its unknown goal!"

At last we came to a place where the encircling moat was spanned by another bridge, and where another gate interrupted the line of the boundary hedge. It was different from the first gate; for it was half transparent like horn, and opened inwards. But through it, in the waning light, I saw again just such a road as I had left—monotonous, dusty, with brown crackling hedges on either side, as far as the eye could reach.

I was strangely disquieted at the sight, which seemed to deprive me of all self-control. A man was passing us, returning for the night to the hills, with a scythe over his shoulder and a can of some liquid in his hand. I forgot the destiny of our race. I forgot the road that lay before my eyes, and I sprang at him, wrenched the can out of his hand, and began to drink.

It was nothing stronger than beer, but in my exhausted state it overcame me in a moment. As in a dream, I saw the old man shut the gate, and heard him say: "This is where your road ends, and through this gate humanity—all that is left of it—will come in to us."

Though my senses were sinking into oblivion, they seemed to expand ere they reached it. They perceived the magic song of nightingales, and the odour of invisible hay, and stars piercing the fading sky. The man whose beer I had stolen lowered me down gently to sleep off its effects, and, as he did so, I saw that he was my brother.

COMMENT AND QUESTION

1. E. M. Forster distrusts science; its product, the machine; and the myth they have both helped to support, the idea of "progress." He exposes in his writing the mechanized and materialistic civilization which prevents man from living "by the essence that is his soul, and the essence, equally divine, that is his body." Many of his stories are fantasies, as is "The Other Side of the Hedge"; the altered perspective points up his meaning.

2. Notice the pedometer. The road is measured in years, not miles. About twenty-five centuries ago the impetus of Greek thought started the Western world in a direction it has since taken. Is there a connection?

3. Notice the two gates. Consider what they are made of, whether they open in or out and on what part of the road, and what the old man says about each gate.

In the *Odyssey* Penelope discusses a dream with the newly-arrived Odysseus, whom she has not yet recognized. Among other things, she says to him: "Stranger, in truth dreams do arise perplexed and hard to tell, dreams which come not, in man's experience, to their full issue. Two gates there are for unsubstantial dreams, one made of horn and one of ivory. The dreams that pass through the carved ivory delude and bring us tales that turn to naught; those that come through polished horn accomplish real things, whenever seen."

What, then, does Forster mean by using these two gates?

4. The meaning of the story is revealed, also, in the difference between the qualities of the road and the qualities of the life on the other side of the hedge.

5. Notice the "educationist" who exhorts on the road but later appears on the other side of the hedge. Are both of these actions in keeping with an "educationist"?

6. Does the concluding line have references beyond the obvious reference to the brother the main character had lost?

THE CAPTIVE

BY CAROLINE GORDON

CAROLINE GORDON (1895–) is a novelist, short story writer, lecturer, and teacher. She was born in Kentucky. She has published a number of novels, including *Aleck Maury, Sportsman* (1934), *The Women on the Porch* (1944), and *The Strange Children* (1951). "The Captive" is from her collection of short stories, *The Forest of the South* (1945). She has written a book of criticism, *How to Read a Novel* (1957).

WE WERE up long before day and were loading the horses at first dawn streak. Even then Tom didn't want to go.

"This ginseng don't have to get to the station," he said, "and as for the money it'll bring, we can get along without that."

"We've been without salt for three weeks now," I told him.

"There's worse things than doing without salt," Tom said.

I knew if he got to studying about it he wouldn't go and I was bound he should make the trip, Indians or no Indians. I slapped the lead horse on the rump. "Go along," I said. "I'd as soon be scalped now and have done with it as keep on thinking about it all the time."

Tom rode off without saying anything more, and I went on in the house and set about my morning work. The children were all stirring by that time. Joe felt mighty big to be the only man on the place. He was telling them what he'd do if Indians came.

"You'd better hush that up," I said. "Can't you get your mind off Indians a minute?"

All that morning, though, I was thinking about what Tom had said and wishing he hadn't had to go. It seemed like I was riding with him most of the day.

"Now he's at West Fork," I'd say to myself, and then after I'd done some more chores, "He'll be about at the crossroads now or maybe Sayler's Tavern." I knew, though, it wasn't much use to be following him that way in my mind. It'd be good dark before he could get home, and my thinking about it wouldn't hurry him.

It was around ten o'clock that I heard the first owl hooting. Over on the mountain, it seemed. Joe was in the yard feeding the chickens and he stopped stock still and threw his head back.

"You hear that, Mammy?" he asked.

I knew then that there must be something wrong with the call, or a boy like Joe wouldn't have noticed it.

I spoke up sharp, though. "I heard it," I said, "and I could hear a heap of other things if I had time to stand around with my ears open. How long you reckon it's going to take you to get those chickens fed?"

We both went on about our business without more talk, but all the time I was saying to myself that if I could get through this and see Tom Wiley riding in at the gate one more time I'd be content to bide without salt the rest of my natural life. I knew it wouldn't do to let down before the children, though, and I kept them busy doing one thing and another till dinner time. It began to rain while we were eating and it rained a long time. After it stopped raining the fog settled down, so thick you could hardly see your hand before you. And all the time the owls were calling. Calling back and forth from one mountain to another. My littlest girl, Martha, got scared, so I made all the children stay in the house and play by the fire whilst I started in on a piece of cloth I'd had in the loom a long time and never could seem to finish. I'd put a stripe through it and I was going to dye it red and make both the girls a dress out of that piece before the winter set in.

By that time the fog had risen as high as the top of the ridges and the whole house was swallowed up in it. The children kept teasing, saying it was good dark now and couldn't they have a candle.

"Yes," I said, "we're here all by ourselves and you want to go lighting candles, so they can't help finding the house."

One of the girls got to crying. "Who's coming?" she said. "Mammy, who you think's coming?"

I saw I'd got them stirred up and I'd have to settle them, for I couldn't stand to be worrying like I was and have the children crying. I gave them all a lump of sugar around and got them started on a play-party. I made out that I had the headache and if they were going to sing they'd have to sing low. It was "Hog Drovers" they were playing.

"Hog-drovers, hog-drovers, hog-drovers we air,
A-courtin' your daughter so sweet and so fair.
Kin we git lodgin' here, O here,
Kin we git lodgin' here?"

I got them started to frolicking and went back to my work. But I couldn't get my mind off something a man said to me once when we were out hunting on the Hurricane, and I made him to go right in on a bear without waiting for the other menfolks to come up.

"You're brash, Jinny," he said, "and you always been lucky, but one of these times you going to be too brash."

Sitting there listening to them owls calling, and wondering how much longer it would be before Tom got home, I got to thinking that maybe this was the time I was too brash. For I knew well there wasn't another woman in the settlements would have undertaken to stay on that place all day with nothing but a parcel of children. Still, I said to myself, it's done now and there's no undoing it. And the first thing I know, Tom will be back, and tomorrow morning it'll fair up, and I'll be thinking what a goose I was to get scared over nothing.

The children were still singing:

"Oh, this is my daughter that sets by my lap.
No pig-stealing drover kin git her from Pap.
You can't git lodgin' here, O here,
You can't git lodgin' here."

I got up and looked out of the window. It seemed to me that the fog was lifting a little. A man was coming up the path. I knew it was a white man by the walk, but I didn't know it was John Borders till he stepped up to the door.

The first thing he asked was where was Tom.

"Gone to the station with a load of ginseng," I told him. "I'm looking for him back now any minute."

He stood there looking off towards the mountain. "How long them owls been calling?" he asked.

"Off and on all evening," I said, "but owls'll hoot, dark days like this."

"Yes," he said, "and some owls'll holler like wolves and gobble like turkeys and every other kind of varmint. Jinny, you better git them children and come over to our house. Ain't no telling when Tom'll be back."

Just then an owl hooted and another one answered him from somewhere on top of the ridge. We both listened hard. It sounded like a real owl calling to his mate, but I was good and scared by that time and I thought I'd best go over to the Borderses'. It was my judgment, though, that there wasn't any hurry. Indians hardly ever come round before nightfall.

I told John that if he'd wait till I'd fastened up the stock I'd go back with him. He said that while I was doing that he'd walk out in the woods a little way. He'd been looking all day for some strayed sheep and hadn't found trace of them, but he thought they might be herded up in that gully by the spring. He went off down the path and I fastened the front door and went out the back way. I didn't fasten the back door, but I kept my eye on it all the time I was worrying with the cattle. Joe was along helping me. The cow was standing there at the pen; so I stopped and milked her while Joe went up in the triangle to look for the heifer. He found her and brought her up to the cowpen just as I finished milking. We fastened both cows up in the stable and Joe went over and saw that all the chickens were up and fastened the door on them. Then we started back to the house with the milk.

We were halfway up the path when we heard the Indians holler. We started for the house on a dead run. I could see Indians in the yard, and one Indian was coming around the house to the back door. I ran faster and slipped in the door ahead of him. Joe was right behind me. The room was so full of Indians that at first I couldn't see any of my children. The Indians was dancing around and hollering and hacking with their tomahawks. I heard one of the children screaming but I didn't know which one it was. An Indian caught me around the waist but I got away from him. I thought, I have got to do something. I fell down on my knees and crawled around between the Indians' legs, they striking at me all the time, till I found Martha, my littlest one, in the corner by the loom. She was dead and I crawled on a little way and found Sadie. She was dead, too, with her skull split open. The baby was just sitting there holding on to the bar of the loom. I caught him in my bosom and held him up to me tight; then I got to my feet. Joe was right behind me all the time and he stood up when I did. But an Indian come up and brained him with a tomahawk. I saw him go down and I knew I couldn't get any more help from him. I couldn't think of anything to do; so I worked my way over towards the door, but there was two or three Indians standing on the porch and I knew there was no use running for it. I just stood there holding the baby while the Indians pulled burning logs out of the fire onto the floor. When the blaze had sprung up they all come out onto the porch.

I made a break and got some way down the path, but an Indian run after me and caught me. He stood there, holding me tight till the other Indians come up; then he laid his hand on my head and he touched the baby too. It seemed he was claiming me for his prisoner. He had rings on his arms and ankles, and trinkets in his ears. I knew he was a chief and I thought he must be a Shawnee. I could understand some of what he said.

He was telling them they better hurry and get away before Tice Harman come home. Another Indian stepped up. I knew him—a Cherokee that come sometimes to the station. Mad Dog they called him. Tice Harman had killed his son. It come to me that they had been thinking all along that they was at Tice Harman's. I jerked my arm away from the Shawnee chief.

"You think you're burning Tice Harman's house," I said. "This ain't Tice Harman's house. It's Tom Wiley's. Tom Wiley. Tom Wiley never killed any Indians."

They looked at each other and I think they was feared. Feared because they had burned the wrong house, but feared too of Tice Harman. Mad Dog said something and laid his hand on his tomahawk, but the old chief shook his head and took hold of my arm again. He spoke, too, but so fast I couldn't tell what he was saying. The Cherokee looked mad but he turned around after a minute and called to the other Indians, and they all left the house and started off through the woods. Mad Dog went first and half a dozen young Indians after him. The old chief and I came last. He had hold of my arm and was hurrying me along, and all the time he kept talking, telling me that he had saved my life, that I was to go with him to his town to be a daughter to him to take the place of a daughter that had died.

I didn't take in much that he was saying. I kept looking back towards the burning house, thinking maybe they wasn't all dead before the Indians set fire to it. Finally I couldn't stand it no longer and I asked the old Shawnee. He pointed to one of the young Indians who was going up the ridge ahead of us. I saw something dangling from his belt and I looked away quick. I knew it was the scalps of my children.

II

We went up over the ridge and then struck north through the woods. I didn't take much notice of where we was going. I had all I could do to keep Dinny quiet—he warn't but ten months old. I let him suck all the way but it didn't do much good. We went so fast it'd jolt out of his mouth and he'd cry louder than ever. The Shawnee would grab my arm and say the other Indians would kill him sure if he kept that up. Finally I got his head down inside the waist of my dress and I held him up against me so tight he couldn't cry, and then I was scared he'd smother, but the Shawnee wouldn't let me stop to find out.

We went on, up one valley and down another, till finally we come out on level land at the foot of a mountain. The old chief made me go first, right up the mountainside. It was worse there than it was in the woods. The laurel and the ivy was so thick that sometimes he'd have to reach ahead of me and break a way through. My arms got numb and wouldn't hold the baby up. It was lucky for me I was crawling up a mountain. I would put him up ahead of me and then crawl to him, and in this way my arms would get a little ease of the burden. The old chief didn't like this, though, and every time it happened he'd slap me and tell me to go faster, go faster or they would surely kill the baby.

We got to the top of the mountain, somehow, and started down. My legs were hurting me now worse than my arms. It was going so straight down the mountainside. The back of my legs got stiff and would jerk me up every time I set my foot down, what they call stifled in a horse. I got on, somehow, though, all through that night and for most of the next day. It was near sundown when we stopped, in a rockhouse [1] at the head of a creek. The Indians must have thought they were too far for any white men to follow them. They made up a big fire and walked around it pretty careless. Two of the young Indians went off in the woods. I heard a shot and they come back dragging a little deer. They butchered it and sliced it down the middle, and slung the two haunches over the fire on forked sticks. The tenderer parts they broiled on rocks that they heated red-hot in the coals. A young buck squatted down by the fire and kept the venison turning. Soon the smell of rich meat cooking rose up in the air. The juices begun dripping down into the blaze and I thought it was a shame for all that gravy to go to waste. I asked the Shawnee to lend me a little kettle he had, and I hung it on a forked stick and caught the juices as they fell, and then poured them back over the meat. When they turned brown and rich I caught the gravy in the little kettle and sopped my fingers in it and let the baby suck them.

The old chief Crowmocker, smiled like he thought a lot of me. "White woman know," he said. "White woman teach Indian women. You make rum?"

I said I didn't know how to make rum, but there was plenty in the settlements and if he would take me back, take me just within a mile or two of the clearing, I'd undertake to furnish him and his men with all the rum they could drink.

He laughed. "White people promise," he said. "You in your cabin you forget poor Indian."

The Cherokee, Mad Dog, had been sitting there broiling the deer nose on a rock that he had got red-hot in the flames. When it was brown he brought it over and gave it to me. Then he went back and sat down, sullen like, not saying anything. The fire shone on his black eyes and on his long beak of a nose. When he moved, you could see the muscles moving, too, in his big chest and up and down his naked legs. An Indian woman would have thought him a fine-looking man, tall and well formed in every way, but it frightened me to look at him. I was glad it was the old chief and not him that had taken me prisoner. I was glad, too, that the chief was old. I'd heard tell how particular the Indians are about things like that. I thought the old chief would likely do what he said and

[1] A rockhouse is not a cave, but a place sheltered by an overhanging ledge of rock.

keep me for his daughter, but if it was Mad Dog he would have me for his wife.

I thought the meat never would get done, but it finally did. The Indians give me a good-size piece off the haunch and I ate it all, except a little piece I put in Dinny's mouth. He spit it out, but I kept putting it back till he got some good of it. Then I took him down to the creek and scooped up water in my hands for him. He'd been fretting because my milk was giving out, but the water and the juice from the meat quieted him a little. After we'd both had all the water we could drink I went back up the hill and sat down on a log with Dinny laying across my knees. It felt good to have his weight off my arms, but I was afraid to take my hands off him. I was feared one of them might come up and snatch him away from me any minute.

He laid there a while a-fretting and then he put his little hand up and felt my face.

"Sadie . . . ," he said. "Sadie . . ."

Sadie was the oldest girl. She played with him a lot and fondled him. He'd go to her any time out of my arms.

I hugged him up close and sang him the song Sadie used to get him to sleep by. "Lord Lovell, he stood at the castle gate," I sang and the tears a-running down my face.

"Hush, my pretty," I said, "hush. Sadie's gone, but Mammy's here. Mammy's here with Baby."

He cried, though, for Sadie and wouldn't nothing I could do comfort him. He cried himself hoarse and then he'd keep opening his little mouth but wouldn't no sound come. I felt him and he was hot to the touch. I was feared he'd fret himself into a fever, but there wasn't nothing I could do. I held his arms and legs to the blaze and got him as warm as I could, and then I went off from the fire a little way and laid down with him in my arms.

The Indians kept putting fresh wood to the fire till it blazed up and lit the whole hollow. They squatted around it, talking. After a while half a dozen of them got up and went off in the woods. The light fell far out through the trees. I could see their naked legs moving between the black trunks. Some of them was dragging up down timber for the fire and some kept reaching up and tearing boughs off the trees. They came back trailing the green boughs behind them. Two or three other Indians come over and they all squatted down and begun stripping the leaves off the switches and binding them into hoops. An Indian took one of the scalps off his belt —Sadie's light hair, curling a little at the ends and speckled now all over with blood. I watched it fall across the bough of maple. I watched till they began stretching the scalp on the hoop and then I shut my eyes.

After a while Crowmocker come over and tied me with some rawhide thongs that he took off his belt. He tied me up tight and it felt good to have the keen thongs cutting into me. I strained against them for a while and then I must have dropped off to sleep. I woke myself up hollering. I thought at first it was the Indians hollering, and then I knew it was me I tried to stop but I couldn't. It would start way down inside me and I would fight to hold it in, but before I knew it my mouth would be wide open and as soon as I'd loose one shriek another would start working its way up and there wasn't nothing I could do to hold it back. I was shaking, too, so hard that the baby rolled out of my arms and started crying.

The old chief got up from where he was sleeping and come over. He stood there looking down at me and then he lighted a torch and went off in the woods a little way. He brought some leaves back with him and he put them to boil in his little kettle. He made me drink some tea from the leaves and he gave the baby some too, and after a while we both went off to sleep.

III

I woke with the old chief shaking me by the arm and telling me it was time to get up. I was still sort of lightheaded and for a minute I didn't know where I was. It was raining hard and so dark you couldn't tell whether it was good day. The Indians had built a fire up under the ledge and were broiling the rest of the venison. I laid there and I saw the light shine on their naked legs and the tomahawks hanging from their belts, and I knew where I was and all that had happened.

The old chief untied the thongs and I stood up with Dinny in my arms. They gave me a little piece of venison and some parched corn. My lips were so swelled I couldn't chew, but I swallowed the corn and I put the meat in my mouth and sucked it till it went away. I felt milk in my breasts and I was glad for the baby. I gave him his dinny but he wouldn't suck. He wouldn't hardly open his eyes. I thought that was from the tea the old Indian had given us and I feared he'd got too much. He was still hot to the touch and I thought he might have got a fever from laying out all night in the rain. I tore off part of my top skirt and I made a sort of sling that I put around my shoulders to carry him in; and I made a cover, too, out of part of the cloth to keep the rain off his little face.

Soon as we had finished eating, the Indians stomped out the fire and scattered the ashes so you couldn't have told there had ever been a camp there, and we started off through the woods.

We hadn't gone far before two of the young Indians left us. I thought they was most likely going back over the trail to watch if anybody was following us. I heard them saying that the folks at the settlement would be sure to send out a party. Some of the Indians thought it wouldn't do no good because the heavy rains had washed out the trail so nobody could find it. But Mad Dog said Tice Harman could follow any trail. I never knew before the Indians was so feared of Harman. They said he was the best hunter among the Long Knives, that he could go as far and stand as much as any Indian, and that they would like for him to come and live with them and be one of their warriors. Mad Dog said now that the only thing was to go so fast and go so far that even Tice Harman couldn't come up with us. He said "O-hi-yo" several times and I judged they meant to make for one of the towns on the river.

It stopped raining after a while but it didn't do much good. It was level ground we was traveling over and the water was standing everywhere, so that half the time you was wading. I knew we was some place high up in the hills, but afterwards I couldn't have told what country I had passed over. I went with my head down most of the time, not seeing anything but the black trunks of the trees going by and the yellow leaves floating in the puddles. Beech woods we must have been in because the leaves was all yellow and little.

We went on like that all day, not stopping to eat anything except some parched corn that the old chief took out of his bag and handed around to us still traveling. Late that evening we come to a water hole. One of the Indians shot a bear and we stopped and built a fire under a cliff. The Indians hadn't no more'n butchered the meat when two scouts come running into camp. They said that white men were following us, on horseback. The Indians all looked scared at this. Crowmocker stood there talking to Mad Dog about what we had best do. I went over and stood by them. Mad Dog said that they ought to kill the child and change the course, that they would have to go faster than ever now and I couldn't keep up, carrying the baby. Crowmocker showed him the sling I had made and said the baby wasn't no burden to me now. He said he had brought me this far and was going to carry me on to his town to teach his women how to weave cloth like the dress I had on.

He told Mad Dog that and then he motioned to me and said, "Go!" I started off, top speed, through the trees. Behind me I could hear the Indians stomping around in the leaves to cover up the signs of the fire. I went on as fast as I could, but every now and then an Indian would shoot past me. Pretty soon they was all ahead except the old chief.

We went down hill towards a hollow that had a little branch running through it. Mad Dog was in the lead, the other Indians right on his heels, jumping over down logs and bushes quick as cats. The old chief stayed by me, and when I'd slow up getting over a log or fall down in the bushes he'd jerk me onto my feet again.

The branch was narrow but running deep with the rains. Mad Dog started wading downstream and the other Indians after him, single file. They hadn't slowed up much and water splashed high. I could see their legs moving through the splashing water. The old chief by my side was breathing hard. I knew he was winded but I thought he would wind quicker than the others. I thought I would keep moving as long as I saw the Indians' legs going on.

The Indian that was in front of me stepped in a hole up to his waist. When he come out of it he took two, three steps and stood still. I knew then that Mad Dog had stopped and I knew he would be coming back down the line. I looked up, but the sides of the gully was too steep. I turned and ran back upstream fast as I could. I heard the breathing close behind me and I knew it was the old chief, and then there was a big splashing. Mad Dog was after me.

I left the water and ran sideways up the gully. The breathing was closer now. I tried to run faster and I caught my foot in a root. They were on me as soon as I went down. Mad Dog grabbed me by both arms. Crowmocker got there a second after, but Mad Dog already had hold of Dinny. I caught at his legs and tried to push them out from under him but he kicked me away. I got up and went at him again but he kicked me down. He kicked me again and then he went on up the side of the gully till he came to a big tree and he held the baby by the feet and dashed his brains out.

I rolled over on my face and I laid there flat on the ground till the old chief come up. He pulled me to my feet and said we would have to run on fast, that the white men were following us on horses. I said no, I wouldn't go, I would stay there with my baby; but he and another Indian took me by the arms and drug me down the stream spite of all I could do.

We went on down the branch a good way. Towards dark we came out on the banks of a river. Water was standing halfway up the trunks of big trees. I saw the current, running fast and covered with black drift, and I didn't believe even an Indian could get across that raging river. But they didn't stop a minute. Crowmocker fell back and two young Indians took hold of my arms and carried me out into the water. The current caught us and swept us off our feet. I couldn't swim much on account of my clothes, but the two young Indians held on to my wrists and carried me on between them. The other Indians come right in after us. They held their guns up high over their heads and swum like boys treading water. I could see their heads bobbing all around me through the black drift and I couldn't see nothing to keep all of us from drowning. They managed to keep out of the drift somehow, though, and all the time they were working towards the other bank till finally we come out in dead water at the mouth of a creek. The Indians that were holding me up stopped swimming all of a sudden, and I knew that we must have got across. It was so dark by that time I couldn't see anything. I got out of the water as best I could and a little way up the creek bank. I fell down there 'mongst some willows. I saw the Indians come up out of the water shaking themselves

like dogs, and I saw them falling down all around me, and then my eyes
went shut.

IV

The old chief woke me up at the first dawn streak. I heard him and I
felt him shaking me, but I didn't get up. As soon as I opened my eyes
the pain in my feet started up. I touched one foot to the ground and it
throbbed worse'n toothache. I knew I couldn't travel any that day and I
didn't care. I turned over on my back and laid there looking up at the sky.
It had cleared off during the night and the stars was shining. The sky was
all a pale gray except for one long sulphur-colored streak where day was
getting ready to break. Behind me the Indians was looking to their guns
and settling their tomahawks in their belts. I watched their heads and
shoulders moving against that yellow light, and I saw one of them take
his tomahawk out and heft it and then try the blade with his finger. I
thought that if I just kept on laying there that maybe he would be the one
to finish me off, and then I thought Mad Dog was quicker and would beat
him to it.

The old chief was still shaking me. "Get up, Jinny. Day come."

"No," I said, "I ain't going to get up."

He took me by the shoulders and tried to pull me to my feet but I
slumped back on the ground. I spoke to him in Shawnee.

"My feet bleed and I cannot travel. Let me die."

He leaned over and looked at my feet and then he called to one of the
young Indians to bring him some white oak bark. When the bark come
he boiled it over the fire and then he took the liquor from the bark and
cooled it with more water and poured it over my feet.

The other Indians had finished scattering the fire and was starting out
through the willows, but Crowmocker just sat there pouring that stuff on
my feet. I could feel the swelling going down and after a while I touched
my feet to the ground. It didn't hurt like it had, and I got up and we
started off. He give me some parched corn and I ate it, walking. He said
we would have to travel fast to catch up with the other Indians. I asked
him if the white people were still following us and he laughed and said no
white men could get across the river. I owned to myself that they couldn't,
and I didn't think any more about them coming after me. I thought the
Indians would probably take me so far away that I'd never again see a
white face.

We caught up with the other Indians towards dark. That night we slept
in a canebrake by a little river. A buffalo was wallowing in the river as
we come up. One of the Indians shot him. They butchered him there in
the water and drug big slabs of the meat up the bank with ropes cut from
the hide. We must have been in Indian country by this time. They didn't
seem to think it made any different how much noise they made. They

made up a big fire to one side of the brake and they were half the night cooking the meat and eating. I went to sleep under a tree with them singing and yelling all around me.

When I woke up the next morning they were having a council. They talked till the sun was high and then they split up into two parties. Mad Dog and three of the young bucks left us and swum across the river. The rest of us kept on up the bank. We traveled all that day through the cane and then we struck a divide and followed it into another valley. We had run out of everything to eat by this time except the strings of jerked meat that they all carried slung around their necks. We stayed two, three days at a buffalo lick, hoping to kill some game, but none came and we went on.

Most of the leaves were off the trees by this time and the nights were cold. I knew it was some time in October that the Indians come and burned our house, but I didn't know how long we'd been on the trail and I didn't have any idea what country we were in.

One morning we come out in some deep narrows just above where two creeks flowed together. A wild-looking place with tumbling falls and big rocks laying around everywhere. I looked up at the cliffs over our heads and I couldn't believe my eyes. They were *painted*: deer and buffalo and turtles big as a man, painted in red and in black on the rock. Some of the young Indians acted like they had never been there before either. They would keep walking around looking at things and sometimes stand and stare at the pictures of wild beasts that were painted everywhere on the smooth rock.

The old chief took a way up the side of the cliffs, the rest of us following. The young Indians went up like deer, but I had to pull myself up by the laurel that grew down in between the rocks. We walked along a narrow ledge and come to a rockhouse. It was the biggest rockhouse ever I saw, run all along one side of the cliff. The old chief uncovered an iron pot from where it was hid in a lot of trash in one corner of the cave and showed me how to set it up on forked sticks. He said that I would have to do all the work around the camp from now on, the way Indian women did, and when the spring rains come and melted the snows he would take me to his town on the Tenassee and I would learn more about Indian ways and be adopted into the tribe in place of his dead daughter.

I thought if he took me there I would never get away and I had it in mind to make a break for it first chance I got. I got hold of two strings of jerked meat and I kept them tied around my waist so I'd be ready when the time came. I thought I would wait, though, and maybe I would find out how far it was to the settlements. I would lie there in my corner of the cave at night, making out I was asleep, and listen to them talking around the fire. I heard them call the names of the creeks that flowed through that valley—Big Paint and Little Mudlick; and further off was another creek, Big Mudlick, where they went sometimes to hunt. The names were strange to me and I never could tell from their talk how far it was to the settlements or even which way to go. I had an idea that the place I was in was secret to the Indians, for it was a wonder to see and yet I had never heard any white body tell of it. I asked Crowmocker what the pictures of deer and buffalo and bear were for and he said they were the Indians' fathers and that I would learn about them when I was adopted into the tribe. Once he pointed some mounds out to me and said they were graves. He said that he and his people always stopped when they come this way to visit the graves of their fathers that was all over the valley.

A spell of fine weather come, late in the fall. Indian summer they call it. We looked out one day and bees were swarming on the cliffside. Crowmocker was mad when he saw them. He said it meant that the white people were coming; that when bees swarmed out of season they were running away from the white people who had scared all the game out of the country and made it so that even bees couldn't live in it. I asked would the white people find their way into this valley and he said they couldn't— that it was a way known only to Indians; that if a white man ever set foot in it the great bear would come down off the wall and crush him in his paws. He said, though, that there would be fighting soon over all the land and a lot of bloodshed.

I knew that was all foolishness about the bear, but I thought likely as not there would be fighting and I wanted to get away worse than ever. One morning I was down in the hollow by myself, gathering wood, and I thought that was the time. Three of the Indians had gone off hunting and I knew the others were laying up in the cave asleep. I didn't think anybody would be following me, for a while, anyhow. I started off, slipping from tree to tree, and I got quite a way up the hollow. I knew nobody was following me, but I would keep looking back over my shoulder all the time. I got to thinking. I didn't have any way to kill game, and nothing to eat but two strings of jerked meat. I didn't even know how far I'd have to go before I came to any settlement. Worst of all, I didn't even know which way to take. Likely as not I'd starve to death in the woods, or freeze if the weather turned. I'd better stay with the Indians, where at least I could sleep warm and eat, if it wasn't anything but parched corn. I picked up my load of wood and got back to camp quick as I could, and didn't none of them ever know I'd been away.

I never tried it again, but sometimes I'd sit there on the edge of the cliff and pick out the way I'd take if I did go. There was a ridge covered with black pines rose up right in front of the rockhouse. I thought if I could once get up there I could get down into the valley easy. I hadn't ever been over there, but I knew what the country would be like. I saw myself slipping along through that divide, around the foot of the mountain and over some more mountains till I'd come out on a clearing. I'd slip up to some cabin, towards dark. They'd think I was an Indian at first, maybe, and then they'd see my eyes was light and they'd take me in and keep me till I could get back to my own folks again.

We stayed in that rockhouse a long time. The leaves all fell off the trees, and one or two light snows fell, but the real cold weather was late coming. The Indians hunted just enough to keep us in meat. They said the pelts were thin that year and not worth taking. Sometimes they would take me along to bring in the game, but mostly they left me to work by myself. When cold weather set in we built big fires in the cave and it was warm inside like a house. When the Indians weren't hunting they would lie around on buffalo skins and sleep. The smoke was terrible and the smell of Indians was all over everything. At first it bothered me, but after a while I got so I didn't notice it.

I wasn't in the cave much, even in bad weather. I had to gather all the firewood. The Indians didn't have an axe and I couldn't get anything but dead branches. There wasn't much down timber on the cliffside; so I'd mostly go up over the cliffs when I was hunting wood. There was a barren there, flat as the palm of your hand and covered with a thin kind of grass. It had plenty of trees on it but they were all twisty and stunted by the wind. The only sizable tree was a big elm. It was peeled for thirty or forty feet and had a rattlesnake painted on it—a monster snake coiling up around the trunk. You could see that snake from everywhere on the barren. I was feared to look at it. The Indians seemed to think a lot of it. Sometimes they would go up there at night and I would hear them singing and dancing and calling to the snake.

Somewhere on the barren there were lead mines. The Indians never let me go to them, but they would go off and stay two, three hours and come back with big balls of lead. They made me smelt it out for bullets. I had to have a mighty fire. It would take me days and days to get up enough wood. I would heap it up in a big pile and then I would kindle the fire and keep it going for hours. When the lead melted, it ran down through little ditches into holes that I had dug to form the bullets. It would take the lead a long time to melt. Sometimes I would be up on the barren from sunup to sundown.

I would sit there and think about my husband and my children. I would wonder whether Tom went out in the woods hunting ginseng the way he used to do, and was he still looking for me or had give me up for dead. When I thought of Tom the house would be there, too, not burning down the way it was last time I saw it, but standing with the rooms just the way they always were. I could see both rooms plain, even to the hole that was burnt in the floor when a big log fell out one night. The children would be playing in and out of the house like they did. It was like they were all living; it was only me that was gone away.

I would think back, too, over things that happened long before ever I was grown and married to Tom Wiley. There was a man named Rayburn stayed at the settlement one winter. Lance Rayburn. A big, strong man and a mighty hunter. We ate bear of his shooting all that fall. He was handy with snares too, and took over a hundred beaver down in the bottom. He courted me some that winter, sitting in front of the fire after the old folks were in bed. I laughed and went on with him, but Tom Wiley had just started a-courting me and all the time my mind was on him more'n it was on the stranger.

Come time for Rayburn to pack up his pelts to take to the station, he saved one out for me. Beaver, and extra fine and soft. He give it to my sister, Sarah, and told her to hand it to me when I come to the house. She made one of the children bring it down to the creek where I was boiling clothes. I laid it there on the grass and I would stop and look at it as I went back and forth with my clothes, and sometimes I would wipe my hands dry and lay them on the soft fur for pleasure in the feel. But all the time I knew I wasn't going to keep it. When Rayburn come towards me through the willows I went to meet him with the pelt in my hands.

"Keep this," I said, "and give it to some girl where you're going."

"Don't you want it?" he asked.

"I ain't taking nothing from you."

He stood there looking at me and all of a sudden his eyes narrowed up like a cat's. "You're full young to be marrying," he said.

"I ain't too young to know my own mind," I told him and before I thought I laughed.

He come towards me, and before I knowed what he was up to he was on me and trying to bear me to the ground. He was a strong man but I was stout, too, and I stood up to him. We was rassling around in the bushes quite some while before he got me down, and then he had to keep both his hands on my chest. I laid there right still, looking up at him.

"What you reckon my pappy'll say when I tell him about this?" I asked.

He laughed, "I ain't a-feared of no Sellards that ever walked," he said, "but that Tom Wiley ain't no manner of man for you," he said.

"You can talk against Tom Wiley and you can hold me here till Dooms-day," I told him, "but it ain't going to do you no good. I ain't going to have none of you no matter what happens."

His face kind of changed. Looked like it hurt him to hear me say it. He got up off me right away and he picked the beaver pelt up from where it lay in the grass and he throwed it hard as he could into the creek.

"It'll git to my girl that way fast as any other," he said.

I watched the pelt floating down the water and onto a rock and then off again. When I turned around he was out of sight and he was gone when I got back to the house. He stayed at the station a while and then he went off in the mountains hunting bear and wasn't ever heard of again.

Some said he was killed by wild beasts. A rifle and a cap that they said was his was found up in the hills. The man that found the rifle kept it, but they give the cap to the Borderses. Wouldn't anybody wear it, and Sally hung it up in the dog alley. I used to look at it every time I passed and wonder whether it had ever been on Lance Rayburn's head and was he dead or still living. And sometimes I'd wonder how it'd been if I'd married him instead of Tom, but I knew all the time I wouldn't ever have married anybody but Tom because he was the one I fancied from the time I was a chap, living neighbor to the Wileys, back in the Roanoke country.

I thought about Lance Rayburn and I thought about a lot of other folks that had come to the settlement and stayed and then gone on and wouldn't anybody know whether they were living still or dead. And I thought about people dead long ago, my old granny back in Carolina, ninety-eight years old and turned simple. She'd sit in the chimney corner all day long, singing the likeliest tunes!

"Pa'tridge in the pea patch," she'd sing and call me to her and fondle me, liking gals, she said, always better than boys.

> "Pa'tridge in the pea patch
> Pickin' up the peas.
> 'Long comes the bell cow
> Kickin' up her heels . . ."

"Oh . . . h, the bell cow," she'd sing and catch me by my little shimmy tail. "O . . . O . . . hh, the bell cow . . ." and hist me up over the arm of her chair. "O . . . O . . . hh, the bell cow, kickin' up her heels. Call the little gal to milk her in the pail."

I used to call those songs to mind when I had to go down to the lick for salt. It was a place I didn't like to go. A deep hollow with three sulphur springs and a lick that covered nigh an acre of ground. The biggest lick ever I saw in my life. The way was white with the bones of beasts, and in between the piled up bones the long furrows that the buffalo made licking the ground for salt. I would walk down those furrows to the spring and fill my bucket with the salty water and go back up the hill to where my kettle was slung between two little birches. Sitting there waiting for the water to boil, I couldn't keep my eyes off the bones. I would take them up in my hand and turn them over and over, wondering what manner of beasts they had belonged to.

Once I made myself a little beast, laying all the bones out on some lacy moss, the front feet stiff like it was galloping off in the woods, the hind legs drawn up under him. A hare it might have been or a little fawn. Or maybe a beast that nobody ever heard of before.

There were beasts come to that lick one time or another not known to man. Bigger'n buffalo they must have been. One thigh-bone, I mind, longer'n I was and twice as big around as two good-sized men.

I thought of a man used to be around the station, Vard Wiley, second cousin to Tom. Folks said he was the biggest liar in the settlements. He would stay off in the woods hunting day after day and never bring in any game except maybe a brace of wild turkeys. And he told tall tales about a lick bigger'n any lick around those parts, where the beasts come up in tens of thousands. He would lay up in a tree all day and watch 'em, he said, and not take a shot for wonder. There were beasts used there, he said, ten times the size of buffalo. He offered to take anybody there and show them the bones, and when they asked him why he didn't bring them back to the settlement he said couldn't no man carry them, nor no two horses.

Folks laughed at him, and the children round the settlement used to sing a song:

> "Vard Wiley's gone west, Vard Wiley's gone east,
> A-huntin' the woods for a monster beast.

> "He'll make him a tent out of the wild beast's hide
> And all the king's horses can stable inside.

> "He'll make him a wagon out of solid bone
> And it'll take ten oxen to draw it home."

I called that song to mind and I thought how if I ever saw Vard Wiley again I'd go up to him and say I knew him to be a truth-teller, and all the people would laugh at me maybe, the way they did Vard Wiley, but all the time I would be knowing it was the truth.

I thought, too, of other tales he told and of jokes he played. Of the time he borrowed my dress and sunbonnet and shawl and went and sat on the creek bank when the schoolmaster was in swimming. He sat there all evening with the sunbonnet hiding his face and old Mister Daugherty shaking his fist at him. "You hussy! You brazen hussy! Don't you know I'm naked?" and finally when he come up out of the water naked as the day he was born Vard took out after him and run him clean to the house. Old Mister Daugherty went around saying there was a woman ought to be run out of the settlements, and Vard would talk to him and make out it was me. But Old Man Daugherty knew wouldn't none of Hezekiah Sellards' daughters be carrying on like that. He was bound it was a woman from Ab's Valley.

I would think about 'em sitting there and arguing about how the hussy ought to be run out of the settlements, and I would laugh all by myself there in the woods. Throw back my head and laugh and then feel silly when the woods give back the echo.

I did a lot of work while I was with the Indians. It was hard on me at first but I got used to it. It was better after Mad Dog left us. The old chief was like a father to me, and the young ones knew I belonged to him and didn't bother me. I slept off by myself in a far corner of the cave and he would wake me up at daybreak and tell me what there was to do that day. He took pains to show me how to flesh pelts and cure them, and he showed me how to split a deer sinew for thread and how to make a whistle to call deer out of birch bark and sticks. And after I got so I could sew skins good he had me make him a pair of leggings and trim them with porcupine quills—porcupine quills colored with some roots he got out of the woods.

It bothered him the way I looked and he made me paint my face the way the Indians did. Fixed me up some of the red root mixed with bear's grease, and after I'd been putting it on my face for a while you couldn't told me from an Indian woman, except for my light eyes.

He'd stay in the cave with me sometimes all day, his buffalo hide wrapped around him so tight that his knees were up against him like a chair. He'd sit there and rock back and forth on his heels and talk while I worked. Down in the hollow the young braves would be practicing their war whoops. He would listen to them and laugh.

"Our young men give the war whoop loudly to cover up their fear of the enemy. It was not so when I was young. There was joy in the war whoop then."

He said he was a chief but he might have been something better. He might have been a medicine man. He had the gift of it from his grandmother. His own mother died when he was born, he said, and his old granny raised him. He told me about how she would take him into the woods with her looking for yarbs and roots, and how she knew where everything grew and which roots would be good to take and which had no strength in them. He said that after I was adopted into the tribe he would tell some of her secrets to me, but the Spirit would be angry if a white woman knew them.

I asked him wouldn't I still be a white woman after I was adopted into the tribe but he said no, the white blood would go out of me and the Spirit would send Indian blood to take its place, and then I would feel like an Indian and know all the Indian ways and maybe get to be a wise woman like his old granny.

He told me about his youngest daughter and how she come by her death, following what she thought was a fawn bleating. They found her days afterward, three enemy arrows in her. Her death had been paid for with three scalps of warriors, and he would say that he didn't grieve over her, but I knew he did. I got to feeling sorry for him sometimes to have lost his daughter that meant so much to him, and then I would think how

I had lost all my children and my husband and I would cry, dropping tears on the skin I was sewing.

I got so after a while that the Indian way of doing things seemed natural to me. I thought nothing of seeing dark faces around me all the time, but in the night sometimes I would dream of white faces. White faces coming towards me through the trees. Or sometimes I would be in a house again and look up all of a sudden and all the faces in the room would be white.

One white face was always coming to me in my dreams: Tice Harman, the man whose house the Indians thought they were burning the day they burned ours. I always thought that if anybody came to save me it would be Tice Harman. I could see him plain in my dreams. A little man, wouldn't weigh more'n a hundred and twenty pounds, but he had a big head. A big head and a big beak of a nose and long yellow hair down to his shoulders. His eyes were blue and in my dreams they glittered like ice. I would dream about Tice Harman and when I waked I would think what I'd heard said of him—how he could go further and stand more than any man in the settlements, and how he loved to fight Indians better'n eat when he was hungry. I would think, too, of how folks said he would bring trouble on the settlements shooting that Indian down when there warn't really any use in it; and I would think that since it was him that brought all my trouble on me, maybe it would be him that would get me away from the Indians. But time went on and nobody came, and after a while I got so I didn't think much about it.

One evening I was gathering wood on the cliffside and I heard a lot of whooping and hollering down near the mouth of the creek. The Indians come out from where they were sleeping back in the cave and stood looking over the falls. A long whoop came and the old chief put his hands to his mouth and answered it. There was more whooping back and forth, and then Mad Dog came up the trail by the falls with about twenty Indians following him. They were painted for war and marched single file, all except the last six or eight. They were in pairs and in the middle of them a white man, walking with his hands tied behind him. A white man? A boy. Couldn't have been more than eighteen years old.

I had to step out of the path to let them by. The dead branches rustled in my hands. The prisoner turned his head. He looked straight into my eyes. It was like he didn't know I was there. I spoke to him.

"I can't do nothing," I said. "I'm a white woman, but I can't do nothing. Christ!" I said, "there ain't nothing I can do."

He kept on looking at me but he didn't speak. They were hurrying him past. I dropped the branches and run after them. Mad Dog called to one of the young bucks and he caught me and held me. I fought him, but he held me till they had all gone up the path.

I went on to the rockhouse and kindled up the fire. After a while Mad Dog come down and told me to cook up some meat quick as I could. There would be singing and dancing, he said; they would want meat all night long.

I looked at him. "A present," I said. "A present for Kagahye-liske's daughter. Give me this boy. He is not good for anything but to gather wood."

His eyes were fierce. "Boy?" he said. "He has this day killed my brother." Then he laughed and smoothed my hair. "Jinny," he said, "pretty Jinny."

I made out I had to see to the fire and walked away. I put some bear meat on to boil and I told him I would call him when it was done, and he went on back up the path.

There was a moon coming. I sat there waiting for the meat to boil and watched it rise over the pines. Up on the barren the Indians were dragging up all the dead branches they could find into one pile. After a while I looked up over the rockhouse and saw the sky all light and knew they had kindled the fire.

The stamping and yelling went on, and every now and then a gun would go off. Then there was running around the tree. You could hear the feet pounding and the long calls. "Ai . . . yi . . . Ai . . . yi . . . Ai . . . yi . . ." One for each man that had died that day. And the sharp cry for the scalp taking. They would act it all out and the boy standing there watching. He was dazed, though; he wouldn't see it for what it was. He wouldn't know what they were doing, might not know what they were going to do. There on the path he looked at me and didn't know me for a white woman. I ought to have found out his name and where he come from. I ought to have done that much. But he wouldn't have answered. And what good would it do his folks . . . if I ever saw white folks again. Then Mad Dog's hand on my hair. "Pretty Jinny . . . pretty Jinny . . ."

The flames shot up and lit the whole valley. The moon looked cold where it hung over the pines. I kept the fire up under the kettle but I couldn't sit still. I walked back and forth in the rockhouse, back and forth, back and forth, waiting for the shrieks to start.

They were a long time coming. I thought maybe it was already going on. Indians can stand there burning and not make a sound, and there have been white men that could. But this was just a boy . . .

The first shriek was long and then they come short and quick, one right after the other. I got over in a corner of the rockhouse and held on tight to a big rock. After a while I let go of the rock and put both fingers in my ears and then I was feared to take them out, thinking it might not be over yet. The Indians were still yelling and stamping. The young ones kept running down and grabbing up chunks of meat from the boiling pot and carrying them up to the barren. I could see the old chief's shadow where he stood on the edge of the cliff calling to the new moon.

When he came down to the rockhouse Mad Dog was with him. They stood there dipping meat up out of the kettle. Mad Dog talked.

"It is too much. For five hundred brooches I could buy a girl of the Wild-Cats, young and swift, a fine worker in beads. A girl like a moonbeam, daughter of a mighty warrior."

His eyes were black in the circles of paint. His tongue showed bright between his painted lips. The red lines ran from his forehead down the sides of his cheeks to make gouts of blood on his chin.

A devil. A devil come straight from hell to burn and murder. Three white men killed that day and the boy brought back to torture. It was him that killed them, him that yelled loudest when the boy was burning. Him that set fire to my house and burned my children . . .

I saw him running through the woods, white men after him. I saw him fall, a dozen bullets in him. But he wouldn't be dead. He would lie there bleeding and look at me out of his painted eyes, and I would go up and stomp on him, stomp him into the dirt . . .

My hands shook so I dropped the sticks I was carrying. I was near enough now to hear all they were saying. Mad Dog was taking little silver brooches out of a buckskin. He poured them out in a pile on a rock and then counted them. The old chief stood there till he got through counting; then he swept them all up into a bag he took from around his neck.

"Brother," he said, "the woman is yours."

Mad Dog had left the fire and was coming towards me. I ran over and caught hold of the old chief's arm. I called him by his Indian name.

"Kagahye-liske, do not give me to this man. He has killed my children and burned my house."

He looked down at me and it was like he'd never seen me before. His face, not painted, was as cruel as the Cherokee's, the eyes bloodshot and the whole face swollen from the meat he had eaten.

"The war whoop drowns sorrow," he said. "This chief is my brother and a mighty warrior. He has this day killed three white men."

I hung on to his arm. "Keep me for one of the young men of your village," I said. "The Cherokee are old women. You have said so and you have promised. You have promised to take me with you wherever you go."

He shook my hands off. "A promise," he said, "to a white coward! Go to your work."

He turned around like he was going to leave the cave. I run after him and caught hold of his knees, but he broke away. Mad Dog come and tied me up tight with thongs that he cut from buffalo hide, and then they both went on up to the barren where the other Indians was still screeching and stamping.

The screeching and stamping went on far into the night. The fire under the kettle went out and it was dark except for a little light from the moon. I laid there on the floor, listening to the Indians and thinking about how it would be when Mad Dog came down to take me for his wife. I laid there, expecting him to come any minute, but the singing and dancing went on and he didn't come, and after a while I went to sleep.

V

The white boy that they had burned came to me while I was asleep. He came carrying a lamp that was made from the bleached skull of a sheep. The brain hollow was filled with buffalo fat and there was a wick in it burning bright. He came walking between the trees like he didn't have need to look where he was going. His hair was light like I had seen it when he passed me there on the path, but it was long, too, like Tice Harman's. His eyes were the same eyes that had looked at me there on the path.

I said to him what I had said there. "I couldn't do nothing," I said. "There wasn't nothing I could do."

He didn't speak—only made signs for me to follow him. I got up and walked after him. The rawhide thongs were still on me but they didn't bind any more and I moved as easy and as light as he did. He went down by the falls and clomb up over the hill to where the elm tree stood that had the big rattlesnake painted on it. He walked past the elm tree and struck out through the black pines that were all over that ridge. Sometimes he would go so fast that I couldn't keep up with him, and then I would stand still and after a while I would see the light flickering through the trees and I would go on to where he was waiting for me. We went on through the pine woods and started down the side of the ridge. I heard water running somewhere far down below. I thought that would be Mudlick Creek, but when I got to it it was a branch I'd never seen before. We crossed it and went on up a path through a clearing. There were little shrubs all around like the ones up on the barren, and in the middle of them was a house. It was my house and yet it wasn't. White all over and the walls so thin you could see the light from the lamp shining through the logs.

People were walking around in the yard and sitting on the doorstep. They moved to let me go through the door, but they didn't speak to me and I didn't speak to them.

The men that were sitting in front of the fire playing draughts didn't even look up when I came in. I went over to the hearth and tried to dry out my clothes. I stood there holding out my hands but no heat came. I looked at the logs and they were white like the timbers of the house, and the same light came from them. I saw that the men playing didn't have a lamp and yet there was light all around them.

People kept walking in and out of the cabin, men and women and little children. I would go up to them and look in their faces, but there wasn't anybody there I knew. I walked round and round the room. Every now and then the people would move out of the way and I would catch sight of the walls. White, with patches of green on them. I put my hand up and felt one of the logs. It was round and cold to the touch. No log at all, but bleached bone. I knew then that all the house was bone, the floor and the walls and the chimney, even the table that the men were playing on, all made from the big bones down at the lick.

One of the men at the table stretched his arm out and pulled me over to him. He had on a beaver cap and his face under it was pale like he'd been in the woods a long time. He looked at me and I saw it was Lance Rayburn. He sang, pulling me up over the arm of his chair:

> "Oh . . . the bell cow, kicking up her heels,
> Call the little gal to milk her in the pail . . ."

Fiddling started up somewhere and all fell to dancing. They danced to one of my old granny's tunes:

> "There was an old lord lived in a northern countree,
> Bowee down, bowee down . . ."

There was bowing back and forth and balancing, and there were figures called, but wasn't any women dancing. I would see something going by and think it was a woman's skirt, but when I got up to it it would be fur or feathers dangling from a belt and all the faces around were dark, not like they were at first.

The great flames went leaping up the chimney, and all of a sudden I knew that they had built that fire to burn somebody by. I looked around for the one they were going to burn but he wasn't there. I said, "They will burn me next," and I saw what they would tie me to—the rattlesnake tree, going straight up from the table through the roof.

I went to the door and I saw through the black trunks a light flickering. I run and Mad Dog and the old chief were after me the way they were that day in the hollow. I thought, "They will kill me now when I go down," and I run faster and then they were both gone away and I was walking through pine woods, the light flickering on ahead of me.

I walked on and come to a creek that run along between wide banks of cane. The light shone on the water and made it light as mist. I stepped in, not knowing whether it was water or mist, and I could feel it coming up around my knees, water and yet not water. I moved along through it light as the wind till I come to where the creek forked. I could see the two forks and the white trunks of the sycamores along the bank, but I didn't know which way to go.

The light was all around me. I could see it shining on the reeds and on the little leaves of the cane and on the water where it broke on the rocks. Behind me there were voices talking.

"Jinny Wiley . . . Jinny Wiley, that was stolen and lived with the Indians . . ."

And then it was the old chief talking to the new moon:

"The white people . . . The white people are all over the land. The beaver makes no more dams and the buffalo does not come to the lick. And bees swarm here in the ancient village. Bees swarm on the graves of our fathers . . ."

The light that had been around me was gone. It was shining now through the tree trunks down a fork of the creek. I waded towards it through the light water, the voices following, and then they were gone and I was standing at the foot of a high mountain. I looked up and saw the light flickering at the top and I clomb towards it, pulling myself up by the scrubs and holly bushes.

I got up on the mountaintop but the young man wasn't there. I walked out onto the edge of a cliff and he was by my side. He said, "Look, Jinny!" and the flame of his lamp leaped up and lighted the whole valley and I looked across a river and saw a fort. I saw the roofs of the houses and the stockade and the timber burned back over the rifle range, and I saw men and women walking around inside the stockade.

I said, "I'm a-going over there," but the young man wasn't with me any more, and the dark that was all around was the inside of the rock-house.

VI

When I woke up the next morning the Indians had a big fire going and were all sitting around eating. I laid there and made out I was still asleep. They had found trace of buffalo down at the lick and were making ready for a big hunt. I thought maybe they would take me along to bring in the game the way they did sometimes, and then I heard Mad Dog say they would leave me tied up in the cave till they got ready to start for their town.

I was laying with my face turned up and I was feared they could tell by my eyes that I wasn't asleep. I give a kind of groan and rolled over on my side. I laid there not moving while the talking went on all around me. Once footsteps come over to the corner where I was laying and I heard something slap down on the ground right by me but I didn't give any sign and the footsteps went away.

I laid there so still that I went to sleep again with the talking and the making ready for the hunt still going on. I was waked up by a kind of roaring sound. At first I thought it was the falls and then I knew the falls wouldn't sound that loud. I opened my eyes. The Indians were all gone and there was a big storm blowing up.

I laid there watching the pine tops lash back and forth in the wind, and the dream I'd had come back into my mind as plain as if it was something that had happened. I thought it was sent to me on purpose to tell me that now was the chance to get away. I knew that if the Indians come back with any game that night they'd feast high again and were more than likely to take me up on the barren and burn me like they done that boy.

I sat up. A piece of meat was lying on the floor right by me. That meant that the Indians would be all gone all day and maybe another day. If I could only get free of the thongs I might get a long way off before they knew I was gone.

There was a knife stuck in a crack of the rock where they laid the meat. If I could only get hold of that! I rolled over and over till I got to the rock and managed to get up on my knees, though the thongs cut into me bad. I could see the handle of the knife sticking up out of the crack and I laid my face down flat on the rock and tried to catch hold of it with my teeth. But it was too far down and all I did was get my mouth full of grit and sand. I gave up and laid down again. The wind wasn't as high as it had been, but the rain was coming down hard. It blew way back into the cave. I laid there with the big drops spattering in my face and a thought came to me. I rolled over to where the rain was pouring down off the roof and I laid there till I was soaked through. All the time I kept straining at the thongs and I could feel them giving a little, the way leather does when it's wet. I kept on, getting them looser and looser till finally I worked my way out of them and stood up free.

I listened and I couldn't hear anything but the roaring of the wind and the beating of the rain on the ledge. I tiptoed to the end of the cave and looked down the path. But I couldn't see any sign of living creature. I dug the knife out from between the rocks and I took the piece of cooked meat and a little kettle that the old chief had left laying around, and went off out of the other end of the cave and along the cliffside.

I kept to the path a little way and then I struck off through the trees down the hillside. The ground was wet and slid from under my feet in big chunks. I caught on to the trees all the way to keep myself from falling. When I got to the bottom I could look back and see where I'd come, as plain as if I'd blazed a trail. I knew I'd have to strike water. I run in among some pines and come to a wet weather branch. I waded right in. It was swift water and full of holes. I would step in one every now and then and go down, but I kept on as fast as I could. I felt all the time like the Indians were after me. I knew they had gone south towards the salt lick and I knew the whole cliffside and the barren was between me and them, but all the time I felt like they were right behind me. When I looked over my shoulder the top boughs of the rattlesnake tree showed from the barren. I was glad when I rounded a bend and it was out of sight.

When I come out to where the branch flowed into the creek I didn't know which way to go, and then I thought that in my dream I was following water and I struck right down the stream. It was harder going here than it was in the branch. The snows melting had filled all the dry weather branches, and muddy water kept running in till you couldn't tell anything about the depth. It was well I was going downstream, but even then the current was a hindrance to me, reaching in and sweeping me off my feet sometimes into a hole that I would have a time getting out of. More than once I was in danger of drowning.

I kept on like this all day. When it was drawing towards dark I crawled up on the bank under some cedars and I laid there and I ate a good-sized piece of the cooked meat I had brought with me. The rain had fallen off to a light drizzle and there was some color in the sky, sign of a clear day tomorrow. There was a flight of little birds over the water and then round and round the tops of the cedars. Some of them lit in the boughs of the tree I was laying under. I could hear them flying in and out and the quick cries and then the twittering as they settled down to roost. It was dark under the trees but the streak of light stayed on the water. I laid here and watched it fade and I wished I could stay there where the cedar boughs were like a little house. I wished I could stay there and not run any more. I thought I would maybe sleep a few minutes and then I could go on faster. But when I shut my eyes I would think I heard the Indians coming through the trees and after a little I got up and went on again.

I tried wading some more but I couldn't make it in the pitch dark. I got up on the bank of the creek and pushed my way through the bushes as best I could. Sometimes the undergrowth would be so thick I couldn't make it, and then I would have to get down in the water again. All the way I was worrying about losing time following the bending and twisting of the creek, and then I would think that was the only sure way to get out of the hill country and I had best stick to water, spite of all the bending.

Sometime during the night I lost my way from the creek and wandered in the pitch dark into a marsh that was all along the creek bottom. More like a bog it was. I couldn't seem to get out of it no matter what I did. I stood there bogged to the knees and couldn't even hear the creek running —nothing but the wind soughing in the trees. And I thought what a lone place it was and if I came on quicksand, as was more than likely, I could go down and even my bones never be found. And I thought of how Lance Rayburn's bones might have been laying all this time in some hollow of the mountain and nothing maybe but squirrels or deer ever going near the place, and it seemed to me I might better have stayed with the Indians. But I knew it wouldn't be any use going back now. They would put the fire to me sure.

I stood there and I heard some wild thing passing. Pit pat pit pat it went; feet falling on dry ground. I pulled out of the muck and made towards the sound, and a deer or something broke through the thicket and went off through the woods.

I followed and come out on high ground, a slope covered with pine needles. I threw myself down flat on my face. I must have gone off to sleep. When I come to myself light was growing through the trees, and all around me I could hear twigs snapping and little rustlings. I got up quick, thinking it was the Indians coming, and then I felt foolish, knowing it was only game stirring at break of day. I saw two deer go by, moving slow over the brown pine needles. The air was so still they didn't get a whiff of me until they were out of the thicket. The buck wheeled so quick he almost knocked the doe over, and then they were both clattering off over the hill.

I went down to the creek bank and washed my face and let the water run over my wrists where they were scratched by the branches. I ate the last of my meat sitting there on a rock. When I got ready to go I found out that one of my strings of jerked meat had slipped off during the night. I couldn't hardly believe it at first. I stood up and felt all over my clothes time and again but it warn't there.

"Well," I said, "it's gone and they ain't no use crying over it, but I wish to God it'd a been the little piece."

I got in the water and started wading again. The creek was shallow for about half a mile and then it run into a bigger creek. The two of them run on before me and I didn't know which way to go. I stood there looking. The sun was up and it shone on the water. I watched the riffles break on the black rocks where the sun caught them, and the place was not the same place I had seen in the dream and yet it was the same because of the light that was over everything.

I remembered the way I took in the dream. "Left I'll go," I said, "like it was in the dream, and if it don't turn out right it's no fault of mine."

I went on, wading half the time. All that day I was thinking about something to eat. Seems like everything good I ever had to eat in my life come back to torment me that day. The smell of herring, cooking, bothered me most. I would see myself, a chap, back in the Roanoke country, broiling herrings over the coals the way children did when their mammy wouldn't give them anything else to eat between meals. I would go over it all, time and again, the herrings hanging in rows in the smokehouse, like tobacco in a barn, and us climbing up on a slab of wood to get at them.

"Three," Dinny, that's my oldest brother, 'd say every time. "Three. You might as well get one apiece while you're at it."

I thought, too, about people wasting things, of a woman I knew used to give all her buttermilk to her pig, and I thought how it was shameful to have no mind for them that might be starving. And I thought how if I could have that pig's dinner one time, or even a moldy piece of bread, the kind I'd thrown away many a time as not good enough for the dogs. And yet I'd been as wasteful as any of them in my day—worse, even, with game. I used to go hunting just for the fun of it. Seemed like there warn't nothing I liked better than sighting down a rifle. Warn't none of the Sellards or Damron boys a better shot than I was, and I could throw a knife with the best of them. That time John and Dick and me and the two Damrons went to Sinking Fork on a big hunt I shot eighteen wild gobblers, and when we loaded up and there were more'n we could carry it was me that said to leave them laying, that there warn't no use in breaking yourself down and the woods full of gobblers. I thought about them gobblers more'n once that day and, Lord, how I wished I could git my hands on a rifle butt just one more time.

I threw my knife once or twice at some small game, mostly rabbits, but it was a rusty old thing and not fitted to the hand the way a knife has to be to turn proper. One rabbit that I hit square in the middle got up and skittered off like nothing had happened, and I saw then it was a waste of time to throw at them.

Late that evening I come on some forward wild greens in a sheltered place on the creek bank. I went down on my knees and gathered every shoot. I found some punk and went up to a rockhouse on the side of the hill and built a little fire way in under the ledge the way I'd seen the Indians do. I knew it was craziness to build a fire, but it might be days before I'd come on any wild greens again. "I'll eat," I said, "varmints or no varmints."

I put my greens on to boil in the little kettle with a piece of the jerked meat and sat there, thinking about how Indians would go up on a cliff to sight over the country and how the least little smoke curling up would be a sign to them. Once I was on the point of putting the fire out but I couldn't bring myself to do it. I feared to feed it much and yet I'd catch myself putting dead twigs to it. It was a long time before the bubbles started rising up in that little old kettle. I sat there rocking on my heels and talking to them.

"Boil," I said, "boil. God's sake, can't you boil no faster'n that? And me setting here starving."

I ate up every mite of the greens and drank the pot liquor and licked the kettle and then I put out down the hill as fast as I could. I could feel my stomach tight under my waistband and strength coming up in me from the vittles and I run faster than I'd ever run before. It was dark under the trees but there was still light down the water courses. I thought how in some cleared place or in a town it wouldn't be dark for two or three hours yet and I saw myself in such a place, moving around and talking to people but staying always in the light. And I said to myself, if I ever got into such a cleared place again it'd be hard to get me to set foot in the woods.

The creek I was following was a master tumbler. Straight down it went over big rocks and the water white everywhere with its dashing. Once I thought I would leave it and strike out through the woods again, and then I thought falling water'd take me out of the hills quicker'n anything else and I'd best stick to it long as I could.

I went on and then all of a sudden I come upon something that froze my guts cold: the print of a foot by the water. I knew it would be a moccasin but I stooped down and looked at it good. I told myself it might be a white man—might be a hunter wearing moccasins like most of 'em did; but I went on a little way and there were three, four footprints in some wet sand and all of them were moccasins. I thought then the game was up or would be directly, but I run on. I run on. I couldn't think of anything else to do.

It was still light when I come out on a big rock by some little falls. I stood there looking and I couldn't believe my eyes. A broad river ran there before me with clearings here and there on the bank and, right across from the rock I was standing on, a fort: a blockhouse with a stockade fence around it and the timber burned back over the rifle range.

I got off the rock and run down towards the water. A woman and some children were walking along outside the stockade. I called to the woman. She give one look at me and turned and run inside the fort, the children after her. I saw the gate swing to behind them and I knew they had shot the bolt.

I tore off my petticoat and waved it over my head and yelled loud as I could:

"Let me in! Let me in, I tell you!"

I could see heads at the upper story and one somebody standing up on a stump to look over the stockade. But nobody answered and there wasn't no sign of the gate opening.

I looked over my shoulder. The woods were dark behind me and there wasn't any sign of Indians, but I knew they'd be coming any minute. I felt like I knew the place in the woods they were at now. I saw them trotting, trotting through the trees, one after another, the way they went.

I thought, "I'll have to do something quick or they'll get me sure, after all my trouble." I started in to swim it but I couldn't make headway against that current. I saw I would be drowning in a minute, and I swum hard and got back to shallow water. It come to me then that the folks in the fort didn't know who I was. I stood up in the water and yelled, loud as I could:

"I'm Jinny Wiley . . . Jinny Wiley that the Indians stole."

The echo come back to me from the woods, but there wasn't any sound from the fort. Then the gate opened a little way and an old man come out with a gun in his hand. He stood there looking at me and he turned around and said something to the folks in the fort and then he started down the path. I watched him coming down over the rifle range, an old man, gray-haired and feeble enough to a been my grandsire. I shouted at him.

"You can't do it. Send some young body over."

He stood on the bank and shouted back at me, his old voice quavering across the water:

"Where'd you come from?"

I jumped up and down and shrieked, top of my voice:

"God's sakes, man, you going to let me die right here before your eyes? I'm white! White, I tell you!"

"All of 'em's gone but me," he said, "and they ain't no canoe."

"Make a raft," I told him.

He nodded his head up and down. I could see his old gray beard a-shaking. "You better be ready to swim for it," he said. "I don't know as I can git across."

He called to the women in the fort and they come and brought an axe. There was a dead mulberry tree on the bank and they went to work felling it. The old man went off in the woods and come back with some grape vine. When the tree fell it split into three logs and he tied them together with a grapevine and then he and the women rolled them down to the water. They handed him two rifles and he laid them on the raft and started poling. The current caught him and he was going downstream. Yelling had started behind me somewhere in the woods. The Indians were coming.

I run down the bank till I got even with the raft and I swum out and clomb aboard. The old man poled hard. We got halfway out in the river and then the vines begun to come loose and the raft was spreading apart. I knelt down and held the logs together with my hands the best I could. The old man fell down on his knees and started praying.

" 'Tain't no use," he said; "we can't make it."

I looked over my shoulder. The Indians were swarming down to the water. I knew they'd be swimming directly. The old man was still praying. I took the pole away from him.

"Go on and pray, you old fool," I said. "I'm a-going to git across this river."

I put all the strength I had into it, and we made some headway. The yelling was closer now. The Indians were in the water. A shot rung out. I hoped to God one of 'em was hit. I poled harder and I saw some willow boughs ahead of me. I reached out and grabbed hold of 'em and we pulled ourselves to shore.

We went up over the rifle range fast as we could. I looked back once. The Indians had left the water and were standing on the bank. I heard Mad Dog calling:

"Whoopee! . . . whoopee! . . . pretty Jinny!"

We went through the gate. I heard the bolt shoot home and I knew I was inside the fort. I fell down on the ground and the women and children come crowding. The Indians were still yelling. I sat up and the high stockade fence was all around me.

"Lord God," I said, "I was lucky to git away from them Indians!"

COMMENT AND QUESTION

1. In one of his poems, Stephen Vincent Benét describes the ghost of Daniel Boone. As Boone goes by at night, phantom deer spring up, and "all lost, wild America is burning in their eyes," "Daniel Boone," *A Book of Americans* (Rinehart, 1933). Lost, wild America burns in this story, too. It is the lost wilderness of America that Miss Gordon recreates here.

2. The story is also a picture of a lost pioneer culture. In alien surroundings Jinny remains what she is, a pioneer white woman. How does she preserve her identity? How do we learn of the culture from which she comes? (The most appealing picture is probably that of Jinny's granny, "turned simple.")

3. A tale about the American Indian can easily become trite, romantic, sentimental, or sensational. "The Captive" avoids all these dangers and achieves, instead, a sober reality. Emotional and sensational details are toned down, so much so that for a brief space the reader wonders how simple, unassuming Jinny, telling the story in her own forthright first person, will communicate her feelings.

But Jinny is far from passive. Early in the story toward the close of section II, there is evidence of Jinny's strong emotional response to the horror of which she has become a part. Again, in the dream in section V, where Jinny gets outside herself, the reader can respond to the full force of the story. What strong emotional associations stimulate the incidents in Jinny's dream?

The rhythm of the prose communicates feeling also. Read aloud any part of section V. Consider also the heightened style in the passages where Crowmocker, Jinny, and Mad Dog speak in Shawnee. Is there justification for the stately, poetic language?

4. Early in the story someone tells Jinny that she is "brash" and "lucky." Do these two words keynote the actions of Jinny throughout the story?

5. Jinny's dream, in its inception and in its consequences, is the most interesting part of "The Captive." The immediate stimulation for the dream is quite clear. But the secondary impulses are strong, too, and have been building for a long time.

In section VI, are the conditions for flight any more favorable than they were in section IV? What, then, spurs a flight in section VI? The obvious answer is not satisfactory. Jinny has a stronger and more subtle reason than the presence of Mad Dog.

This subtle reason explains, in part, the force of the dream in the story. Are you willing to accept the dream simply as a supernatural presage or omen? Does Jinny use the dream as an explicit guide? Compare the flame of the young man's lamp as it lights the whole valley (end of section V) with the light breaking over everything on the first morning of Jinny's flight. Is not the relationship poetic rather than explicit?

Jinny's dream has a powerful psychological function. When a human being springs into action, he draws deep down upon all his resources. Would you be willing to accept Jinny's dream as the plan of her unconscious?

THE SECOND DEATH

BY GRAHAM GREENE

GRAHAM GREENE (1904–   ) was born in England and educated at Oxford. He has been a film critic for the *Spectator* and wrote the script for two highly successful motion pictures, "The Fallen Idol," and "The Third Man." He has written three plays and many mystery or detective stories. Of his nine novels, three in particular have established him among the foremost living novelists. These three novels, *The Power and the Glory* (1940), *The Heart of the Matter* (1948), and *The End of the Affair* (1951) are powerful studies of sin, guilt, and redemption. Greene's *In Search of a Character: Two African Journals* (1962) illuminates his recent novel, *A Burnt-Out Case* (1961). His short stories appear in *Nineteen Stories* (1949) and *Twenty-One Stories* (1954).

SHE FOUND me in the evening under trees that grew outside the village. I had never cared for her and would have hidden myself if I'd seen her coming. She was to blame, I'm certain, for her son's vices. If they were vices, but I'm very far from admitting that they were. At any rate he was generous, never mean, like others in the village I could mention if I chose.

I was staring hard at a leaf or she would never have found me. It was dangling from its twig, its stalk torn across by the wind or else by a stone one of the village children had flung. Only the green tough skin of the stalk held it there suspended. I was watching closely, because a caterpillar was crawling across the surface, making the leaf sway to and fro. The caterpillar was aiming at the twig, and I wondered whether it would reach it in safety or whether the leaf would fall with it into the water. There was a pool underneath the trees, and the water always appeared red, because of the heavy clay in the soil.

I never knew whether the caterpillar reached the twig, for, as I've said, the wretched woman found me. The first I knew of her coming was her voice just behind my ear.

"I've been looking in all the pubs for you," she said in her old shrill voice. It was typical of her to say "all the pubs" when there were only two in the place. She always wanted credit for trouble she hadn't really taken.

I was annoyed and I couldn't help speaking a little harshly. "You might have saved yourself the trouble," I said, "you should have known I wouldn't be in a pub on a fine night like this."

The old vixen became quite humble. She was always smooth enough when she wanted anything. "It's for my poor son," she said. That meant that he was ill. When he was well I never heard her say anything better than "that dratted boy." She'd make him be in the house by midnight every day of the week, as if there were any serious mischief a man could get up to in a little village like ours. Of course we soon found a way to cheat her, but it was the principle of the thing I objected to—a grown man of over thirty ordered about by his mother, just because she hadn't a husband to control. But when he was ill, though it might be with only a small chill, it was "my poor son."

"He's dying," she said, "and God knows what I shall do without him."

"Well, I don't see how I can help you," I said. I was angry, because he'd been dying once before and she'd done everything but actually bury him. I imagined it was the same sort of dying this time, the sort a man gets over. I'd seen him about the week before on his way up the hill to see the big-breasted girl at the farm. I'd watched him till he was like a little black dot, which stayed suddenly by a square grey box in a field. That was the barn where they used to meet. I've very good eyes and it amuses me to try how far and how clearly they can see. I met him again some time after midnight and helped him get into the house without his mother knowing, and he was well enough then—only a little sleepy and tired.

The old vixen was at it again. "He's been asking for you," she shrilled at me.

"If he's as ill as you make out," I said, "it would be better for him to ask for a doctor."

"Doctor's there, but he can't do anything." That startled me for a moment, I'll admit it, until I thought, "The old devil's malingering. He's got some plan or other." He was quite clever enough to cheat a doctor. I had seen him throw a fit that would have deceived Moses.

"For God's sake come," she said, "he seems frightened." Her voice broke quite genuinely, for I suppose in her way she was fond of him. I couldn't help pitying her a little, for I knew that he had never cared a mite for her and had never troubled to disguise the fact.

I left the trees and the red pool and the struggling caterpillar, for I knew that she would never leave me alone, now that her "poor boy" was asking for me. Yet a week ago there was nothing she wouldn't have done to keep us apart. She thought me responsible for his ways, as though any mortal man could have kept him off a likely woman when his appetite was up.

I think it must have been the first time I had entered their cottage by the front door since I came to the village ten years ago. I threw an amused glance at his window. I thought I could see the marks on the wall of the ladder we'd used the week before. We'd had a little difficulty in putting it straight, but his mother slept sound. He had brought the ladder down from the barn, and when he'd got safely in, I carried it up there again. But you could never trust his word. He'd lie to his best friend, and when I reached the barn I found the girl had gone. If he couldn't bribe you with his mother's money, he'd bribe you with other people's promises.

I began to feel uneasy directly I got inside the door. It was natural that the house should be quiet, for the pair of them never had any friends to stay, although the old woman had a sister-in-law living only a few miles away. But I didn't like the sound of the doctor's feet as he came downstairs to meet us. He'd twisted his face into a pious solemnity for our benefit, as though there was something holy about death, even about the death of my friend.

"He's conscious," he said, "but he's going. There's nothing I can do. If you want him to die in peace, better let his friend go along up. He's frightened about something."

The doctor was right. I could tell that as soon as I bent under the lintel and entered my friend's room. He was propped up on a pillow, and his eyes were on the door, waiting for me to come. They were very bright and frightened, and his hair lay across his forehead in sticky stripes. I'd never realized before what an ugly fellow he was. He had sly eyes that looked at you too much out of the corners, but when he was in ordinary health, they held a twinkle that made you forget the slyness. There was something pleasant and brazen in the twinkle, as much as to say, "I know I'm sly and ugly. But what does that matter? I've got guts." It was that twinkle, I think, some women found attractive and stimulating. Now when the twinkle was gone, he looked a rogue and nothing else.

I thought it my duty to cheer him up, so I made a small joke out of the fact that he was alone in bed. He didn't seem to relish it, and I was beginning to fear that he too was taking a religious view of his death, when he told me to sit down, speaking quite sharply.

"I'm dying," he said, talking very fast, "and I want to ask you some-thing. That doctor's no good—he'd think me delirious. I'm frightened, old man. I want to be reassured," and then after a long pause, "someone with common sense." He slipped a little farther down in his bed.

"I've only once been badly ill before," he said. "That was before you settled here. I wasn't much more than a boy. People tell me that I was even supposed to be dead. They were carrying me out to burial when a doctor stopped them just in time."

I'd heard plenty of cases like that, and I saw no reason why he should want to tell me about it. And then I thought I saw his point. His mother had not been too anxious once before to see if he were properly dead, though I had little doubt that she made a great show of grief—"My poor boy. I don't know what I shall do without him." And I'm certain that she believed herself then, as she believed herself now. She wasn't a murderess. She was only inclined to be premature.

"Look here, old man," I said, and I propped him a little higher on his pillow, "you needn't be frightened. You aren't going to die, and any-way I'd see that the doctor cut a vein or something before they moved you. But that's all morbid stuff. Why, I'd stake my shirt that you've got plenty more years in front of you. And plenty more girls too," I added to make him smile.

"Can't you cut out all that?" he said, and I knew then that he had turned religious. "Why," he said, "if I lived, I wouldn't touch another girl. I wouldn't, not one."

I tried not to smile at that, but it wasn't easy to keep a straight face. There's always something a bit funny about a sick man's morals. "Any-way," I said, "you needn't be frightened."

"It's not that," he said. "Old man, when I came round that other time, I thought that I'd been dead. It wasn't like sleep at all. Or rest in peace. There was someone there, all round me, who knew everything. Every girl I'd ever had. Even that young one who hadn't understood. It was before your time. She lived a mile down the road, where Rachel lives now, but she and her family went away afterwards. Even the money I'd taken from mother. I don't call that stealing. It's in the family. I never had a chance to explain. Even the thoughts I'd had. A man can't help his thoughts."

"A nightmare," I said.

"Yes, it must have been a dream, mustn't it? The sort of dream people do get when they are ill. And I saw what was coming to me too. I can't bear being hurt. It wasn't fair. And I wanted to faint and I couldn't, because I was dead."

"In the dream," I said. His fear made me nervous. "In the dream," I said again.

"Yes, it must have been a dream—mustn't it?—because I woke up. The curious thing was I felt quite well and strong. I got up and stood in the road, and a little farther down, kicking up the dust, was a small crowd, going off with a man—the doctor who had stopped them burying me."

"Well," I said.

"Old man," he said, "suppose it was true. Suppose I had been dead. I believed it then, you know, and so did my mother. But you can't trust her. I went straight for a couple of years. I thought it might be a sort of second chance. Then things got fogged and somehow . . . It didn't seem really possible. It's not possible. Of course it's not possible. You know it isn't, don't you?"

"Why no," I said. "Miracles of that sort don't happen nowadays. And anyway, they aren't likely to happen to you, are they? And here of all places under the sun."

"It would be so dreadful," he said, "if it had been true, and I'd got to go through all that again. You don't know what things were going to happen to me in that dream. And they'd be worse now." He stopped and then, after a moment, he added as though he were stating a fact, "When one's dead there's no unconsciousness any more for ever."

"Of course it was a dream," I said and squeezed his hand. He was frightening me with his fancies. I wished that he'd die quickly, so that I could get away from his sly, bloodshot and terrified eyes and see something cheerful and amusing, like the Rachel he had mentioned, who lived a mile down the road.

"Why," I said, "if there had been a man about working miracles like that, we should have heard of others, you may be sure. Even poked away in this god-forsaken spot," I said.

"There were some others," he said. "But the stories only went round among the poor, and they'll believe anything, won't they? There were lots of diseased and crippled they said he'd cured. And there was a man, who'd been born blind, and he came and just touched his eyelids and sight came to him. Those were all old wives' tales, weren't they?" he asked me, stammering with fear, and then lying suddenly still and bunched up at the side of the bed.

I began to say, "Of course they were all lies," but I stopped, because there was no need. All I could do was to go downstairs and tell his mother to come up and close his eyes. I wouldn't have touched them for all the money in the world. It was a long time since I'd thought of that day, ages and ages ago, when I felt a cold touch like spittle on my lids and opening my eyes had seen a man like a tree surrounded by other trees walking away.

COMMENT AND QUESTION

1. One incident from "The Second Death" has a parallel in the Gospel of St. Luke 7:11–16. "At that time Jesus went into a city that is called

Naim: and there went with Him His disciples, and a great multitude. And when He came nigh to the gate of the city, behold a dead man was carried out, the only son of his mother; and she was a widow, and a great multitude of the city was with her. Whom when the Lord had seen, being moved with mercy toward her, He said to her: Weep not. And He came near, and touched the bier. (And they that carried it stood still.) And He said: Young man, I say to thee, arise. And he that was dead sat up, and began to speak. And He gave him to his mother."

2. In "The Second Death" neither mother, son, narrator, nor town has a name. The only name mentioned is that of Rachel, a Jewish name. Do these facts indicate a relationship with the Biblical story?

3. The subjects of sin, guilt, repentance, and moral responsibility are recurring themes in the writing of Greene. Have the experiences of the narrator been like those of the son? Whose story is this? The son's or the narrator's?

4. The keen eyesight of the narrator is stressed throughout the story. Why? What connection is there between the open eyes of the dead man in the last paragraph and the "cold touch" on the eyes of the narrator?

5. The people in this story—mother, son, narrator—are decidedly unpleasant. Did the author have a purpose in establishing this quality?

6. Is this story intended to be a parable?

THE SNOWS OF KILIMANJARO

BY ERNEST HEMINGWAY

ERNEST HEMINGWAY (1898-1961) was born in Oak Park, Illinois. In the First World War he served in an ambulance unit on the Italian front and was wounded. After the war he was a newspaper correspondent in Paris and became a member of the group of American expatriates. He was a correspondent also in the Spanish Civil War. He travelled widely. He has had a profound and international influence on the writing of fiction. Among his best-known novels are *The Sun Also Rises* (1926), *A Farewell to Arms* (1929), *For Whom the Bell Tolls* (1940), *Across the River and Into the Trees* (1950), and *The Old Man and the Sea* (1952), for which he was awarded the Pulitzer Prize in 1953. In 1954 he won the Nobel Prize for Literature. Forty-nine of his stories are collected in the volume *The Short Stories of Ernest Hemingway* (1953).

Kilimanjaro is a snow covered mountain 19,710 feet high, and is said to be the highest mountain in Africa. Its western summit is called the Masai "Ngàje Ngài," the House of God. Close to the western summit there is the dried and frozen carcass of a leopard. No one has explained what the leopard was seeking at that altitude.

"THE MARVELLOUS thing is that it's painless," he said. "That's how you know when it starts."

"Is it really?"

"Absolutely. I'm awfully sorry about the odor though. That must bother you."

"Don't! Please don't."

"Look at them," he said. "Now is it sight or is it scent that brings them like that?"

The cot the man lay on was in the wide shade of a mimosa tree and as he looked out past the shade onto the glare of the plain there were three of the big birds squatted obscenely, while in the sky a dozen more sailed, making quick-moving shadows as they passed.

"They've been there since the day the truck broke down," he said. "Today's the first time any have lit on the ground. I watched the way they sailed very carefully at first in case I ever wanted to use them in a story. That's funny now."

"I wish you wouldn't," she said.

"I'm only talking," he said. "It's much easier if I talk. But I don't want to bother you."

"You know it doesn't bother me," she said. "It's that I've gotten so very nervous not being able to do anything. I think we might make it as easy as we can until the plane comes."

"Or until the plane doesn't come."

"Please tell me what I can do. There must be something I can do."

"You can take the leg off and that might stop it, though I doubt it. Or you can shoot me. You're a good shot now. I taught you to shoot didn't I?"

"Please don't talk that way. Couldn't I read to you?"

"Read what?"

"Anything in the book bag that we haven't read."

"I can't listen to it," he said. "Talking is the easiest. We quarrel and that makes the time pass."

"I don't quarrel. I never want to quarrel. Let's not quarrel any more. No matter how nervous we get. Maybe they will be back with another truck today. Maybe the plane will come."

"I don't want to move," the man said. "There is no sense in moving now except to make it easier for you."

"That's cowardly."

"Can't you let a man die as comfortably as he can without calling him names? What's the use of slanging me?"

"You're not going to die."

"Don't be silly. I'm dying now. Ask those bastards." He looked over to where the huge, filthy birds sat, their naked heads sunk in the hunched feathers. A fourth planed down, to run quick-legged and then waddle slowly toward the others.

"They are around every camp. You never notice them. You can't die if you don't give up."

"Where did you read that? You're such a bloody fool."

"You might think about some one else."

"For Christ's sake," he said, "That's been my trade."

He lay then and was quiet for a while and looked across the heat shimmer of the plain to the edge of the bush. There were a few Tommies that showed minute and white against the yellow and, far off, he saw a herd of zebra, white against the green of the bush. This was a pleasant camp under big trees against a hill, with good water, and close by, a nearly dry water hole where sand grouse flighted in the mornings.

"Wouldn't you like me to read?" she asked. She was sitting on a canvas chair beside his cot. "There's a breeze coming up."

"No thanks."

"Maybe the truck will come."

"I don't give a damn about the truck."

"I do."

"You give a damn about so many things that I don't."

"Not so many, Harry."

"What about a drink?"

"It's supposed to be bad for you. It said in Black's to avoid all alcohol. You shouldn't drink."

"Molo!" he shouted.

"Yes Bwana."

"Bring whiskey-soda."

"Yes Bwana."

"You shouldn't," she said. "That's what I mean by giving up. It says it's bad for you. I know it's bad for you."

"No," he said. "It's good for me."

So now it was all over, he thought. So now he would never have a chance to finish it. So this was the way it ended in a bickering over a drink. Since the gangrene started in his right leg he had no pain and with the pain the horror had gone and all he felt now was a great tiredness and anger that this was the end of it. For this, that now was coming, he had very little curiosity. For years it had obsessed him; but now it meant nothing in itself. It was strange how easy being tired enough made it.

Now he would never write the things that he had saved to write until he knew enough to write them well. Well, he would not have to fail at trying to write them either. Maybe you could never write them, and that was why you put them off and delayed the starting. Well he would never know, now.

"I wish we'd never come," the woman said. She was looking at him holding the glass and biting her lip. "You never would have gotten anything like this in Paris. You always said you loved Paris. We could have stayed in Paris or gone anywhere. I'd have gone anywhere. I said I'd go anywhere you wanted. If you wanted to shoot we could have gone shooting in Hungary and been comfortable."

"Your bloody money," he said.

"That's not fair," she said. "It was always yours as much as mine. I left everything and I went wherever you wanted to go and I've done what you wanted to do. But I wish we'd never come here."

"You said you loved it."

"I did when you were all right. But now I hate it. I don't see why that had to happen to your leg. What have we done to have that happen to us?"

"I suppose what I did was to forget to put iodine on it when I first scratched it. Then I didn't pay any attention to it because I never infect. Then, later, when it got bad, it was probably using that weak carbolic solution when the other antiseptics ran out that paralyzed the minute blood vessels and started the gangrene." He looked at her, "What else?"

"I don't mean that."

"If we would have hired a good mechanic instead of a half baked kikuyu driver, he would have checked the oil and never burned out that bearing in the truck."

"I don't mean that."

"If you hadn't left your own people, your goddamned Old Westbury, Saratoga, Palm Beach people to take me on——"

"Why, I loved you. That's not fair. I love you now. I'll always love you. Don't you love me?"

"No," said the man. "I don't think so. I never have."

"Harry, what are you saying? You're out of your head."

"No. I haven't any head to go out of."

"Don't drink that," she said. "Darling, please don't drink that. We have to do everything we can."

"You do it," he said. "I'm tired."

Now in his mind he saw a railway station at Karagatch and he was standing with his pack and that was the headlight of the Simplon-Orient cutting the dark now and he was leaving Thrace then after the retreat. That was one of the things he had saved to write, with, in the morning at breakfast, looking out the window and seeing snow on the mountains in Bulgaria and Nansen's Secretary asking the old man if it were snow and the old man looking at it and saying, No, that's not snow. It's too early for snow. And the Secretary repeating to the other girls, No, you see. It's not snow and them all saying, It's not snow we were mistaken. But it was the snow all right and he sent them on into it when he evolved exchange of populations. And it was snow they tramped along in until they died that winter.

It was snow too that fell all Christmas week that year up in the Gauertal, that year they lived in the woodcutter's house with the big square porcelain stove that filled half the room, and they slept on mattresses filled with beech leaves, the time the deserter came with his feet bloody in the snow. He said the police were right behind him and they gave him woolen socks and held the gendarmes talking until the tracks had drifted over.

In Schrunz, on Christmas day, the snow was so bright it hurt your eyes when you looked out from the weinstube and saw every one coming home from church. That was where they walked up the sleigh-smoothed urine-yellowed road along the river with the steep pine hills, skis heavy on the shoulder, and where they ran that great run down the glacier above the Madlener-haus, the snow as smooth to see as cake frosting and as light as powder and he remembered the noiseless rush the speed made as you dropped down like a bird.

They were snow-bound a week in the Madlener-haus that time in the blizzard playing cards in the smoke by the lantern light and the stakes were higher all the time as Herr Lent lost more. Finally he lost it all. Everything, the skischule money and all the season's profit and then his capital. He could see him with his long nose, picking up the cards and then opening, "Sans Voir." There was always gambling then. When there was no snow you gambled and when there was too much you gambled. He thought of all the time in his life he had spent gambling.

But he had never written a line of that, nor of that cold, bright Christmas day with the mountains showing across the plain that Barker had flown across the lines to bomb the Austrian officers' leave train, machine-gunning them as they scattered and ran. He remembered Barker afterwards coming into the mess and starting to tell about it. And how quiet it got and then somebody saying, "You bloody murderous bastard."

Those were the same Austrians they killed then that he skied with later. No not the same. Hans, that he skied with all that year, had been in the Kaiser-Jägers and when they went hunting hares together up the little valley above the saw-mill they had talked of the fighting on Pasubio and of the attack on Pertica and Asalone and he had never written a word of that. Nor of Monte Corno, nor the Siete Commum, nor of Arsiedo.

How many winters had he lived in the Voralberg and the Arlberg? It was four and then he remembered the man who had the fox to sell when they had walked into Bludenz, that time to buy presents, and the cherry-pit taste of good kirsch, the fast-slipping rush of running powder-snow on crust, singing "Hi! Ho! said Rolly!" as you ran down the last stretch to the steep drop, taking it straight, then running the orchard in three turns and out across the ditch and onto the icy road behind the inn. Knocking your bindings loose, kicking the skis free and leaning them up against the wooden wall of the inn, the lamplight coming from the window, where inside, in the smoky new-wine smelling warmth, they were playing the accordion.

"Where did we stay in Paris?" he asked the woman who was sitting by him in a canvas chair, now, in Africa.

"At the Crillon. You know that."

"Why do I know that?"

"That's where we always stayed."

"No. Not always."

"There and at the Pavillion Henri-Quatre in St. Germain. You said you loved it there."

"Love is a dunghill," said Harry. "And I'm the cock that gets on it to crow."

"If you have to go away," she said, "is it absolutely necessary to kill off everything you leave behind? I mean do you have to take away everything? Do you have to kill your horse, and your wife and burn your saddle and your armour?"

"Yes," he said. "Your damned money was my armour. My Swift and my Armour."

"Don't."

"All right. I'll stop that. I don't want to hurt you."

"It's a little bit late now."

"All right then. I'll go on hurting you. It's more amusing. The only thing I ever really liked to do with you I can't do now."

"No, that's not true. You liked to do many things and everything you wanted to do I did."

"Oh, for Christ sake stop bragging, will you?"

He looked at her and saw her crying.

"Listen," he said. "Do you think that it is fun to do this? I don't know why I'm doing it. It's trying to kill to keep yourself alive, I imagine. I was all right when we started talking. I didn't mean to start this, and now I'm crazy as a coot and being as cruel to you as I can be. Don't pay any attention, darling, to what I say. I love you, really. You know I love you. I've never loved any one else the way I love you."

He slipped into the familiar lie he made his bread and butter by.

"You're sweet to me."

"You bitch," he said. "You rich bitch. That's poetry. I'm full of poetry now. Rot and poetry. Rotten poetry."

"Stop it, Harry, why do you have to turn into a devil now?"

"I don't like to leave anything," the man said. "I don't like to leave things behind."

                              *   *   *

It was evening now and he had been asleep. The sun was gone behind the hill and there was a shadow all across the plain and the small animals were feeding close to camp; quick dropping heads and switching tails, he watched them keeping well out away from the bush now. The birds no longer waited on the ground. They were all perched heavily in a tree.

There were many more of them. His personal boy was sitting by the bed.

"Memsahib's gone to shoot," the boy said. "Does Bwana want?"

"Nothing."

She had gone to kill a piece of meat and, knowing how he liked to watch the game, she had gone well away so she would not disturb this little pocket of the plain that he could see. She was always thoughtful, he thought. On anything she knew about, or had read, or that she had ever heard.

It was not her fault that when he went to her he was already over. How could a woman know that you meant nothing that you said; that you spoke only from habit and to be comfortable? After he no longer meant what he said, his lies were more successful with women than when he had told them the truth.

It was not so much that he lied as that there was no truth to tell. He had had his life and it was over and then he went on living it again with different people and more money, with the best of the same places, and some new ones.

You kept from thinking and it was all marvellous. You were equipped with good insides so that you did not go to pieces that way, the way most of them had, and you made an attitude that you cared nothing for the work you used to do, now that you could no longer do it. But, in yourself, you said that you would write about these people; about the very rich; that you were really not of them but a spy in their country; that you would leave it and write of it and for once it would be written by some one who knew what he was writing of. But he would never do it, because each day of not writing, of comfort, of being that which he despised, dulled his ability and softened his will to work so that, finally, he did no work at all. The people he knew now were all much more comfortable when he did not work. Africa was where he had been happiest in the good time of his life, so he had come out here to start again. They had made this safari with the minimum of comfort. There was no hardship; but there was no luxury and he had thought that he could get back into training that way. That in some way he could work the fat off his soul the way a fighter went into the mountains to work and train in order to burn it out of his body.

She had liked it. She said she loved it. She loved anything that was exciting, that involved a change of scene, where there were new people and where things were pleasant. And he had felt the illusion of returning strength of will to work. Now if this was how it ended, and he knew it was, he must not turn like some snake biting itself because its back was broken. It wasn't this woman's fault. If it had not been she it would have been another. If he lived by a lie he should try to die by it. He heard a shot beyond the hill.

She shot very well this good, this rich bitch, this kindly caretaker and destroyer of his talent. Nonsense. He had destroyed his talent himself. Why should he blame this woman because she kept him well? He had destroyed his talent by not using it, by betrayals of himself and what he believed in, by drinking so much that he blunted the edge of his perceptions, by laziness, by sloth, and by snobbery, by pride and by prejudice, by hook and by crook. What was this? A catalogue of old books? What was his talent anyway? It was a talent all right but instead of using it, he had traded on it. It was never what he had done, but always what he could do. And he had chosen to make his living with something else instead of a pen or a pencil. It was strange, too, wasn't it, that when he fell in love with another woman, that woman should always have more money than the last one? But when he no longer was in love, when he was only lying, as to this woman, now, who had the most money of all, who had all the money there was, who had had a husband and children, who had taken lovers and been dissatisfied with them, and who loved him dearly as a writer, as a man, as a companion and as a proud possession; it was strange that when he did not love her at all and was lying, that he should be able to give her more for her money than when he had really loved.

We must all be cut out for what we do, he thought. However you make your living is where your talent lies. He had sold vitality, in one form or another, all his life and when your affections are not too involved you give much better value for the money. He had found that out but he would never write that, now, either. No, he would not write that, although it was well worth writing.

Now she came in sight, walking across the open toward the camp. She was wearing jodhpurs and carrying her rifle. The two boys had a Tommie slung and they were coming along behind her. She was still a good-looking woman, he thought, and she had a pleasant body. She had a great talent and appreciation for the bed, she was not pretty, but he liked her face, she read enormously, liked to ride and shoot and, certainly, she drank too much. Her husband had died when she was still a comparatively young woman and for a while she had devoted herself to her two just-grown children, who did not need her and were embarrassed at having her about, to her stable of horses, to books, and to bottles. She liked to read in the evening before dinner, and she drank Scotch and soda while she read. By dinner she was fairly drunk and after a bottle of wine at dinner she was usually drunk enough to sleep.

That was before the lovers. After she had the lovers she did not drink so much because she did not have to be drunk to sleep. But the lovers bored her. She had been married to a man who had never bored her and these people bored her very much.

Then one of her two children was killed in a plane crash and after that was over she did not want the lovers, and drink being no anæsthetic she had to make another life. Suddenly, she had been acutely frightened of being alone. But she wanted some one that she respected with her.

It had begun very simply. She liked what he wrote and she had always envied the life he led. She thought he did exactly what he wanted to. The steps by which she had acquired him and the way in which she had finally fallen in love with him were all part of a regular progression in which she had built herself a new life and he had traded away what remained of his old life.

He had traded it for security, for comfort too, there was no denying that, and for what else? He did not know. She would have bought him anything he wanted. He knew that. She was a damned nice woman too. He would as soon be in bed with her as any one; rather with her, because she was richer, because she was very pleasant and appreciative and because she never made scenes. And now this life that she had built again was coming to a term because he had not used iodine two weeks ago when a thorn had scratched his knee as they moved forward trying to photograph a herd of waterbuck standing, their heads up, peering while their nostrils searched the air, their ears spread wide to hear the first noise that would send them rushing into the bush. They had bolted, too, before he got the picture.

Here she came now.

He turned his head on the cot to look toward her. "Hello," he said.

"I shot a Tommy ram," she told him. "He'll make you good broth and I'll have them mash some potatoes with the Klim. How do you feel?"

"Much better."

"Isn't that lovely? You know I thought perhaps you would. You were sleeping when I left."

"I had a good sleep. Did you walk far?"

"No. Just around behind the hill. I made quite a good shot on the Tommy."

"You shoot marvellously, you know."

"I love it. I've loved Africa. Really, If *you're* all right it's the most fun that I've ever had. You don't know the fun it's been to shoot with you. I've loved the country."

"I love it too."

"Darling, you don't know how marvellous it is to see you feeling better. I couldn't stand it when you felt that way. You won't talk to me like that again, will you? Promise me?"

"No," he said. "I don't remember what I said."

"You don't have to destroy me. Do you? I'm only a middle-aged woman who loves you and wants to do what you want to do. I've been destroyed two or three times already. You wouldn't want to destroy me again, would you?"

"I'd like to destroy you a few times in bed," he said.

"Yes. That's the good destruction. That's the way we're made to be destroyed. The plane will be here tomorrow."

"How do you know?"

"I'm sure. It's bound to come. The boys have the wood all ready and the grass to make the smudge. I went down and looked at it again today. There's plenty of room to land and we have the smudges ready at both ends."

"What makes you think it will come tomorrow?"

"I'm sure it will. It's overdue now. Then, in town, they will fix up your leg and then we will have some good destruction. Not that dreadful talking kind."

"Should we have a drink? The sun is down."

"Do you think you should?"

"I'm having one."

"We'll have one together. *Molo, letti dui whiskey-soda!*" she called.

"You'd better put on your mosquito boots," he told her.

"I'll wait till I bathe . . ."

While it grew dark they drank and just before it was dark and there was no longer enough light to shoot, a hyena crossed the open on his way around the hill.

"That bastard crosses there every night," the man said. "Every night for two weeks."

"He's the one makes the noise at night. I don't mind it. They're a filthy animal though."

Drinking together, with no pain now except the discomfort of lying in the one position, the boys lighting a fire, its shadow jumping on the tents, he could feel the return of acquiescence in this life of pleasant surrender. She *was* very good to him. He had been cruel and unjust in the afternoon. She was a fine woman, marvellous really. And just then it occurred to him that he was going to die.

It came with a rush; not as a rush of water nor of wind; but of a sudden evil-smelling emptiness and the odd thing was that the hyena slipped lightly along the edge of it.

"What is it, Harry?" she asked him.

"Nothing," he said. "You had better move over to the other side. To windward."

"Did Molo change the dressing?"

"Yes. I'm just using the boric now."

"How do you feel?"

"A little wobbly."

"I'm going in to bathe," she said. "I'll be right out. I'll eat with you and then we'll put the cot in."

So, he said to himself, we did well to stop the quarrelling. He had never quarrelled much with this woman, while with the women that he loved he had quarrelled so much they had finally, always, with the corrosion of the quarrelling, killed what they had together. He had loved too much, demanded too much, and he wore it all out.

He thought about alone in Constantinople that time, having quarrelled in Paris before he had gone out. He had whored the whole time and then, when that was over, and he had failed to kill his loneliness, but only made it worse, he had written her, the first one, the one who left him, a letter telling her how he had never been able to kill it. . . . How when he thought he saw her outside the Regence one time it made him go all faint and sick inside, and that he would follow a woman who looked like her in some way, along the Boulevard, afraid to see it was not she, afraid to lose the feeling it gave him. How every one he had slept with had only made him miss her more. How what she had done could never matter since he knew he could not cure himself of loving her. He wrote this letter at the Club, cold sober, and mailed it to New York asking her to write him at the office in Paris. That seemed safe. And that night missing her so much it made him feel hollow sick inside, he wandered up past Taxim's, picked a girl up and took her out to supper. He had gone to a place to dance with her afterward, she danced badly, and left her for a hot Armenian slut, that swung her belly against him so it almost scalded. He took her away from a British gunner subaltern after a row. The gunner asked him outside and they fought in the street on the cobbles in the dark. He'd hit him twice, hard, on the side of the jaw and when he didn't go down he knew he was in for a fight. The gunner hit him in the body, then beside his eye. He swung with his left again and landed and the gunner fell on him and grabbed his coat and tore the sleeve off and he clubbed him twice behind the ear and then smashed him with his right as he pushed him away. When the gunner went down his head hit first and he ran with the girl because they heard the M. P.'s coming. They got into a taxi and drove out to Rimmily Hissa along the Bosphorus, and around, and back in the cool night and went to bed and she felt as over-ripe as she looked but smooth, rose-petal, syrupy, smooth-bellied, big-breasted and needed no pillow under her buttocks, and he left her before she was awake looking blousy enough in the first daylight and turned up at the Pera Palace with a black eye, carrying his coat because one sleeve was missing.

That same night he left for Anatolia and he remembered, later on that trip, riding all day through fields of the poppies that they raised for opium and how strange it made you feel, finally, and all the distances seemed wrong, to where they had made the attack with the newly arrived Constantine officers, that did not know a god-damned thing, and the artillery had fired into the troops and the British observer had cried like a child.

That was the day he'd first seen dead men wearing white ballet skirts and upturned shoes with pompons on them. The Turks had come steadily and lumpily and he had seen the skirted men running and the officers shooting into them and running then themselves and he and the British observer had run too until his lungs ached and his mouth was full of the taste of pennies and they stopped behind some rocks and there were the Turks coming as lumpily as ever. Later he had seen the things that he could never think of and later still he had seen much worse. So when he got back to Paris that time he could not talk about it or stand to have it mentioned. And there in the café as he passed was that American poet with a pile of saucers in front of him and a stupid look on his potato face talking about the Dada movement with a Roumanian who said his name was Tristan Tzara, who always wore a monocle and had a headache, and, back at the apartment with his wife that now he loved again, the quarrel all over, the madness all over, glad to be home, the office sent his mail up to the flat. So then the letter in answer to the one he'd written came in on a platter one morning and when he saw the handwriting he went cold all over and tried to slip the letter underneath another. But his wife said, "Who is that letter from, dear?" and that was the end of the beginning of that.

He remembered the good times with them all, and the quarrels. They always picked the finest places to have the quarrels. And why had they always quarrelled when he was feeling best? He had never written any of that because, at first, he never wanted to hurt any one and then it seemed as though there was enough to write without it. But he had always thought that he would write it finally. There was so much to write. He had seen the world change; not just the events; although he had seen many of them and had watched the people, but he had seen the subtler change and he could remember how the people were at different times. He had been in it and he had watched it and it was his duty to write of it; but now he never would.

"How do you feel?" she said. She had come out from the tent now after her bath.

"All right."

"Could you eat now?" He saw Molo behind her with the folding table and the other boy with the dishes.

"I want to write," he said.

"You ought to take some broth to keep your strength up."

"I'm going to die tonight," he said. "I don't need my strength up."

"Don't be melodramatic, Harry, please," she said.

"Why don't you use your nose? I'm rotted half way up my thigh now. What the hell should I fool with broth for? Molo bring whiskey-soda."

"Please take the broth," she said gently.

"All right."

The broth was too hot. He had to hold it in the cup until it cooled enough to take it and then he just got it down without gagging.

"You're a fine woman," he said. "Don't pay any attention to me."

She looked at him with her well-known, well-loved face from *Spur* and *Town and Country*, only a little the worse for drink, only a little the worse for bed, but *Town and Country* never showed those good breasts and those useful thighs and those lightly small-of-back-caressing hands, and as he looked and saw her well known pleasant smile, he felt death come again. This time there was no rush. It was a puff, as of a wind that makes a candle flicker and the flame go tall.

"They can bring my net out later and hang it from the tree and build the fire up. I'm not going in the tent tonight. It's not worth moving. It's a clear night. There won't be any rain."

So this was how you died, in whispers that you did not hear. Well, there would be no more quarrelling. He could promise that. The one experience that he had never had he was not going to spoil now. He probably would. You spoiled everything. But perhaps he wouldn't.

"You can't take dictation, can you?"

"I never learned," she told him.

"That's all right."

There wasn't time, of course, although it seemed as though it telescoped so that you might put it all into one paragraph if you could get it right.

There was a log house, chinked white with mortar, on a hill above the lake. There was a bell on a pole by the door to call the people in to meals. Behind the house were fields and behind the fields was the timber. A line of lombardy poplars ran from the house to the dock. Other poplars ran along the point. A road went up to the hills along the edge of the timber and along that road he picked blackberries. Then that log house was burned down and all the guns that had been on deer foot racks above the open fire place were burned and afterwards their barrels, with the lead melted in the magazines, and the stocks burned away, lay out on the heap of ashes that were used to make lye for the big iron soap kettles, and you asked Grandfather if you could have them to play with, and he said, no. You see they were his guns still and he never bought any others. Nor did he hunt any more. The house was rebuilt in the same place out of lumber now and painted white and from its porch you saw the poplars and the lake beyond; but there were never any more guns. The barrels of the guns that had hung on the deer feet on the wall of the log house lay out there on the heap of ashes and no one ever touched them.

In the Black Forest, after the war, we rented a trout stream and there were two ways to walk to it. One was down the valley from Triberg and around the valley road in the shade of the trees that bordered the white road, and then up a side road that went up through the hills past many small farms, with the big Schwarzwald houses, until that road crossed the stream. That was where our fishing began.

The other way was to climb steeply up to the edge of the woods and then go across the top of the hills through the pine woods, and then out to the edge of a meadow and down across this meadow to the bridge. There were birches along the stream and it was not big, but narrow, clear and fast, with pools where it had cut under the roots of the birches. At the Hotel in Triberg the proprietor had a fine season. It was very pleasant and we were all great friends. The next year came the inflation and the money he had made the year before was not enough to buy supplies to open the hotel and he hanged himself.

You could dictate that, but you could not dictate the Place Contrescarpe where the flower sellers dyed their flowers in the street and the dye ran over the paving where the autobus started and the old men and the women, always drunk on wine and bad marc; and the children with their noses running in the cold; the smell of dirty sweat and poverty and drunkenness at the Café des Amateurs and the whores at the Bal Musette they lived above. The Concierge who entertained the trooper of the Garde Republicaine in her loge, his horse-hair-plumed helmet on a chair. The locataire across the hall whose husband was a bicycle racer and her joy that morning at the Cremerie when she had opened L'Auto and seen where he placed third in Paris-Tours, his first big race. She had blushed and laughed and then gone upstairs crying with the yellow sporting paper in her hand. The husband of the woman who ran the Bal Musette drove a taxi and when he, Harry, had to take an early plane the husband knocked upon the door to wake him and they each drank a glass of white wine at the zinc of the bar before they started. He knew his neighbors in that quarter then because they all were poor.

Around that Place there were two kinds; the drunkards and the sportifs. The drunkards killed their poverty that way; the sportifs took it out in exercise. They were the descendants of the Communards and it was no struggle for them to know their politics. They knew who had shot their fathers, their relatives, their brothers, and their friends when the Versailles troops came in and took the town after the Commune and executed any one they could catch with calloused hands, or who wore a cap, or carried any other sign he was a working man. And in that poverty, and in that quarter across the street from a Boucherie Chevaline and a wine co-operative he had written the start of all he was to do. There never was another part of Paris that he loved like that, the sprawling trees, the old white plastered houses painted brown below, the long green of the autobus in that round square, the purple flower dye upon the paving, the sudden drop down the hill of the rue Cardinal Lemoine to the River, and the other way the narrow crowded world of the rue Mouffetard. The street *that ran up toward the Pantheon and the other that he always took with the bicycle, the only asphalted street in all that quarter, smooth under the tires, with the high narrow houses and the cheap tall hotel where Paul Verlaine had died. There were only two rooms in the apartments where they lived and he had a room on the top floor of that hotel that cost him sixty francs a month where he did his writing, and from it he could see the roofs and chimney pots and all the hills of Paris.*

From the apartment you could only see the wood and coal man's place. He sold wine too, bad wine. The golden horse's head outside the Boucherie Chevaline where the carcasses hung yellow gold and red in the open window, and the green painted co-operative where they bought their wine; good wine and cheap. The rest was plaster walls and the windows of the neighbors. The neighbors who, at night, when some one lay drunk in the street, moaning and groaning in that typical French ivresse that you were propaganded to believe did not exist, would open their windows and then the murmur of talk.

"Where is the policeman? When you don't want him the bugger is always there. He's sleeping with some concierge. Get the Agent.*" Till some one threw a bucket of water from a window and the moaning stopped. "What's that? Water. Ah, that's intelligent." And the windows shutting. Marie, his femme de menage, protesting against the eight-hour day saying, "If a husband works until six he gets only a little drunk on the way home and does not waste too much. If he works only until five he is drunk every night and one has no money. It is the wife of the working man who suffers from this shortening of hours."*

"Wouldn't you like some more broth?" the woman asked him now.

"No, thank you very much. It is awfully good."

"Try just a little."

"I would like a whiskey-soda."

"It's not good for you."

"No. It's bad for me. Cole Porter wrote the words and the music. This knowledge that you're going mad for me."

"You know I like you to drink."

"Oh yes. Only it's bad for me."

When she goes, he thought. I'll have all I want. Not all I want but all there is. Ayee he was tired. Too tired. He was going to sleep a little while. He lay still and death was not there. It must have gone around another street. It went in pairs, on bicycles, and moved absolutely silently on the pavements.

No, he had never written about Paris. Not the Paris that he cared about. But what about the rest that he had never written?

What about the ranch and the silvered gray of the sage brush, the quick, clear water in the irrigation ditches, and the heavy green of the alfalfa. The trail went up into the hills and the cattle in the summer were shy as deer. The bawling and the steady noise and slow moving mass raising a dust as you brought them down in the fall. And behind the mountains, the clear sharpness of the peak in the evening light and, riding down along the trail in the moonlight, bright across the valley. Now he remembered coming down through the timber in the dark holding the horse's tail when you could not see and all the stories that he meant to write.

About the half-wit chore boy who was left at the ranch that time and told not to let any one get any hay, and that old bastard from the Forks who had beaten the boy when he had worked for him stopping to get some feed. The boy refusing and the old man saying he would beat him again. The boy got the rifle from the kitchen and shot him when he tried to come into the barn and when they came back to the ranch he'd been dead a week, frozen in the corral, and the dogs had eaten part of him. But what was left you packed on a sled wrapped in a blanket and roped on and you got the boy to help you haul it, and the two of you took it out over the road on skis, and sixty miles down to town to turn the boy over. He having no idea that he would be arrested. Thinking he had done his duty and that you were his friend and he would be rewarded. He'd helped to haul the old man in so everybody could know how bad the old man had been and how he'd tried to steal some feed that didn't belong to him, and when the sheriff put the handcuffs on the boy he couldn't believe it. Then he'd started to cry. That was one story he had saved to write. He knew at least twenty good stories from out there and he had never written one. Why?

"You tell them why," he said.

"Why what, dear?"

"Why nothing."

She didn't drink so much, now, since she had him. But if he lived he would never write about her, he knew that now. Nor about any of them. The rich were dull and they drank too much, or they played too much backgammon. They were dull and they were repetitious. He remembered poor Julian and his romantic awe of them and how he had started a story once that began, "The very rich are different from you and me." And how some one had said to Julian, Yes, they have more money. But that was not humorous to Julian. He thought they were a special glamourous race and when he found they weren't it wrecked him just as much as any other thing that wrecked him.

He had been contemptuous of those who wrecked. You did not have to like it because you understood it. He could beat anything, he thought, because no thing could hurt him if he did not care.

All right. Now he would not care for death. One thing he had always dreaded was the pain. He could stand pain as well as any man, until it went on too long, and wore him out, but here he had something that had hurt frightfully and just when he had felt it breaking him, the pain had stopped.

He remembered long ago when Williamson, the bombing officer, had been hit by a stick bomb some one in a German patrol had thrown as he was coming in through the wire that night and, screaming, had begged every one to kill him. He was a fat man, very brave, and a good officer, although addicted to fantastic shows. But that night he was caught in the wire, with a flare lighting him up and his bowels spilled out into the wire, so when they brought him in, alive, they had to cut him loose. Shoot me, Harry. For Christ sake shoot me. They had had an argument one time about our Lord never sending you anything you could not bear and some one's theory had been that meant that at a certain time the pain passed you out automatically. But he had always remembered Williamson, that night. Nothing passed out Williamson until he gave him all his morphine tablets that he had always saved to use himself and then they did not work right away.

Still this now, that he had, was very easy; and if it was no worse as it went on there was nothing to worry about. Except that he would rather be in better company.

He thought a little about the company that he would like to have.

No, he thought, when everything you do, you do too long, and do too late, you can't expect to find the people still there. The people all are gone. The party's over and you are with your hostess now.

I'm getting as bored with dying as with everything else, he thought.

"It's a bore," he said out loud.

"What is, my dear?"

"Anything you do too bloody long."

He looked at her face between him and the fire. She was leaning back in the chair and the firelight shone on her pleasantly lined face and he could see that she was sleepy. He heard the hyena make a noise just outside the range of the fire.

"I've been writing," he said. "But I got tired."

"Do you think you will be able to sleep?"

"Pretty sure. Why don't you turn in?"

"I like to sit here with you."

"Do you feel anything strange?" he asked her.

"No. Just a little sleepy."

"I do," he said.

He had just felt death come by again.

"You know the only thing I've never lost is curiosity," he said to her.

"You've never lost anything. You're the most complete man I've ever known."

"Christ," he said. "How little a woman knows. What is that? Your intuition?"

Because, just then, death had come and rested its head on the foot of the cot and he could smell its breath.

"Never believe any of that about a scythe and a skull," he told her. "It can be two bicycle policemen as easily, or be a bird. Or it can have a wide snout like a hyena."

It had moved up on him now, but it had no shape any more. It simply occupied space.

"Tell it to go away."

It did not go away but moved a little closer.

"You've got a hell of a breath," he told it. "You stinking bastard."

It moved up closer to him still and now he could not speak to it, and when it saw he could not speak it came a little closer, and now he tried to send it away without speaking, but it moved in on him so its weight was all upon his chest, and while it crouched there and he could not move, or speak, he heard the woman say, "Bwana is asleep now. Take the cot up very gently and carry it into the tent."

He could not speak to tell her to make it go away and it crouched now, heavier, so he could not breathe. And then, while they lifted the cot, suddenly it was all right and the weight went from his chest.

It was morning and had been morning for some time and he heard the plane. It showed very tiny and then made a wide circle and the boys ran out and lit the fires, using kerosene, and piled on grass so there were two big smudges at each end of the level place and the morning breeze blew them toward the camp and the plane circled twice more, low this time, and then glided down and levelled off and landed smoothly and, coming walking toward him, was old Compton in slacks, a tweed jacket and a brown felt hat.

"What's the matter, old cock?" Compton said.

"Bad leg," he told him. "Will you have some breakfast?"

"Thanks. I'll just have some tea. It's the Puss Moth you know. I won't be able to take the Memsahib. There's only room for one. Your lorry is on the way."

Helen had taken Compton aside and was speaking to him. Compton came back more cheery than ever.

"We'll get you right in," he said. "I'll be back for the Mem. Now I'm afraid I'll have to stop at Arusha to refuel. We'd better get going."

"What about the tea?"

"I don't really care about it you know."

The boys had picked up the cot and carried it around the green tents and down along the rock and out onto the plain and along past the smudges that were burning brightly now, the grass all consumed, and the wind fanning the fire, to the little plane. It was difficult getting him in, but once in he lay back in the leather seat, and the leg was stuck straight out to one side of the seat where Compton sat. Compton started the motor and got in. He waved to Helen and to the boys and, as the clatter moved into the old familiar roar, they swung around with Compie watching for wart-hog holes and roared, bumping, along the stretch between the fires and with the last bump rose and he saw them all standing below, waving, and the camp beside the hill, flattening now, and the plain spreading, clumps of trees, and the bush flattening, while the game trails ran now smoothly to the dry waterholes, and there was a new water that he had never known of. The zebra, small rounded backs now, and the wildebeeste, big-headed dots seeming to climb as they moved in long fingers across the plain, now scattering as the shadow came toward them, they were tiny now, and the movement had no gallop, and the plain as far as you could see, gray-yellow now and ahead old Compie's tweed back and the brown felt hat. Then they were over the first hills and the wildebeeste were trailing up them, and then they were over mountains with sudden depths of green-rising forest and the solid bamboo slopes, and then the heavy forest again, sculptured into peaks and hollows until they crossed, and hills sloped down and then another plain, hot now, and purple brown, bumpy with heat and Compie looking back to see how he was riding. Then there were other mountains dark ahead.

And then instead of going on to Arusha they turned left, he evidently figured that they had the gas, and looking down he saw a pink sifting cloud, moving over the ground, and in the air, like the first snow in a blizzard, that comes from nowhere, and he knew the locusts were coming up from the South. Then they began to climb and they were going to the East it seemed, and then it darkened and they were in a storm, the rain so thick it seemed like flying through a waterfall, and then they were out and Compie turned his head and grinned and pointed and there, ahead, all he could see, as wide as all the world, great, high, and unbelievably white in the sun, was the square top of Kilimanjaro. And then he knew that there was where he was going.

Just then the hyena stopped whimpering in the night and started to make a strange, human, almost crying sound. The woman heard it and stirred uneasily. She did not wake. In her dream she was at the house on Long Island and it was the night before her daughter's début. Somehow her father was there and he had been very rude. Then the noise the hyena made was so loud she woke and for a moment she did not know where she was and she was very afraid. Then she took the flashlight and shone it on the other cot that they had carried in after Harry had gone to sleep. She could see his bulk under the mosquito bar but somehow he had gotten his leg out and it hung down alongside the cot. The dressings had all come down and she could not look at it.

"Molo," she called, "Molo! Molo!"

Then she said, "Harry, Harry!" Then her voice rising, "Harry! Please, Oh Harry!"

There was no answer and she could not hear him breathing.

Outside the tent the hyena made the same strange noise that had awakened her. But she did not hear him for the beating of her heart.

COMMENT AND QUESTION

1. *The attitude of defeat.* A Hemingway character can usually express his attitude toward life in the simple phrase: "You can't win." The more admirable Hemingway character usually adds: "But you can be brave." These two phrases constitute a Hemingway code. Is this code apparent in this story? Is Harry brave? Or is defeat dominant here?

When "The Snows of Kilimanjaro" opens, the chips are down for Harry. He is engaged in a final judgment of his life.

a. *Harry and Helen.* Does Harry love his wife? Has he ever loved her? Perhaps one should ask: Has he ever loved her as a "wife"? Although Harry and Helen are married, the reader knows that Helen is not Harry's "wife" in any true sense. Do you think that Harry recognizes this truth clearly enough for it to add to his personal tragedy? Or does he seem unaware of this particular defeat?

b. *Harry's talent.* What part did Helen play in the loss of Harry's talent? Does Harry blame Helen completely? Does Harry seem deeply disturbed about the loss of his talent?

c. *Harry's attitude toward defeat.* Harry thinks: "You spoiled everything." The "you" refers to himself. Is Harry's reflection correct? Or does he have a code that ultimately gives some meaning to his life?

The reader should withhold final judgment on the defeat in Harry's life until he has considered the story as a whole.

2. *The importance of physical sensations.* A Hemingway character usually finds that truth and reality are limited to his sense experiences. To think is not to live, at least not to live realistically.

Notice the contrast between the italicized portions and the rest of the story. The italicized portions emphasize physical sensations. What, then, does the rest of the story emphasize? Why are these two activities so sharply divided in this story? Is it significant that Harry's illness is painless?

What is the range of Harry's sense experience? He comments that death is the only experience he has never had. If so, has his range of sense experience been limited?

3. *The death.* Is the death in this story inglorious, grotesque, and filthy? Consider the following:

    a. The trivial accidents which lead to the infection.

    b. The three or four shapes or forms in which death or the thought of death becomes tangible, beginning with the buzzards.

    c. The physical characteristics of Harry's malady. Is the death in this story ironic? Could big game hunting be part of an italicized section?

4. *Spoiling the last experience.* Stoicism in the face of death is a virtue Hemingway grants to many of his characters. Does Harry succeed in his desire to keep from spoiling the last experience? Does he display any stoicism? Any kindliness and courage? What of his wife?

Since Harry had fulfilled himself once in life (as the italicized portions show), the most important statement here is: "I've been writing." Properly related to Harry's defeat and to the italicized portions, this statement gives some dignity and significance to the death.

5. *The italicized portions.* Read aloud, these portions of the story reveal the cadence and rhythm of Hemingway's best prose, his skill in poetic repetition and variation of a theme. The first italicized portion speaks of snow like a theme in music. Why should snow come to Harry's mind? How does the second italicized portion grow out of Harry's quarreling with Helen? What stimulates the last italicized reflection? All of these portions are closely integrated with the main story although they could exist independently.

Do these portions merely represent stories that Harry wants to write? Or is a dying man fulfilling himself in them as he had done once before in his life? If so, is the fulfillment limited to physical sensations gained through love, sports, nature, fighting? Or are there other values? Does Harry have conceptions of courage, defeat, violence, cruelty, and injustice? In other words, does he have a code? Which seems dominant, however, the code or the physical sensations?

Violence, which is characteristic of Hemingway's writing, occurs here in the italicized portions. Would violence be a natural part of Hemingway's attitude toward life?

AN ANALYSIS OF THE SCENE IN THE AIRPLANE

The most interesting problem in "The Snows of Kilimanjaro" is reflected in the following questions: Does the story have spiritual values? Does Hemingway give spiritual significance to a defeated man in the episode where the airplane is flying toward Kilimanjaro, also known **as** the House of God? Is the scene in the airplane intended to be a mystical experience? Some critics have answered "Yes" to all these questions.

But the scene in the airplane disturbs many readers, including the critics who find spiritual values in the story. One critic feels that Hemingway "muffed" what was intended to be a mystical experience because he did not prepare the reader properly nor develop a lofty tone. Another critic feels that a snow-capped mountain as a symbol of the House of God is too trite and conventional to have much force.

Actually the scene does not seem to be intended to be a mystical experience. A more believable explanation is that the scene in the airplane is an hallucination. Much in this scene is dependent upon the sense impressions which have stimulated Harry in the story. Notice that the death occurs when the cot is lifted (p. 264). This lifting sensation is part of the hallucination of the airplane, for the boys pick up the cot and carry it. It is difficult to get Harry into the airplane because of the position of his leg, and this position is explained in the final scene (p. 266). The coming of the airplane had been discussed by Helen and Harry. And the rain that falls during the flight had been a matter of dispute also (p. 259).

The gradual diminution of Harry's powers is one of the effective parts of this story. Notice how his powers fail from the first sentence through the "whispers" (p. 259), to statements by Harry which Helen does not hear (p. 264). Harry's whirling sensations end in an hallucination, and the scene in the airplane is made up of a series of physical sensations and a series of thoughts that he can no longer logically piece together.

The grotesque details of the hallucination are also in keeping with the grotesque details of the death, like the reference to the bicycle policemen. Compie's grin as he indicates Kilimanjaro is the final grotesque touch. The reader should note also that the description of Kilimanjaro preceding the story has ironic overtones. The fantastic detail of the leopard in a description of the House of God supports the irony. If no one can explain what the leopard was seeking, no one can explain what the two men in the airplane are seeking. Furthermore, without thought mysticism does not exist, and Harry's reflections do not rise far above physical sensation.

Nothing in the story prepares the reader for a belief in a spiritual home. Little in the scene in the airplane supports the belief. The conclusion is that the scene can hardly be called a mystical experience and that Hemingway did not intend to give spiritual significance to a dying, defeated man in "The Snows of Kilimanjaro."

In "The Second Death" Greene tries to achieve a mystical experience. Compare these two stories. Study the development of tone in both and you will come to a clearer understanding of the purpose of Greene and the purpose of Hemingway.

THE BENCH OF DESOLATION

BY HENRY JAMES

HENRY JAMES (1843–1916) is the most distinguished member of a distinguished American family. His father was Henry James, the philosopher, and his brother was William James, the philosopher and psychologist. Born in America, he travelled a good deal in England and Europe, and finally settled in England when he was thirty-two. He became a British subject in 1915. In spite of this background, he is usually considered an American writer. Americans figure prominently in many of his better known novels like *The Ambassadors* (1903), *The American* (1877), *Daisy Miller* (1879), *Portrait of a Lady* (1881), and *The Golden Bowl* (1904). A penetrating psychological and moral insight pervades his numerous stories and novels. James is the author, also, of a good deal of criticism, collected in *The Art of the Novel* (1934). Today James is being acclaimed not only as the classic critic of the technique of fiction but also as the foremost American writer of fiction.

SHE HAD practically, he believed, conveyed the intimation, the horrid, brutal, vulgar menace, in the course of their last dreadful conversation, when, for whatever was left him of pluck or confidence—confidence in what he would fain have called a little more confidently the strength of his position—he had judged best not to take it up. But this time there was no question of not understanding, or of pretending he didn't; the ugly, the

awful words, ruthlessly formed by her lips, were like the fingers of a hand
that she might have thrust into her pocket for extraction of the monstrous
object that would serve best for—what should he call it?—a gage of battle.

"If I haven't a very different answer from you within the next three
days I shall put the matter into the hands of my solicitor, whom it may
interest you to know I've already seen. I shall bring an action for 'breach'
against you, Herbert Dodd, as sure as my name's Kate Cookham."

There it was, straight and strong—yet he felt he could say for himself,
when once it had come, or even, already, just as it was coming, that it
turned on, as if she had moved an electric switch, the very brightest light
of his own very reasons. There *she* was, in all the grossness of her native
indelicacy, in all her essential excess of will and destitution of scruple; and
it was the woman capable of that ignoble threat who, his sharper sense
of her quality having become so quite deterrent, was now making for him
a crime of it that he shouldn't wish to tie himself to her for life. The vivid,
lurid thing was the reality, all unmistakable, of her purpose; she had
thought her case well out; had measured its odious, specious present-
ability; had taken, he might be sure, the very best advice obtainable at
Properley, where there was always a first-rate promptitude of everything
fourth-rate; it was disgustingly certain, in short, that she'd proceed. She
was sharp and adroit, moreover—distinctly in certain ways a masterhand;
how otherwise, with her so limited mere attractiveness, should she have
entangled him? He couldn't shut his eyes to the very probable truth that
if she should try it she'd pull it off. She *knew* she would—precisely; and her
assurance was thus the very proof of her cruelty. That she had pretended
she loved him was comparatively nothing; other women had pretended it,
and other women too had really done it; but that she had pretended he
could possibly have been right and safe and blest in loving *her*, a creature
of the kind who could sniff that squalor of the law-court, of claimed damages and brazen lies and published kisses, of love-letters read amid obscene
guffaws, as a positive tonic to resentment, as a high incentive to her course
—this was what put him so beautifully in the right. It was what it meant
in a woman all through, he said to himself, the mere imagination of such
machinery. Truly what a devilish conception and what an appalling
nature!

But there was no doubt, luckily, either, that he *could* plant his feet the
firmer for his now intensified sense of these things. He was to live, it
appeared, abominably worried, he was to live consciously rueful, he was
to live perhaps even what a scoffing world would call abjectly exposed;
but at least he was to live saved. In spite of his clutch of which steadying
truth, however, and in spite of his declaring to her, with many other
angry protests and pleas, that the line of conduct she announced was
worthy of a vindictive barmaid, a lurking fear in him, too deep to counsel
mere defiance, made him appear to keep open a little, till he could some-

how turn round again, the door of possible composition. He had scoffed at her claim, at her threat, at her thinking she could hustle and bully him—"Such away, my eye, to call back to life a dead love!"—yet his instinct was ever, prudentially but helplessly, for gaining time, even if time only more woefully to quake, and he gained it now by not absolutely giving for his ultimatum that he wouldn't think of coming round. He didn't in the smallest degree mean to come round, but it was characteristic of him that he could for three or four days breathe a little easier by having left her under the impression that he perhaps might. At the same time he could not have said—what had conduced to bring out, in retort, her own last word, the word on which they had parted—"Do you mean to say you yourself would now be *willing* to marry and live with a man of whom you could feel, the thing done, that he'd be all the while thinking of you in the light of a hideous coercion?" "Never you mind about *my* willingness," Kate answered; "you've known what that has been for the last six months. Leave that to me, my willingness—I'll take care of it all right; and just see what conclusion you can come to about your own."

He was to remember afterwards how he had wondered whether, turned upon her in silence while her odious lucidity reigned unchecked, his face had shown her anything like the quantity of hate he felt. Probably not at all; no man's face *could* express that immense amount; especially the fair, refined, intellectual, gentlemanlike face which had had—and by her own more than once repeated avowal—so much to do with the enormous fancy she had originally taken to him. "Which—frankly now—would you personally *rather* I should do," he had at any rate asked her with an intention of supreme irony: "just sordidly marry you on top of this, or leave you the pleasure of your lovely appearance in court and of your so assured (since that's how you feel it) big haul of damages? Shan't you be awfully disappointed, in fact, if I don't let you get something better out of me than a poor, plain, ten-shilling gold ring and the rest of the blasphemous rubbish, as we should make it between us, pronounced at the altar? I take it, of course," he had swaggered on, "that your pretention wouldn't be for a moment that I should—after the act of profanity—take up my life with you."

"It's just as much my dream as it ever was, Herbert Dodd, to take up mine with *you*! Remember for me that I can do with it, my dear, that my idea is for even as much as that of you!" she had cried; "remember that for me, Herbert Dodd; remember, remember!"

It was on this she had left him—left him frankly under a mortal chill. There might have been the last ring of an appeal or a show of persistent and perverse tenderness in it, however preposterous any such matter; but in point of fact her large, clean, plain brown face—so much too big for her head, he now more than ever felt it to be, just as her head was so much too big for her body, and just as her hats had an irritating way of

appearing to decline choice and conformity in respect to *any* of her dimen-
sions—presented itself with about as much expression as his own shop-
window when the broad, blank, sallow blind was down. He was fond of
his shop-window with some good show on; he had a fancy for a good
show and was master of twenty different schemes of taking arrangement
for the old books and prints, "high-class rarities" his modest catalogue
called them, in which he dealt and which his maternal uncle, David
Geddes, had, as he liked to say, "handed down" to him (his widowed
mother had screwed the whole thing, the stock and the connection and
the rather bad little house in the rather bad little street, out of the ancient
worthy, shortly before his death, in the name of the youngest and most
interesting, the "delicate" one and the literary, of her five scattered and
struggling children); he could enjoy his happiest collocations and con-
trasts and effects, his harmonies and varieties of toned and faded leather
and cloth, his sought color-notes and the high clearnesses, here and there,
of his white and beautifully figured price-labels, they could please him
enough in themselves almost to console him for not oftener having to
break, on a customer's insistence, into the balanced composition; but the
dropped expanse of time-soiled canvas, the thing of Sundays and holidays,
with just his name, "Herbert Dodd, Successor," painted on below his
uncle's antique style, the feeble penlike flourishes already quite archaic,
this ugly vacant mask, which might so easily be taken for the mask of
failure, somehow always gave him a chill.

That had been just the sort of chill—the analogy was complete—of Kate
Cookham's last look. He supposed people doing an awfully good and sure
and steady business, in whatever line, could see a whole front turned to
vacancy that way, and merely think of the hours off represented by it.
Only for this—nervously to bear it, in other words, and Herbert Dodd,
quite with the literary temperament himself, was capable of that amount
of play of fancy, or even of morbid analysis—you had to be on some foot-
ing, you had to feel some confidence, pretty different from his own up to
now. He had never *not* enjoyed passing his show on the other side of the
street and taking it in thence with a casual obliquity; but he had never
held optical commerce with the drawn blind for a moment longer than he
could help. It *always* looked horribly final and as if it never would come
up again. Big and bare, with his name staring at him from the middle, it
thus offered in its grimness a turn of comparison for Miss Cookham's
ominous visage. She never wore pretty, dotty, transparent veils, as Nan
Drury did, and the words "Herbert Dodd"—save that she had sounded
them at him there two or three times more like a Meg Merrilies or the
bold bad woman in one of the melodramas of high life given during the
fine season in the pavilion at the end of Properley Pier—were dreadfully,
were permanently seated on her lips. *She* was grim, no mistake.

That evening, alone in the back room above his shop, he saw so little what he could do that, consciously demoralised for the hour, he gave way to tears about it. Her taking a stand so incredibly "low," that was what he couldn't get over. The particular bitterness of his cup was his having let himself in for a struggle on such terms—the use, on her side, of the vulgarest process known to the law: the vulgarest, the vulgarest, he kept repeating that, clinging to the help rendered him by this imputation to his terrorist of the vice he sincerely believed he had ever, among difficulties (for oh he recognized the difficulties!) sought to keep most alien to him. He knew what he was, in a dismal, downtrodden sphere enough—the lean young proprietor of an old business that had itself rather shrivelled with age than ever grown fat, the purchase and sale of second-hand books and prints, with the back street of a long-fronted south-coast watering-place (Old Town by good luck) for the dusky field of his life. But he had gone in for all the education he could get—his educated customers would often hang about for more talk by the half-hour at a time, he actually feeling himself, and almost with a scruple, hold them there; which meant that he had had (he couldn't be blind to that) natural taste and had lovingly cultivated and formed it. Thus, from as far back as he could remember, there had been things all round him that he suffered from when other people didn't; and he had kept most of his sufferings to himself—which had taught him, in a manner, *how* to suffer, and how almost to like to.

So, at any rate, he had never let go his sense of certain differences, he had done everything he could to keep it up—whereby everything that was vulgar was on the wrong side of his line. He had believed, for a series of strange, oppressed months, that Kate Cookham's manners and tone were on the right side; she had been governess—for young children—in two very good private families, and now had classes in literature and history for bigger girls who were sometimes brought by their mammas; in fact, coming in one day to look over his collection of students' manuals, and drawing it out, as so many did, for the evident sake of his conversation, she had appealed to him that very first time by her apparently pronounced intellectual side—goodness knew she didn't even then by the physical!—which she had artfully kept in view till she had entangled him past undoing. And it had all been but the cheapest of traps—when he came to take the pieces apart a bit—laid over a brazen avidity. What he now collapsed for, none the less—what he sank down on a chair at a table and nursed his weak, scared sobs in his resting arms for—was the fact that, whatever the trap, it held him as with the grip of sharp murderous steel. There he was, there he was; alone in the brown summer dusk—brown through *his* windows—he cried and he cried. He shouldn't get out without losing a limb. The only question was which of his limbs it should be.

Before he went out, later on—for he at last felt the need to—he could, however, but seek to remove from his face and his betraying eyes, over

Robbins & Lawrence pepperbox pistol. (Courtesy Los Angeles County Museum of Natural History)

Considering all its features, the Robbins & Lawrence pepperbox was quite unlike the Allen, Blunt & Syms, and other types. Based on patents issued to George Leonard in September of 1849 and July of 1850, the Robbins & Lawrence was a breech-loading single-action arm with a five-shot nonrotating barrel group and a revolving striker, concealed within the frame, which fired each barrel in succession. The barrel group was made in two sections, front and rear, and hinged to the frame as a unit.

The long front section was held against the short rear section by screw threads on the axis pin, and the Robbins & Lawrence was technically a multishot screw-barrel pistol. Unscrewing the front section allowed the shooter to push a ball into the rear of each of the rifled bores; with powder and ball inserted, the shooter screwed the front section tightly against the rear section, then pushed down a latch on top of the frame, which allowed the entire barrel group to pivot downward as a unit to expose longitudinally mounted nipples set into its rear face. What appeared to be a ring trigger was actually a cocking lever; pulling it retracted and rotated the striker (by means of longitudinal and diagonal grooves cut into its surface), which remained at full-cock until the shooter pressed a convex trigger to fire one of the barrels.[35]

The Robbins & Lawrence was probably on the market by mid-1851, and was still available in December of 1854; at that time an official of the company, which was then engaged in the manufacture of the Sharps rifle, wrote that the price for the "patent revolving pistol . . . now made is $12 at retail."[36]

The "Maynard Primer" revolver mentioned by Al-bright represented an attempt by Massachusetts Arms to gain a share of the repeating-handgun market without infringing upon Colt's patent. Made in .28 and .31 caliber, these guns had manually rotated cylinders; to make them more appealing to the gun-buying public they also incorporated a Maynard primer in the frame, operating in conjunction with a single frame-mounted nipple instead of one behind each chamber. This obviated the need for capping five or six separate nipples. Although a hand-rotated revolver was generally more reliable than the mechanically rotated type, it was far slower in firing second or third shots, and there is little doubt that the vast majority of handgun buyers preferred mechanically rotated arms, whether revolvers or pepperboxes. When Granville Stuart and his family started west in 1852, his father carried what Stuart described as a small, .25 caliber "Maynard's patent" revolver. (He also commented that: "No one would carry such a pistol nowadays, but revolvers were just invented.") And in December of 1854 James Bailey of Sacramento offered "a few of Maynard's celebrated Pocket Pistols, Self-Primers."[37]

By 1853 Massachusetts Arms was experimenting with various methods of rotating the cylinder by means of the trigger, but the firm confined these methods chiefly to its .28 caliber pocket revolver; most of the .31 caliber arms continued to be made with manually rotated cylinders. Under a patent issued to Joshua Stevens in January of 1855 the company made about 1600 pocket revolvers with trigger-revolved cylinders, but these still required manual cocking. Thus, like the Warner arms, advertised again in 1855 by a San Francisco firm, the new Massachusetts Arms revolvers were

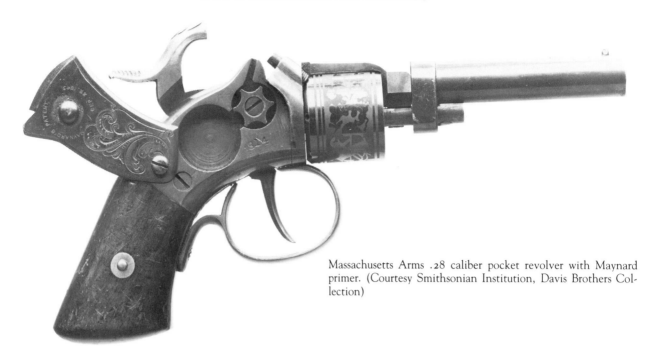

Massachusetts Arms .28 caliber pocket revolver with Maynard primer. (Courtesy Smithsonian Institution, Davis Brothers Collection)

little competition for the Colt, which by that time fairly flooded the western market.[38]

One dealer, Charles Hummel of San Antonio, was an agent for both Colts and for Whitney arms (including Whitney's "Mississippi rifles, revolvers, breechloaders and ordinary carbines.") His selection very probably embraced the manually rotated .31 caliber revolvers with solid frames of brass which Whitney made in the early 1850s, but Hummel's big sellers were Colt .44 Dragoons and .36 Navies. In 1854 he wrote to jobber Armand Soubie of New Orleans that "my affairs are quiet, but more Colt pistols can always be sold." Although Hummel once commented that Dragoons sold better than the lighter .36s, his letters nevertheless reflected the persistent popularity of the latter models. One of his 1855 advertisements, in fact, made special reference to a small lot of "Colt's Navy Pistols, with Ivory Handles, and finely engraved, in cases." To counter the problem of rusting during shipment along the Gulf Coast, he ordered in 1856 "another dozen military Colt galvanized [nickel-plated?] pistols and a half dozen not galvanized if they are the same price as the Navy, I could have sold a great many Navy pistols, Have you sent them yet?"[39]

Early in 1854 a party led by Major John C. Fremont encountered between fifty and sixty mounted Ute warriors armed with rifles and bows and arrows. As a civilian with the Fremont group later recounted:

[Fremont] tore a leaf from his journal, and handing it to me, said: here take this, and place it against a tree, and at a distance near enough to hit it every time, discharge your Colt's Navy six shooters, fire at intervals of from ten to fifteen seconds—and call

the attention of the Indians to the fact, that it is not necessary for white men to load their arms. I did so; after the first shot, they pointed to their own rifles, as much as to say they could do the same, (if they had happened to have the powder), I, without lowering my arm, fired a second shot, this startled them. I discharged it a third time—their curiosity and amazement were increased: the fourth time, I placed the pistol in the hands of the chief and told him to discharge it, which he did, hitting the paper and making another impression of the bullet. The fifth and sixth times two other Indians discharged it, and the whole six barrels being now fired it was time to replace it in my belt. I had another one already loaded, which I dexterously substituted, and scared them into an acknowledgment that they were all at our mercy, and we could kill them as fast as we liked, if we were so disposed.

Frederick Law Olmsted, whose party journeyed through the Southwest in the mid-1850s, had high praise for the Navy Colt:

Of the Colt's we cannot speak in too high terms. Though subjected for six or eight months to rough use, exposed to damp grass, and to all the ordinary neglects and accidents of camp travel, not once did a ball fail to answer the finger. Nothing got out of order, nothing required care; not once, though carried at random, in coat-pocket or belt, or tied thumping at the pommel, was there an accidental discharge. . . . Before taking them from home we gave them a trial alongside every rival we could

French dueling pistols by Le Page of Paris, used 13 September 1859 in the formal duel between former California Supreme Court Chief Justice David S. Terry and the U.S. senator from California David C. Broderick. Each pistol is inscribed on a plate on the left side "Hon. David S. Terry SAN FRANCISCO." The pistols were also used two years earlier in another California duel. (Courtesy Mrs. W. H. Wood and Wells Fargo Bank History Room)

hear of, and we had with us an unpatented imitation, but for practical purposes one Colt we found worth a dozen of all others. Such was the testimony of every old hunter and ranger we met. There are probably in Texas about as many revolvers as male adults, and I doubt if there are one hundred in the state of any other make. . . . After a little practice we could very surely chop off a snake's head from the saddle at any reasonable distance, and across a fixed rest could hit an object of the size of a man at ordinary rifle range. One of our pistols was one day submerged in a bog for some minutes, but on trial, though dripping wet, not a single barrel missed fire. A border weapon, so reliable in every sense, would give brute courage to even a dyspeptic tailor.[40]

Target or dueling-style pistol with adjustable single set trigger and 17³/4 in. overall length, marked on the top barrel flat "H. E. DIMICK ST. LOUIS." (Courtesy Missouri Historical Society)

Evidently Henry Deringer's pocket pistols did not lag very far behind the Colts in popularity; in September of 1855 T. J. Albright of St. Louis advertised "450 pair single & double Pistols; 80 d[itt]o Belt, and Deringer and Duelling d[itt]o."[41]

But California was Deringer's real marketplace, and his little pistol came in for increasing notice there in the middle and late 1850s. After the much-publicized shooting of General W. H. Richardson by gambler Charles Cora in November of 1855, San Francisco firearms dealer A. J. "Natchez" Taylor testified that Cora had often appeared at his shop to have him load the pair of "Derringers" the gambler carried. Richardson himself had a Deringer at the time of the shooting, though he had never had a chance to use it. Ned McGowan, acquitted of involvement in the murder of California editor James King in May of 1856, described his personal armament as a Deringer-type pistol in each coat pocket, another pair in his trousers pockets, a Bowie knife, and finally a six-shooter in his belt![42]

As had been the case in San Diego in 1852, Deringers occasionally represented the weapons of choice in the duels that occurred with almost monotonous frequency in the California of the 1850s. Newspapers sometimes printed advance notices of such events, and some duelists even sent formal engraved invitations to their friends. A. J. Taylor, one of the earliest Deringer dealers on the West Coast, devoted a large part of his business to the dueling trade, even operating a shooting gallery where individuals could practice for a duel. One of his 1856 advertisements, in fact, listed "genuine Derringer Pistols, and a large assortment of English Duelling and Colt's Pistols." With "the true objectivity of a professional man, Natchez would then supply weapons for both sides for a price." Although the formalities did require a pair of smoothbore pistols, Californians, like other westerners, tended to be in-

formal on such occasions and used anything that was handy.[43]

However, there was no shortage of true dueling pistols on the frontier of the 1850s. Dealers such as F. H. Clark, T. J. Albright, Henry Griffiths, and others had them readily available. Equally well suited for the duel were the elegant half-stocked "target" pistols in the French style, made by Horace Dimick of St. Louis and by Thomas Bailey of New Orleans. Still, a favorite weapon for these affairs of honor was the Navy Colt. With these guns the common procedure was to stand back to back, walk five paces, then turn and fire at leisure until one participant was down or until both revolvers were empty. At Contra Costa the politician David Broderick and Judge J. Caleb Smith shot it out with Navies at twelve paces, both firing at random until each had only a single round left in his revolver. When a shot finally drew blood, both duelists bowed, shook hands, and departed the scene, having satisfactorily defended their individual honors.[44]

Not all duels ended in tragedy or even in minor blood-letting. In a Nevada City encounter the playful friends of a fiddler and a male singer loaded the opponents' pistols with "bullets" of currant jelly, which gave the appearance of spattered blood without its unpleasantness.[45]

A casual frontier duel may even have involved pepperboxes, although with their smooth bores and small calibers the multibarreled guns were hardly suitable for such use. As close-range self-defense weapons, however, they remained in evidence in the West throughout the 1850s.

In 1854 Thomas P. Wheelock joined the Allen firm, which then became Allen, Thurber, and Co. Two years later Thurber retired, whereupon the company name changed to Allen & Wheelock, with Ethan Allen still at the helm. Although Allen probably held onto the lion's share of the pepperbox market, there

A pair of Colt Dragoon .44s, a large Bowie knife, and a stern countenance complement this image of a Kansas brigand, Charles Metz (alias Marshall Cleveland). A member of a free-state "jayhawker" band of ruffians in the 1850s, he served briefly as a captain with the Seventh Kansas Cavalry before resuming his former life as a guerrilla. The Dragoon he holds appears to be one of the Third Model .44s fitted with an adjustable long-range rear sight for use with a detachable shoulder stock. (Courtesy Kansas State Historical Society)

was no shortage of other contenders for the position. For instance, the Manhattan Firearms Manufacturing Company, whose principal business was pepperboxes and single-shot pistols, was not even organized until May of 1855. In September of 1855 T. J. Albright of St. Louis, besides listing "100 Colt's Pistols, assorted sizes," offered "150 4, 5, 6, and 7 barrel Revolvers." Those with four, five, and six barrels were probably of American manufacture; the seven-barreled pistol, however, may well have been a foreign item.[46]

While pepperboxes made by Manhattan may or may not have reached the frontier (although the company's later percussion revolvers did), the pepperboxes made by a man who subsequently became closely allied with this company did reach both Kansas and California. Thomas K. Bacon had worked for Allen & Thurber until mid-1847, when the firm moved from Norwich to Worcester. Bacon remained in Norwich, and by the spring of 1850 had started his own business under the name of Bacon & Company.[47]

Bacon evidently favored the underhammer design, because both his pepperboxes and some of his single-shot pistols incorporated this feature. Unlike many other underhammer guns, however, the hammer spurs of Bacon's guns were contoured and positioned to allow easy cocking by the trigger finger, a good selling point. Bacon pepperboxes were normally six-shot single-action mechanically rotated arms in .30 caliber; because of the underhammer and single-action feature the Bacon could have made good use of sights, but like most other pepperboxes it had none. In 1856 O.H. Bogart's Sportsman's Emporium of San Francisco offered "Colts and Mariette Revolvers, Derringer, and Bacons Pistols." Another Bacon, found in Kansas prior to 1909, was probably a veteran of the "Bleeding Kansas" troubles of the 1850s.[48]

The Bacon, however, was not the only pepperbox to see action in Kansas. In September of 1856 a Kansas settler wrote in his diary: "I will buy a pepperbox $6." And on one occasion William Phillips, reporting on conditions there for the New York Tribune, had to

W. F. N. Arny, a free-state leader and agent for the National Kansas Committee, in disguise in Missouri in 1856. His brace of revolvers appears to be Colt 1851 Navies. (Courtesy Kansas State Historical Society)

Kansas abolitionist John Brown's Colt M1851 (No. 51010) given to him by W. F. N. Arny. (Courtesy Kansas State Historical Society)

surrender his arms to a proslavery officer. Phillips "had an excellent six-shooter in my belt, and a four-barrelled French revolver in my pocket; I took out the latter and handed it to [Marshal] Jones." Phillips's "French revolver" was probably a Mariette pepperbox, mentioned in the 1856 Sportsman's Emporium ad and presumably the original basis for the Blunt & Syms. The major difference between the two was that the Mariette had separate turn-off barrels instead of a barrel group made from a single block of iron. Although the Belgian model could have as many as twenty-four barrels, four-barrel and six-barrel versions seem to have been especially popular.[49]

The ubiquitous Colts, of course, were also in strong evidence in Kansas. Philips noted that "on the part of the pro-slavery men, Clarke was armed with a small five-inch Colt's revolver, while Colonel Burns had a navy revolver, which is heavier and carries a much larger ball." Testimony regarding the arms sent to John Brown and his abolitionists in Kansas included these remarks:

Question. Did John Brown receive any arms in any form from the [Massachusetts State Kansas] committee, or any members of the committee?

Answer. The committee sent him twenty-five navy revolvers of Colt's manufacture, by Mr. Arny, but they never reached him. I think it was in August, 1856. They were sent to Lawrence, and were stored there a short time, subject to Brown's order. He did not appear to claim them, and they were loaned to a military company in Lawrence called the Stubbs. . . .

Brown was also the recipient of other revolvers, made by Colt's old rival, the Massachusetts Arms Company. After the abolitionist's abortive attack on Harper's Ferry in 1859, army officers recovered "102 Massachusetts Arms Company pistols and 58 Massachusetts

Arms Company powder flasks," as well as 102 Sharps carbines. As the Senate committee investigating the incident concluded:

They had two hundred Sharp's carbines and two hundred revolver pistols and about one thousand pikes, together with a quantity of clothing and ammunition. The carbines and revolvers had been procured by contributions in Massachusetts, in 1856, and forwarded to Iowa to be sent into Kansas for the aid and in the defense of the free-State people in the struggle then existing there, and they had been intrusted to John Brown for that purpose, together with the ammunition.

As Brown himself stated, the revolvers were "a little under the Navy size," and other evidence shows that the guns were .31 caliber Massachusetts Arms hand-rotated revolvers with Maynard primers and 6 in. barrels.[50]

Again, however, these guns were little competition for Colt. Although Colt's Dragoon, Navy, and pocket models sold as fast as he could make them, in 1856 he brought out a solid-frame sidehammer revolver, a companion piece to the larger revolving rifles and shotguns with the same design. Mechanically no different from the long guns, these revolvers were commonly available with 3½ in or 4½ in. round or octagon barrels, bored to .28 or .31 caliber respectively. Besides its solid frame and sidehammer, this model differed from earlier production-model Colts in having a rack and pinion or "creeping" loading lever and a "sheath trigger," in which a trigger-like projection on the underside of the frame housed the real trigger. Although the sidehammer revolver passed through a number of variations and improvements, it fell short of the success of Colt's other guns; by the mid-1850s, however, the Colt name alone was enough to ensure at least a respectable sale of any gun stamped with it. J. A.

Cased Colt Root Model pocket revolver, presented by Maj. Frank North to Buffalo Bill Cody on the latter's birthday in 1870. (Courtesy Saunders Memorial Museum, Berryville, Ark.)

Henry's advertisement in the *Arkansas Gazette* in December of 1856 for "Colt's New Pocket Repeater" almost certainly referred to the sidehammer pistol. Of two examples of Colt .28 caliber M1855 revolvers carried to early California (and now in the Sutter's Fort collection), one has a standard 3 1/2 in. barrel, but the barrel of the other is only 1 3/4 in. long. While not especially commonplace, the practice of cutting off Colt barrels extended to Navy and Dragoon as well as to later models.[51]

Advertisements by dealers in the West during the late 1850s show the multiplicity of handguns available to anyone having the purchase price, but as usual Colts were the big sellers. From 1857 through 1859 dealers in California, Arizona, Texas, Nebraska, and Kansas sold these guns: Spatz, Newhouse, and Co. of San Francisco offered "Cases [of] Colt's eight-inch Army Pistols"; A. S. Parker and Co. of Atchison, Kansas, offered "Colt's 4, 5 and 6 inch Revolvers, [and] Rifles and Shot Guns, a great variety"; and White and Granger of Ft. Buchanan, Arizona, listed "Colt's Navy Six-Shooter Pistols." While traveling down the Santa Fe Trail in 1857, William Napton noted that:

Reece was mounted on his splendid iron gray and I on my trained buffalo horse, each of us having a pair of Colt's navy revolvers, of six chambers in

holsters. [But] Hines, an assistant wagonmaster of one of the trains, suggested to me that I should use his pair of heavy Colt's army revolvers, which, he said, carried a heavier ball and were more effective in killing buffalo than mine.

Granville Stuart considered his Navy Colt a "mighty good weapon" and often used it to take deer and similar game at one hundred yards. The armament Bill Hamilton and a companion took with them into the Blackfoot country in 1858 evidently included special-order Colts:

Each of us had a Sharp's rifle, abundance of cartridges, and tape caps. . . . Besides this, we each had two Colts, twelve inch barrel, six shooters, with skeleton stock; these pistols would kill two hundred yards. We also packed a heavy doubled barrelled shot gun, which we used for guard at night; in addition to these I had my Derringers and McKay had his bows and arrows. . . .[52]

Attempts to circumvent Colt's patent continued to crop up. In June of 1857 Kemp & Frodsham of Omaha offered "Colt's Revolving pistols, all sizes, Single and Double Pocket Pistols, and Ells' Patent Revolvers." First patented in August of 1854 by Josiah Ells of Pittsburgh, early examples of this gun resembled a

Colt's Repeaters.

RECEIVED Colt's Repeating and Collin's self-cocking Pistols—also Colt's New Pocket Repeater, and for sale by   J. A. HENRY.

Oct. 25th, 1856.

Arkansas Gazette (Little Rock), Dec. 1856.

COLT'S NAVY SIX-SHOOTER PISTOLS.

For sale by

WHITE & GRANGER,

mar. 10   At Fort Buchanan.

Arizona Weekly, June 1859.

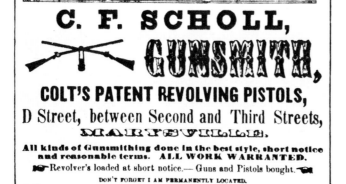

M. FREIDE,

211 *Broadway, one door north of Cherry-st.*

wholesale and retail dealer in

Guns, Rifles, Revolvers, Bowie-Knives, &c.,

AND AGENT FOR COLT'S IMPROVED REVOLVERS.

And keeps on hand all other trimmings necessary to an out fit for a Pike's Peak Emigrant. Come—examine—buy!

From Parker and Huyett's *Illustrated Miners' Hand-Book and Guide to Pike's Peak,* published in St. Louis in 1859.

C. F. SCHOLL,

GUNSMITH,

COLT'S PATENT REVOLVING PISTOLS,

D Street, between Second and Third Streets,

MARYSVILLE.

All kinds of Gunsmithing done in the best style, short notice and reasonable terms. ALL WORK WARRANTED.

☞ Revolver's loaded at short notice.— Guns and Pistols bought. ☜

DON'T FORGET I AM PERMANENTLY LOCATED.

G. & O. Amys' Marysville [California] *Directory, 1857.* (Courtesy Bancroft Library, University of California)

cross between a pepperbox and a conventional revolver. The frame had neither top- nor bottomstraps, and only the threads at the front of the cylinder pin held the barrel in place; the gun also had a bar hammer, which contributed to its pepperbox-like appearance. In a subsequent model, shown in a patent issued in April of 1857, Ells reinforced the frame with top- and bottomstraps, although he retained the bar hammer. Among the internal features of this model was a pawl which also acted as a cylinder bolt. Ells subsequently made a double-action revolver much more conventional in appearance; the exact type sold by

Kemp & Frodsham is uncertain, but it was probably the solid-frame bar-hammer depicted in Ells's 1857 patent.[53]

REVOLVERS FROM ABROAD: THE ADAMS AND THE TRANTER

Other revolvers, bigger and better than the Ells, also appeared in the West at this time. A gunsmith traveling across the plains in 1857 with an army survey party occasionally repaired civilian weapons in his spare time, sometimes charging as much as a dollar for a single screw; one gun he specifically recalled working on was "an English revolver of a new pattern," probably a Beaumont-Adams or a competing design made by William Tranter of Birmingham.[54]

Originally patented in February of 1851 by Robert Adams of London, the Adams was the first conventional English revolver to seriously threaten the Colt; during London's Great Exhibition it aroused considerable interest among firearms experts. Prior to the exhibition the usual type of British "revolver" was the pepperbox; in September of 1851, in fact, the *Illustrated London News* stated that

> The American revolving pistols differ from those commonly seen in England in the circumstances of their only having one barrel, a fixture, the compound breeching made to revolve, whereas in the English revolving pistol the barrels themselves turn on a pivot.

Although the process took time, the Adams was to dislodge the Colt and the English-made pepperboxes from their favored positions.[55]

The London partnership of Deane, Adams, & Deane commonly offered the Adams in the usual three sizes: holster, belt, and pocket; or .50, .44, and .31 calibers, all of which had five-shot cylinders. Externally the revolvers were notable because their hammers had no cocking spurs; the weapons were true "self-cocking" arms, designed to be fired only by a long pull on the trigger. This did not allow the precise aiming possible in the single-action Colt, but was somewhat faster for the average hand to operate. In terms of general construction, a major point in Adams's favor was the overall ruggedness of his arms. The octagon barrel and solid frame were forged from one piece, as were the trigger and cylinder bolt. The self-cocking mechanism was easily as simple as Colt's single-action design, and was perhaps even better suited for long and hard use. Also, the largest production-model Adams was a .50 caliber arm, potent enough for almost any job required of a handgun and still some twenty ounces lighter than the Colt Dragoon. As some pistoleers pointed out, however, the Adams had its disadvantages as well.

Colt First Model .44 Dragoon (No. 3262), modified for ease of handling and concealment by cutting the 7½ in. barrel to 2½ in. and removing the loading-lever assembly. Evidence indicates that the gun may be one of two used by Deputy U.S. Marshal William Stokes when in 1877 he arrested John D. Lee hiding in a pigpen. Lee was convicted as the leader of the band of Mormons who in 1857 at Mountain Meadows almost entirely wiped out a band of about 140 Arkansas and Missouri emigrants; he was executed in 1877. (Courtesy Utah State Historical Society)

George Armstrong Custer as a West Point cadet in a classic pose with a Colt M1855 Root Model pocket revolver. (From *The Custer Album*, courtesy Dr. Lawrence A. Frost)

Because of Colt's patents the Adams had no recoil shield behind the cylinder and no mechanical loading lever, both highly desirable additions. And the Colt Navy and Dragoon models had six- rather than five-shot cylinders.[56]

To settle the question of which revolver was the better, firing tests took place at Woolwich in September of 1851, during which the Adams edged out its rival. Other trials followed: in an 1852 test in South Africa, the Colt badly defeated its English competitor. Colt himself had already made arrangements to secure a hold on the English market by setting up shop in London, and by early 1853 his factory there was turning out both 1849 pocket and 1851 Navy revolvers, later completing some 700 third-model Dragoons. Adams countered by taking out a U.S. patent on his revolver in May of 1853, but the following year the British Navy ordered 9500 Navy Colts; moreover, after official tests, the British Army purchased no fewer than 14,000 Colt Navies in 1855.[57]

Adams was enjoying good civilian sales, however, and his opportunity for a military market was soon to appear. In February of 1855 Lt. Frederick Beaumont of the Royal Engineers patented a modification of Adams's lockwork which permitted single-action as well as self-cocking fire—in short, a true double-action design. About a month after the patent date the British Army ordered 100 Beaumont-Adams revolvers for trials, and thousands more subsequently. Partly because of

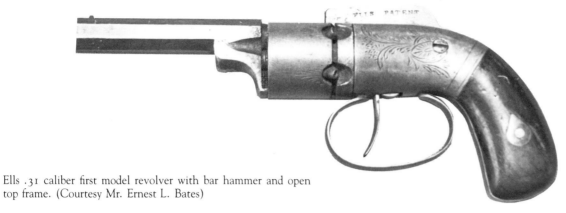

Ells .31 caliber first model revolver with bar hammer and open top frame. (Courtesy Mr. Ernest L. Bates)

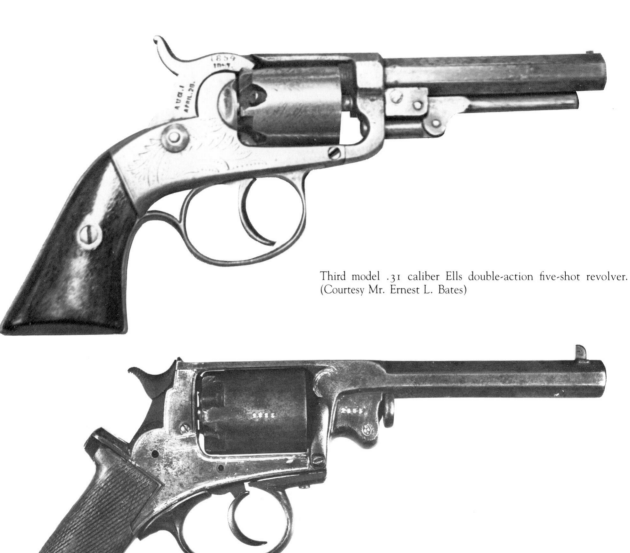

Third model .31 caliber Ells double-action five-shot revolver. (Courtesy Mr. Ernest L. Bates)

A Belgian-made licensed copy of an English Model 1855 Beaumont-Adams five-shot double-action percussion revolver of about 54 bore (.45 caliber). This specimen is attributed—but without documentation—to "Wild Bill" Hickok. It was donated to the Kansas State Historical Society in 1934 by the widow of a Hickok biographer. (Courtesy Kansas State Historical Society)

Tranter .38 caliber (80 bore) engraved two-trigger revolver (above) imported from England by A. B. Griswold & Co. of New Orleans about 1860. The Kerr 54 bore (about .45 caliber) below is another English-made revolver which found some favor among American buyers. (Courtesy Mr. E. Lee Manning, Jr.)

this, Colt began closing up his London factory late in 1856.[58]

Evidently Adams was as aware of the American commercial market as Colt was of the British. It was very probably a Deane & Adams revolver which the adventurous Englishman William Chandless carried in 1855 while working as a freighter between Atchison and Salt Lake City. En route to Salt Lake the train got word of a band of Pawnees in its vicinity, resulting in the rapid distribution of arms and ammunition to the teamsters. Wrote Chandless: "The rifles were what are called 'yager' but rather old ones formerly belong-ing to the government. . . . the supply was insuffi-cient, and I did not get one, which I cared little about, having a D. and A." Once in Salt Lake Chandless bought a "pistol case" and belt at Brigham Young Jr.'s saddle shop, noting later that: "If any one should buy a secondhand D. and A., first quality, middle size, No. 14,007, and with it a white leather case, let him know and appreciate the latter as the workmanship of young

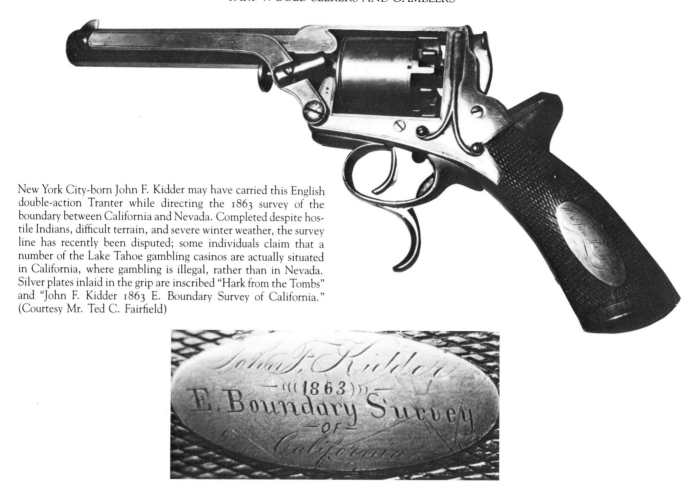

New York City-born John F. Kidder may have carried this English double-action Tranter while directing the 1863 survey of the boundary between California and Nevada. Completed despite hostile Indians, difficult terrain, and severe winter weather, the survey line has recently been disputed; some individuals claim that a number of the Lake Tahoe gambling casinos are actually situated in California, where gambling is illegal, rather than in Nevada. Silver plates inlaid in the grip are inscribed "Hark from the Tombs" and "John F. Kidder 1863 E. Boundary Survey of California." (Courtesy Mr. Ted C. Fairfield)

Brig." In March of 1856 T. J. Albright of St. Louis advertised "Sharpe's Rifles, and the celebrated Dean's Revolvers, the most formidable weapons in use." In view of the date, Albright's "celebrated Dean's Revolvers" could have been either the self-cocking Adams or early examples of the Beaumont-Adams double-action arms. Deane, Adams, & Deane did make the first few Beaumont-Adams guns, most of which had mechanical loading levers patented by Adams himself in 1854, but the partnership broke up in August of 1856, to be succeeded by the London Armoury Company.[59]

For American buyers, however, the old name apparently stuck. In 1858 and 1859, for example, at least three dealers—Lownes, Orgill & Co. and F. H. Clark of Memphis, and D. Kernaghan & Co. of New Orleans—listed "Dean's" or "Dean and Adams'" arms. More correctly, Schuyler, Hartley & Graham offered the "Adams" in the *Kansas Herald* early in 1859. But in 1864 a California dealership listed "Dean & Adams'" revolvers among its other wares.[60]

Another gunmaker who managed to get a fair number of his revolvers into American hands was William Tranter of Birmingham. Tranter had patented a percussion pepperbox in October of 1849, but his two revolver patents, one in January of 1853 and the other

in August of 1856, proved to be far more important. The distinguishing characteristic of the majority of Tranter percussion revolvers was the use of two triggers, with the second trigger projecting below the trigger guard and operated by the middle finger of the shooting hand. This lower trigger, however, was actually a cocking lever: pulling it revolved the cylinder and forced the hammer to full-cock, where it remained until the shooter pressed the upper trigger to fire. Used in this way the revolver was a lever-cocked single-action, but it would act as the usual self-cocking arm if the shooter pulled both triggers simultaneously.[61]

While Tranter's 1853 patent covered his two-trigger revolver, the 1856 patent pertained to both a two-trigger and a single-trigger design. The single-trigger model, resembling the Beaumont-Adams, did not have the ungainly appearance of the older two-trigger arm, but the latter was apparently the more popular. Made in several variations, it was available in barrel lengths from 4½ in. to 7½ in. and in at least six calibers, with .36, .44, and .50 the most common. Among American dealers, Hyde & Goodrich of New Orleans imported many two-trigger .44s, and may have started this practice as early as the mid-1850s. But they were not the only firm to handle the arm; F. H. Clark of Memphis had them by September of 1858, and pre-

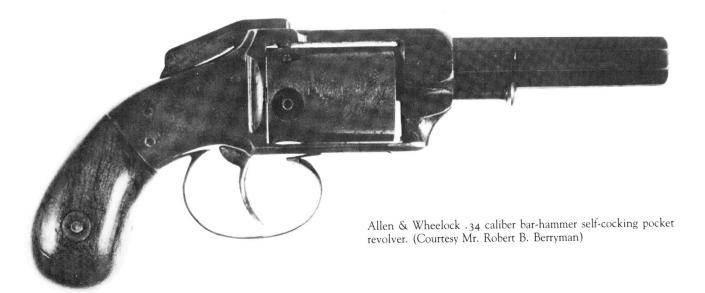

Allen & Wheelock .34 caliber bar-hammer self-cocking pocket revolver. (Courtesy Mr. Robert B. Berryman)

sumably the "Yantess" revolvers offered in the *Kansas Herald* early in 1859 were Tranters as well. (The unusual spelling in the ad probably resulted from the typesetter's misinterpretation of handwritten copy.) Charles Kittredge of St. Louis, who advertised himself as an "Importer of Guns" late in 1859, is also known to have sold Tranter's revolvers. Both dealers often stamped the guns with their own names, but one rusted two-trigger .36 caliber model with 4 1/2 in. barrel (now in the Sutter's Fort collection) has no dealer markings, and could have reached California in a number of ways.[62]

MORE RIVALS FOR COLT AND DERINGER

Tranter and Adams managed to gain a share of the American market not only because their guns were genuinely good, but also because their designs did not infringe upon Colt's patents. Most American manufacturers, their efforts to develop commercially successful revolvers forestalled by Colt, had to wait until Colt's patents expired, and for that reason 1857 was a big year for them. Colt's patent extension lapsed in February, leaving the field open for anyone able to offer a reasonably good design. Within a year Allen & Wheelock, Massachusetts Arms, Remington, Warner, Whitney, and a new firm, Smith & Wesson, all had mechanically rotated revolvers ready for the market. Even some little-known proprietary designs appeared, two of which were the products of New Orleans makers. The LeMat, initially patented in 1856, was a single-action arm with a shot barrel mounted under its conventional revolver barrel; it was to see limited use by the Confederacy during the Civil War. Less familiar was the five-shot double-action sidehammer revolver made by Thomas Bailey.[63]

Like LeMat, Allen & Wheelock and Massachusetts Arms were probably working on their entries well before the expiration of Colt's patent. Allen's model, a solid-frame bar-hammer five-shot revolver made in .31 and .34 caliber, clearly showed its pepperbox heritage; and although the firm manufactured this gun for several years, another more sophisticated model soon appeared beside it. Massachusetts Arms abandoned its .31 caliber manually rotated Maynard-primer revolver, and altered its trigger-rotated .28 caliber model so that the hammer instead of the trigger effected cylinder rotation. Far better guns, however, were the company's .31 and .36 caliber copies of the Beaumont-Adams double-action, made under license from the parent firm and protected by Adams's U.S. patent of 1853.[64]

Serviceable, well-made revolvers also came from Eli Whitney, Jr., who had made the Walker Colts for their inventor and who had supplied many Mississippi rifles both to the government and to the civilian market. Whitney had manufactured two models of hand-rotated revolvers in the early 1850s, then turned his attention to the mechanically rotated "Walking Beam" guns patented by Fordyce Beals in September of 1854. The *Scientific American* brought these guns to public notice in 1855, but not until the lapse of Colt's patent was Whitney really in a position to make a strong bid for the revolver market.[65]

In 1857 his firm made about 300 revolvers which were almost exact copies of the Navy Colt, but also came out with a new solid-frame six-shot "Navy" revolver of Whitney's design with a 7 1/2 in. octagon barrel. In November of that year Whitney wrote the chief of ordnance offering "my own new model" Navy revolvers at twelve dollars each, presumably early ex-

Whitney-Beals .28 caliber "walking beam" iron-frame pocket revolver. (Courtesy Mr. H. Paul Wilson)

Whitney .36 caliber revolver (No. 10988) owned by Hugh A. Cook, Franklin County (Kansas) sheriff and representative to the 1865 Kansas legislature. (Courtesy Kansas State Historical Society)

Allen & Wheelock percussion belt-model revolver excavated in Kansas. (Courtesy Mr. John Biringer Miller) amples of his solid-frame .36, and also brought out a scaled-down .31 caliber five-shot pocket version of this gun, which like the larger size was first made without and then with an attached loading lever. Following the two solid-frame models was another pocket revolver, also with a solid frame but having a sheath trigger instead of the conventional trigger and guard; except for its centrally mounted hammer, the new pocket arm was quite similar to the Colt sidehammer model patented in 1855.[66]

A revolver resembling the Whitney Navy which was actually made in the West, although in very small numbers, was the Shawk & McLanahan. Assembled near St. Louis about 1858, this was another solid-frame six-shot .36 caliber weapon, but its frame was brass instead of iron and its 8 in. barrel was round instead of octagonal. Total production was probably fewer than 100 guns.[67]

Coming onto the market beside Allen & Wheelock's bar-hammer revolver was the firm's new solid-frame single-action sidehammer revolver, incorporating features patented by Allen in January and December of 1857. Externally this gun resembled the Colt sidehammer of 1855, with a hammer on the right side of the frame and a cylinder pin entering from the rear. Internally, however, this pistol differed from and was more reliable than the Colt, having a rotating recoil plate locked to the rear of the cylinder, a longitudinally sliding cylinder bolt activated by a spring-loaded stud in the top of the tumbler, and a rammer housed in the barrel lug and operated by a pivoting trigger guard. Allen & Wheelock made this revolver in barrel lengths from 2 in. to 8½ in. and in four frame sizes according to caliber: .28, .31, .34, and .36.[68]

Like most other Allen guns the sidehammer revolvers sold well; the "Allen's Pistols" offered in 1858 by Lownes, Orgill & Co. and F. H. Clark of Memphis undoubtedly included examples of these guns. More specifically, T. J. Albright's advertisement in the *Arkansas Gazette* in February of 1859 listed "Allen's New Patent Repeater of all sizes, from 3 to 8 inch." In the fall of that year another St. Louis dealer, Charles Kittredge, advertised Allen's pistols with an illustration of the sidehammer revolver. And at least one Allen sidehammer (now in the Pioneer Museum in Colorado Springs) came to Colorado during the rush of 1859.[69]

In the spring of 1859 gunsmith John Biringer left the employ of the Tryon concern in Philadelphia and traveled west, setting up his own shop in Leavenworth. Before leaving Tryon he bought individual samples of Colt, Whitney, and Warner revolvers, and six pairs of Allens, plus another Allen he described as a "No. 2 4 in." These may well have been single-shot pistols, but when Biringer opened his Leavenworth shop for business, he listed in his books "Allens Revolvers" with 3 in. to 6 in. barrels; based on the supply of extra Allen parts he had on hand, he evidently expected these guns to be among his best sellers.[70]

Biringer's stocks also included Colts with 4 in. to 6 in. barrels, Whitney "Colts Patern . . . 3 in," and Warner "3 in" and "4 in" revolvers. Based on a patent for a pawl design issued to Warner in July of 1857, these guns were conventional-looking single-action solid-frame pocket arms, made first in .28 and later in .31 caliber. Unlike Warner's earlier handguns the new revolvers proved fairly successful, with production eventually reaching some 9000 arms. At least one other western dealer, N. O. Kernaghan of New Orleans, was selling Warners by 1859.[71]

Allen, Massachusetts Arms, Warner, and Whitney had all made inroads into the handgun business in the years before 1857, but of these four only Allen had experienced real success. With the expiration of Colt's patent, however, E. Remington & Sons, rifle and shotgun manufacturers of long standing, took their first step into a field that would prove highly profitable for them. They entered modestly enough, with a five-shot .31 caliber single-action pocket model patented by Fordyce Beals in June of 1856. In May of 1857 Beals got another patent on this gun, but since the first few examples do not carry the latter date, the revolver may have reached the market a month or two before that. The Beals pocket model went through three versions, all of which had solid frames with externally mounted pawls. The first type, advertised as "A Superior Article" in an 1858 brochure, had a conventional trigger and guard, differing in this feature from the second type, which had a sheath trigger. The third type, based on a cylinder-pin/loading-lever patent issued to Beals in September of 1858, also had a sheath trigger but was somewhat larger than the other two, and in the contours of its barrel lug and loading lever resembled the big .36 and .44 caliber Remingtons which were to follow it. (By August of 1859 Remington was advertising this gun in the East as a "Pocket And Belt Size Revolver.")[72]

While all three Beals models were single-action arms, a designer named Joseph Rider patented a new five-shot double-action pocket revolver in May of 1859 that would become one of Remington's biggest sellers. The distinguishing external feature of this arm was its "mushroom" cylinder, in which the front half was of uniform diameter but the rear half tapered inward from rear to front. Also, unlike most double-action handguns, the Remington Rider had no prawl at the top of the grip, but a streamlined S-shaped frame-backstrap contour instead. The revolver was mechanically

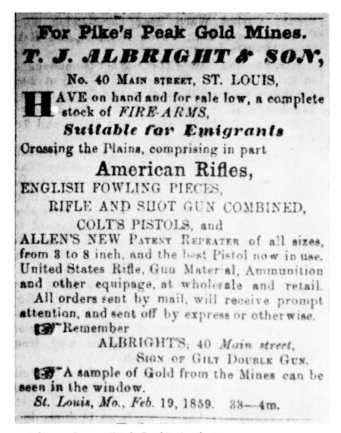

Arkansas Gazette (Little Rock), April 1859.

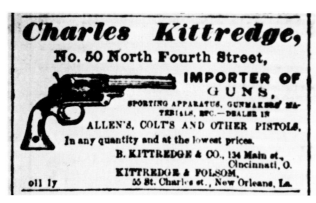

Missouri Democrat (St. Louis), Oct. 1859.

New Orleans *Picayune*, April 1861.

reliable, having among other things a cylinder bolt similar to that in the Adams revolvers, and it far outsold all the Beals pocket models combined. Taylor & Churchill enthusiastically advertised this gun in the New Orleans *Picayune* in April of 1861: "Three Hundred Ryder's patent Self-Cocking Revolvers, pocket size, Only Nine Dollars Each."[73]

Even with the availability of the Colt, Allen, Massachusetts Arms, Warner, Whitney, and Remington revolvers, single-shot pistols remained highly popular items. One .36 caliber bar-hammer screw-barrel Allen (now with the Colorado State Historical Society) came to Cherry Creek with a Colorado settler in 1859, and a member of the party which broke Dr. John Doy out of a Kansas jail in the same year wore a pistol of this type (but with a 2 in. barrel), on a thong around his neck. Another bar-hammer pistol of the same size was found near Ft. Kearny, Nebraska, and may also date from the late 1850s. An older style of screw-barrel pocket pistol made by Beckwith of London, with thumb-cocked center hammer, folding trigger, and sliding safety behind the hammer, was found in Cherry Creek in the 1880s and probably also reached Colorado during its gold-rush period. A pair of similar pistols fabricated by Patrick of Liverpool, but without the sliding safeties, were bought about 1865 by an early settler of the Pike's Peak region.[74]

Henry Deringer's little pistol also held onto its popularity: between 1856 and 1866 Deringer sold more than 5000 pairs, about four-fifths of which went onto the market between 1856 and 1861. The gun's popularity, however, did not stem entirely from this quantity, but from sales of the many copies which began appearing on the market in the late 1850s. So widespread did this copying become that late in the summer of 1859 Deringer himself inserted an open letter in the columns of the *Alta California*, warning that "several dishonest persons have manufactured and offered for sale a counterfeit or imitation of my celebrated pistols, fraudulently stamping them with my name. . . . this fraud [has] been extensively practiced in San Francisco." In Deringer's eyes a major offender was A. J. Plate of San Francisco, who bought about 54 pairs from Deringer's New York agents, Folsom & Stevens, in 1858. However, in that year Charles Schlotterbeck, one of Deringer's workmen, left Philadelphia for San Francisco, establishing a business relationship with Plate soon after his arrival. In 1860 Henry Schlotterbeck, a brother who had left Deringer's employ the previous year, formed "Slotter & Co." in Philadelphia with other Deringer workmen. With Charles Schlotterbeck as unofficial agent in California, Slotter & Company began supplying Plate not only with muzzle-loading rifles, but with very close copies of Deringer

Members of the rescue party which in 1859 freed Dr. John Doy (seated) from the jail at St. Joseph, Mo., after he had been kidnapped and jailed for stealing slaves and setting them free. The man second from right carries an Allen-style bar-hammer self-cocking pistol on a cord about his neck, while his companion (fourth from left) wears a U.S. Model 1832 heavy artillery short sword, of Roman pattern. (Courtesy Kansas State Historical Society)

pocket pistols. While some of these guns were plainly stamped "Slotter & Co.," most of those made through 1863 were marked as Deringer products. Furthermore, Slotter sold Deringers not only to Plate but also to Robert Liddle and Wilson & Evans, as well as to dealers in Oregon and Nevada. Exasperated, Deringer initiated legal action against Plate in November of 1863 which, nearly six years later, finally resulted in Deringer's favor.[75]

But the Slotter-Plate activities did not cause all Deringer's problems; besides Klepzig & Co. of San Francisco, gunmakers in many other parts of the West stood ready to supply customers with their own Deringer-style pocket pistols. Two Houston makers, Schmidt and Erichson, fabricated creditable copies of the arm, but there were a number of others also, including Dickson of Louisville, Trumpler of Little Rock, and Dimick of St. Louis. Even Tufts & Colley of New York, who advertised "guns, rifles, [and] pistols" in the Dallas Herald and the Galveston News for 1859, made "Deringer patt'n" handguns. Dealers in Mississippi River

ports such as F. Glassick & Co. and Schneider & Co. of Memphis (who maintained an on-again, off-again partnership with one another), Samuel O'Dell of Natchez, Louis Hoffman of Vicksburg, and T. F. Guion of New Orleans also made or sold Deringer copies.[76]

In all probability the eastern-made Deringer copies marked "Gillespie," "R. P. Bruff," and "Seaver" also reached the frontier, because during the late 1850s their makers advertised repeatedly (as did Tufts & Colley) in western newspapers. As early as 1854 Wolfe, Gillespie & Co. of New York had offered "Colt's and Derringer Pistols" in the Galveston News; and in the fall of 1858 (some two years after the company name had become Wolfe, Dash, & Fisher), the partners were still advertising "fine Rifles and Pistols, of their own manufacture, marked 'Gillespie'" in the New Orleans Picayune. These Gillespie pistols included derringers which, except for their cast-steel barrels, were fairly close copies of Henry Deringer's product. Contemporary with Wolfe, Dash & Fisher was another New York partnership, that of Bruff, Brother & Seaver. In

"Buffalo Bill" Cody's pair of Henry Deringer, Jr., pocket pistols. Each is inscribed on a silver shield inset in the stock "W. F. Cody 1865." (Courtesy Sotheby Parke Bernet, Los Angeles)

Pair of percussion derringer pistols made by G. Erichson of Houston, Texas. Each has a five-point star inset in the wrist, perhaps representative of its Texas origin. (Courtesy Winchester Repeating Arms Co., Division of Olin Industries, Inc.)

1856 this firm had simply offered "Colt's and Deringer Pistols," but by mid-1860 the partners were styling themselves "Manufacturers of Rifles and Derringer Pistols" in the *Picayune,* and were undoubtedly the sources for the steel-barrel Deringer copies carrying "R. P. Bruff" or "Seaver" markings.[77]

Countering the many Deringer copyists were H. G. Newcomb and L. Swett & Co. of Vicksburg, J. B. Gilmore of Shreveport, A. Millspaugh of Washington, Louisiana, Hyde & Goodrich of New Orleans, and the established California houses, all of whom provided an outlet for the genuine Deringer-made article. At least one dealer, F. H. Clark of Memphis, sold both the genuine article and reproductions of his own manufacture. Other merchants probably did this also; the "Derringer's Silver-Mounted Pocket Pistols" listed by D. Kernaghan & Co. of New Orleans in 1858 and 1859 may have included both originals and imitations.[78]

Whether made by Deringer or by an imitator, the little pistols had no trouble finding buyers. When J. Ross Browne and his companions were at Camp Drum in 1863,

we heard a good deal about the lively condition of society in and around Los Angeles. It was not considered safe for a man to travel about, even within a few miles of camp, without a double-barrelled shot-gun, a revolver, a bowie-knife, and two Derringer pistols.

Asbury Harpending, describing his own experiences in California in 1863, wrote that:

In those days everyone carried a derringer, which looked like a sort of toy pistol, but was really one of the most deadly close-range emergency weapons ever invented by the evil genius of man. Each person had a pet place for keeping his derringer secreted, but handy. For myself, I carried one in a specially prepared pocket inside of the right cuff of my coat. Just a practiced twitch, and I could have it in my hand ready for use in an instant.[79]

OLDER PEPPERBOXES AND NEWER REVOLVERS

The new revolvers flooding the market failed to lessen the popularity of the single-shot pistol, nor did they displace the percussion pepperbox. Features of the patent issued to Allen in January of 1857, although described in connection with a conventional revolver, also went into a new four-shot pepperbox. Unlike Allen's earlier models, the axis pin in the new gun did not extend entirely through the barrel group; instead, it was a tapered post only about 7/8 in. long, which allowed a barrel group of smaller diameter.[80]

DERINGER PISTOLS.

PHILADELPHIA, June 18th, 1859.
MESSRS. CHARLES CURRY & BROTHER, No. 8, Battery street, San Francisco, California: Gents—As several dishonest persons have manufactured and offered for sale a counterfeit or imitation of my celebrated pistols, fraudulently stamping them with my name, and thus imposing on the public; this fraud having been extensively practiced in San Francisco, California, with a view to prevent it in future, I have constituted you my AGENTS for the sale of the DERINGER PISTOL in California. I wish you to caution all persons infringing on my rights either as manufacturers or venders, that I shall, on conviction, prosecute them to the utmost extent of the law. Those wishing to obtain a genuine Deringer pistol will therefore call upon you, as I have no other authorized agent in California.
au1 1m   HENRY DERINGER.

Alta California (San Francisco), Sept. 1859.

Percussion pepperboxes held onto some of their popularity well into the 1860s. During the Pike's Peak rush a St. Louis observer made this reference to the gold-seekers' armament, which included an oblique mention of pepperboxes:

frightful looking bowie knives manufactured for the special purpose of disemboweling the Indians around Pike's Peak; many-muzzled pistols and guns, intended to be used by one Pike's Peaker, when he proposes to let a little daylight through the proportions of another. . . .

While crossing the plains about 1861 Samuel Clemens—better known as Mark Twain—took amused notice of a traveling companion's problems with one such gun:

George Bemis . . . wore in his belt an old original "Allen" revolver, such as irreverent people called a "pepperbox." Simply drawing the trigger back, cocked and fired the pistol. As the trigger came back, the hammer would begin to rise and the barrel to turn over, and presently down would drop the hammer, and away would speed the ball. To aim along the turning barrel and hit the thing aimed at was a feat which was probably never done with an "Allen" in the world. But George's was a reliable weapon, nevertheless, because as one of the stage-drivers afterward said, "If she didn't get what she went after, she would fetch something else." And so she did. She went after a deuce of spades nailed against a tree, once, and fetched a mule standing about thirty yards to the left of it. Bemis did not want the mule; but the owner came out with a double-barreled shotgun and persuaded him to buy it, anyhow. It was a cheerful weapon the "Allen." Sometimes all its six barrels would go off at once, and then there was no safe place in all the region round about, but behind it.

Later in the journey, Clemens and Bemis unwisely joined in a buffalo hunt while waiting for their mud wagon to be repaired. The hunt ended in disgrace for them when a wounded bull chased Bemis nearly two miles and forced him up a tree. Mellowing somewhat as he recovered from the disaster, Bemis recalled the ridicule coming from those who had witnessed the event: "It was not funny. . . . I should have shot that long gangly lubber they called Hank, if I could have done it without crippling six or seven other people— but of course I couldn't, the old "Allen's" so confounded comprehensive."[81]

A rusted six-shot bar-hammer pepperbox with a 5 in. barrel group, found in Russell's Gulch, Colorado, is probably a relic of the Pike's Peak rush; another pepperbox, of the same general style but much smaller, was found along the Missouri River in Montana, and may have been dropped by one of the region's early gold-seekers. In contrast to the bar-hammer models, a pepperbox imported by Lewis & Tomes, which came to the Denver area about 1863, has seven barrels and a thumb-cocked center hammer. More representative were the bar-hammer Allens and their long-time rival, the concealed-hammer Blunt & Syms. A notice in an 1860 New York directory by John G. Syms, "Late with Blunt & Syms," offered "Six-Barrelled Pistols," and a price list issued by Tryon of Philadelphia in 1864 included, among the Allen & Wheelock revolvers and single-shots, Allen's "four barrel, self-cocking pistol."[82]

By the close of the 1850s, however, revolvers were finally outdistancing pepperboxes in popularity, especially the revolvers made by Colt. When young Libeus Barney was in Denver in October of 1859, "I witnessed a duel between Mr. P. McClure, the challenging party, and Mr. R. E. Whitsett; their weapons were Colt's navies; distance, ten paces." Teamsters encountered on the plains by Richard F. Burton in 1860 wore:

> a broad leather belt [which] supports on the right a revolver, generally a Colt's Navy or medium size (when Indian fighting is expected, the large dragoon pistol is universally preferred); and on the left in a plain black sheath, or sometimes in the more ornamental Spanish scabbard, is a buckhorn or ivory handled bowie-knife. . . . A glance through the wagon awning shows guns and rifles stowed along the side.

Based on his frontier experiences, Burton offered some sage advice to those contemplating a westward journey:

> For weapons I carried two revolvers: from the moment of leaving St. Jo to the time of reaching Placerville or Sacramento the pistol should never be absent from a man's right side—remember it is handier there than on the other—nor the bowie knife from his left. Contingencies with Indians and others may happen, when the difference of a second saves life: the revolver should therefore be carried with its butt to the fore, and when drawn it should not be levelled as in target practice, but directed toward the object, by means of the right forefinger laid flat along the cylinder while the medius draws the trigger.

> The instinctive consent between eye and hand, combined with a little practice, will soon enable the beginner to shoot correctly from the hip; all he has to do, is to think that he is pointing at the mark, and pull. As a precaution, especially when mounted upon a kicking horse, it is wise to place the cock upon a capless nipple rather than trust to the intermediate pins. In dangerous places the revolver should be discharged and reloaded every morning, both for the purpose of keeping the hand in, and to do the weapon justice. A revolver is an admirable tool when properly used; those, however, who are too idle or careless to attend to it, had better carry a pair of "Derringers."[83]

Although they may have been unaware of Burton's recommendations, prospectors en route to the Colorado goldfields were no less fond of revolvers. As the Missouri Republican described the "wheel-barrow or hand-cart chap":

> [He] is dressed in a coon-skin cap, red flannel shirt— plentifully besprinkled with buttons and flashy devices of animated creation—with corduroy pants and water-proof boots (with flaming red tops), that come up to his thigh. A leather belt encircles his middle (he has no waist), in which is hung a dirk-knife and a colt's revolver. In his cart is a pair of blankets, a bacon ham, three slices of jerked beef, a few pounds of crackers, and a jug of whiskey. . . .[84]

Colts were also favorites with express companies and other concerns whose businesses involved physical risk. Near Salt Lake City Richard Burton met a Pony Express rider named Jim, who carried "two Colt's revolvers, of the dragoon or largest size, considering all others too small." Navy Colts, however, were apparently more popular with other express riders, if only because of their lighter weight; the rider's primary mission was to get the mail through, and his instruc-

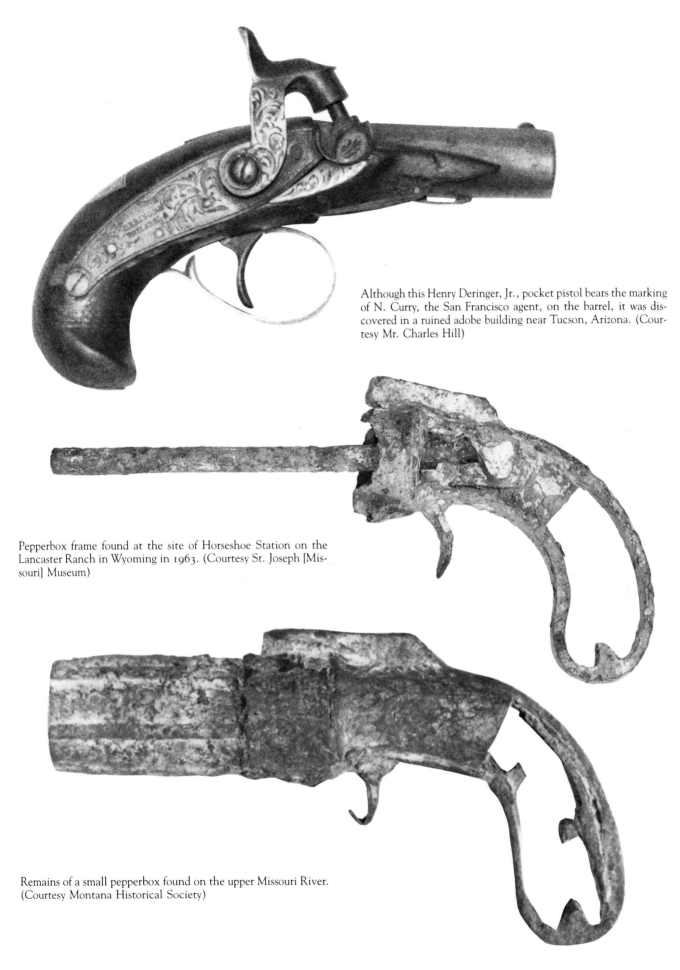

Although this Henry Deringer, Jr., pocket pistol bears the marking of N. Curry, the San Francisco agent, on the barrel, it was discovered in a ruined adobe building near Tucson, Arizona. (Courtesy Mr. Charles Hill)

Pepperbox frame found at the site of Horseshoe Station on the Lancaster Ranch in Wyoming in 1963. (Courtesy St. Joseph [Missouri] Museum)

Remains of a small pepperbox found on the upper Missouri River. (Courtesy Montana Historical Society)

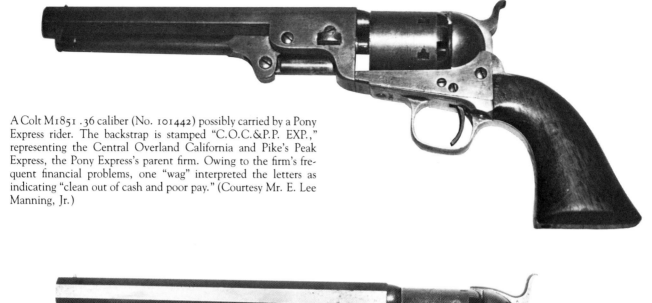

A Colt M1851 .36 caliber (No. 101442) possibly carried by a Pony Express rider. The backstrap is stamped "C.O.C.&P.P. EXP.," representing the Central Overland California and Pike's Peak Express, the Pony Express's parent firm. Owing to the firm's frequent financial problems, one "wag" interpreted the letters as indicating "clean out of cash and poor pay." (Courtesy Mr. E. Lee Manning, Jr.)

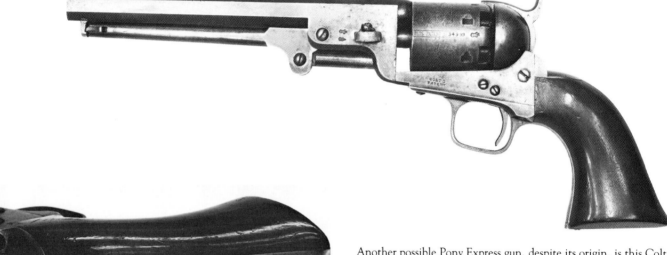

Another possible Pony Express gun, despite its origin, is this Colt M1851 (No. 34999) manufactured in London, England in 1855. The backstrap inscription may represent the Leavenworth & Pike's Peak Express, organized in February of 1859. Bankrupt by year's end, its assets were taken over by Russell, Majors & Waddell and the firm was renamed the Central Overland California and Pike's Peak Express. (Courtesy Mr. John G. Hamilton)

tions were to depend on his mount's speed and endurance to get him out of any trouble—the weapon was to be used only as a last resort. For added firepower a rider might carry a single revolver with an extra loaded cylinder; just before riding across Nevada late in 1860, "Pony Bob" Halsam "adjusted . . . my Colt's revolver, with two cylinders ready for use in case of an emergency."[85]

Halsam had reason to be apprehensive, for at that time Indians were disrupting express service in both Nevada and Utah. William W. Finney, general agent of the Pacific, rushed to Carson City to aid Division Superintendent Bolivar Roberts in restoring regular service, putting out an appeal to residents of Sacramento to equip twenty-five men for an armed expedition to Salt Lake City. The people came up with

the money for provisions and salaries and with most of the 25 Sharps rifles and 25 Colt Dragoons Finney requested. The Pony Express also procured 106 "Army sized revolvers," very probably Dragoons, from the commander of the Department of Utah at Camp Floyd to defend company property. According to the agreement, company officials would either return the guns in good order or pay for them.[86]

Express riders, of course, were not the only plains travelers to demand abundant firepower. John Cremony, who spent years among the Apaches during the 1850s and early 1860s, habitually carried "four Colt's six-shooters, two in my saddle-holsters and two in my belt, with a large bowie knife."[87]

Although the Colt firm continued shipping the Dragoon through most of 1861, in 1860 Colt introduced

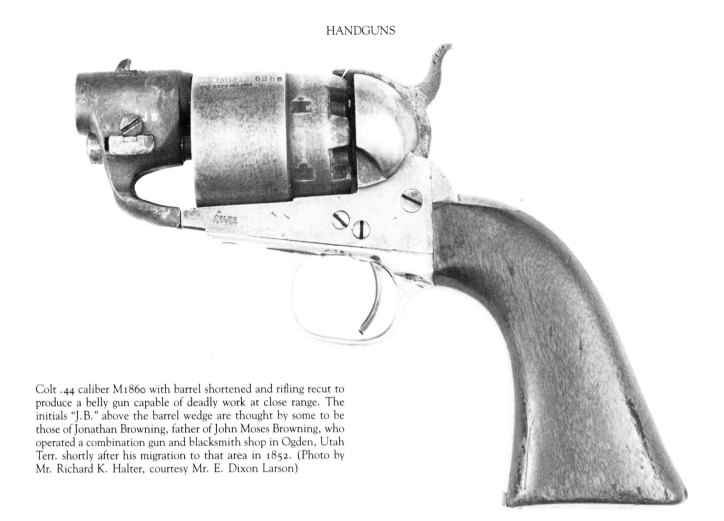

Colt .44 caliber M1860 with barrel shortened and rifling recut to produce a belly gun capable of deadly work at close range. The initials "J.B." above the barrel wedge are thought by some to be those of Jonathan Browning, father of John Moses Browning, who operated a combination gun and blacksmith shop in Ogden, Utah Terr. shortly after his migration to that area in 1852. (Photo by Mr. Richard K. Halter, courtesy Mr. E. Dixon Larson)

a replacement for this gun, his .44 caliber six-shot "New Model Army Pistol." The distinctive features of the new gun were its rebated cylinder and rack and pinion or "creeping" loading lever, and its lighter weight: due to the use of improved "Silver Steel," it weighed some twenty-three ounces less than its predecessor. Such an arm obviously had a ready market in the West, and by September of 1860 J. A. Henry of Little Rock, among others, was able to offer "a lot of Colt's new Silver Steel Revolvers." Two more new Colts built on the same lines, a six-shot Navy and a five-shot "Police" revolver, came out the following year. At about the same time Colt also brought out a .36 caliber pocket model, with a five-shot rebated cylinder but with the old style of loading lever. This was an apparent duplication of effort, since the Police revolver was also a five-shot .36, having a fluted cylinder and the newer loading lever, and proved somewhat more popular. Nevertheless, some of the old-style .36 pocket guns did reach the West: one such model (now in the Wells Fargo Bank History Room) has "Wells Fargo Express— Nevada Office" engraved on its backstrap.[88]

Colt's Model 1860 Army became the most popular handgun of the Civil War, and a civilian favorite soon after its introduction, but the new 1861 Navy never came close to achieving the popularity of the "Old

Model Navy" of 1851. In 1863 a cased pair of heavily engraved 1851 Navies, complete with accessories (and now in the Colorado State Historical Society collection), went to Captain Byron Ayers of the Second Kansas Volunteers, a gift from John Ross, chief of the Cherokees. When Montana outlaw Jack Slade got into a brawl in a Virginia City saloon at about the same time, the bartender "raised a big Colt's navy revolver in front of Slade and declared himself to take a hand in the fight and Slade then weakened and said: 'Let us quit.'"[89]

Evidently Colt's Police revolver (which is now often referred to as the Model 1862 although it was on the market a year before that) had a definite appeal for westerners. During the trial of George Ives in Virginia

Arkansas Gazette (Little Rock), Sept. 1860.

Colt .44 caliber M1860 Army with the rammer and loading lever removed and the barrel cut to a more convenient length for concealment. The revolver belonged to the Mormon Porter Rockwell, sometimes referred to as "the destroying angel." (Courtesy Utah State Historical Society)

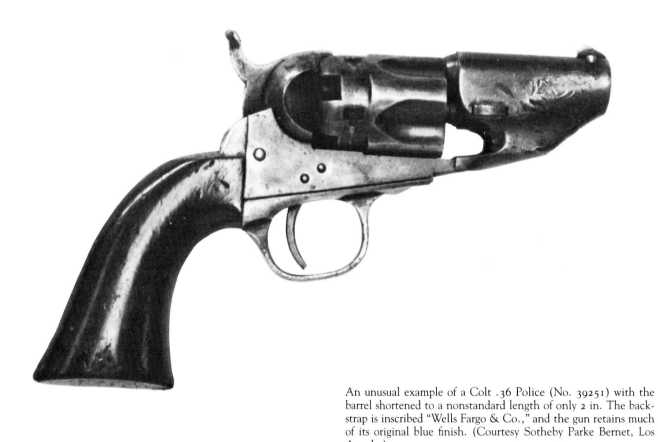

An unusual example of a Colt .36 Police (No. 39251) with the barrel shortened to a nonstandard length of only 2 in. The backstrap is inscribed "Wells Fargo & Co.," and the gun retains much of its original blue finish. (Courtesy Sotheby Parke Bernet, Los Angeles)

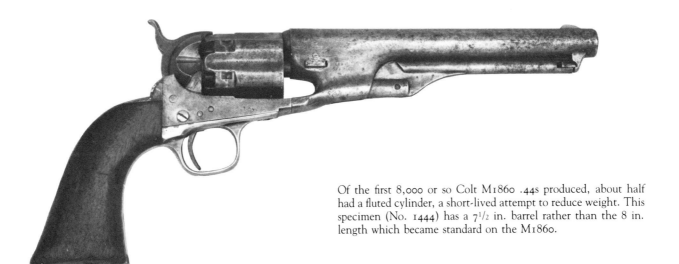

Of the first 8,000 or so Colt M1860 .44s produced, about half had a fluted cylinder, a short-lived attempt to reduce weight. This specimen (No. 1444) has a 7½ in. barrel rather than the 8 in. length which became standard on the M1860.

Quantrill guerrillas Arch Clement, Dave Pool, and Bill Hendricks, each armed with a pair of Colt revolvers. The unholstered handguns include two M1860 .44s, at left. (Courtesy Library of Congress)

This cross-eyed westerner holds his Colt M1851 Navy in a classic pose in an ambrotype from the Civil War period. (Courtesy Mr. Herb Peck, Jr.)

City in 1863, Judge Wilbur Sanders wore "a heavy overcoat with deep side pockets, in each of which I had carried a new Colt's police pistol." Police revolvers with barrels shortened to 2 in. or 2½ in. seem to have acquired a certain popularity in the West as "hide-out" or "belly guns": one of these (now with the California Historical Society) has ivory grips; another, found in Eldorado County, California, has three chambers still loaded. In general the neat workmanship noticeable in connection with these cut-down Colts, including the professional job of filling in the rammer holes in the barrel lugs, suggests that the Colt factory itself may have shortened the barrels rather than individual gunsmiths. James B. Hume, a Wells Fargo detective, carried a M1860 Army with its barrel shortened in a similar manner.[90]

In spite of the voracious demands of the Ordnance Department, which began sweeping up most of the New Model Army .44s in June of 1861 and gathered in many other Colts besides, the Colt factory was still able to supply the civilian market with all the revolvers it could handle. By July of 1863 Henry Folsom of St. Louis had on hand "500 Colt's Revolvers, assorted sizes"; S. B. Shaw, a competitor in the same city, was more explicit, offering in October of 1863 "100 Colt's Army Revolvers, 700 Colt's Navy Revolvers, 500 Colt's 6, 5, and 4 Inch Revolvers, [and] 100 Colt's 6½ and 5½ Inch d[itt]o." The latter could have been either the .36 caliber pocket models or the Police revolvers, both of which were available in those barrel lengths. At about the same time, Neosfield & Mitchell of Leavenworth accepted delivery of a shipment of 50 Model 1861 Navies from the Colt factory. In an advertisement appearing in June of 1864, which also offered Wesson rifles and Sharps carbines, Henry Folsom declared: "Important to Veteran Regiments and Emigrants to Idaho . . . Colt's Pistols of all sizes, among which are 200 new model Armies. . . ." In contrast, Unger & Brother, advertising in San Francisco two months later, offered "Colt's Navy Pistols, New And Old Models."[91]

Reflecting the popularity of the older Colts were the .31 and .36 caliber revolvers made by the Manhattan Firearms Manufacturing Company, which bore a strong resemblance to the Colt models of 1849 and 1851. Based on patents issued in May and December of 1859, Manhattan's .31 caliber arm, on the market by the fall of that year, was a five-shot weapon distinguished by a removeable sideplate in the frame and by ten bolt notches in the cylinder. The .36 caliber "Navy" revolver, which came out at about the same time, also had a five-shot cylinder with ten bolt notches, but lacked the detachable sideplate. About 1860 Manhattan modified the .31 caliber gun to incorporate a six-shot cylinder with twelve notches, but this revolver was less popular than the .36, and production of it probably stopped near the close of 1862. However, the bigger model continued in production until well after the Civil War. In March of 1864 Benjamin Kittredge, a Cincinnati arms dealer, patented a spring plate for the Manhattan Navy which when attached to the face of the standing breech prevented any backflash from the percussion caps, but Manhattan had been making limited use of this plate for some time prior to the patent.[92]

Some Manhattans may have reached the West under the auspices of Kittredge himself, who often shipped guns down the Ohio River to the Mississippi. In any event, during the Civil War Manhattans were on the frontier in some quantity: in October of 1863, for example, S. B. Shaw of St. Louis listed no fewer than 1500 Manhattan Navy revolvers with 6½ in. barrels, and another 500 with 4 in. and 5 in. barrels. By the summer of 1864 another dealer, John Biringer of Leav-

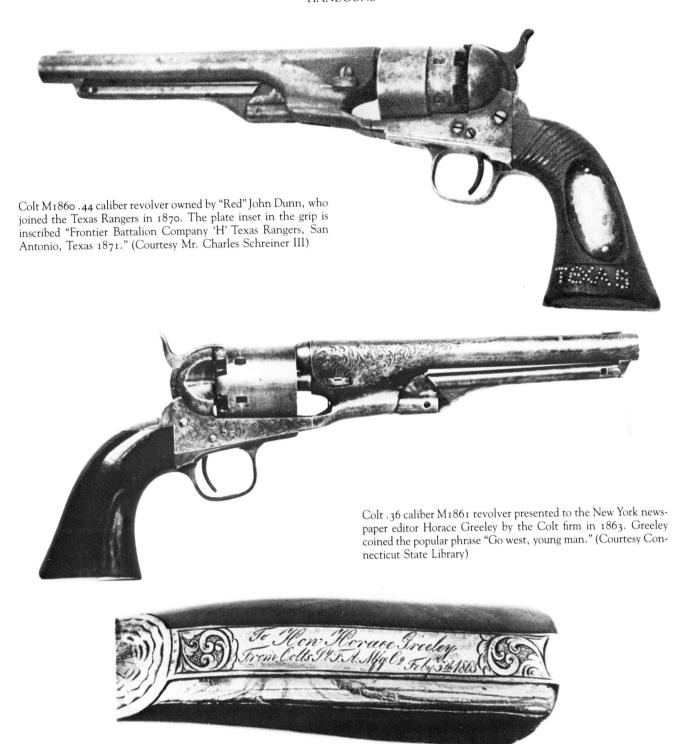

Colt M1860 .44 caliber revolver owned by "Red" John Dunn, who joined the Texas Rangers in 1870. The plate inset in the grip is inscribed "Frontier Battalion Company 'H' Texas Rangers, San Antonio, Texas 1871." (Courtesy Mr. Charles Schreiner III)

Colt .36 caliber M1861 revolver presented to the New York newspaper editor Horace Greeley by the Colt firm in 1863. Greeley coined the popular phrase "Go west, young man." (Courtesy Connecticut State Library)

enworth, was doing a brisk business in Manhattans, especially those with 6½ in. barrels.[93]

Colt's handgun line was much more diversified than Manhattan's, but another manufacturer, Remington, was soon able to match Colt model for model. About 1860 Remington brought out the first of its belt and holster revolvers, a single-action solid-frame six-shot model made in .36 and .44 caliber versions. This revolver was based on the loading-lever/cylinder-pin patent granted to Fordyce Beals in September of 1858,

and first used in his third-model pocket revolver. Because the new revolvers were stamped "Beals' Patent" on the barrel, they were often referred to as Beals revolvers instead of Remingtons, and Union purchasing agents who bought such guns from July through December of 1861 listed them under both names.[94]

A patent issued to William Elliot in December of 1861, again on the loading-lever/cylinder-pin assembly, resulted in a modification of the big Beals: the new 1861 model, which actually appeared about the

Manhattan .31 caliber revolver, a major competitor of the Colt .31 caliber Model 1849 pocket revolver, which it resembles closely. (Courtesy Union Pacific Railroad Museum)

Heavily corroded Remington New Model percussion revolver found along the Santa Fe Trail in Haskell County, in southwestern Kansas. (Courtesy Kansas State Historical Society) middle of 1862, came in the usual .36 and .44 caliber versions, but differed from the Beals in having a channel cut in the upper rear section of the loading lever and an integral metal web under the lever, presumably to stiffen it. Still another patent on the loading-lever/cylinder-pin assembly, this one issued to Samuel Remington in March of 1863, resulted in the "New Model" series, which included not only the large .36 and .44 caliber guns but, in short order, a .36 caliber double-action belt model, a .31 caliber five-shot sheath-trigger pocket revolver, and, somewhat later, a .36 caliber five-shot single-action "Police" model.[95]

Apparently Union purchases of the large-frame Remington-Beals revolvers temporarily prevented most of them from reaching the frontier market. In December of 1862, however, an issue of the *Missouri Democrat* carried the following notice: "Remington's Army and Navy Revolver Has been approved by the U.S. Board of Ordnance, and is now largely used in the service." The address given in the notice was that of the factory in Ilion, New York, and Remington often placed its own advertisements in western newspapers rather than leaving that job to its dealers. In July of 1863 Henry Folsom of St. Louis offered "100 Beale's Navies" along with various other revolvers, but two months later the Remington firm again placed its own ad for "Remington's Army and Navy Revolvers!," this time showing a cut of the New Model .44. A heavily rusted Remington .44 found in Colorado, either a Beals or an early 1861 model, has had its barrel shortened to about 3 in., reflecting the frontier practice of cutting down the barrels of large-caliber revolvers that was perhaps most common in connection with Colts.[96]

Not to be outdone by his rivals in Ilion and Hartford, Allen brought out a new solid-frame percussion revolver about 1861 which departed from his earlier sidehammer models in several respects. Made in .36 and .44 caliber sizes, the new revolver had a centrally mounted hammer, a cylinder pin entering from the front, a pivoting (instead of a sliding) cylinder bolt, and no recoil plate behind the cylinder. The loading lever, however, was like that in the sidehammer guns, with the rammer forced into the chamber mouths by a hinged trigger guard. Late in 1861 Union authorities bought a small quantity of Allen revolvers on the open market in Boston; presumably most of these were the big centerhammer models (because a centerhammer Allen .44 is one of five revolvers illustrated in the Atlas for the *Official Records*), but the purchases may also have included some of the .36 caliber sidehammer arms. For the benefit of civilian buyers, an Allen advertisement of the 1860s declared the centerhammer .44 "unsurpassed for simplicity, strength, power of penetration, or accuracy of shooting."[97]

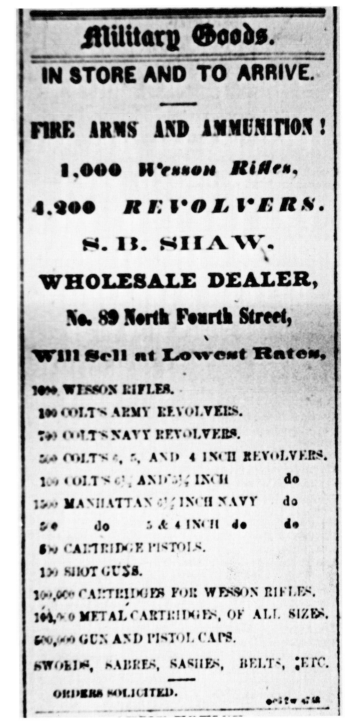

Missouri Democrat (St. Louis), Oct. 1863.

Although more closely associated with military use, the double-action revolver made by Eben T. Starr also reached the frontier civilian market: in February of 1861 O. S. Jennings of New Orleans offered "Navy Pistols. Starr's Patent Self-Cocking and Hair-Trigger Revolving Pistols, Six-Shooters."[98]

SMITH AND WESSON AND THE RIMFIRE CARTRIDGE REVOLVER

Percussion revolvers by Colt, Adams, Tranter, Remington, Warner, Whitney, Allen & Wheelock, Massachusetts Arms, and Manhattan offered everything the conservative handgun buyer could want. But late in 1857 a radically new revolver appeared on the market, one that would eventually render all percussion revolvers obsolete. While it incorporated some interesting mechanical details, the revolver itself was less important than the cartridge it chambered—a self-contained metallic round. The priming compound was spun into a hollow rim at the base or "head" of the cartridge case; this rim, of larger diameter than the case body, was struck by the hammer nose to ignite the priming, and the cartridge thus earned the name "rimfire."

Broken frame of a Remington .44 caliber New Model percussion revolver, found in Virginia City, Nevada.

REMINGTON'S ARMY AND NAVY REVOLVER

HAS BEEN APPROVED BY THE U. S. Board of Ordnance, and is now largely used in the service.

Circulars with prices to the Trade, furnished on application. Address,

de10 3m L 498   E. REMINGTON & SONS, Ilion, New York.

Missouri Democrat (St. Louis), Dec. 1862.

Since this cartridge fit into the chamber from the rear, it required a chamber bored through from end to end and not closed at the rear by a nipple as in percussion revolvers. This little detail—a bored-through chamber—was to give Horace Smith and Daniel B. Wesson the same monopoly over early rimfire-cartridge revolvers that Colt had enjoyed with his early percussion revolvers. Smith and Wesson, however, were not the first to come up with the idea of a bored-through chamber; after they had worked out the details of their revolver, they found that a young inventor named Rollin White had patented such a chamber in April of 1855. So in November of 1856 the two partners concluded an agreement with White to use his idea in exchange for cash payment plus royalty.[99]

Made from late 1857 to 1860, Smith & Wesson's first-model, first-issue revolver underwent at least six variations, but its basic features remained the same. Termed the "No. 1, Or Seven Shooter" in an 1858 circular, it was a seven-shot .22 caliber single-action arm with a brass frame and sheath trigger. The $3^3/_{16}$ in. ribbed octagon barrel was hinged at the front of the topstrap and locked in place at the front of the bottomstrap. Swinging up the barrel allowed the cylinder, which rotated on integral centers instead of on a separate cylinder pin, to drop out for loading. To eject the fired cases the shooter passed each chamber over a fixed ejector rod which was rigidly mounted under the barrel. The spring-loaded cylinder bolt, which lay longitudinally in the topstrap, was disengaged by a cleverly designed two-piece hammer. The upper part, comprising the cocking spur and hammer nose, pivoted on the lower part; when the shooter's thumb pressed the cocking spur backward and downward the hammer nose swung upward, lifting the cylinder bolt to allow the cylinder to rotate. F. H. Harrington, Daniel Wesson's nephew, patented this feature in June

Men identified as Frank and Jesse James. Frank (left) holds a Colt M1851 or similar revolver, while Jesse has a percussion Remington (c. 1867). (Courtesy Denver Public Library, Western History Dept.)

Allen & Wheelock .44 caliber percussion revolver.

of 1858, although the revolver itself was on the market more than six months before that.[100]

Hinging the barrel at the front of the topstrap was not a strong system, and the two-piece hammer was harder to make than the usual one-piece type; but the real disadvantage of this revolver was its small caliber, the load for which soon came to be standardized at 4 grains of powder and a 29 grain bullet, hardly adequate for the demands of frontier service. While Smith and Wesson undoubtedly realized this, the .22 Short cartridge resulted from necessity rather than preference. The copper used for the cartridge case had to be soft and thin enough for the hammer nose to dent it, and because of this the shock of firing often caused the case head to bulge or rupture. A badly bulged case head, wedged between the cylinder and the standing breech, could jam the cylinder. This happened so frequently, in fact, that the first examples of the Smith & Wesson had a recoil plate behind the cylinder which rotated with it, to prevent just such an occurrence.[101]

But because arms designers saw the possibilities of the rimfire cartridge, considerable talent went into its improvement, and after making about 3000 guns, Smith & Wesson discontinued the rotating recoil plate. As the cartridge itself improved, however, the number of gunmakers who wanted to design their own guns for it also increased. By mid-1858 Allen and Wheelock had introduced a seven-shot sidehammer .22 of their own, though Allen did not get a patent on the mechanical details until November of that year. While this was a sturdier design than the Smith & Wesson, it was also a flagrant infringement of the Rollin White patent: on behalf of Smith & Wesson, White instituted a lawsuit against Allen late in 1859, but the suit did not come to a conclusion until four years later, and Allen himself evidently regarded this point as a minor deterrent. Other manufacturers were almost as quick to adopt the bored-through cylinder, thus partially depriving Smith & Wesson of a market that was legally theirs. Nevertheless the first-issue Smith & Wessons sold well: although the firm delivered only a handful late in 1857, by September of 1858 more than

Henry Folsom ad from the *Missouri Democrat* (St. Louis), July 1863.

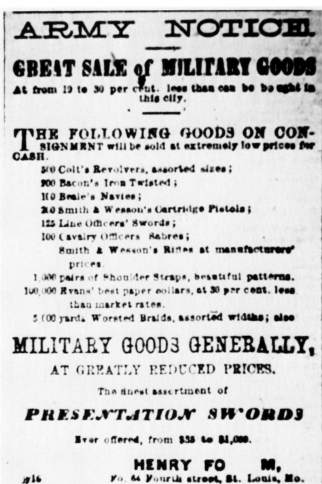

Smith & Wesson .22 caliber First Model revolvers, First Issue (above) and Second Issue. At top is a gutta-percha case of the type which was available for these guns. (Courtesy Mr. E. Lee Manning, Jr.)

800 .22s had come out of the factory. In March of that year the firm had appointed Joseph W. Storrs of New York its general sales agent, and Storrs distributed most of the first-issue models to other dealers, presumably including a dealer or two in the West.[102]

In 1860, after completing about 11,500 of the old first-issue models, the two partners brought out a new .22, differing from the last variation of the older model chiefly in the cylinder-locking arrangement: a one-piece hammer patented in July of 1859 displaced the two-piece type, with the raised, wedge-shaped nose of the new hammer acting on a split flat spring attached to the underside of the top-mounted cylinder bolt. While this design simplified manufacture, Smith and Wesson were still losing part of the cartridge-revolver market to their competitors. In 1861 the partners initiated a second lawsuit against Herman Boker &

Company of New York, the agent for .22 caliber cartridge revolvers made by Manhattan Arms Company. Late in that year J. W. Storrs testified that the revolvers infringing upon Rollin White's patent had appeared on the market in this order: Allen & Wheelock, Bacon, Manhattan, Union Arms, Prescott, Pond, "and a few more"; the "few more" undoubtedly included a highly advanced revolver patented by Daniel Moore in September of 1860. Other testimony gave a slightly different order, which included Warner and "Sharps & Hawkins," but the real point was that by late 1861 there were several competing handguns on the market which violated Smith & Wesson's patent rights.[103]

In mid-1861 Smith & Wesson introduced their "No. 2" or "Belt Pistol," a scaled-up version of their .22 with a six-shot cylinder and iron frame, available with 4 in., 5 in., or 6 in. barrel. It was chambered for a new cartridge, the .32 Long rimfire, which helped account for the model's great popularity: by 1864, in fact, the company was nearly two years behind on orders. Assisting in this happy circumstance was the fact that in October of 1862 the court decided the Boker case in Smith & Wesson's favor, after which Bacon, Moore, Pond, and Warner turned over their stocks of revolvers to Smith & Wesson, while other manufacturers simply withdrew their arms from the market. Two exceptions to this were Allen and E. A. Prescott, who blithely continued making metallic-cartridge revolvers until an injunction issued in November of 1863 stopped them.[104]

Since J. W. Storrs handled the distribution of most of the early Smith & Wessons, the time when they first reached the West is uncertain, but they were there no later than 1860. Charles Curry was advertising them by August of that year, as was J.A. Henry of Little Rock a month later. In 1861 the humorist Samuel ("Mark Twain") Clemens selected one as personal armament before crossing the country on his personal journey of discovery:

> I was armed to the teeth with a pitiful little Smith & Wesson's seven-shooter, which carried a ball like a homeopathic pill, and it took the whole seven to make a dose for an adult. But I thought it was grand. It appeared to me to be a dangerous weapon. It only had one fault—you could not hit anything with it. One of our "conductors" practiced awhile on a cow with it, and as long as she stood still and behaved herself she was safe. . . .

John Nelson would have agreed with Sam Clemens's analysis. While working as a teamster near Denver at about the same time, Nelson accidently killed a mule. Although he offered to pay for it, the wagonmaster threatened to lock him up. Nelson started to walk

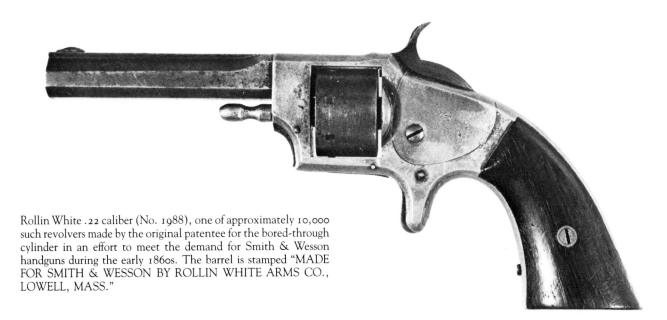

Rollin White .22 caliber (No. 1988), one of approximately 10,000 such revolvers made by the original patentee for the bored-through cylinder in an effort to meet the demand for Smith & Wesson handguns during the early 1860s. The barrel is stamped "MADE FOR SMITH & WESSON BY ROLLIN WHITE ARMS CO., LOWELL, MASS."

away when the wagon boss pulled a little Smith & Wesson: Nelson "looked at the tiny pistol, laughed, and told him to go on shooting. That popgun wouldn't hurt me." The boss fired all seven shots—and missed with every bullet![105]

In 1862 Benjamin Kittredge of Cincinnati ordered no fewer than 2600 Smith & Wesson .32s, some of which probably went farther west. By March of 1863 T. J. Albright was offering "Smith & Wesson's, and other Cartridge Pistols"; in July Henry Folsom listed "200 Smith & Wesson's Cartridge Pistols," and two months later Horace Dimick announced "2000 Revolvers Just received of Colt's, Smith & Wesson's, and other Makers. . . ." James Miller, who ran a mercantile establishment in Salt Lake City, noted in December of 1864 that a shoplifter had stolen a Smith & Wesson worth $28, but Miller later recovered the gun from an auction house.[106]

Of the patent-infringement revolvers that J. W. Storrs and others had enumerated as being on the market late in 1861, at least five of them—the Bacon, Moore, Pond, Prescott, and Warner—reached the West. With the legal decision of 1862 in their favor, Smith and Wesson licensed Bacon, Moore, Pond, and Warner to complete the revolvers then in the process of manufacture, whereupon the two partners bought these revolvers at wholesale and distributed them to dealers to sell at the usual retail prices. Prescott and Ethan Allen continued selling their guns on their own until the 1863 injunction put a stop to the practice.[107]

Advertisements of Allen's guns by individual frontier dealers were apparently few and far between in the early 1860s; an Allen & Wheelock ad in an 1863 San Francisco business directory gave the address of the home office in Worcester rather than that of a

West Coast agent. However, it is highly probable that those houses such as Albright, Dimick, and Charles Kittridge, all of which had handled Allen percussion handguns, continued to deal in Allen & Wheelock cartridge models. In August of 1864, in fact, Nathaniel Curry & Brother specifically listed "Colt's, Derringer's, Smith & Wesson's, Sharp's and Allen & Wheelock's Pistols."[108]

Where Smith and Wesson were concerned, Allen was probably the most worrisome of all the makers of revolvers with bored-through cylinders. Not only were his guns mechanically sound and well made, but his name was as well established as Colt's. Furthermore, his company was soon able to offer a line of metallic-cartridge handguns ranging in caliber from .22 to .44.

In its solid frame, side-mounted hammer, and cylinder pin entering from the rear, the Allen seven-shot sheath-trigger .22 patented in November of 1858 resembled his then-current percussion revolver; however, in July of 1860 the Worcester inventor patented a six-shot sidehammer .32 with cylinder pin entering the frame from the front, and most of his small-frame cartridge revolvers made thereafter took that form. Smith & Wesson did not begin delivery of its .32 rimfire revolver until late June of 1861, but Allen's .32 was undoubtedly on the market months before that. With either make, the shooter had to remove the cylinder for loading and remove it again to eject the fired cases, but the Allen had the important advantage of a solid rather than a hinged frame.[109]

Not content to rest on his laurels, and possibly wary of violating Smith & Wesson's patent rights, Allen patented in September of 1860 not a gun but a "lipfire" cartridge. This cartridge was very similar to the usual rimfire except that, instead of having a rim entirely

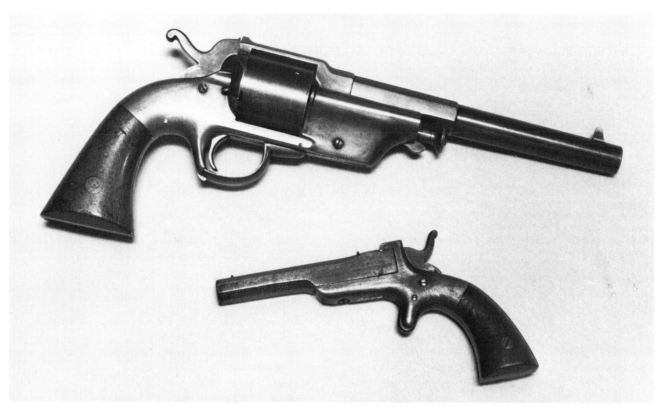

Above, Allen & Wheelock .44 caliber lipfire revolver. Production of similar revolvers was halted by court action, following Rollin White's successful defense of his patent on the bored-through cylinder. On this model and the percussion Allen & Wheelock revolvers which followed, the trigger guard served a dual purpose as the loading lever or ejector, depending upon the type of ignition system used. Below is a .32 caliber single-shot Allen & Wheelock pistol with side-swinging barrel.

surrounding the case head, Allen designed a small lip, or segment of a rim, projecting from an otherwise rimless case. Another provision of this patent, and probably more important than the lip itself, was "a stronger head or end to the cartridge, which obviates the difficulty of the swelling back of the head of the cartridge, as is common in other modes of construction."[110] The segmental rim also saved about seven-eighths of the priming compound required for a normal rimfire case of similar size.

Presumably the first of the Allen lipfire revolvers to reach the market was a sheath-trigger model designed for the "No. 52" or .32 caliber lipfire cartridge. Generally this model resembled the Allen .32 rimfire revolver, with a side-mounted hammer and cylinder pin entering from the front, but it had a mechanical extractor on the upper left side of the frame ahead of the cylinder, and a hinged loading gate behind it. Allen's provision for incorporating a stronger head in his lipfire cases, however, allowed him to design cartridges considerably more powerful than the .32, and in September of 1861 he patented a large-frame lipfire revolver intended specifically for such cartridges. While the sheath-trigger .32 lipfire followed the lines of Allen's .32 rimfire revolver, the large-frame lipfire was quite similar to Allen's big centerhammer percussion

revolver, with a center-mounted hammer, cylinder pin entering from the front, and an ejector operated by the trigger guard, which was merely a clever modification of the loading lever used in his percussion arms. The big lipfires were made in two sizes, one for the No. 56 cartridge and the other for the No. 58, or calibers .36 and .44 respectively.[111]

Contemporary with Allen's .44 lipfire were two other metallic-cartridge revolvers of like caliber, the Moore and the Pond, both of which chambered the .44 rimfire round; Moores and Ponds of this size, however, were made in extremely limited numbers and constituted little threat to the Allen, which in any event fired a cartridge with a more strongly built case.

Probably the last of the Allen lipfires to be introduced was a little seven-shot centerhammer sheath-trigger model, chambered for the No. 50 or .25 caliber cartridge. Externally this gun was a noticeable departure from other Allens; its frame was contoured like those of the Smith & Wesson and the majority of other pocket-size cartridge revolvers of the 1860s. The .25 caliber revolver was on the market only briefly, however, before the injunction issued in November of 1863 took effect; a Tryon price list put out in January of 1864 included the entire line of lipfire revolvers in calibers .25, .32, .36, and .44, but a list which came out eight months later, while pricing the line of Allen percussion handguns and single-shot cartridge rifles and pistols, did not even mention the lipfires.[112]

Prolific as he was, Allen was far from the only manufacturer to cause Smith & Wesson problems, even though most of the other makers proved more tractable. Eventually Lucius W. Pond, Daniel Moore, Thomas K. Bacon, and James Warner surrendered their existing stocks of revolvers to Smith & Wesson, but each maker managed to get some of his products onto the market before the courts ruled in Smith & Wesson's favor.

The Pond cartridge revolver, patented in July of 1860 by A. J. Gibson and made in Worcester, Allen's home town, had a tip-up barrel like that of the Smith & Wesson, but the Pond barrel was hinged via the topstrap to the standing breech, and dropped into a long slot in the bottomstrap for locking. This arrangement gave the barrel-frame assembly more rigidity than it had in the Smith & Wesson (whose barrel was hinged to the front of the topstrap), and in addition the cylinder of the Pond was permanently attached to the barrel and swung upward with it, making it more convenient for the shooter to load or eject the cases.[113]

Commonly made with an iron frame (though sometimes brass was used), the Pond probably first appeared as a six-shot .44 rimfire with a 7¹/₄ in. barrel, but the six-shot .32 caliber model, available with 4 in., 5 in., or 6 in. octagon barrel, was by far the more popular. Between January of 1863 and August of 1864 Pond turned over more than 4800 of his revolvers to Smith & Wesson, and some Ponds reached the West under the auspices of Smith & Wesson's dealers. One such revolver (now with the Kansas State Historical Society), stamped "Manuf'd For Smith & Wesson" on its 6 in. barrel, was the property of James Montgomery, a noted Kansas free-stater. Pond had managed to make and sell about 2000 of his guns before Smith & Wesson stepped in, and a few of these earlier arms may have gone west also. In an attempt to keep his business solvent without having to deal with the Springfield partnership, Pond brought out .22 and .32 caliber "separate chambers" revolvers in 1864, based on patents issued to J. H. Vickers the previous year, but the new guns met with only limited success.[114]

Somewhat more numerous than the Pond patent-infringement arms were the revolvers made by Daniel Moore of Brooklyn, New York. Patented in September of 1860, the Moore's basic design was a forerunner of many later cartridge revolvers: the barrel-cylinder assembly rested on a longitudinal pivot at the front of the bottomstrap; pressing a catch in the recoil shield allowed the barrel and cylinder to rotate to the right as a unit through an arc of about 20 degrees, exposing

the chambers on the right side of the cylinder for loading. A detachable ejector rod under the barrel knocked out the fired cases. To help hold the assembly together during the shock of firing, Moore extended the rear of the cylinder pin well past the cylinder, and enlarged it into a collar which engaged a keyhole slot in the face of the standing breech. Like the Pond, a very few Moore revolvers had iron frames and six-shot cylinders chambered for the .44 rimfire cartridge, but most of them were seven-shot .32s, with brass frames and 4 in., 5 in., or 6 in. octagon barrels. As mechanically advanced as the Moore was, it bore an external resemblance to .31 caliber, open-frame percussion revolvers such as the Colt 1849 pocket model.[115]

Following the legal settlement, Smith & Wesson claimed more than 5000 Moore revolvers, which received the Smith & Wesson stamp on their barrels before going to individual dealers. But Moore had sold well over 4000 before coming to terms, and his arms would have ranked among the most popular of all early cartridge revolvers had it not been for his legal difficulties. In April of 1863 Horace Dimick of St. Louis received 50 Moores from Smith & Wesson, and the guns undoubtedly went to other western dealers also.[116] Like Pond, Moore was reluctant to give up the revolver business, and the gun he designed to evade Rollin White's patent for the bored-through chamber was to prove surprisingly successful.

Still another maker to run afoul of the Rollin White patent was Thomas Bacon, who had already encountered reverses in the armsmaking field. After his original firm of Bacon & Co. failed, Bacon worked briefly for Manhattan; then, in November of 1858, he formed another concern, the Bacon Manufacturing Company. Like other gunmakers Bacon was well aware of the advantages of metallic-cartridge pistols, and a Bacon advertisement in an 1862 Norwich business directory showed no fewer than eight different handguns. Two of these—a revolver quite similar to the Colt 1849 pocket model and a centerhammer single-shot pistol with sheath trigger—were percussion guns, but the other six all chambered rimfire cartridges. Aside from a "Single Cartridge Pistol" there were five cartridge revolvers: a solid-frame seven-shot .22 also made in a six-shot .25 caliber version, and scaled-up solid-frame models in .32 and .38 rimfire. Besides these there were two hinged-frame revolvers in .22 and .32 caliber, both of which strongly resembled the first-model Smith & Wesson. However, the company made very few of the hinged-frame models, and it was the solid-frame rimfires with which Bacon captured his share of the cartridge-revolver market.[117]

The most popular of the solid-frame models was the .32, which had a sheath trigger, removeable sideplate,

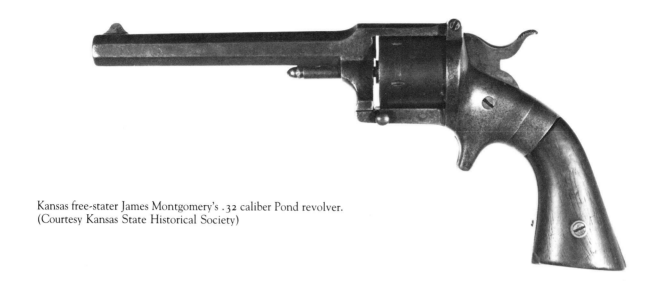

Kansas free-stater James Montgomery's .32 caliber Pond revolver.
(Courtesy Kansas State Historical Society)

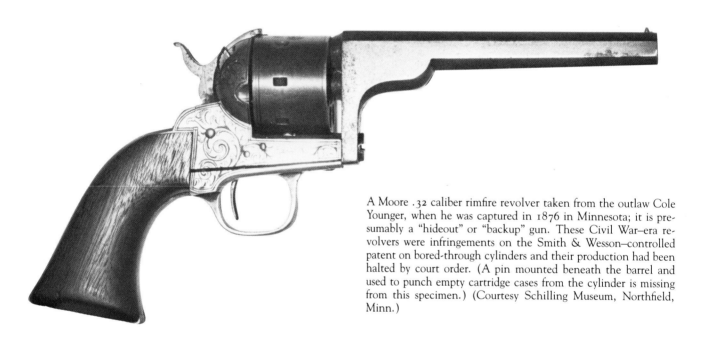

A Moore .32 caliber rimfire revolver taken from the outlaw Cole
Younger, when he was captured in 1876 in Minnesota; it is presumably a "hideout" or "backup" gun. These Civil War–era revolvers were infringements on the Smith & Wesson–controlled
patent on bored-through cylinders and their production had been
halted by court order. (A pin mounted beneath the barrel and
used to punch empty cartridge cases from the cylinder is missing
from this specimen.) (Courtesy Schilling Museum, Northfield,
Minn.)

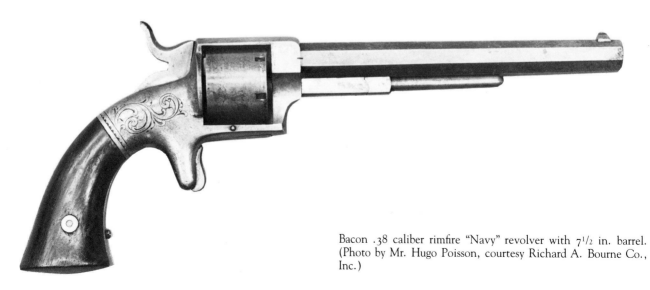

Bacon .38 caliber rimfire "Navy" revolver with 7½ in. barrel.
(Photo by Mr. Hugo Poisson, courtesy Richard A. Bourne Co.,
Inc.)

and octagon barrel. More suitable for the frontier, however, was the Bacon "American Navy" revolver, a large sheath-trigger model with 7 1/2 in. octagon barrel and a six-shot cylinder chambered for the .38 rimfire cartridge. The Bacon Navy went through several variations, none of which altered the basic design until, in May of 1862, Charles W. Hopkins patented a revolver with a "swing-out" cylinder. In principle this design was similar to that of the earlier Moore, but in the latter the entire barrel-cylinder assembly swung to one side: in the Hopkins, only the cylinder, housed in a solid frame, swung outward. Because it was among the earliest of the true swing-out cylinder designs, the Hopkins was also somewhat ahead of its time: nearly thirty years would pass before American and foreign handgun manufacturers made extensive use of this principle. Hopkins's patent involved a vertical arm, or "crane," at the front of the cylinder which rested on a longitudinal pivot in the bottomstrap; pushing a catch protruding from the front of the frame allowed the cylinder and crane to pivot to the right, through an arc of about 20 degrees, exposing the right side of the cylinder for loading from the rear. Only the lock at the front of the frame held the cylinder-crane assembly in place, and because of this it would develop looseness after a period of hard use. In spite of this, however, the Bacon revolvers incorporating Hopkins's patent showed considerable commercial promise. Bacon applied it to the .22, .32, and .38 solid-frame revolvers, but before sales became widespread Smith & Wesson took over Bacon's inventory.[118]

Although Smith & Wesson retailed most of the Hopkins or "patent" revolvers, Bacon had sold more than 5000 of the "pin" or "old style" solid-frame models before the courts interfered. In April of 1863, Henry Folsom of St. Louis advertised: "Bacon's New Model Cartridge Revolver—Henry Folsom . . . Having Secured the Exclusive Agency for the sale of the above Revolvers, is prepared to supply the trade in quantities. . . ." His inventory included the .38 "Navy" as well as the smaller guns.[119]

Through late 1863 and into early 1864 Folsom offered, among a host of other guns, "200 Bacon's New Models," which presumably included both the old-model and Hopkins-patent arms. Early in 1864 Smith & Wesson took delivery of about 1100 Bacon revolvers for resale, a number which comprised both the old-style and swing-out cylinder guns in .22, .32, and .38 calibers; since Folsom was also a Smith & Wesson dealer, some of his later Bacons may have come from that source. Those Bacons released for sale by Smith & Wesson had the Rollin White patent date stamped on their cylinders.[120]

Campbell & Richardson's *St. Louis Business Directory for 1863.*

The Hopkins-patent .32 sold well enough to prompt Smith & Wesson to place additional orders for it, but by that time two other Bacon principals, H. A. Briggs and Samuel S. Hopkins, had improved Charles Hopkins's original design. Patented in January of 1864, the Briggs & Hopkins revolver had a cylinder which swung outward on two cranes, front and rear, and a thumb-operated latch at the rear of the cylinder instead of the front. Like Daniel Moore's design, the Briggs & Hopkins would probably have achieved notable commercial success, but the Bacon firm made comparatively few of them. Thomas Bacon himself, evidently unhappy over the settlement with Smith & Wesson, had left the Bacon Manufacturing Company in December of 1863, and the following year formed the Bacon Arms Company, which began making .31

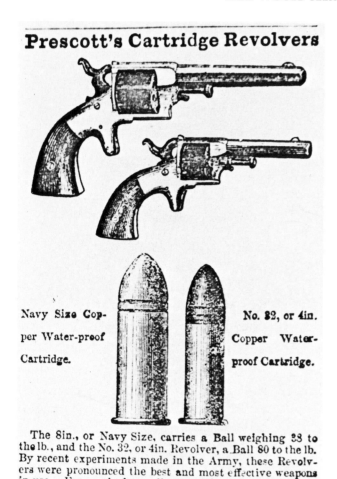

Prescott's Cartridge Revolvers

Navy Size Copper Water-proof Cartridge.

No. 32, or 4in. Copper Water-proof Cartridge.

The 8in., or Navy Size, carries a Ball weighing 23 to the lb., and the No. 32, or 4in. Revolver, a Ball 80 to the lb. By recent experiments made in the Army, these Revolvers were pronounced the best and most effective weapons in use. For particulars call or send for a Circular to
MERWIN & BRAY, Sole Agents,
No. 245 Broadway, N. Y.

Harper's Weekly, January 1862.

THE WESSON RIFLE!
Colt's Revolvers,
Manhattan Revolvers
SMITH & WESSON REVOLVERS,
Prescott's Revolvers,
SWORDS, SABRES,
SASHES, BELTS, FIELD GLASSES
THE PLACE TO BUY THEM CHEAPEST,
No. 89 North Fourth Street
ST. LOUIS.
S. B. SHAW,
WHOLESALE DEALER AND SOLE AGENT
FOR THE
WESSON RIFLE CARBINE,
THE BEST RIFLE IN THE SERVICE,
As testified to by prominent Army Officers everywhere.

This is just the right Gun to have on the Kansas Border—sure fire—long range—perfectly accurate, and can be fired six times in a minute. It is a true unflinching friend all the time. Send for REVOLVERS and RIFLES to
S. B. SHAW,
au24 2w r839. No. 89 North Fourth street.

Missouri Democrat (St. Louis), Aug. 1863.

caliber solid-frame sheath-trigger percussion revolvers and .22 caliber pepperboxes stamped with the date of one of William Elliot's 1860 patents.[121]

Apparently not all the patent-infringement revolvers which crossed the Mississippi were advertised by the dealers who handled them. In June of 1863, for example, Smith & Wesson shipped 25 Warner revolvers to Horace Dimick in St. Louis. In July of 1857 James Warner had patented the mechanical features of a solid-frame percussion pocket revolver which sold fairly well. With the availability of metallic cartridges, Warner modified his revolver to chamber such ammunition, although in appearance the cartridge arm was highly similar to its percussion predecessor. It had a solid frame with the cylinder bolt in the topstrap, a 3 in. round barrel, and a five-shot cylinder chambered for the .30 caliber rimfire cartridge. Unlike most other pocket-size cartridge revolvers of the time, the Warner had a conventional trigger and guard, and a hinged loading gate behind the cylinder, although the shooter had to remove the cylinder pin to eject the fired cases. Warner put about 2500 of his revolvers on

the market before coming to terms with Smith and Wesson, who appropriated another 1395. Besides Dimick, Benjamin Kittredge of Cincinnati was also the recipient of these arms, most of which Warner surrendered to Smith & Wesson between January and August of 1863. As was the case with the Bacon arms, the Warners retailed by Smith & Wesson had the Rollin White patent date stamped on the cylinders. (Foiled in his attempt to make and market cartridge revolvers, Warner nevertheless sold 4001 breech-loading carbines to the Union government in 1864–65.)[122]

Although Pond, Moore, Bacon, and Warner all came to terms with Smith & Wesson, one manufacturer who refused to bargain was Edwin A. Prescott of Worcester; like Allen, he continued making revolvers until the injunction of 1863 put a stop to his operations. Apparently Prescott's first attempt at arms manufacture was a .31 caliber brass-frame sheath-trigger percussion pocket revolver, incorporating a cylinder bolt and antifouling device patented by Prescott in October of 1860. Realizing that metallic cartridges were the coming thing, however, Prescott soon had a diversified

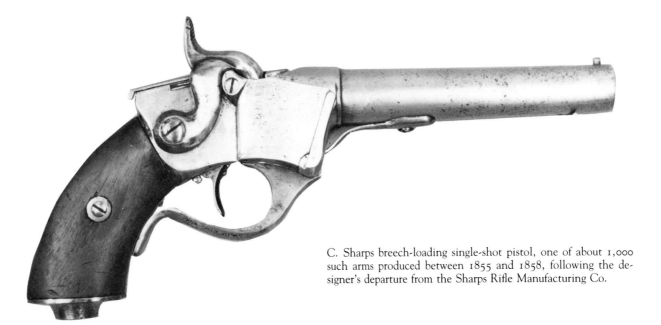

C. Sharps breech-loading single-shot pistol, one of about 1,000 such arms produced between 1855 and 1858, following the designer's departure from the Sharps Rifle Manufacturing Co.

line of rimfire revolvers on the market. Aside from various .22 caliber models, he brought out a six-shot solid-frame .32 closely resembling his percussion revolver, and a big six-shot .38. Made first with an iron and then with a brass frame, the .38 retained the frame contour of the .32, but had a long 7¼ octagon barrel and a conventional trigger and guard instead of a sheath trigger. Another Prescott revolver, presumably appearing after the above models, was again in .32 caliber, but except for its solid frame of brass and its cylinder pin, the gun was outwardly almost identical to the Smith & Wesson No. 2.[123]

At least two sizes of the Prescott cartridge revolver were on the market by January of 1862, but apparently few if any examples came west until 1863. In August of that year, S. B. Shaw of St. Louis advertised not only Wesson rifles and Colts, Manhattan, and Smith & Wesson revolvers, but Prescotts as well; although he gave no specifics, his supply presumably included both the .32s and .38s.[124]

While Smith and Wesson brought no fewer than four cartridge-handgun makers to heel and forced two others to stop production, still other makers managed to elude their grasp. This group included foreign manufacturers, makers of single- or multibarreled pistols, and designers of metallic-cartridge revolvers without bored-through cylinders.

A foreign manufacturer whose pinfire arms achieved a fair prominence in this country was Eugene LeFaucheux of Paris. More than 12,000 of the big single-action revolvers LeFaucheux had patented in 1854 went to the Union government during the Civil War, but the Paris inventor also made double-barreled pistols, self-cocking pocket revolvers, and pepperbox-like

"fist pistols," all widely copied by other French and Belgian gunmakers. One LeFaucheux 7 mm (.28 caliber) pinfire pocket revolver with folding trigger (now in the Sutter's Fort collection), which came to California with an early settler, is identical to that shown in the 1864 Schuyler, Hartley, & Graham catalog.[125]

RIMFIRE PISTOLS, RIMFIRE PEPPERBOXES, AND NOVEL CARTRIDGE REVOLVERS

American handgun makers desiring to use conventional rimfire cartridges in their arms, but not willing to risk a court fight over the matter, could compromise by making cartridge pepperboxes or single-shot pistols. Not all manufacturers of such arms introduced their designs simply to evade the Rollin White patent, however; Christian Sharps, for example, by far the most famous maker of cartridge pepperboxes, had patented his basic idea for a four-shot percussion pepperbox as early as December of 1849. After leaving the Sharps Rifle Manufacturing Company late in 1853, Sharps moved to Philadelphia, where he made small quantities of breech-loading percussion pistols, pistol-carbines, and percussion pocket revolvers. A patent issued to Sharps in January of 1859 for a "revolver," however, led him into the handgun business in a big way.[126]

The 1859 patent covered a four-barreled metallic-cartridge pistol which was basically a modification of his percussion pepperbox of 1849. Arranged in the form of a square, the barrel group in Sharps's design did not revolve, but slid forward in the frame for loading; a pivoting spring-loaded catch, engaging a lug on the underside of the barrel group, locked the barrels against the standing breech for firing. In lieu of a revolving barrel group Sharps employed a rotating

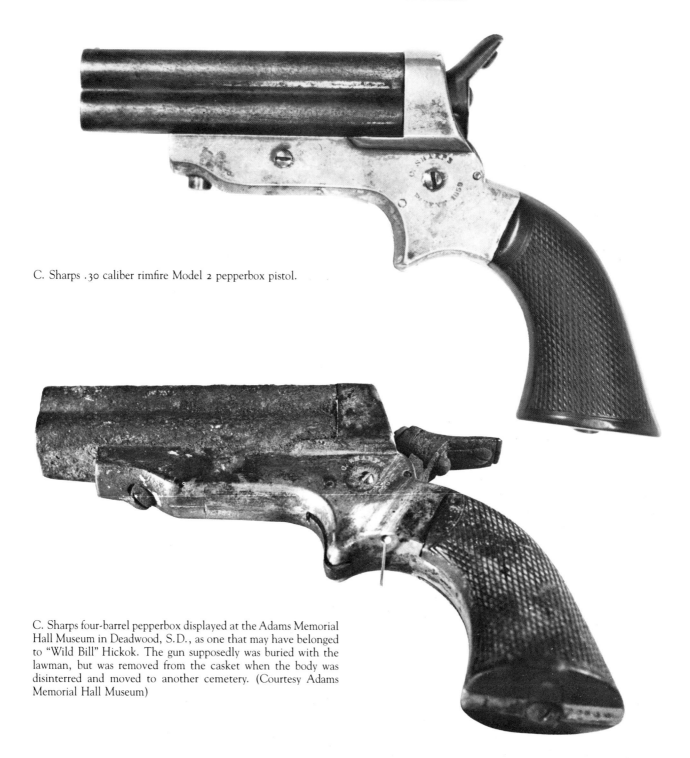

C. Sharps .30 caliber rimfire Model 2 pepperbox pistol.

C. Sharps four-barrel pepperbox displayed at the Adams Memorial Hall Museum in Deadwood, S.D., as one that may have belonged to "Wild Bill" Hickok. The gun supposedly was buried with the lawman, but was removed from the casket when the body was disinterred and moved to another cemetery. (Courtesy Adams Memorial Hall Museum)

firing pin on the hammer face, acted upon by a pawl on the side of the hammer, to discharge each barrel in succession. Fundamentally the design was somewhat more reliable than a conventional revolver, and it gave rise to many copies both here and abroad.

The earliest models of the four-barrel Sharps were in .22 caliber, with 2½ in. barrel groups, brass frames, and sheath triggers. Since the first few examples have no patent date, they were probably on the market by the close of 1858. A year or so later Sharps added a scaled-up version of this pistol to his line, with a 3 in. barrel group chambered for the .30 caliber rimfire round.[127]

One of these pistols, presumably in .22 caliber, was presented to Lord George Berkeley when he was in St. Louis in the fall of 1859. Berkeley described it as:

the most perfect little *bijou* of a revolver I ever saw in my life. The makers of this perfect little weapon, which is highly finished and handsome enough to be worn on a chain at a lady's waist, are [C.] Sharp and Co., Philadelphia, and for which in 1852 [*sic*]

332

they had a patent. In size it is so small that I carried it in my waistcoat-pocket, and in execution so effective that at eight yards I could shoot as correctly, if not more so, than I could with my favourite pair of John Manton duelling-pistols, as they used to be called, and the little conical ball propelled by cartridge, at ten yards would go through a half-inch deal board. This little pistol is a four-barrel revolver, loading at the breech, but revolving in the hammer, each cock of the hammer bringing into its proper place the right nipple or peg for concussion on the respective cartridges. I have been told (I never saw it so used) that this deadly little weapon is made to come into play in those brutal and bloody "difficulties," as they call them—they cannot, indeed, be called duels—which, I regret to say, so frequently disgrace society in the United States.[128]

By 1862 the talented inventor had formed a partnership with William Hankins, also of Philadelphia, and previously the maker of small solid-frame percussion pocket revolvers. The partners opened a new factory which initially concerned itself with the manufacture of carbines and rimfire cartridges, but operations soon shifted to pistols. The long arms which came from the factory were the Sharps & Hankins sliding-barrel guns patented in July of 1861, but the firm also made a new iron-frame four-barrel, with $3^{1}/_{2}$ in. barrel group chambered for the .32 Long rimfire round. Like the earlier pistols this gun went through several variations, chiefly involving the location of the rotating firing pin and the presence or absence of an extractor. Despite its advantages—an iron frame and the use of a more powerful cartridge—the Sharps & Hankins four-barrel did not prove quite as popular as the brass-frame .22 and .30 caliber models. For use at close range, however, it was a reliable pocket pistol.[129]

In the case of the Sharps and other multibarreled pistols with fixed barrel groups, "close range" meant about ten yards. The inaccuracy of these guns at distances beyond card-table range resulted from the difficulty in boring four barrels in a single block of iron so that each barrel was parallel to the others (difficult even today). Furthermore, as was the case with double rifles, the line of recoil for the upper left barrel differed considerably from that for the lower right barrel, a factor particularly noticeable with the Sharps & Hankins .32 Long model: the point of impact for the lower right barrel might be fairly close to the point of aim, whereas the upper left barrel would throw its bullet high and wide of the target.[130]

Again, however, the Sharps was a dependable little gun, and sold nearly as fast as its designer could man-

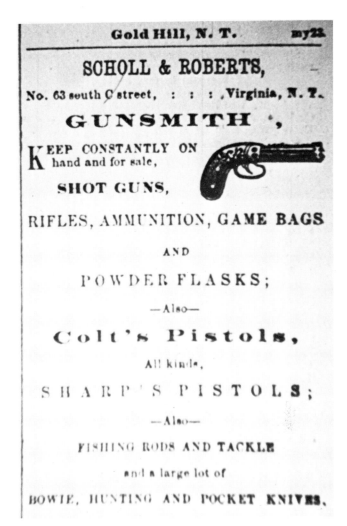

Gold Hill (Nevada) *Daily Morning Message,* June 1864.

Ad from *Leslie's Weekly,* September 1861, illustrating the Remington-Elliot "zig-zag" cartridge pepperbox.

Starr .32 caliber rimfire four-barrel pepperbox.

ufacture it. Charles Curry was advertising Sharps pistols by August of 1860, although some, such as the brass-frame model presented to Lord Berkeley, reached the West before that. One Sharps & Hankins .32 was found on the Sutter's Fort grounds during excavations there in the 1890s, and another was picked up in Ponca Park, Colorado. [131]

Although the Sharps was the best-known cartridge pepperbox, Remington also brought out a line of its own, based primarily on two patents issued to William Elliot in May of 1860. The first model to be produced was a six-barreled .22 with a revolving barrel group and a ring trigger; pushing and pulling the trigger rotated the barrel group, by means of longitudinal and diagonal grooves on its periphery, and cocked and dropped the hammer. Loading was effected through a small loading port in the top of the standing breech. [132]

Advertised as "Elliot's Pocket Revolver" in September of 1861, this gun gave way within two years to a new design having fixed barrels and a rotating striker. Made in both five-barreled .22 and four-barreled .32 versions, this pistol was much more successful than the revolving-barrel or "zig-zag" arm. While retaining the ring trigger, the new gun had a barrel group whose breech end swung upward for loading when the shooter released a latch in front of the trigger. Apparently the five-shot .22 was as popular as the four-shot .32, even in the West: one .22 was discovered in Sacramento during construction there in 1919, and another was

found near Cripple Creek, Colorado. A .32 caliber model (now with the Colorado State Historical Society) was the property of an early resident of Central City. [133]

Other makes of cartridge pepperboxes—the four-barreled Starr, six-barreled Bacon, and eight-barreled Rupertus—never achieved the prominence of the Remington or Sharps.

Like the metallic-cartridge pepperboxes, single-shot pistols were no infringement of the Rollin White patent, and many such guns in .22, .30, and .32 rimfire appeared on the market in the early 1860s. The barrels of the Wesson, the Driscole, and the Stafford (styled an "Automatic Pistol" by its maker) rested on transverse pivots, so that their muzzles tipped down for loading; the Allen, the Bacon, the Morgan & Clapp, and the Lombard had vertically pivoted barrels whose breech ends swung to one side; the barrels of the Dickinson and the later Rupertus, resting on longitudinal pivots, rotated to one side and downward; and the Taylor had a longitudinally sliding barrel. Except for the Rupertus, which was available in a .38 rimfire version, these pistols did not have the big bores which characterized the older percussion Deringer. [134]

Among the first designers to correct this situation was the energetic Daniel Moore, who in February of 1861 patented an all-metal sheath-trigger breech-loading derringer chambered for a .41 caliber metallic cartridge. Like the barrels of the Dickinson and the

Rupertus pistols, the 2½ in. barrel of the Moore rotated to the right and downward, on a longitudinal pivot, for loading. One interesting thing about this pistol was that Moore originally designed it for a centerfire cartridge, although almost all the production models took the .41 rimfire round, which thereafter became the standard load for cartridge derringers.[135]

Because the first examples of the Moore are stamped "Patent Applied For," they were probably on the market by the time the patent was issued. The Moore became one of the most popular pistols of its type, coming early to the attention of Californians: during the Deringer vs. Plate trial, John R. Evans and H. H. Wilson testified that:

> Since 1860 a number of new and improved pistols have come upon the market of the world, and especially California. There has been introduced the Sharp pistol, Smith & Weston, the breech-loading Deringer, the Remington Deringer and others. . . . We had orders for various kinds of pistols—the "Moore Deringer," the "Slotter Deringer" and other kinds of Deringers, and we bought all these kinds. Moore's Deringer has the word "Deringer" on it, I think. It is a breech-loader. . . .[136]

Other cartridge pistols of large caliber, most notably the Hammond, soon followed the Moore. Unlike the Moore and most of the other early cartridge pistols, however, the sheath-trigger "Bulldog" pistol patented by Henry Hammond in October of 1864 had a fixed barrel and moveable breechblock; for loading, the breechblock swung to one side on a massive longitudinal pivot, lying below the bore axis, which joined barrel to frame. Made by the Connecticut Arms & Manufacturing Company in barrel lengths of 4 in. and occasionally 6½ in., the Hammond was larger and heavier than other pistols of its type because it chambered the .44 rimfire cartridge.[137]

A new Remington, made under patents issued to Joseph Rider in December of 1863 and November of 1864, had a breechblock pivoting at its lower front corner, which swung or "rolled" backward and downward for loading. It was locked in place by an L-shaped hammer, whose long horizontal arm turned on a pivot set well in front of the breechblock pivot. As the hammer swung upward to fire, lugs on its horizontal arm rose into engagement with bearing surfaces on the front face of the breechblock below the breechblock pivot, preventing the block from tilting backward at the moment of discharge. To permit this locking arrangement, a slot was cut vertically through the center of the block, which gave the gun its common nickname of "split-breech pistol." Although it was in-

itially made in small calibers and short barrel lengths, a later popular version of this arm had a 4 in. round barrel chambered for the .41 rimfire cartridge.[138]

Both Hammond and Remington also incorporated their breech designs into single-shot cartridge carbines: Remington sold the government 20,000 carbines of this type between September of 1864 and May of 1866, examples of which underwent postwar Ordnance trials alongside the Hammond. Although the Hammond carbine was unsuccessful, the split-breech Remington was to form the basis for one of the most successful single-shot rifles of later years.[139]

Another .41 rimfire derringer that probably reached the market by the close of 1865 was patented by Ethan Allen in March of that year. The new gun had an automatic extractor (the subject of Allen's patent) but otherwise incorporated the same vertically pivoted barrel design used in his earlier .32 rimfire pistols.[140]

Rather than make cartridge pepperboxes or single-shot pistols, a few manufacturers chose to design cartridge revolvers loading from the front of the cylinder, which allowed them to leave a wall of metal at the rear of each chamber and thus evade Rollin White's patent. While there were many experiments with such designs, only three became really successful: the Plant, the Moore, and the Slocum.

Probably the earliest to appear on the market was that made by the Plant Manufacturing Company of New Haven, Connecticut. Based on a cartridge and cylinder patent issued to Willard Ellis and John White in July of 1859, the Plant was quite similar to the first-model, first-issue Smith & Wesson in construction, with its barrel hinged to the front of a topstrap which also carried the cylinder bolt. Other features, such as the sheath trigger and fixed ejector rod under the barrel, were also like those in the Smith & Wesson, but the Plant was much larger, with a 6 in. octagon barrel and a six-shot cylinder chambered for a special .42 caliber "cup-primer" cartridge.[141]

In July of 1863 Ellis and White took out a second patent on a refined version of this cartridge, and a second-model Plant was on the market by March of 1864. Made in two basic sizes, .42 and .28 caliber, the new model had a solid frame, first of iron and then of brass, a Colt-type cylinder bolt housed within the frame, and a sliding ejector behind the cylinder patented by Henry Reynolds in May of 1864.[142]

The cup-primer cartridge, which slipped into the chamber from the front, had a metallic case with a concave head; the beak-like hammer nose which struck the case passed through one of six small holes bored into the rear face of the cylinder; these holes were smaller than the chamber diameter and did not constitute a violation of Rollin White's patent. Both the

Plant .42 caliber front-loading revolver.

Moore's Patent .32 caliber front-loading "teat-fire" revolver and cartridge, one of the most popular of the Smith & Wesson competitors. After 1864 these arms were produced by the National Arms Co., which was bought out by Colt in 1870. (Courtesy Mr. E. Lee Manning, Jr.)

large and small solid-frame models achieved respectable sales, their distribution handled by Merwin & Bray of New York, who were also agents for the Ballard rifle. One factor which undoubtedly helped sell these guns was that they were available with optional percussion cylinders, an obviously worthwhile accessory. Also, a few enterprising gunsmiths found it a simple matter to modify the .42 caliber models so that they would chamber the standard .41 rimfire cartridge. However, the small .28 caliber pocket revolver seems to have been somewhat more popular than the larger arm; Benjamin Kittredge retailed a quantity after stamping the barrels with his name, and a few .28 caliber cup-primer cartridge cases recently found at the site of Bent's Fort in Colorado indicate that the pocket model had a following even in the West, whose inhabitants generally preferred bigger handguns. By October of 1865 at least one dealer on the Missouri River, M. W. Calhoun of Atchison, was advertising the large-frame Plants as "Merwin & Bray's Patent Copper Cartridge and loose ammunitions Loading Revolvers . . . shooting a ball larger than Colt's navy."

Within a year a number of other dealers on the frontier would also be selling this arm.[143]

A second type of front-loading revolver was that designed by Daniel Moore, who seemed never to run out of ideas. Although Smith & Wesson had control of his side-swing .32 rimfire revolvers, his breech-loading derringer was selling well, and in April of 1863 he patented a front-loading "teat-fire" revolver. In this design the chambers were not bored all the way through; instead, a teat-like projection at the rear of the cartridge case which contained the priming protruded through a small aperture at the rear of each chamber.[144]

In its most common form the Moore, which was on the market by April of 1864, had an open-top brass frame with sheath trigger and "parrot-beak" or "bird's-head" butt, a six-shot cylinder, and a 3 1/4 in. round barrel. Subsequent patents covering the cartridge, cylinder bolt, and a pivoting ejector refined the arm, helping to make it the most popular of all the evasions of the Rollin White patent. And, like conventional rimfire revolvers, the Moore was soon on its way to frontier dealers.[145]

Unlike the Plant and the Moore, the revolver patented by Frank Slocum in April of 1863 used conventional .32 rimfire cartridges. To effect this without infringing upon the White patent Slocum designed a "side-loading" revolver, in which the chambers were not integral parts of the cylinder, but separate forward-sliding tubes. After pushing aside a catch at the rear of each chamber tube and sliding the tube forward, the shooter dropped a cartridge into it, then pulled it back and locked it in place. Again, the hammer nose struck the cartridge rims through slits in a circular wall which formed the rear face of the cylinder. Made by the Brooklyn Arms Company with a solid frame of brass, the sheath-trigger Slocum had a five-shot cylinder, a 3 in. round barrel, and an ejector rod on the right side of the frame ahead of the cylinder.[146]

In January of 1865 T. J. Albright of St. Louis advertised Slocum's side-loading revolver as "The Model Pocket Pistol Of The Age." A short time prior to this Daniel Moore's firm had become the National Arms Company, and the "National Revolvers" offered by Reno Beauvais in May of 1865 were simply the teat-fire Moores stamped with the new name. National also modified the Moore all-metal derringer, giving it a larger butt with wood grips and calling it the "No. 2"; the all-metal or "No. 1," however, continued in production unchanged. Aside from its handguns, National was another manufacturer which submitted a breech-loading carbine for postwar Ordnance trials.[147]

PERCUSSION VERSUS CARTRIDGE ARMS

Whether single-shot pistol, pepperbox, or revolver, a handgun using fixed ammunition exclusively quite obviously depended upon such ammunition for proper performance. In the more settled frontier locales like St. Louis and San Francisco, metallic cartridges were readily available, but this was not the case in the more remote areas, where percussion revolvers remained highly popular throughout the 1860s. One example of this is the fact that a fire destroyed the Colt factory early in February of 1864, and within a month a group had formed the Metropolitan Arms Company, whose chief business was the manufacture of .36 caliber percussion revolvers which were almost exact copies of contemporary Colt models. Although Metropolitan made a few facsimiles of Colt's 1861 Navy and Police revolvers, most of its production efforts centered around copies of the 1851 Navy. Among the retailers of this gun was Horace Dimick of St. Louis, whose name sometimes appeared on the barrels.[148]

By the close of the 1850s, when the carrying of conventional revolvers had become commonplace, interest had also developed in methods of bringing them

A .28 caliber front-loading Plant with the cylinder removed to show its rear face.

into action as rapidly as possible. The speed with which a frontiersman could draw and shoot his revolver soon assumed an importance second only to the accuracy of his fire. After mentioning the Sharps four-barrel pistol given to him in St. Louis in 1859, Lord George Berkeley repeated the stories he had heard of typical confrontations between two westerners:

Supposing one free citizen to deem himself free to take the life of another, and to enter at once, without counsel or friendly and cool advice, into a "shooting difficulty," he puts his hand, containing a six-barrel revolver, into his bosom, cocked and ready for use, and walks out for the purpose of meeting his victim. He sees his unconscious victim approaching, and, suddenly confronting him, revolver, though concealed in his hand, ready for momentary action . . . he calls his victim a liar, and bids him draw and defend himself. Supposing that the unprepared victim does not possess Sharp's little "pocket compeller," but has in a pocket a revolver, if, on the word to draw, his hand attempts to do [it], his bloody antagonist shoots him dead before he can touch his weapon. If, on the contrary, the supposed victim is duly prepared for any emergency, and happens to have in his pocket "Sharp's compeller," he temporizes with his foe somewhat in this fashion: "Guess, neighbour, you're mighty sharp on me, you air; I don't want none o' this. Carn't we better fix it no how? Jest you suppose now, if 't warn't be best for you and I to see if we can't call in a mediator?" All this time the intended but unwilling-to-be victim is apparently only fumbling nervously in the pocket of his coat, but really he is bringing the muzzle of his little compeller into the front corner of his pocket, and levelling that pocket corner, which of course his downcast eye can see, at the fourth or fifth button, as the case may be, of his adversary's waistcoat. Having perfected his aim while temporising in speech, he shoots his opponent through the heart, lungs, or body, no matter which, and effectually unsteadies his neighbour's aim.[149]

Guns, Rifles, Pistols.

N. CURRY & BROTHER

HAVE CONSTANTLY ON hand a splendid assortment of Double Guns of every description, also Henry's Repeating Rifles, Spencer's Rifles, Sharp's Sporting Rifles and Sharp's Carbines, Colt's Revolving Rifles, Wurfflein's, Slotter's, J. E. Evans' and Leman's Rifles; Colt's, Derringer's, Smith & Wesson's, Sharp's and Allen & Wheelock's Pistols, Powder Flasks, Shot Pouches, Powder, Shot, Caps, Wads, Eley's Wire Cartridges, Henry's Rifle Cartridges, etc., etc.

Repairing of every description done and warranted.

N.B.—Sole Agents for the genuine Derringer Pistols for the Pacific Coast. Wholesale and retail, by
N. CURRY & BROTHER,
317 Battery street, between Clay and Commercial streets. San Francisco,   au17-tf

Alta California (San Francisco), Aug. 1864.

Those without benefit of a Sharps pocket pistol instead practiced the rapid-draw-and-fire technique, and during the early 1860s this technique saw repeated use in the more lawless areas of the West. Thomas Dimsdale, who took up residence in Virginia City, Montana, in mid-1863, had this to say regarding outlaw Henry Plummer and his self-cocking sidearm: "Plummer was the quickest hand with his revolver of any man in the mountains. He could draw the pistol and discharge the five loads in three seconds." Judged by later standards this was something less than lightning-fast, but it was evidently fast enough in the Montana of the 1860s. Other acquaintances of Plummer left these impressions:

one might as well have looked into the eyes of the dead for some token of a human soul as to have sought it in the light gray orbs of Plummer. Their cold, glassy stare defied inquisition. They seemed to be gazing through you at some object beyond, as though you were transparent. While other men laughed or pitied or threatened with their eyes, his had the same half-vacant stare, no matter how moving the story or tragic the spectacle. . . . To his enemies [any] magnanimity was more seeming than real. He always proffered them the advantage in drawing the pistol, but he knew that the instance would be very rare, where, even thus favored, his antagonist could anticipate him in its deadly use.[150]

But there were also law-abiding Montanans just as skillful as Plummer. Dimsdale gave this description of the capture of Dutch John Wagner by vigilante Neil Howie:

[Howie] determined to arrest the robber at all risks, single-handed. He called out, "Hallo, Cap! hold on a minute." Wagner wheeled his horse half round, and Neil, fixing his eyes upon him, walked straight towards him with empty hands. His trusty revolver hung at his belt, however, and those who have seen the machine-like regularity and instantaneous motion with which Howie draws and cocks a revolver, as well as the rapidity and accuracy of his shooting, well know that few men, if any, have odds against him in an encounter with fire-arms. . . . he arrived within a few steps of the Dutchman, [then] broke the silence with the order, "Give me your gun and get off your mule."[151]

Presumably the revolvers used in such encounters were percussion arms. By 1863 the larger dealers in the West could generally offer their customers a wide choice of both percussion and cartridge handguns, but the cap-and-ball arms were as much in evidence as the newer types. In May of 1864 Wilson & Evans of San Francisco advertised not only Smith & Wessons and breech- and muzzle-loading derringers, but also Colt, Remington, and "Dean & Adams" revolvers. During the same year Nathanial Curry & Brother offered pistols by Colt, Sharps, and Smith & Wesson, also noting that their partnership was the "authorized Agents for Deringer Pistols in California." In May of 1865 Reno Beauvais of St. Louis had on hand "National, Sharp's and Smith & Wesson's Revolvers [with] Fixed Ammunition for all sized revolvers and rifles"; alongside the cartridge arms Beauvais also offered "Shot Guns, Colt's, Manhattan, Remington, [and] Whitney Revolvers and Rifles." Advertising at the same time, Carlos Gove of Denver did not even mention cartridge pistols, but instead listed "Colt's Navy and Dragoon Revolvers, [and] Remington's Dragoon Revolvers."[152] For his trip west in 1865, Samuel Bowles of the Springfield (Massachusetts) *Republican* received a Smith & Wesson .32. He seemed a little disappointed when he later reported to his paper that Indians along the route to Denver had given his party a wide berth, perhaps because of the travelers' "innumerable Colts', Smith & Wessons', Remingtons', Ballards' and double-barreled shotguns."[153]

The Rollin White patent did not expire until 1869; only then would metallic-cartridge handguns seriously threaten the dominance of the percussion revolver in the West.

· PART VI ·

NATIVE AMERICANS:
Indian Arms
1803–1865

◆

EXCEPT FOR the visit of a trapper or trader, most of the Indians living in the lands west of the Mississippi early in the nineteenth century had little contact with whites. Yet they were feeling the effects of white civilization: by 1800 the horses introduced by the Spanish had drastically altered the way of life of many tribes, giving them a mobility never before possible. The horse, in fact, became such a critical factor in the economy of the Plains tribes that the capture or destruction of a tribe's pony herd became a major objective of any opposing force. Firearms also had an important effect on Indian life, giving the tribes that acquired them a substantial advantage over their gunless neighbors. Other less benign "gifts" provided by whites were whiskey, widely used as a trade item, and diseases against which the Indians lacked immunity. In 1837, for example, a smallpox epidemic among tribes on the upper Missouri decimated the Blackfeet and reduced the Mandans from a population of more than one thousand to fewer than one hundred, while cholera struck the Pawnees a severe blow in 1849.

During the early 1800s the trappers and traders entering the trans-Mississippi country from the east often adopted Indian ways, and thus did not present a true picture of white civilization, or of the threat to Indian culture which it posed. The tribes learned a good deal more about whites in 1830, however, when, under the Indian Removal Act, Congress authorized President Andrew Jackson to exchange land beyond the Mississippi for coveted Indian-occupied lands in the East. For ceding these lands the Indians were promised the western land grants in perpetuity, plus assistance in resettlement; any resistance to relocation, however, would be met with military force. Most of the eastern tribes acquiesced without violence, but there was a notable exception: the Seminoles, whose unwillingness to move brought on the Seminole War of 1836–42. Despite this resistance the government, with the army's assistance, had by 1842 shifted some eighty

thousand Indians from their lands in the East. The removal of the Five Civilized Tribes—the Cherokees, Chickasaws, Choctaws, Creeks, and Seminoles—subjected many families to immense suffering, giving the name "Trail of Tears" to their route westward. The relocation of these tribes was an irony, for by the 1830s they were well advanced in adopting white customs. Many were raising crops and livestock for a living; the Cherokees even had their own constitution, their own newspaper, and were preparing to establish a public school system. (Not long after their arrival in Indian Territory, the Cherokees started publishing the first newspaper in what was to become Oklahoma.)

The Indian Trade and Intercourse Act of 1834 had defined the new "Indian country" as that region west of the Mississippi outside the borders of Louisiana, Arkansas, and Missouri; but before the end of the decade an influx of white settlers moved that boundary west of the ninety-fifth meridian. In 1838 Congress designated the area roughly comprising the present state of Oklahoma and part of Kansas as Indian Territory, to be a "permanent home" for the tribes removed from the East. Garrisons at a string of army posts were to enforce the ban on white intrusion and protect the eastern Indians from any hostility they might encounter from Indians already living in the territory. However, pressure from land-hungry whites soon made the term "permanent Indian frontier" a meaningless one. During and after the 1840s emigrants bound for the Pacific Coast cut new paths through the Indian lands. Initially the tribes were tolerant of occasional bands of travelers and even of the presence of military outposts, but their resentment grew in proportion to the increasing press of whites and the resulting destruction of game. In an 1847 circular aimed at emigrants on the Oregon Trail, Oregon Territorial Governor George Abernethy noted that "small parties of two or three [travelers] are sometimes stripped of their property while on their way to this Territory, perhaps because a preceding party promised to pay the

Indians for something . . . and failed to fulfill their promise. This will show you the necessity of keeping your word with them in all cases." Unfortunately, any number of emigrants—and government officials as well—failed to heed this advice.

Oregon had its own problems. The territory's Cayuse Indians, becoming hostile to missionaries Marcus Whitman and Henry Spaulding, attacked the Whitman mission in November of 1847, killing Whitman and his wife Narcissa. Efforts of a peace commission to maintain some sort of order were disrupted by a volunteer military force bent upon punishing virtually any Indians it might encounter. Finally, however, the volunteers realized they were promoting a warlike union of all the tribes in the Columbia Basin and returned home.

The Indians found new reason to fear white settlement in 1850, when Congress passed the Oregon Donation Land Law, opening land to homesteading without regard to Indian rights. Even less fortunate than those in Oregon were California's Digger Indians, who were unlucky enough to reside in the gold country exploited by the "'49ers." Able to offer little effective resistance, the Diggers were almost annihilated by disease, starvation, and violence. California's governor echoed a growing sentiment among westerners when in 1851 he proclaimed that "a war of extermination will continue to be waged until the Indian race becomes extinct." Experienced frontiersmen such as Tom Fitzpatrick, former trapper and later government agent for the tribes on the high plains, warned of the growing plight of the Indians and the impact that westward emigration was having on them, but to little avail. Emigration continued unabated, increasing the pressure on the western tribes.

To help protect travelers on the Oregon Trail the army had organized the Regiment of Mounted Rifles in 1846, had built Fort Kearny on the Platte in 1848, and had converted Forts Laramie, Hall, and Vancouver from fur-trading stations to military outposts. Travelers on the Santa Fe Trail were to expect protection from Forts Atkinson and Union. As was true throughout the West, however, the garrisons at these points—sometimes fewer than fifty men—were generally too small and isolated to do much more than "show the flag." With the Indians becoming increasingly restive, the need for additional measures to control them became apparent. Treaties negotiated in 1851 and 1853 at Forts Laramie and Atkinson respectively provided for annuity payments to restrain warriors from molesting traffic on the Oregon and Santa Fe routes. But in 1854 Kansas and Nebraska were organized as territories, preempting much of the land previously set aside as the "Permanent Indian Frontier."

The tribes of the southern plains and the arid Southwest—the Comanches, Kiowas, Utes, Navajos, and several of the Apache subtribes—had been warring against whites and against each other for a century or two prior to the 1850s. But not until that decade did the warriors of the central plains and the areas around California rise up in concerted efforts to drive out white settlers. The killing of an emigrant's wandering cow by a Sioux brave in the summer of 1854, and the rash handling of the incident by an army detachment, brought on a general war with the Sioux. A press of gold-seekers through the lands of the Yakimas in 1855 precipitated an uprising by the tribes of the Pacific Northwest. And in 1856 a misunderstanding about the ownership of stolen horses resulted in an outbreak by the Cheyennes. By the fall of 1858 the army had decisively scattered the northwestern tribes, but the successes it scored against the Sioux and Cheyenne were only temporary. Equally short-lived were the army's victories over the southwestern tribes; by 1864 only the Navajos had suffered a definitive defeat. Sioux, Cheyenne, Comanche, Kiowa, and other tribes would continue to war against whites well into the 1870s—and some of the Apaches would still be at war ten years after that.

·17·

INDIAN ARMS

INDIGENOUS WEAPONS

ALTHOUGH firearms were to assume ever-increasing importance for the Indians of the 1800s, never did they completely lay aside the indigenous weapons: the bow, the lance, and the war club. Because it threw a projectile the bow was, in a sense, the predecessor of the gun, and in skilled hands it could easily prove as effective as the clumsy flintlock smoothbores carried by the earliest explorers. A traveler bound for Oregon in 1832 found Blackfeet warriors armed with "muskets, bows, and arrows. . . . The bows are made of walnut, about three feet long, and the string of the sinews of the buffalo, all calculated for great elasticity, and will reach an object at a surprising distance. It was to us a much more terrific weapon of war than a musket."[1]

If the hunting arrow driven by such a bow did not strike bone, it sometimes tore completely through the game. Furthermore, arrowheads made of soft hoop iron were even capable of penetrating bone. Iron for arrowheads came from various sources—either from barter with traders or from the salvage of abandoned iron-bound items. An oft-repeated saying on the frontier credited the Indians with being able to steal the iron tires from a wagon while it was moving at the gallop![2]

Artist George Catlin left a vivid description of the typical Indian armament he saw during his travels in the 1830s:

An Indian . . . mounted on a fleet and well-trained horse, with his bow in his hand, and his quiver slung on his back, containing an hundred arrows, of which he can throw fifteen or twenty in a minute, is a formidable and dangerous enemy. Many of them also ride with a lance of twelve or fourteen feet in length with a blade of polished steel; and all of them (as a protection for their vital parts), with a shield or arrow-fender made of the skin of the buffalo's neck, which has been smoked and hardened with glue extracted from the hoofs. These shields are arrow-proof, and will glance off a rifle-shot with perfect effect by being turned obliquely, which they do with great skill.

The scalping-knife . . . which is carried under the belt, is the form of knife most generally used in all parts of the Indian country, where knives have been introduced. It is a common and cheap butcher knife with one edge, manufactured at Sheffield, in England, perhaps, for a sixpence; and sold to the poor Indian in these wild regions for a horse. If I should live to get home, and should ever cross the Atlantic with my Collection, a curious enigma would be solved for the English people, who may inquire for a scalping-knife, when they find that every one in my Collection (and hear also, that nearly every one that is to be seen in the Indian country, to the Rocky Mountains and the Pacific Ocean) bears on its blade the impress of G.R., which they will doubtless understand.

Pipe tomahawks are the most valued of an Indian's weapons, inasmuch as they are a matter of luxury, and useful for cutting his fire-wood, etc., in time of peace; and deadly weapons in time of war, which they use in the hand, or throw with unerring and deadly aim.[3]

Josiah Gregg, who spent many months in the Southwest, had this to say on the subject of Indian arms of the 1830s and early 1840s:

The arms of the wild Indians are chiefly the bow and arrows, with the use of which they become remarkably expert. A dextrous savage will lay a wager at short shots, against many riflemen. . . . While the musketeer will load and fire once, the bowman will discharge a dozen arrows, and that, at distances under fifty yards, with an accuracy nearly equal to the rifle.

The usual length of the Indian bow is about three feet, though it is sometimes as much as four. It is generally made of elastic wood, yet elk's horn is occasionally used. . . . Bows have also been made . . . of a pair of buffalo ribs. . . . The arrows are generally about thirty inches long, and pointed with iron, though the primitive flint points are still met with among some of the wildest tribes. Besides these, the lance or spear, the use of which they may have learned from the Mexicans, is an effective weapon in the charge as well as the chase. Many are also provided with the North-western fusil, and some have rifles. Very few, however, have acquired the dexterity of our frontier Indians with this deadly weapon. But no Indian deems his equipage complete without a 'scalping-knife'; yet among the western prairie Indians the tomahawk is but little known. They employ, in its stead, the war-club or 'war-hawk,' which are bludgeons with an encased stone for a head in the former, and with a transverse blade or spike in its place in the latter. Many are provided with shields of raw buffalo or elk skin. . . .[4]

Elsewhere Gregg offered additional comments about the lance, and presented a comparison of the efficiency in hunting buffalo of primitive weapons as opposed to firearms:

both Indians and Mexicans often chase [buffalo] with a long-handled spear or lance, which, if the horse be well trained, is still a more expeditious mode of killing them than with the bow and arrow. An expert lancer will enter a drove, and drawing up alongside, will pierce buffalo after buffalo until several are brought down. In default of bow or lance, they chase with the fusil, but seldom so successfully as with the former weapons. The Americans generally prefer 'running' with the horseman's pistol; yet the Indian is apt to kill double as many with his arrows or lance.[5]

In the mid-1840s the army lieutenant James Carleton noted that:

the Dahcotahs [Sioux] have many short fusees amongst them, which they have procured from the American Fur Company, and a very few rifles. But with these weapons they are not expert. Their main dependence either in war or the chase, is upon their bows and arrows, their lances and their shields. Their bows are not over three feet long, but are very stout.

The lances are about 7 feet long. Just where the blades unite with the shafts, are usually fastened large tassels of war-eagle feathers. These lances are not thrown like the javelin, but are used principally to thrust down their antagonists when on foot, and in the charge against horsemen.[6]

Another traveler described the Caw Indians as using lances with six-foot shafts and three-foot blades to hunt buffalo from horseback, although like the Sioux the Caws undoubtedly used them against human adversaries also.[7]

Soldiers who served with Eugene Bandel in the mid-1850s were impressed with the skill in archery displayed by Sioux Indian youths:

All of them . . . from boys of six years of age up, have their bows and a quiver full of arrows, and the accuracy with which they shoot is almost unbelievable. We would often let the boys, with their little bows, shoot (at twenty paces) three and five cent pieces out of a post which we had split at the top and in which we had fastened the coin; and almost every time they did it.[8]

Perhaps the most qualified observer regarding the effect of the bow and arrow in warfare was the army doctor. One of these serving in the Southwest wrote in 1862 that: "An expert bowman can easily discharge six arrows per minute, and a man wounded with one is almost sure to receive several arrows. . . . We have not seen more than one or two men wounded by a single arrow only."[9]

At times even whites made use of the bow and arrow. James P. Beckwourth, a prominent mulatto trapper and scout, told his biographer that in the early 1820s he had practiced extensively with the bow and was quite proficient in its use. When a band of Arapaho braves stole a rifle from the five trappers with whom he was working, the whites managed to seize two Indian guns and five bows with quivers. In later life William T. Hamilton wrote that of the group of trappers he accompanied into the mountains in 1842, two men had bows and arrows and were experts with them.[10]

FIREARMS

While whites might occasionally borrow Indian weapons, Indians were much more eager to lay hands on the whites' firearms. With the possible exception of the horse, few commodities introduced by whites had as dramatic an effect on the culture of eighteenth- and nineteenth-century Indian tribes as did the gun. For decades the possession of firearms was a significant factor in intertribal relationships, with those tribes lucky enough to own guns maintaining a distinct advantage over their less-fortunate neighbors.[11]

A gun trade among many of the western Indians was already well established when Lewis and Clark headed up the Missouri. As early as the 1750s French traders entering New Mexico reported that the Wichitas were trading French guns to the Comanches for horses. Although few in number, the Otos had acquired a good supply of firearms by 1775, and did not hesitate to use them on Pawnee raiders. In 1795 one observer wrote from an Omaha village on the Platte that the warriors were knowledgeable enough about firearms to want only English guns "and not the French ones, which burst in their hands." At about the same time, travelers on the upper Missouri noted that the Gros Ventre and Mandan tribes were well supplied with javelins, guns, pistols, and ammunition obtained from the British at the Montreal and Hudson's Bay posts.[12]

In contrast to the use of firearms as trade goods by the British and French, Spanish authorities in the Southwest generally prohibited trading guns to Indians; but other tribes, acting from the comfortable position of "middlemen" and not at all concerned with white regulations, saw to it that the Indians living in Spanish territory obtained guns anyway. The whites, however, later took over much of the southwestern arms trade. In 1830 Antonio Comaduran reported to his Mexican superiors that when questioned as to the source of their arms, hostile Apaches claimed they came from Anglo-Americans who "gave them guns and powder and other necessities for which the Apaches gave them mules and horses." Comaduran also reported that the Apaches had indicated that the Americans had advised them not to make peace with the Mexicans "because if they hurried and made war on us, the Anglo-Americans would aid them, and they would make an end to us." Such a report was particularly alarming to provincial authorities in view of the fact that those arms available to militia forces in northern Mexico were often limited in quantity and quality.[13]

During their upriver journey in 1804–5, Lewis and Clark took particular note of Indians' guns. In 1804 Clark described the Teton Sioux as "badly armed with fusees" and noted that the Rickarees or Arikara had the same type of gun. Many such arms came into Indian hands as a result of an annual Sioux trade fair held in late spring, where Sissetons and Yanktons met traders who brought them guns, powder, ball, kettles, axes, and various other European trade goods. "Through such trading," Lewis observed, "[the] Sioux manage to be well supplied enabling them to maintain their superiority on that section of the Missouri." (In 1795 a Frenchman named Trudeau had noticed the same thing, stating that the fear with which other tribes on the Missouri and near the Black Hills regarded the Teton Sioux stemmed mainly from the fact that the Sioux had many guns, while others had few.)[14]

The Rickarees relied heavily on the Sioux for their guns and ammunition, and it was their policy to remain on agreeable terms with the latter until they could develop other sources of supply. Clark observed that among the Rickarees, Minatarees, and Mandans a gun and its accessories (or a good horse) were roughly equal in value to two tail feathers from an eagle, highly

prized plumes which were used as decorations in a warrior's hair or in the mane and tail of a favorite mount.[15]

Farther west the explorers encountered other evidence of the extensive firearms trade. In October of 1805, in a village in what is now Oregon, the party "Saw a british musket copper tea kettles & C. . . ."; a few days later "2 Indians came to us from a village below who had red and blue cloth blankets which appeared new one had a brass musket and powder flask a little powder & C."[16]

Although Spanish authorities confiscated most of Zebulon Pike's papers, he managed in 1810 to prepare a detailed account of his expedition to the Southwest, which included a unique estimate of the number of firearms possessed by the various tribes he had encountered during his travels. Presumably most of these arms were "Northwest Guns," the most common term for the light full-stocked smoothbore musket designed for the Indian trade. Widespread sales of these arms by the Hudson's Bay and the Mackinaw companies led to the use of two other popular names, the "Hudson's Bay fuke" and "Mackinaw gun," as well as the catch-all terms "fusil" or "fusee"; but the name "Northwest gun" was used for this arm even before the formation of the famous Montreal trading company of that name, and the guns were listed in that manner in advertisements, fur-company inventories, and U.S. government contracts.[17]

Early in its history the Northwest gun acquired certain characteristics which distinguished it from other lightweight flintlock muskets. The barrel was almost always octagonal at the rear, becoming round a foot or so forward of the breech. It was inletted into a full stock which extended almost to the muzzle, and held in place by crosspins. The flat brass buttplate was secured by nails or screws, but the practical-minded Indians often removed it for use as a hide scraper. The really important characteristics of the Northwest gun, however, were an unusually large sheet-iron trigger guard, permitting use while wearing mittens or gloves, and a brass serpent- or dragon-shaped sideplate opposite the lock. Evidently this plate stemmed from a similar device on some light British "Queen Anne" military muskets sent to the American colonies at the end of the seventeenth century. Whatever its origin, the serpent sideplate represented a hallmark of quality to the Indian, and its presence on a Northwest gun was often essential to sales. Besides looking for the serpent sideplate, a potential purchaser might also check for other markings; Northwest guns sold by the Hudson's Bay Company were often stamped with a unique symbol, a "seated fox in a tombstone," while those sold by the North West Company had a "fox in a circle." Some later American and Belgian arms carried similar markings to ensure the confidence of customers already familiar with their appearance on the English guns.[18]

These guns frequently had barrel lengths of 30, 36, 42, or 48 inches, but the Indians who used them sometimes shortened them considerably. The owner might do this to make the gun easier to reload on horseback, but the extrashort barrels often resulted from burst muzzles. To the Indians guns were tools, and like their horses they expected them to perform their function with little or no care on the owners' part. Carelessness in loading, or allowing the muzzle to become obstructed with dirt or snow, could cause a burst barrel, whereupon a warrior cut the barrel off below the break and continued using the gun. In fact, he would use it until it simply wore out, then save the parts for other purposes. Altered sections of barrel, for example, would work as hide scrapers, and at least one warrior, a Blackfoot photographed on a Canadian reservation in the 1880s, wore a breastplate or chest ornament comprising two strips of furs and the serpent sideplates from half a dozen Northwest guns.[19]

In terms of actual performance, the Northwest gun was generally a well-made, dependable arm, as it had to be to withstand the rough treatment it usually got. Even better made was the "Chief's Gun," a Northwest arm "of Better quality and better finished" than the

Mid-eighteenth-century French smoothbore trade gun of about .55 caliber, representative of guns available to Indians from French traders throughout much of that century. The 48 in. barrel is octagonal for about nine inches at the breech and then round to the muzzle. Stamped at the rear of the lockplate is a stylized club, bow, and quiver. (Courtesy Museum of the Fur Trade, Chadron, Neb.)

In 1833–34, the artist Karl Bodmer accompanied Prince Maximilian on a journey up the Missouri River. He painted representatives of many of the Indian tribes which they observed, faithfully recording details of their dress, hair styles, ornaments, and even the large trigger guards on the North West guns with which these two Assiniboin warriors were armed.

standard article, often having a silver nameplate in the stock. Indians were demanding customers, and despite occasional references to the reportedly inferior quality of these arms, traders' efforts to introduce lesser-quality weapons to their buyers usually evoked scorn and a demand for refund or exchange.[20]

Besides its ruggedness, the qualities which ensured the gun's continued popularity were its suitability for either a single ball or a shot change, its light weight, and its low price. (There is no truth to the old story that the cost to an Indian was a stack of pelts piled high enough to reach the muzzle of a Northwest gun standing on its butt.) With its light smoothbore barrel the gun could not compete at long range with rifled arms, but recent firing tests show that when carefully loaded the gun will put single patched balls into a 6 in. circle at 45 yards. In practice, however, Indians often did not exert such care in loading.[21]

Just when the first Northwest gun appeared is uncertain. The earliest known example, dated 1777, was the product of an English maker named Sandwell, although similar guns were available decades before that; due to hard usage, however, existing specimens of eighteenth-century trade guns are very rare.[22]

What is certain is the popularity of English-made guns, which Indians strongly preferred to American or Belgian copies: Barnett, Bond, W. Chance & Son, Grice, Ketland, Parker Field & Company, Sargent Brothers, and Wheeler all manufactured flintlock Northwest guns at one time or another. In fact, American fur companies often bought their trade guns from English makers, and in many instances even the U.S. Office of Indian Trade had to rely on foreign Northwest guns to meet Indian demands, although it made at least one early attempt to substitute American guns.[23]

In 1795 Congress had established the Indian factory

Indian hide scrapers made from sections of North West trade gun barrels. (Courtesy National Park Service)

system to promote trade with the tribes and protect them from exploitation by private traders and their alcohol. The government set up twenty-eight "factories" or trading posts at which federal employees exchanged quality goods for the Indians' furs. Despite the fact that factory employees were less knowledgeable of Indian customs and less skilled in dealing with them than were the commercial traders, the plan was generally successful until, in 1822, Congress abolished it under pressure from private trading companies.[24]

In 1807, to supply the factories with smoothbores, Secretary of War Henry Dearborn ordered the production of 1200 light .54 caliber "carbines or Indian guns," with 34 in. barrels and pin-fastened full stocks. According to Springfield records the armory completed 600 of these in 1809 and 602 in 1810, but apparently these smoothbores proved inappropriate for their intended purpose. Early in 1809 the superintendent of the Indian Trade Office requested a Philadelphia dealer to get:

> 100 of the real North West guns by Barnett or Ketland. . . . they are to be known by the large guard of iron, by three screw pins to the lock, by one screw only (which passes quite through the stock) being used to secure the upper part of the guard and the lower part of the barrel; and above all by a brass mounting [the serpent sideplate] opposite to the lock. . . . If those bought by you are not of this kind they will not answer any purpose and need not be sent.

Some of the Springfield carbines acquired bayonet studs and went to West Point for use by cadets, but as late as 1848 there were still 690 others on hand at the armory.[25]

In the face of competition from the English-made Northwest guns, American manufacturers of trade muskets experienced little success until the 1840s. In 1827 and 1828 the American Fur Company did order several hundred Northwest guns, with blued 30 to 48 in. barrels and varnished stocks, from Henry's Bolton Gun Works in Pennsylvania, but Henry's efforts to secure repeat orders were disappointing. In August of 1827 John Jacob Astor himself wrote Henry to say that: "our Agent in the interior . . . complains of the quality of both the Guns & Rifles which you made for us this spring." Also, the company could get good-quality guns from Europe for from $4.50 to $5.75 each. Company officials often reminded Henry of this fact: in November of 1828, for instance, the gunmaker found this note appended to an order: "Our people like your *sample* guns of *last* spring well enough, but at the same price they prefer those we get from England." Months later, in July of 1829, Ramsay Crooks wrote, criticizing the blue finish of Henry's Northwest guns as unequal to the "bright lively blue" of the English guns, and adding that one of Henry's guns had burst because the barrel was too thin. During that same year the company imported 450 Northwest guns from England and 500 from Liege, Belgium. Interestingly enough, the specifications for these guns called for "Barnett" markings on the lockplates regardless of the actual source of manufacture, because at that time Barnett was a leading producer of Northwest guns for the Hudson's Bay Company.[26]

In May of 1825, near the Bear River, Peter Skene Ogden of Hudson's Bay had encountered a small band of Indians who had "4 Guns (Barnets) & altho' one had 1802 marked on the lock & another 1817 Still they were in good order & appeared as if they were taken out of the Store only a few days Since." Elsewhere Ogden noted the widespread use of English guns among the Snake Indians: "they have a number of American Knives and trinkets amongst them but all their Fire Arms except one Rifle have come from our quarter; although not more than 100 men came to our Camp they had sixty Guns. . . ." A letter from the American Fur Company to James Henry in 1836 again stressed the Indians' preference for English guns, stating that "we cannot hold out any encouragement for North West guns. Our people will not take any but the English."[27]

The four to six dollars the trader had to give for a Northwest gun was small compared to the profit he might realize from it. In the winter of 1812–13 the price for a good gun at the Pacific Fur Company's Spokane outpost was a minimum of twenty beaver pelts, while a few "short ones" changed hands for fifteen pelts. At that time the wholesale price of a trade gun was about one pound seven shillings, while the average value of the twenty pelts was about twenty-five pounds! In July of 1826, near the Great Salt Lake, William Ashley transferred his trading outfit to the firm of Smith, Jackson, and Sublette, preparing in-

Three flintlock North West trade guns. From top: 1820 Wilson found in a stone fort in the Owl Creek Mountains of Wyoming; imitation Barnett discovered in 1910 with a skeleton in a cave on Heart Mountain in Wyoming; Barnett with a lock dated 1870 found along the Yellowstone River, not far from the site of Custer's defeat of 1876. The latter gun has been shortened drastically and the buttstock altered, possibly for more convenient use on horseback. (Courtesy Museum of the Fur Trade, Chadron, Neb.)

voices for the items to be turned over; the prices on these invoices showed how much higher trade goods were in the mountains than they were nearer their points of origin, as at St. Louis. Gunpowder of "first and second quality" went for $1.50 per pound, shot for $1.25 per pound, lead for casting balls for $1 a pound, butcher knives for 75¢ each, three-point blankets for $9.00 each, gray cloth of common quality for $5.00 per yard, and Northwest fusils for a healthy $24.00 each.[28]

The traders naturally passed on such prices to the Indians, many of whom paid willingly because the ownership of a gun was so important. Chinooks and Clatsops living near Astoria in 1812 had only a few firearms, but their presence was significant:

> Their arms are principally Bows and Arrows, Iron and bone Bludgeons, with a few muskets, which they are extremely fond of, and so much is their effect dreaded by the surrounding tribes (who have few or none) that a dosen on either side are sufficient to decide their most obstinate conflicts. . . .[29]

While Indians often used their guns against each other, they were no more reluctant to use them on whites. One of the best-known examples of this was the attack on William Ashley's party by the Arikara in the spring of 1823; in a letter to the *Missouri Republican* Ashley claimed that the attackers had numbered about 600, perhaps three-fourths of whom had "London fusils." He probably credited the smoothbores

with underserved performance, however, when he wrote that they "carry a ball with great accuracy and force and which [the Arikara] use with as much expertness as any man I ever saw handle firearms." Some twenty years later Bill Hamilton's camp of trappers suffered a night attack by Indians armed in the same manner. As Hamilton described it, "we fired at the flashes of the Indian guns; these were Hudson Bay flintlocks and made a very decided flash when discharged. The weapon is not over-effective, but will do damage at short range.[30]

White hunters sometimes used Northwest guns as well. In the winter of 1833–34 Warren Angus Ferris of the American Fur Company mentioned the difficulty he and a companion had in hunting deer on snowshoes. They had no rifles for the hunt and therefore experienced only moderate success: "We each possessed a fusil brought to the country expressly for the Indian trade, a light kind of gun which is only used by the hunters on our side of the mountains for running buffalo. However, my companion appeared quite expert with his weapon, and made several very good shots with it."[31]

Through the 1830s most of the Northwest guns used on the frontier came from English makers, but American manufacturers equipped to supply rifles to the Indians still found a reasonably good market. Although the smoothbore trade musket was the more representative Indian firearm, some tribes had demonstrated a preference for rifles even before the coming of Lewis and Clark. Soon after the Revolution an

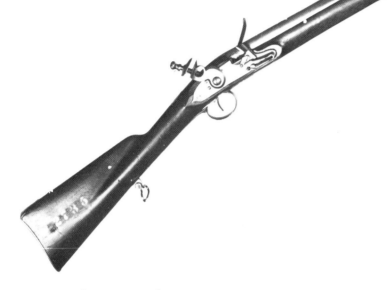

U.S. Model 1807 carbine, sometimes referred to as the "Indian carbine." Although originally intended for distribution to friendly Indians or sale at Indian "factories," few if any were used for the intended purpose. (Courtesy West Point Museum)

American trader named William Burnett reported that tribes in what is now Michigan would have nothing to do with smoothbores, but wanted rifles. And early in the life of the government's factory system, officials found rifles to be important items in factory inventories. In September of 1803 Tench Coxe of the Government Purveyor's Office ordered 50 flintlock rifles from Peter Gonter of Lancaster, Pennsylvania, to be delivered to the Chickasaw Indian factory, and a partial list of makers who supplied rifles to the factories between 1806 and 1812 included such prominent names as Henry Deringer, Jr., Jacob Dickert, Frederick Goetz, John Guest, Christopher Gumpf, and John Miles.[32]

In an 1807 letter to Jacob Dickert and Henry DeHuff, Coxe gave a fairly detailed description of the rifles the government was ordering for the Indians at that time:

They are to be common, plain rifles substantially made. The barrel to be three feet and two inches in length. The workmanship to be such as to pass a strict & rigorous inspection. The calibre such as to fit balls of half an ounce weight. The finishing, (if the work be good & substantial) will be sufficient, if not inferior to those commonly made for ordinary use. The barrels would be preferred round (instead of eight square) from the tail pipe or lower thimble to the muzzle; but of the [same] thickness [as] the flat part or thinnest part of the octagonal barrels. The price that will be paid for the rifle complete, will be ten dollars cash.

(In addition to rifles, Coxe ordered from some of the gunsmiths "bells for cows, horses & sheep for the Indian stores.")[33]

Depending on specifications in individual orders, rifles made for the Indians might differ from Coxe's description. Barrels could be as long as 48 in., but more often fell between 42 in. and 46 in., with calibers ranging between .42 and .53. Mountings such as trigger guard, buttplate, plain patchbox cover, and ramrod thimbles were usually brass. Gunmakers usually charged the government from $10.50 to $12.50 apiece for such rifles, adding 50¢ each for rifles "ornamented on the Breach with silver stars and half moons" or with other decorative inlays. One contract with Deringer in 1811 called for a dozen rifles to be highly finished, and inlaid with stars or eagles, and cost the government $22.50 apiece. Presumably such ornate guns were presented to selected chiefs or other distinguished members of a tribe.[34]

Even after the termination of the factory system in 1822, the government found it necessary to continue to purchase rifles (as well as Northwest guns) for distribution to Indians as treaty or annuity payments. In 1825, for example, Menard & Valle of Kaskaskia delivered to the Wea Indians "10 Rifles Gumph" as part of their annual annuity. A year later the firm distributed "14 Best Lancaster Rifles @ $18 [ea.]" to the Kickapoos for the same reason. After the War of 1812 the United States established what it felt would be a permanent Indian Territory west of Arkansas and Lou-

Two views of the remains of a flintlock North West trade gun with distinctive dragon sideplate, found in the Snake River in Idaho. (Courtesy Idaho Historical Society)

isiana. Tribes were encouraged to move from their lands east of the Mississippi into these areas, and during the later years of the Monroe administration relocation became the official policy of the government. Treaties with many of the relocating tribes—including the Cherokees, Chocktaws, and Creeks between 1817 and 1832—specifically called for the payment of a rifle with ammunition to each warrior emigrating to the West. By 1837 approximately half of the twenty thousand warriors who had been persuaded to relocate westward had received guns from the federal government.[35]

During the 1830s government contracts for Indian rifles called for significant quantities of both flintlock and percussion arms, which in the main came from Henry Deringer, George and Edward Tryon, Henry Leman, and Jacob Fordney. Deringer's preeminence was due largely to his past performance with Indian rifles. In 1829 the superintendent of Indian Affairs wrote that:

[Deringer] had made Rifles for the Indian Trade during a large portion of the time General Mason had superintended it. . . . among his greatest dif-

ficulties was that of getting good Rifles—But he at last found out Mr. Derenger—and since he had employed him he had never had trouble either in bad guns, or want of punctuality of delivery. . . . I continued to send Mr. Derenger orders, and found him faithful. Moreover the Indians all seek his guns, and know his name as well as if they could read. . . .

Between September of 1831 and April of 1833 Deringer sent the government 2150 Indian rifles; another 500 came from George Tryon at the same time. One of Deringer's shipments comprised "217 percussion and 93 flint-lock rifles complete, at $12.50 per rifle; 217,000 percussion caps at 80 cents per thousand; [and] 310 woolen covers at 37½ cts. . . ." The Chocktaws at Fort Smith, Oklahoma, showed a definite preference for the Deringer rifles, as long as they were flintlocks—when the Indians received a delivery of 550 rifles, they returned the 200 percussion arms included in the shipment for exchange.[36]

Another government invitation for proposals for Indian rifles, issued by the War Department's Office of Indian Affairs in July of 1837, called for a total of 4500 arms, each proposal to be accompanied by a pattern gun meeting these general specifications:

The rifles wanted are such as have heretofore been furnished to emigrating Indians. They may be described in general terms as carrying balls of which a pound of lead will not make less than forty-five, nor more than one hundred, and must be of a length and weight corresponding properly with the size of the ball. Each gun is to be accompanied by moulds, wiper, and such other implements as are necessary to make a complete equipment.

Each rifle is to be enclosed in a first rate woollen cover, securely packed in strong boxes, and not less

Well-worn example of a shortened flintlock North West gun, found in the Cajon Pass between the San Gabriel and San Bernardino mountains of California. The pass was a southeast gateway for overland travel to the coast after the early 1830s. Below is a Joslyn breech-loading carbine, used by Amasa Lyman, one of the Mormon leaders of the colonists who came to the San Bernardino Valley as early as 1851. Both guns are displayed at the San Bernardino County (Cal.) Museum.

In 1792 the U.S. government began procuring rifles from various Pennsylvania makers to equip the army's rifle companies, raised in that year. In 1794 and again in 1807 additional contracts were let for the purchase or manufacture of similar rifles. Initially these arms were for the army, but later several hundred were distributed to friendly Indian tribes, either as gifts or annuity payments, or by sale through government-run trading posts ("factories"). Typical characteristics, particularly of those rifles manufactured under the 1807 contracts, as was this specimen by Christopher Gumpf of Lancaster, Pa., were a simple brass patchbox cover and a .54 caliber round/octagonal barrel, which sometimes bore a proofmark at the breech. Some of those rifles intended for Indian use were specifically ordered with "silver stars and thumbpiece" inlays. (Courtesy West Point Museum)

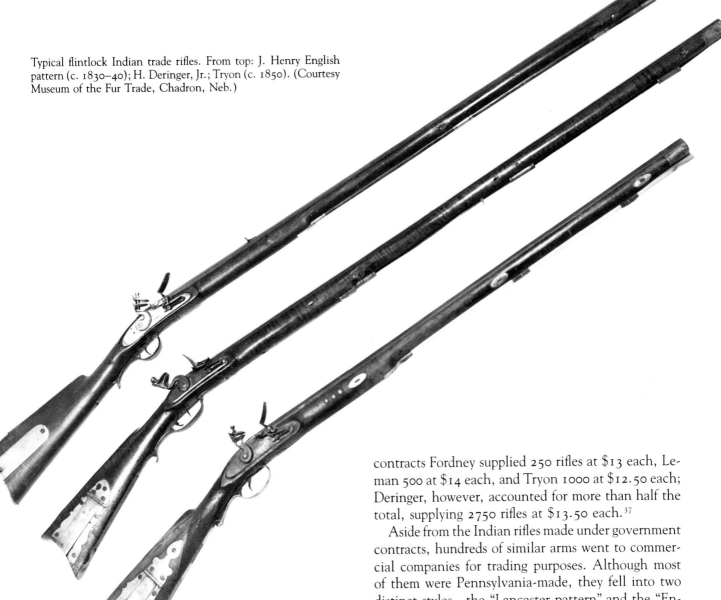

Typical flintlock Indian trade rifles. From top: J. Henry English pattern (c. 1830–40); H. Deringer, Jr.; Tryon (c. 1850). (Courtesy Museum of the Fur Trade, Chadron, Neb.)

than twenty, nor more than twenty-five in each box.

. . . Before any rifles are received, they will be rigidly and thoroughly inspected, and proved by an officer of the same department; they will not be received, unless they conform in all respects to the patterns.

As a result of the contractor's proposals, early in November the War Department let contracts for "rifles for Indians" to four well-known makers—Deringer, Tryon, Leman, and Fordney—all of whom would have to complete their guns within one year. Under these contracts Fordney supplied 250 rifles at $13 each, Leman 500 at $14 each, and Tryon 1000 at $12.50 each; Deringer, however, accounted for more than half the total, supplying 2750 rifles at $13.50 each.[37]

Aside from the Indian rifles made under government contracts, hundreds of similar arms went to commercial companies for trading purposes. Although most of them were Pennsylvania-made, they fell into two distinct styles—the "Lancaster pattern" and the "English pattern." As suggested by its name, the Lancaster pattern was basically a Kentucky (named after the seat of Kentucky-rifle manufacture, Lancaster, Pennsylvania), with full-length maple stock and semifancy brass mountings. English-pattern rifles were slightly less expensive, with simple rectangular patchbox covers and rather straight, thick walnut stocks. After J. J. Henry designed his "Scroll Guard" or "New English" rifle in 1834, the older arm became, appropriately enough, the "Old English" pattern, and was so listed in subsequent orders. One order from Ramsay Crooks late in 1840 (on behalf of Pierre Chouteau & Co.) called for:

50 Rifles *new* English pattern 3 feet 6 inch barrels 32 Balls
　　　　　　　　　　　　　　　　　　　　to the lb @ $11.50
50　" 　old 　　" 　　 " 　3 " 6 " . . .
100　" 　Lancaster 　　" 　3 ft 6 to 3 ft 8 inch "
　　　　　　　　　　　　　　　35 to 40 Balls 　" 　" 　" [38]

Flintlock rifle of 1820s vintage, by Henry Deringer, Jr. The stock has been partially covered in leather and bears an Apache Indian clan marking. (Courtesy Arizona Historical Society)

Between 1835 and 1842 the American Fur Company ordered some 1300 Lancaster-pattern rifles from John Joseph Henry and his son James; in 1837, in fact, Crooks wrote Henry that "we would like to give you this year the making of all our Rifles if you will undertake it, and not disappoint us." Until about 1840 these arms were flintlocks, with barrels typically 42 in. to 44 in. long, and with calibers between .49 and .53, but after that some orders began to call for percussion rifles, and the caliber decreased to about .47. Apparently the Henry firm was also the American Fur Company's sole source for the English-pattern rifles, but this style never proved quite as popular for the Indian trade as did the Lancaster patterns.[39]

Despite the appearance of percussion arms in Indian hands, the demand for flintlocks continued to be strong. In January of 1844 the Office of Indian Affairs ordered "for the use of the Pawnee Indians 40 Short rifles to measure 32 Inches in the Barrel bored for Sixty Balls to the pound with substantial flint locks." And as late as 1853 Indian trader George Ewing, in an order for various rifles for his St. Louis agency, specifically noted: "no percussion Locks wanted this year."[40]

While these rifles were made specifically for the Indians, white traders and trappers bought them as well. In general they were high-quality arms, in part because Indians would avoid buying a gun with obvious defects. In December of 1837, in fact, Ramsay Crooks of the American Fur Company warned James Henry that "the outside of the barrels of the Lancaster pattern [you sent us] have so many flaws as will injure their sale for the Indians cannot be persuaded that such external imperfection does not extend to the interior of the rifle."[41]

Although the American Fur Company did business with the Henry concern on a large scale through the 1820s, 1830s, and early 1840s, Henry seldom enjoyed the benefits of a government contract during this time. Nevertheless, his firm's civilian business was more than sufficient to keep it occupied. In January of 1843 the Ewing brothers informed James Henry that "our Indian trade West of the Mississippi river calls for a large supply of Indian Rifles of peculiar styles & kinds to suit our different posts." To fill this need the Ewings began ordering fairly large lots of rifles on a regular basis; one 1844 order alone asked for some 270 "English pattern" and scroll-guard rifles. The latter were to have "a handsome maple stock, handsome brass mountings—a good heavy barrell—from 42 to 46 inches long . . . bore to be from 40 to 55 or 60 Balls to the pound—The Lock must be good and no *mistake*—if this fails, the gun is worthless, so put on the same quality of Lock which you put on the Eng Pat Rifle only not quite so large—say 5 inches—& of a more fancy finish."[42]

On the other hand, Henry Leman tried for years to interest the American Fur Company in his rifles, without success, but following his 1837 contract with the government his prospects brightened considerably, and

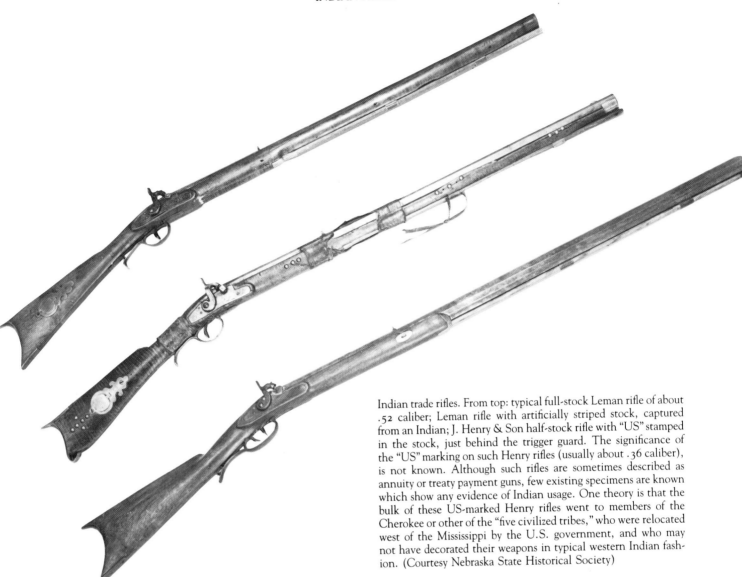

Indian trade rifles. From top: typical full-stock Leman rifle of about .52 caliber; Leman rifle with artificially striped stock, captured from an Indian; J. Henry & Son half-stock rifle with "US" stamped in the stock, just behind the trigger guard. The significance of the "US" marking on such Henry rifles (usually about .36 caliber), is not known. Although such rifles are sometimes described as annuity or treaty payment guns, few existing specimens are known which show any evidence of Indian usage. One theory is that the bulk of these US-marked Henry rifles went to members of the Cherokee or other of the "five civilized tribes," who were relocated west of the Mississippi by the U.S. government, and who may not have decorated their weapons in typical western Indian fashion. (Courtesy Nebraska State Historical Society)

his shop made plain but sturdy Indian rifles, in ever-increasing numbers, until he eventually became perhaps the best-known manufacturer of these arms. Frontier dealers sold Leman rifles to both red and white customers from the 1840s until well after the close of the Civil War.[43]

With the rising popularity of rifled arms among the Indians, certain tribes became particularly well versed in their use. A traveler noted in 1840 that the Osages fired their rifles every morning and renewed the charges. All their arms were flintlocks, he observed; they were unwilling to accept percussion weapons since they found large quantities of flint readily available. Moreover, a gunsmith provided by the U.S. government kept their rifles in good repair.[44]

The Sacs, Foxes, and Potawatomies who roamed the country near the Missouri River adopted many customs from the whites, and these tribes were well armed with rifles. The Potawatomies were accustomed to firing from horseback while hunting, and trained their horses to remain still while they rested their rifles in the crotch of two long crossed sticks for more accurate shooting; through such techniques these warriors earned a reputation among neighboring tribes as very capable marksmen.[45]

Indians able to make full use of the rifle's capabilities often showed little interest in unrifled weapons, and in 1840, when James Henry tried to sell the American Fur Company smoothbore rifles for the Indian trade, Ramsay Crooks replied tersely:

We said in ours of July 29 that the smooth bored rifles would not suit us. The more we reflect upon it the more we are satisfied that they will not answer at all for our Indian trade. When the Indians use a rifle it must be a real one, and they will not carry a smooth bore of such weight so long as they can get a North West gun.[46]

Still, rifles by no means eclipsed the popularity of the trade musket. Although English guns dominated

the market through the 1830s, American-made Northwest guns became more plentiful during the 1840s, largely because of government contracts. In January of 1839 Deringer received a contract from the War Department for an unspecified number of "Guns for Indians" at $8 each, similar (but not identical) to Northwest guns, and additional contracts to other makers followed. Early in 1841 Tryon signed a government trade-musket contract for $1700 worth of arms, and in 1842 Henry Leman contracted for another 500 at $7 each. Then, in March of 1844, Henry Deringer agreed to supply 6460 at $4.75 apiece, and a year later, with a government order for 830 at $5.50 each, Tryon began sending out a steady stream of Northwest guns, supplying the War Department with a total of more than 5500 by the close of 1855. The bulk of the Tryon trade guns had 36 in. barrels, while the balance had 42 in. barrels. Many of Leman's Northwest guns also had 36 in. barrels, as well as facsimiles of the Hudson's Bay "seated fox in a tombstone" stamped on the lockplates.[47]

The Indians' firearms, of course, were not limited to trade muskets and rifles made especially for them; plains rifles, military rifles and muskets, shotguns, and pistols sometimes came into their hands as gifts or as the spoils of war. In the 1820s Peter Ogden mentioned giving two pistols to Indians who had acted as emissaries for him, and on one occasion Solomon Carvalho, who accompanied Fremont on his 1853–54 expedition, traded his double-barreled shotgun to Walkara, a Ute chief, for a horse. Carvalho also described the expertise of the Delawares then in Kansas in hunting with rifles:

> A Delaware Indian, in hunting buffaloes, when near enough to shoot, rests his rifle on his saddle, balances himself in the stirrup on one leg; the other is thrown over the rifle to steady it. He then leans on one side, until his eye is on a level with the object, takes a quick sight, and fires while riding at full speed, rarely missing his mark, and seldom chasing one animal further than a mile.[48]

In 1854 a rifle-carrying hunting party of about one hundred Sacs and Foxes came under attack by a large war party near the Kansas River. The attackers were generally armed with bows and arrows or smoothbore trade guns, and as a result the Sacs and Foxes, firing by relays so that some of their rifles were always loaded,

U.S. M1841 "Mississippi" rifle showing probable evidence of Indian usage: the stock has been repaired with rawhide, and brass tacks have been added for decorative purposes. (Courtesy Museum of the Fur Trade, Chadron, Neb.)

A white scout and a Yuma Indian with a half-stock muzzle-loading rifle, photographed about 1862 near Fort Yuma, Arizona Terr. (Courtesy Smithsonian Institution)

kept the war party from approaching closely enough to do any serious damage with their shorter-ranged weapons.[49]

As Indians made wider and more expert use of firearms, so did white hunters continue using Indian guns for hunting, particularly for buffalo. Rudolph Friederich Kurz left a detailed description of one form of buffalo hunting he observed during his travels in the late 1840s:

> When running buffaloes, the hunters do not use rifle-patches but take along several balls in their mouths; the projectile thus moistened sticks to the powder when put into the gun. In the first place, on buffalo hunts, they do not carry rifles, for the reason that they think the care required in loading them takes too much time unnecessarily when shooting at close range and, furthermore, they find rifle balls too small. The hunter chases buffaloes at full gallop, discharges his gun, and reloads without slackening speed. To accomplish this he holds the weapon close within the bend of his left arm and, taking the powder horn in his right hand, draws out with his teeth the stopper, which is fastened to the horn to prevent its being lost, shakes the requisite amount of powder into his left palm, and again closes the powder horn. Then he grasps the gun with his right hand, holding it in a vertical position, pours the powder down the barrel, and gives the gun a sidelong thrust with the left hand, in order to shake the powder well through the priming hole into the touchpan (hunters at this place [Fort Union] discard percussion caps as not practical).
>
> Now he takes a bullet from his mouth and with his left hand puts it into the barrel, where, having been moistened by spittle, it adheres to the powder. He dares never hold his weapon horizontal, that is, in the position taken when firing, for fear that the ball may stick fast in its course, allowing sufficient air to intervene between powder and lead to cause an explosion and splinter the barrel. So long as the ball rolls freely down there is no danger. Hunters approach the buffaloes so closely that they do not take aim but, lifting the gun lightly with both hands, point in the direction of the animal's heart and fire. They are very often wounded in the face and hands by the bursting gun barrels, which, especially when the weather is extremely cold, are shattered as easily as glass.

Kurz also described a hunt on the Yellowstone River, during which Battiste Lafontaine raced a mile in six minutes while shooting twelve cows. Owen Mac-Kenzie, Kurz noted, could load and shoot fourteen times in one mile, "but does not invariably hit the object at which he aims."[50]

Bursting gun barrels were not the only source of danger in running buffalo. John Townsend left this account:

> an unpleasant accident happened to one of our men, named McCarey. He had been running a buffalo, and was about reloading the gun, which he had just discharged, when the powder in his horn was ignited by a burning wad remaining in the barrel; the horn was burst to fragments, the poor man dashed from his horse, and his face, neck, and hands, burnt in a shocking manner.[51]

Francis Parkman, anxious to try a smoothbore for hunting buffalo, borrowed a loaded gun—quite possibly a Northwest gun—from Deslauriers. During the chase Parkman found that he had only rifle balls in his pouch, "too large for pistols and too small for the gun. I loaded the gun . . . but as often as I leveled it to fire, the bullets would roll out of the muzzle and the gun returned only a report like a squib, as the powder harmlessly exploded." When he dismounted to gather dry grass to use as wadding a wounded buffalo bounded toward him, forcing him to remount quickly. With commendable ingenuity he yanked a few fringes from the seam of his buckskin trousers and, using these as wadding, reloaded and dispatched the beast.[52]

Parkman also presented some general observations on this style of hunting, which largely confirmed Kurz's description:

> The chief difficulty in running buffalo . . . is that of loading the gun or pistol at full gallop. Many hunters for convenience' sake carry three or four bullets in the mouth; the powder is poured down the muzzle of the piece, the bullet dropped in after it, the stock struck hard upon the pommel of the saddle, and the work is done. The danger of this is obvious. Should the blow on the pommel fail to send the bullet home, or should the bullet, in the act of aiming, start from its place and roll towards the muzzle, the gun would probably burst in discharging. Many a shattered hand and worse casualties besides have been the result of such an accident. To obviate it, some hunters make use of a ramrod, usually hung by a string from the neck, but this materially increases the difficulty in loading. The bows and arrows which the Indians use in run-

ning buffalo have many advantages over firearms, and even white men occasionally employ them.[53]

Smoothbores used for a purpose more violent than buffalo hunting were in especially wide evidence during the Sioux uprising in Minnesota in 1862. Many of these guns, however, were not trade muskets, but double-barreled shotguns captured from local settlers. John F. Bishop of the Fifth Minnesota Infantry mentioned such guns in his vivid account of the battle of Redwood:

> Indians rushed in upon us from behind, firing mostly double-barrel shotguns. . . . Then a hand-to-hand encounter took place, every man fighting the best he knew how to cut his way out of the terrible looking mob behind us. They were all painted and naked, except breech-clouts. Sergeant Trescott of Chatfield, two others and myself, tried to cut our way through, in order to get into the ferryman's log house or barn, which stood on opposite sides of the road leading to the ferry on our side of the river. Trescott fell about two hundred feet from the house; the others fell before they reached it, shot by Indians inside the house or barn. Both were full of Indians. I could not stop to argue right of passage, but darted through between the buildings. . . . a large sized ball shivered the stock of my musket and cut a flesh wound in the thigh, but not a very serious one. A little beyond the ferry-house I met an Indian with a double shotgun; he gave me the contents of both barrels, which struck the sand in the road at my feet; he was excited, I suppose, as well as myself. We both commenced loading; he had both barrels loaded as I rammed my cartridge home. A gun barrel then came up under my left arm. Supposing it to be an Indian in my rear about to use his hatchet, I did not turn to see how it was to be done; the gun went off and the Indian fell and the road was clear once more.

Despite the effectiveness of the bow at distances under fifty yards, Indians clung tenaciously to what firearms they had, crude though they might sometimes be. One of George Ruxton's hunting companions in the 1840s was a Potawatomie who carried a rifle which authorities had presented to him for bringing in four prisoners during the Canadian Rebellion; the Indian prized the weapon on this account, but Ruxton described it as "a most delapidated affair, the lock being tied on by a thong of buckskin, and the stock broken in many places." Even if the gun itself was serviceable, the ammunition fired from it might not be. After a sharp fight with Apaches in Arizona about 1864 Daniel Conner reported that "one of the guns we captured

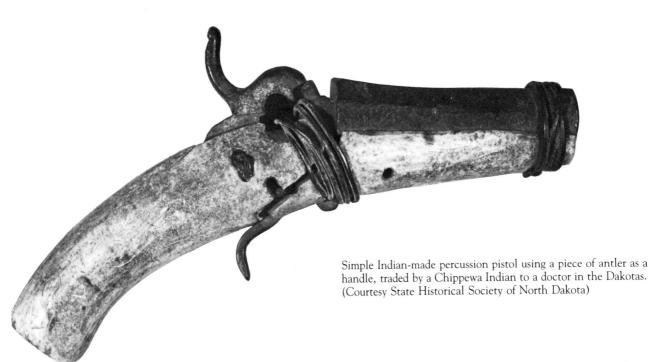

Simple Indian-made percussion pistol using a piece of antler as a handle, traded by a Chippewa Indian to a doctor in the Dakotas. (Courtesy State Historical Society of North Dakota)

In 1831 William P. Richardson, subagent for the Iowa Indians, accompanied a group of chiefs to Paris as guests of King Louis Philippe. This pair of cased LePage dueling pistols was presented by the French king to one of the chiefs, who later gave the set to Richardson. (Courtesy St. Joseph [Missouri] Museum)

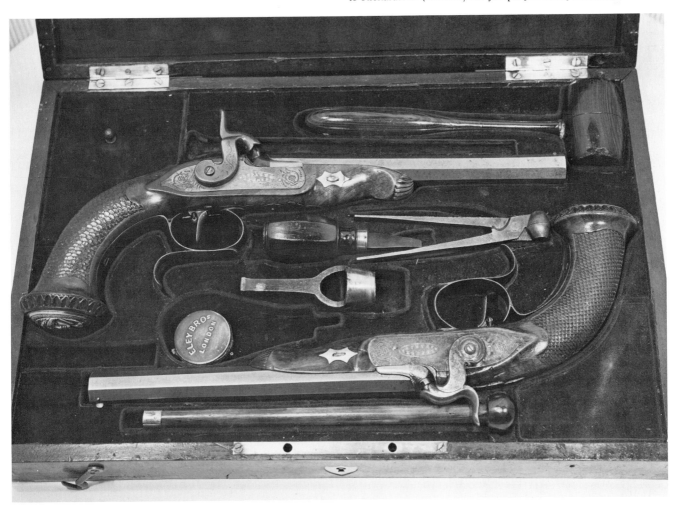

was a small, single barrel shotgun, brass mounted, and of English manufacture, and it was loaded with a ball that looked as though it had been beaten into its spherical shape by hand."[54]

Although some flintlock Northwest guns underwent conversion to the percussion system, and others acquired percussion locks during manufacture, gunmakers continued turning out flintlock trade muskets well into the 1870s. By that time, however, the Indians who used firearms for fighting rather than hunting had found that Northwest guns and muzzle-loading rifles were not nearly as effective as the breechloaders and repeaters that began coming into their hands after the Civil War.

Cut-down Colt M1855 revolving rifle found north of McKenzie, North Dakota on the site of a skirmish between Indians and Gen. H. H. Sibley's troops during his 1863 campaign against the Sioux. (Courtesy State Historical Society of North Dakota).

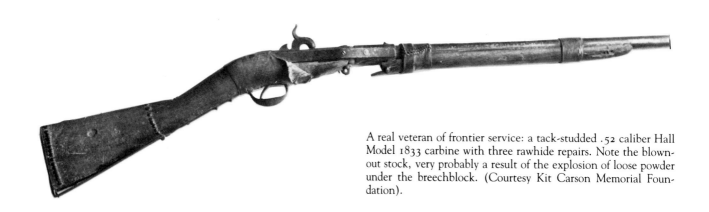

A real veteran of frontier service: a tack-studded .52 caliber Hall Model 1833 carbine with three rawhide repairs. Note the blown-out stock, very probably a result of the explosion of loose powder under the breechblock. (Courtesy Kit Carson Memorial Foundation).

NOTES

CHAPTER 1

1. *American State Papers, Military Affairs* (Washington, 1832–61), 1: 110; cited hereafter as *ASP, MA*. Maj. James E. Hicks, *U.S. Military Firearms, 1776–1956* (1940; reprint ed., La Canada, Cal., 1962), 14. Col. Berkeley R. Lewis, *Small Arms and Ammunition in the United States Service* (Washington, 1956), 49 and pl. 11. Meriwether Lewis, *The Lewis and Clark Expedition* (1814; reprint ed., Philadelphia and New York, 1961), 1: xix.

2. Joe Kindig, Jr., *Thoughts on the Kentucky Rifle in Its Golden Age* (York, Pa., 1960). Henry J. Kauffman, *The Pennsylvania-Kentucky Rifle* (Harrisburg, Pa., 1960), 19 and passim. Capt. John G. W. Dillin, *The Kentucky Rifle* (1924; reprint ed., York, Pa., 1959).

3. *ASP, MA*, 1: 679. Donald Jackson, ed., *Letters of the Lewis and Clark Expedition, with Related Documents, 1783–1854* (Urbana, Ill., 1962), 40, 70–75.

4. Quotation from Hicks, *Military Firearms*, 25. *ASP, MA*, 1: 679; 2: 481.

5. Col. Arcadi Gluckman, *Identifying Old U.S. Muskets, Rifles & Carbines*, rev. ed. (Harrisburg, Pa., 1965), 162–64.

6. Jackson, *Lewis and Clark Letters*, 97–98. Quotation in Hicks, *Military Firearms*, 25.

7. Milo M. Quaife, ed., *The Journals of Captain Meriwether Lewis and Sergeant John Ordway . . .* (Madison, Wis., 1916), 367. Reuben Gold Thwaites, ed., *Original Journals of the Lewis and Clark Expedition* (New York, 1904), 5: 241.

8. Quotation from Stuart E. Brown, Jr., *The Guns of Harper's Ferry* (Berryville, Va., 1968), 32.

9. Thwaites, *Lewis and Clark Journals*, 4: 257; 5: 181; 7: 98.

10. Quotation from Carl P. Russell, *Firearms, Traps, and Tools of the Mountain Men* (New York, 1967), 40.

11. Howard L. Blackmore, *Hunting Weapons* (New York, 1971), 315–24.

12. Quaife, *Lewis and Ordway Journals*, 31.

13. Thwaites, *Lewis and Clark Journals*, 2: 98, 363; 4: 11.

14. Maj. Z[ebulon] M. Pike, *An Account of Expeditions to the Sources of the Mississippi, and through the Western Parts of Louisiana . . .* (1810; reprint ed., Ann Arbor, Mich., 1966), 39.

15. Ibid., 46.

16. *ASP, MA*, 1: 158.

17. Pike, *Account of Expeditions*, 37.

18. Ibid., 53.

19. Ibid., 174.

20. Ibid., 182, 184.

21. *ASP, MA*, 1: 190.

22. Francis Paul Prucha, *The Sword of the Republic* (New York, 1969).

23. *ASP, MA*, 1: 604, 679; 2: 481.

24. Gluckman, *Muskets, Rifles & Carbines*, 162–64. House Doc. 44, 24th Cong., 1st Sess., Serial No. 287.

25. Gluckman, *Muskets, Rifles & Carbines*, 165. Hicks, *Military Firearms*, 41–42, 47.

26. Quotation in Gluckman, *Muskets, Rifles & Carbines*, 405.

27. *ASP, MA*, 2: 481. Gluckman, *Muskets, Rifles & Carbines*, 166–68.

28. House Doc. 47, 16th Cong., 1st Sess., Serial No. 33. *ASP, MA*, 2: 599–608. Senate Ex. Doc. 54, 30th Cong., 1st Sess., Serial No. 509. Gluckman, *Muskets, Rifles & Carbines*, 168–72.

29. R. T. Huntington, *Hall's Breechloaders*, ed. Nancy Bagby (York, Pa., 1972), 5–8, 180—87, 333–38. Claud E. Fuller, *The Breech-Loader in the Service* (1933; reprint ed., New Milford, Conn., 1965), 17–26. [Frank M. Sellers], *The William M. Locke Collection* (East Point, Ga., 1973), 30, 35, 491–92. See also *Niles' Register*, 24 May 1817.

30. Huntington, *Hall's Breechloaders*, 7–10, 350–51.

31. Ibid., 12, 14–16, 271–73. *ASP, MA*, 2: 672, 834; 6: 104–111. House Doc. 47, 16th Cong., 1st Sess., Serial No. 33.

32. No rifles appear in the list of 1818 contracts; see *ASP, MA*, 1: 851–55.

33. Capt. John R. Bell, *The Journal of Captain John R. Bell, official Journalist for the Stephen H. Long Expedition . . .*, ed. Harlin M. Fuller and LeRoy R. Hafen (Glendale, Cal., 1957), 105, 109–110. Edwin James, comp., *Account of an Expedition from Pittsburgh to the Rocky Mountains . . .* (1823; reprint ed., Ann Arbor, Mich., 1966), 1: 451.

34. *ASP, MA*, 2: 507–11. Surgeon John Gale, *The Missouri Expedition, 1818–1820*, ed. Roger L. Nichols (Norman, Okla., 1969), 57.

CHAPTER 2

1. Col. Berkeley R. Lewis, *Small Arms and Ammunition in the United States Service* (Washington, 1956), 85, 109–11. Senate Ex. Doc. 15, 25th Cong., 1st Sess., Serial No. 309.

2. Lewis, *Small Arms and Ammunition*, 107–10.

3. *American State Papers, Military Affairs* (Washington, 1832–61), 1: 45, 55, 110, 304; 2: 499; cited hereafter as *ASP, MA*. Col. Arcadi Gluckman, *Identifying Old U.S. Muskets, Rifles & Carbines*, rev. ed. (Harrisburg, Pa., 1965), 39–42. Maj. James E. Hicks, *U.S. Military Firearms, 1776–1956* (1940; reprint ed., La Canada, Cal., 1962), 14–16. Ordnance returns of the 1795–1820 period usually refer to the U.S. muskets made in those years as "French pattern" or "Charleville pattern" arms, and do not use a model/year designation. In a number of cases, these early model/year designations were coined much later by arms historians and collectors.

4. *ASP, MA*, 1: 110, 120, 130–32. Some of the contracts for this musket were actually let in 1794, a year before Springfield began manufacturing it. For the 1794 contracts, see *ASP, MA*, 1: 65, 110, and Gluckman, *Muskets, Rifles, & Carbines*, 48–49. For the 1798 contracts, see *ASP, MA*, 1: 120; Gluckman, 53–63; and Hicks, *Military Firearms*, 19–23, wherein is reproduced a typical 1798 contract. Some of the 1798 contractors appear in *American State Papers, Finance*, 1: 785–86, 789, 792, 799.

5. Gluckman, *Muskets, Rifles & Carbines*, 51–53. *ASP, MA*, 1: 199, 256, 679; 2: 481.

6. Gluckman, *Muskets, Rifles & Carbines*, 62–63. Hicks, *Military Firearms*, 19–20, 42–43. *ASP, MA*, 1: 679–80; 2: 478, 481.

7. Donald Jackson, ed., *Letters of the Lewis and Clark Expedition, with Related Documents, 1789–1854* (Urbana, Ill., 1962), 97. Reuben Gold Thwaites, ed., *Original Journals of the Lewis and Clark Expedition* (New York, 1904), 2: 143; 5: 342. Milo M. Quaife, ed., *The Journals of Captain Meriwether Lewis and Sergeant John Ordway . . .* (Madison, Wis., 1916), 382.

8. *ASP, MA*, 1: 190. Clarence Edwin Carter, comp. and ed., *The Territorial Papers of the United States* (Washington, 1934–62), 14: 146.

9. Donald Jackson, ed., *The Journals of Zebulon Montgomery Pike, with Letters and Related Documents* (Norman, Okla., 1966), 1: 53. Major Z[ebulon] M. Pike, *An Account of Expeditions to the Sources of the Mississippi and through the Western Parts of Louisiana . . .* (1810; reprint ed., Ann Arbor, Mich., 1966), 148.

10. Jackson, *Pike Journals*, 1: 102, 365.

11. John N. George, *English Guns and Rifles* (Plantersville, S.C., 1947), 223–26 and pl. 15.

12. *ASP, MA*, 1: 158. Quaife, *Lewis and Ordway Journals*, 220. Bernard De Voto, ed., *The Journals of Lewis and Clark* (Boston, 1953), 150. Thwaites, *Lewis and Clark Journals*, vol. 5, 391.

13. Pike, *Account of Expeditions*, 2, 8, 15, 23.

14. *ASP, MA*, 1: 328. Hicks, *Military Firearms*, 31–36; a typical 1808 contract is reproduced on 33–34. Gluckman,

Muskets, Rifles & Carbines, 83–85. Older texts on the subject tend to regard this musket as a new model, but more recent texts do not. Considerable correspondence pertaining to the 1808 contracts is in the records of the Bolton Gun Works, Microfilm reel 1, J. J. Henry Papers, Eleutherian Mills Historical Library, Wilmington, Del.

15. Hicks, *Military Firearms*, 39–41. *ASP, MA*, 2: 481, 505. Gluckman, *Muskets, Rifles & Carbines*, 103–7.

16. *ASP, MA*, 2: 523–24.

17. Ibid., 2: 481. Gluckman, *Muskets, Rifles & Carbines*, 115–22, 405. Hicks, *Military Firearms*, 49–50.

18. *ASP, MA*, 2: 481. Gluckman, *Muskets, Rifles & Carbines*, 115–16.

19. Capt. John R. Bell, *The Journal of Captain John R. Bell, Official Journalist for the Stephen H. Long Expedition . . .*, ed. Harlin M. Fuller and LeRoy R. Hafen (Glendale, Cal., 1957), 105. Edwin James, comp., *Account of an Expedition from Pittsburgh to the Rocky Mountains . . .* (1823; reprint ed., Ann Arbor, Mich., 1966), 1: 451. *ASP, MA*, 2: 478, 481, 505, 507.

CHAPTER 3

1. Samuel E. Smith, "The Single Shot Martial Pistols of the U.S.," in James E. Serven, ed., *The Collecting of Guns* (Harrisburg, Pa., 1964), 106–7.

2. Ibid. 108. Maj. James E. Hicks, *U.S. Military Firearms, 1776–1956* (1940; reprint ed., La Canada, Cal., 1962), 23–25. See also *American State Papers, Finance*, 1: 792.

3. Donald Jackson, ed., *Letters of the Lewis and Clark Expedition, with Related Documents, 1783–1854* (Urbana, Ill., 1962), 91, 97. Reuben Gold Thwaites, ed., *Original Journals of the Lewis and Clark Expedition* (New York, 1904), 4: 336.

4. Thwaites, *Lewis and Clark Journals*, 5: 223–34.

5. Mrs. Dunbar Rowland, ed., *Life, Letters and Papers of William Dunbar* (Jackson, Miss., 1930), 249.

6. Major Z[ebulon] M. Pike, *An Account of Expeditions to the Sources of the Mississippi and through the Western Parts of Louisiana . . .* (1810; reprint ed., Ann Arbor, Mich., 1966), 57.

7. Hicks, *Military Firearms*, 26. Smith, "Single Shot Martial Pistols," 109. *American State Papers, Military Affairs* (Washington, 1832–61), 1: 190, 679; 2: 481; cited hereafter as *ASP, MA*. Maj. Arcadi Gluckman, *United States Martial Pistols and Revolvers* (Buffalo, N.Y., 1944), 39–40.

8. Pike, *Account of Expeditions*, 174.

9. Smith, "Single Shot Martial Pistols," 106, 108–9. Hicks, *Military Firearms*, 29–30.

10. Smith, "Single Shot Martial Pistols," 109. Hicks, *Military Firearms*, 36–39. *ASP, MA*, 2: 481.

11. Hicks, *Military Firearms*, 44–46. Smith, "Single Shot Martial Pistols," 107, 109.

12. Gluckman, *Pistols and Revolvers*, 47–49. Hicks, *Military Firearms*, 45.

13. Quotation from Col. Arcadi Gluckman, *Identifying Old U.S. Muskets, Rifles & Carbines*, rev. ed. (Harrisburg, Pa., 1965), 406.

14. Hicks, *Military Firearms*, 57. Smith, "Single Shot Martial Pistols," 110.

15. Smith, "Single Shot Martial Pistols," 107, 110–11. Hicks, *Military Firearms*, 27–29. ASP, MA, 2: 478, 507.

16. Smith, "Single Shot Martial Pistols," 110–11. ASP, MA, 2: 481, 532–33, 573. Gluckman, *Pistols and Revolvers*, 56–57. Hicks, *Military Firearms*, 59–60. House Doc. 47, 16th Cong., 1st Sess., Serial No. 33. Capt. John R. Bell, *The Journal of Captain John R. Bell, Official Journalist for the Stephen H. Long Expedition . . .*, ed. Harlin M. Fuller and LeRoy R. Hafen (Glendale, Cal., 1957), 105. Edwin James, comp., *Account of an Expedition from Pittsburgh to the Rocky Mountains . . .* (1823; reprint ed., Ann Arbor, Mich., 1966), 1: 451.

CHAPTER 4

1. Washington Irving, *The Adventures of Captain Bonneville* (Norman, Okla., 1961), 360–61. See also the reminiscences of George Yount, in *California Historical Society Quarterly*, April 1923: 30.

2. Donald Chaput, "The Samopal Rifle," *The Gun Report*, June 1974: 34–37.

3. Ledgers of Bryan & Morrison, 1803–1810, microfilm reels 26 and 27, Pierre Menard Papers, Illinois State Historical Library, Springfield, Ill. Joe Kindig, Jr., *Thoughts on the Kentucky Rifle in Its Golden Age* (York, Pa., 1960). Henry J. Kauffman, *The Pennsylvania-Kentucky Rifle* (Harrisburg, Pa., 1960), 19 and *passim*. Capt. John G. W. Dillin, *The Kentucky Rifle* (1924; reprint ed., York, Pa., 1959). Daniel E. Hartzler, *Arms Makers of Maryland* (York, Pa., 1977), 142, 145. Alexander Ross, *Adventures of the First Settlers on the Oregon or Columbia River* (1849; reprint ed., Ann Arbor, Mich., 1966), 224. Carl P. Russell, *Firearms, Traps, and Tools of the Mountain Men* (New York, 1967), 55–56. A good example of Creamer's work has a .50 caliber octagon barrel, 44⁷/₁₆ in. long, and raised scroll carving on the stock; see *Muzzle Blasts*, May 1969, p. 2.

4. Little Rock *Arkansas Gazette*, 11 Dec. 1819.

5. Dillin, *The Kentucky Rifle*.

6. N. Bosworth, *A Treatise on the Rifle, Musket, Pistol, and Fowling-Piece* (1846; reprint ed., Huntington, W. Va., n.d.), 19,40. Ross, *The First Settlers*, 198. *American Turf Register and Sporting News*, Oct. 1831: 66–67. See also Maria R. Audubon, ed., *Audubon and His Journals* (New York, 1899), 2: 460–62.

7. Quotation from Alexander Ross, *The Fur Hunters of the Far West* (Norman, Okla., 1956), 212. LeRoy R. Hafen and Ann W. Hafen, eds., *Rufus B. Sage: His Letters and Papers, 1836–1847* (Glendale, Cal., 1956), 1: 184.

8. Charles E. Hanson, Jr., *The Plains Rifle* (Harrisburg, Pa., 1960), 5–8.

9. Pierre Menard Business Papers, 1774–1825, microfilm reel 11, Menard Papers. Charles E. Hanson, Jr., *The Hawken Rifle: Its Place in History* (Chadron, Neb., 1979), 73. John E. Parsons, "Gunmakers for the American Fur Company," *New York Historical Society Quarterly*, April 1952: 182.

10. Photostat in Kauffman, the *Pennsylvania-Kentucky Rifle*, 148. Memo of 31 Dec. 1830, Bolton Gun Works Records, microfilm reel 1, J. J. Henry Papers, Eleutherian Mills Historical Library, Wilmington, Del. Parsons, "American Fur Company," 184–86. *Spirit of the Times*, 27 Oct. 1832.

11. Astor to Henry, 6 Oct. 1825, microfilm reel 1, Henry Papers.

12. Memo of 31 Dec. 1830, microfilm reel 9, Henry Papers.

13. Am. Fur Co. order of 20 Oct. 1832, microfilm reel 9, Henry Papers.

14. *American Turf Register*, April 1833: 411.

15. Am. Fur Co. order of 12 Sept. 1833, microfilm reel 9, Henry Papers.

16. Parsons, "American Fur Company," 182, 186–88. James Austin Hanson and Kathryn J. Wilson, *The Mountain Man's Sketch Book* (Canyon, Tex., 1976), 1: 43. Quotation in Carl P. Russell, *Guns on the Early Frontiers* (Berkeley and Los Angeles, 1957), 319. Hanson, *The Hawken Rifle*, 66–67.

17. Sites order of 18 July 1835, microfilm reel 9, and Holmes-Swanwick letter of 4 Sept. 1838, microfilm reel 2, Henry Papers.

18. Charles Z. Tryon, *The History of a Business Established One Hundred Years Ago* (Philadelphia, 1911). James E. Serven, "Tryon Gunmaking Firm Grew with the Nation," *American Rifleman*, Dec. 1970: 38–42. Tryon order of Jan 1818, microfilm reel 9, Henry Papers. Senate Doc. 512, 23rd Cong., 1st Sess., Serials No. 244 and No. 248. House Doc. 174, 25th Cong., 2nd Sess., Serial No. 327.

19. Jocelyn, Darling & Co.'s *American Advertising Directory For Manufacturers and Dealers*, 1832. *American Turf Register*, May 1837: 409. Hanson and Wilson, *Mountain Man's Sketch Book*, 48. Quotation in Hanson, *The Hawken Rifle*, 79.

20. Serven, "Tryon Gunmaking Firm," 39.

21. Hanson, *The Plains Rifle*, 26, 43, 78. Russell, *Guns on the Early Frontiers*, 131, 134, 139–41. Frank M. Sellers, *American Gunsmiths: A Source Book* (Highland Park, N.J., 1983). Kauffman, *The Pennsylvania-Kentucky Rifle*, 123 and *passim*. See also Col. Robert E. Gardner, *Small Arms Makers* (New York, 1963), 75. Hanson and Wilson, *Mountain Man's Sketch Book*, 1: 48.

22. Item WR-13. For a description of the rifle that Davy Crockett supposedly took to Texas, see James Wilson Nichols, *Now You Hear My Horn*, ed. Catherine W. McDowell (Austin, 1967), 13–14.

23. Paxton's *New Orleans Directory & Register*, 1822. See also the St. Charles *Missourian*, 24 June 1820 and 27 June 1821. Hanson, *The Plains Rifle*, 51–52. Frederic L. Billon, *The Annals of St. Louis in Its Territorial Days* (St. Louis, 1888), 155. *American State Papers, Indian Affairs* (Washington, 1832–34), 2: 290–93. St. Louis *Enquirer*, 14 April 1819. Solomon Migneron may have been related to François Migneron, who, in partnership with Andrew Lauderville, was a St. Louis gunsmith even before 1800. See *Outposts of the Mississippi* (1799?), cited in Sellers, *American Gunsmiths*.

24. Hanson, *The Hawken Rifle*, 7–10, 85, 92–93. Amer-

ican State Papers, Indian Affairs, 2: 293. "The Old Gun-maker," clipping from the St. Louis *Globe-Democrat*, c. 1882, Jacob and Samuel Hawken Papers, Missouri Historical Society, St. Louis, Mo.: cited hereafter as "Hawken interview."

25. Quotation in Dale L. Morgan, ed., *The West of William H. Ashley* (Denver, 1964), 9.

26. "Hawken interview." Quotations in Morgan, *William H. Ashley*, 198. Hanson, *The Plains Rifle*, 40.

27. Hanson, *The Hawken Rifle*, 31. Capt. James Hobbs, *Wild Life in the Far West* (1872; reprint ed., Glorieta, N.M., 1969), 22. "Hawken interview."

28. Orders to the Bolton Gun Works, microfilm reel 9, Henry Papers. George Frederick Ruxton, *Life in the Far West*, ed. LeRoy R. Hafen (Norman, Okla., 1951), 54–55. See also note 11 above.

29. Hanson, *The Plains Rifle*, 37–38, 42–43, 111. Zenas Leonard, *Narrative of the Adventures of Zenas Leonard* (1839; reprint ed., Ann Arbor, Mich., 1966), 4. Clyde and Mae Reed Porter, comps., *Matt Field on the Santa Fe Trail*, ed. John E. Sunder (Norman, Okla., 1960), 172–74.

30. Hanson, *The Plains Rifle*, 37–38.

31. Lewis Winant, *Early Percussion Firearms* (New York, 1959), 7, 32–50. House Rpt. 53, 28th Cong., 2nd Sess., Serial No. 468. Howard L. Blackmore, *Guns and Rifles of the World* (New York, 1965), 46–47. Quotation in Robert Held, *The Age of Firearms* (New York, 1957), 175. *Arkansas Gazette*, 25 Jan. and 5 Dec. 1832. Crooks to Henry, 30 March 1830, microfilm reel 2, Henry Papers.

32. Martin Ridge and Ray Allen Billington, *America's Frontier Story* (New York, 1969), 479. George W. Kendall, *Narrative of an Expedition across the Great South-Western Prairies . . .* (1845; reprint ed., Ann Arbor, Mich., 1966), 1: 57.

33. Quotation in Russell, *Guns on the Early Frontiers*, 332. F. G. Young, ed., *The Correspondence and Journals of Captain Nathaniel J. Wyeth, 1831–1836* (1899; reprint ed., New York, 1973), 238. Osborne Russell, *Journal of a Trapper*, ed. Aubrey L. Haines (Lincoln, Neb., 1965), 66. Lt. Col. Peter Hawker, *Instructions to Young Sportsmen . . .* (Philadelphia, 1846), 412–13. Josiah Gregg, *Commerce of the Prairies*, ed. Max L. Moorhead (Norman, Okla., 1954), 321–22.

34. "Invoice of Goods receiv'd . . . from Liverpool," Dec. 1818, microfilm reel 9, Henry Papers. Quotation from Held, *The Age of Firearms*, 157.

35. Ledgers of Pierre Menard, 1820–25, microfilm reel 18, Menard Papers. See notes 11 and 17 above. Quotation in Hanson, *The Hawken Rifle*, 75.

36. "Columbia Inventory for Outfit," 1823, Hudson's Bay Company Archives, B.239/aa/6, 189, Hudson's Bay Co., Beaver House, London. Frederick Merk, ed., *Fur Trade and Empire: George Simpson's Journal* (Cambridge, Mass., 1931), 173. Marvin C. Ross, ed., *The West of Alfred Jacob Miller, 1837*, rev. ed. (Norman, Okla., 1968), 02.

37. John N. George, *English Guns and Rifles* (Plantersville, S.C., 1947), pl. 11. W. Keith Neal and D. H. L. Back, *The Mantons: Gunmakers* (New York, 1966), pl. 30.

Orders to the Bolton Gun Works, fall 1831 and summer 1836, microfilm reel 9, Henry Papers. *American Turf Register*, April 1833: 414. See also William Fraser Tolmie's journal, in *Washington Historical Quarterly*, July 1912: 240.

38. Hanson, *The Plains Rifle*, 41–42. *Museum of the Fur Trade Quarterly*, Winter 1969: 1. John D. Baird, *Hawken Rifles, The Mountain Man's Choice* (Franklin, Ind., 1968).

39. Based largely on the authors' survey of existing Hawken rifles. See also works cited above.

40. Hanson, *The Plains Rifle*, 41–42. W. T. Hamilton, *My Sixty Years on the Plains* (Norman, Okla., 1960), 72. Russell, *Firearms, Traps, and Tools*, 90–92.

41. Quotations in Hanson, *The Plains Rifle*, 52–53.

42. St. Louis *Missouri Argus*, 15 May 1835. Hanson, *The Hawken Rifle*, 17.

43. Hanson, *The Plains Rifle*, 31, 44, 75–77. Quincy (Ill.), *Whig*, 7 Dec. 1839. Col. Arcadi Gluckman and L. D. Satterlee, *American Gun Makers* (Harrisburg, Pa., 1953), 123–24. Leman letterhead ("Established 1834"), and Ewing to Henry, 24 Oct. 1848, microfilm reel 2, Henry Papers. House Doc. 174, Serial No. 327. Quotations in Russell, *Guns on the Early Frontiers*, 321. Gardner, *Small Arms Makers*, 115. Jackson Arms (Dallas, Tex.) Catalog 18, item 426.

44. Herschel C. Logan, *The Pictorial History of the Underhammer Gun* (New York, 1960). Marius B. Peladeau, "Underhammer Firearms," *American Rifleman*, April 1966: 23–25. See also Nichols, *Now You Hear My Horn*, 23.

45. Photostat in Hanson, *The Hawken Rifle*, 77.

46. Albright order of July, 1847, microfilm reel 9, Henry Papers. Senate Ex. Doc. 54, 30th Cong., 1st Sess., Serial No. 509. Senate Ex. Doc. 43, 29th Cong., 1st Sess., Serial No. 472. Gregg, *Commerce of the Prairies*, 342.

47. Alvan Clark essay, in *American Repertory of the Arts, Sciences, and Useful Manufactures*, April 1841: 164–69; also in *Spirit of the Times*, 24 April 1841. U.S. Patent No. 1565 of 24 April 1840.

48. Clark, in *American Repertory*, 167.

49. Ibid. 168. Ned H. Roberts, *The Muzzle Loading Cap Lock Rifle* (1944; reprint ed., Harrisburg, Pa., 1958), 15.

50. Clark, in *American Repertory*, 167–68.

51. Quotation in Charles T. Haven and Frank A. Belden, *A History of the Colt Revolver* (New York, 1940), 293. Edwin Wesson Order Book, 1839–1847, Edwin Wesson Papers, Connecticut Historical Society, Hartford, Conn.

52. Young, *Wyeth's Correspondence and Journals*, 113. Irving, Smith & Hyslop orders of 1818 and 1819, and Jos. Cooper orders, 1830–37, microfilm reel 9, and Ewing to Henry, 18 Jan. 1843, microfilm reel 2, Henry Papers. Quotation in Hanson, *The Hawken Rifle*, 71.

53. *American Turf Register*, August 1844: 502.

54. Hanson, *The Hawken Rifle*, 70, 72. *Arkansas State Gazette*, 25 March 1840.

55. Kendall, *Narrative of an Expedition*, 1: 22, 203. Hanson, *The Hawken Rifle*, 37, 72.

56. Letter from Carl A. Ray, Mississippi State Department of Archives and History, to the authors, 3 May 1974. *Mississippi Free Trader and Natchez Gazette*, 2 Oct. 1845.

Hanson, *The Plains Rifle*, 47, 87, 112. Jackson Arms (Dallas, Tex.) Catalog 18, item 376.

57. Monterey *Californian*, 15 March 1848.

58. Russell, *Guns on the Early Frontiers*, 73–75. Letter from Dale Archibald, Oregon Historical Society, to the authors, 31 August 1973.

59. Burlington *Hawk Eye*, 4 Jan. 1844. James J. Webb, *Adventures in the Santa Fe Trade*, ed. Ralph P. Bieber (Glendale, Cal., 1931), 116–17.

60. Lewis H. Garrard, *Wah-To-Yah and the Taos Trail* (Norman, Okla., 1966), 233.

61. Senate Doc. 229, 26th Cong., 2nd Sess., Serial No. 378.

62. George, *English Guns and Rifles*, 278–81.

63. Hawker, *Instructions to Young Sportsmen*, 29. John Palliser, Esq., *Solitary Rambles and Adventures of a Hunter in the Prairies* (London, 1853), vii.

64. Albright orders of 2 Nov. 1844 and 19 Dec. 1846, microfilm reel 9, and Albright to Henry, 16 July 1848, microfilm reel 2, Henry Papers.

65. Quotation in Hanson, *The Hawken Rifle*, 33. François des Montaignes, "The Plains," *Western Journal and Civilian*, Sept. 1853: 442.

66. William Elsey Connelley, ed., *Doniphan's Expedition and the Conquest of New Mexico and California* (Kansas City, 1907), 388. Garrard, *Wah-To-Yah*, 118. George Douglas Brewerton, *Overland with Kit Carson* (New York, 1930), 184. James B. Marsh, *Four Years in the Rockies* (Newcastle, Pa., 1884), 41.

67. Quotation in Dale L. Morgan, *Jedediah Smith and the Opening of the West* (New York, 1953), 241. David H. Coyner, *The Lost Trappers* (Cincinnati, 1859), 107–8.

68. James Ripley Jacobs, *The Beginning of the U.S. Army, 1783–1812* (Princeton, N.J., 1947), 135. *Spirit of the Times*, 15 Sept. 1838.

69. Dillin, *The Kentucky Rifle*, 50–51 and pls. 39, 72. *American Turf Register*, April 1833: 415. Russell, *Journal of a Trapper*, 88. *California Historical Society Quarterly*, April 1923: 47. Randolph B. Marcy, *Thirty Years of Army Life on the Border* (1866; reprint ed., Philadelphia and New York, 1963), 390.

70. Francis Parkman, *The Oregon Trail*, ed. E. N. Feltskog (Madison, Wis., 1969), 357. Reuben Gold Thwaites, ed., *Early Western Travels, 1748–1846* (Cleveland, 1904–7), 8: 103. *Spirit of the Times*, 27 Jan. and 3 Feb. 1838. Baron de Berenger, *Helps and Hints How to Protect Life and Property* (London, 1835), 90–91.

71. Dillin, *The Kentucky Rifle*, 50–51. For a description of a common loading procedure, see *Audubon and His Journals*, 2: 492.

72. Ross, *The Fur Hunters*, 29, 38.

73. Thwaites, *Early Western Travels*, 21: 217–18. Frederick Gerstaecker, *Wild Sports in the Far West* (Boston, 1866), 125. Quotation in Hanson, *The Plains Rifle*, 55.

74. Ruxton, *Life in the Far West*, 10. Parkman, *The Oregon Trail*, 29, 39.

75. Palliser, *Solitary Rambles*, ix–x.

76. Clyde and Mae Reed Porter, comps., *Ruxton of the Rockies*, ed. LeRoy R. Hafen (Norman, Okla., 1950), 83. Ruxton, *Life in the Far West*, 10.

77. George Frederick Ruxton, *Adventures in Mexico and the Rocky Mountains* (1847; reprint ed., Glorieta, N.M., 1973), 264–65.

78. Grant Foreman, *Marcy and the Gold Seekers . . .* (Norman, Okla., 1939), 6–7.

79. [Frank M. Sellers], *The William M. Locke Collection* (East Point, Ga., 1973), 488, 491. U.S. pats. 1461, of 31 Dec. 1839 and 1810, of 8 Oct. 1840. *Spirit of the Times*, 5 Feb. 1842. U.S. pat 747, of 25 May 1838. Claud E. Fuller, *The Breech-Loader in the Service, 1816–1917* (1933; reprint ed., New Milford, Conn., 1965), 63–71. Senate Misc. Doc. 9, 30th Cong., 2nd Sess., Serial No. 533. See also Heinrich Leinhard, *From St. Louis to Sutter's Fort, 1846*, trans. and ed. Erwin G. and Elizabeth K. Gudde (Norman, Okla., 1961), 34.

80. Joseph Milton Nance, *After San Jacinto: The Texas-Mexican Frontier, 1836–1841* (Austin, 1963), 93. Michael J. Koury, *Arms for Texas* (Ft. Collins, Colo., 1973), 52–58, 76.

81. Robert M. Reilly, *United States Military Small Arms, 1816–1865* (Baton Rouge, La., 1970), 136–39. Senate Misc. Doc. 9, Serial No. 533. Andrew F. Lustyik, "Jenks Carbine—Gun with a Jinx," *American Rifleman*, April 1969: 18–20.

82. *Niles' Register*, 31 Dec. 1814. *American State Papers, Military Affairs* (Washington, 1832–61), 4: 187, 302, 616. See also Lt. Col. B. R. Lewis, "The First U.S. Repeaters," *American Rifleman*, Dec. 1949: 38–42.

83. Quotation in Russell, *Guns on the Early Frontiers*, 308. House Doc. 50, 21st Cong., 2nd Sess., Serial No. 207. Frank M. Sellers and Samuel E. Smith, *American Percussion Revolvers* (Ottawa, 1971), 101–5.

84. Ibid. 102–3.

85. U.S. pat. 9430X of 25 Feb. 1836; reproduced in Haven and Belden, *The Colt Revolver*, 541–48.

86. William B. Edwards, *The Story of Colt's Revolver* (Harrisburg, Pa., 1953), 58–63. James E. Serven, *Colt Firearms from 1836* (Harrisburg, Pa., 1979), 298–313. U.S. pat. 1304 of 29 Aug. 1839.

87. Edwards, *Colt's Revolver*, 58–63. Serven, *Colt Firearms*, 298–313, 324. James Henry to P. Lawton, 9 Aug. 1839, microfilm reel 9, Henry Papers. Senate Doc. 196, 26th Cong., 2nd Sess., Serial No. 378.

88. Edwards, *Colt's Revolver*, 77. Serven, *Colt Firearms*, 316–24.

89. *Spirit of the Times*, 7 July 1838. These prices soon dropped to more reasonable levels; see *Spirit of the Times*, 15 Sept. 1838. Senate Doc. 29, 25th Cong., 1st Sess., Serial No. 309.

90. New Orleans *Picayune*, 1 Feb. and 28 March 1838.

91. Gregg, *Commerce of the Prairies*, 229. Edwards, *Colt's Revolver*, 93–101. Quotations in Haven and Belden, *Colt Revolver*, 304, 309. Koury, *Arms for Texas*, 29–38.

92. Nance, *After San Jacinto*, 93. Koury, *Arms For Texas*, 40–41.

93. *Missouri Republican*, 9 Feb. and 1 March 1841. Ken-

dall, *Narrative of an Expedition*, 1: 203. See also quotation in Hanson, *The Hawken Rifle*, 78, and Parsons, "American Fur Company," 192.

94. Edwards, *Colt's Revolver*, 127–36.

95. U.S. pat. 188, of 28 April 1837. Russell, *Guns on the Early Frontiers*, 78–80. Sellers, *The Locke Collection*, 422, 485–86. Serial No. 309.

96. Senate Doc. 29, Serial No. 309.

97. *Mechanics' Magazine* (N.Y.), Sept. 1836, Jan. 1837, and April 1837; *Spirit of the Times*, 5 Nov. 1836; *American Turf Register*, Dec. 1836: 170, Jan. 1837: 225. A. W. F. Taylerson, R. A. N. Andrews and J. Frith, *The Revolver, 1818–1865* (New York, 1968), 295 and pl. 32.

98. Hanson, *The Hawken Rifle*, 76. Gregg, *Commerce of the Prairies*, 325. Nichols, *Now You Hear My Horn*, 64–65. Gen. Thomas J. Green, *Journal of the Texian Expedition against Mier . . .* (New York, 1845), 83.

99. U.S. pat 707, of 24 April 1838. Sellers and Smith, *American Percussion Revolvers*, 111–13.

100. Sellers and Smith, *American Percussion Revolvers*, 111–13. Quotation in Hanson, *The Hawken Rifle*, 80.

101. Edwin Bryant, *What I Saw in California . . . 1846–47* (Santa Ana, Cal., 1936), 146–47.

102. Photostat in Hanson, *The Hawken Rifle*, 77. Logan, *The Underhammer Gun*, 184–85, 188–89.

103. John Browning and Curt Gentry, *John M. Browning, American Gunmaker* (Garden City, N.Y., 1964), 9–10, 225.

104. Ibid. "Diary of the Mormon Battalion Mission," John D. Lee, ed. Juanita Brooks, *New Mexico Historical Review*, July 1967: 185, 189. William Clayton, *William Clayton's Journal* (1921; reprint ed., New York, 1973), 119.

105. Browning and Gentry, *John M. Browning*, 19, 226. Sellers and Smith, *American Percussion Revolvers*, 21.

106. Sellers and Smith, *American Percussion Revolvers*, 21.

107. LeRoy R. Hafen and Ann W. Hafen, eds., *Fremont's Fourth Expedition* (Glendale, Cal., 1960), 183.

CHAPTER 5

1. Washington Irving, *The Adventures of Captain Bonneville*, ed. Edgeley W. Todd (Norman, Okla., 1961), 19. Washington Irving, *A Tour on the Prairies*, ed. John Francis McDermott (Norman, Okla., 1956), 67. Josiah Gregg, *Commerce of the Prairies*, ed. Max L. Moorhead (Norman, Okla., 1954), 33.

2. John George, *English Guns and Rifles* (Plantersville, S.C., 1947), 187–220. Robert Held, *The Age of Firearms* (New York, 1957), 136–37, 159–61.

3. Quotation in Col. Arcadi Gluckman, *Identifying Old U.S. Muskets, Rifles, and Carbines*, rev. ed. (Harrisburg, Pa., 1965), 77. *Museum of the Fur Trade Quarterly*, Summer 1975: 10–11, Fall 1979: 5–11.

4. John Palliser, Esq., *Solitary Rambles and Adventures of a Hunter in the Prairies* (London, 1853), viii–ix. Ledgers of Bryan & Morrison, 1812, microfilm reel 27, Pierre Menard Papers, Illinois State Historical Library, Springfield, Ill.

Quotation in Carl P. Russell, *Guns on the Early Frontiers* (Berkeley and Los Angeles, 1957), 135, 232–33. Capt. John G. W. Dillin, *The Kentucky Rifle* (1924; reprint ed., York, Pa., 1959), 40, 71 and pl. 80. Quotations in Charles E. Hanson, Jr., *The Plains Rifle* (Harrisburg, Pa., 1960), 8, 36. *Museum of the Fur Trade Quarterly*, Fall 1979: 10.

5. George, *English Guns and Rifles*, 223–26. Held, *The Age of Firearms*, 102–4.

6. John E. Parsons, "Gunmakers for the American Fur Company," *New York Historical Society Quarterly*, April 1952: 192.

7. H. M. Brackenridge, *Views of Louisiana . . .* (1814; reprint ed., Ann Arbor, Mich., 1966), 201.

8. John Bradbury, *Travels in the Interior of America . . .* (1817; reprint ed., Ann Arbor, Mich., 1966), 27–28. Ross Cox, *The Columbia River*, ed. Edgar I. Stewart and Jane R. Stewart (Norman, Okla., 1957), 94.

9. Alexander Ross, *Adventures of the First Settlers on the Oregon or Columbia River* (1849; reprint ed., Ann Arbor, Mich., 1966), 84. House Doc. 45, 17th Cong., 2nd Sess., Serial No. 78. Alexander Ross, *The Fur Hunters of the Far West*, ed. Kenneth A. Spaulding (Norman, Okla., 1956), 146, 240. Russell, *Guns on the Early Frontiers*, 65–67. Kaskaskia (Ill.) *Western Intelligencer*, 5 Aug. 1818. See also Frederick Merk, ed., *Fur Trade and Empire; George Simpson's Journal* (Cambridge, Mass., 1931), 60.

10. T. D. Bonner, *The Life and Adventures of James P. Beckwourth* (New York, 1858), 77, 79. Gregg, *Commerce of the Prairies*, 33. See also Capt. James Hobbs, *Wild Life in the Far West* (1872; reprint ed., Glorieta, N.M., 1969), 73.

11. Maurice S. Sullivan, *The Travels of Jedediah Smith* (Santa Ana, Cal., 1934), 78, 128.

12. Summary in David Lavender, *Bent's Fort* (Garden City, N.Y., 1954), 126.

13. Clark's Report of 1830, in *Oregon Historical Quarterly*, March 1947: 31–32.

14. Charles Larpenteur, *Forty Years a Fur Trader on the Upper Missouri* (Chicago, 1933), 67–69. See also Maria R. Audubon, ed., *Aububon and His Journals* (New York, 1899), 2: 181, 191.

15. Joseph Milton Nance, *Attack and Counter-Attack* (Austin, 1964), 598–621. See also Sidney B. Brinckerhoff and Pierce A. Chamberlain, *Spanish Military Weapons in Colonial America, 1700–1821* (Harrisburg, Pa., 1972).

16. George Douglas Brewerton, *Overland with Kit Carson* (New York, 1930), 59–60. Albert Pike, *Prose Sketches and Poems Written in the Western Country*, ed. David J. Weber (Albuquerque, N.M., 1967), 243. Gregg, *Commerce of the Prairies*, 155. Senate Ex. Doc. 54, 30th Cong., 1st Sess., Serial No. 509.

17. Michael J. Koury, *Arms for Texas* (Ft. Collins, Co., 1973), 12–19. Joseph Milton Nance, *After San Jacinto: The Texas-Mexican Frontier, 1836–1841* (Austin, 1963), 92. House Ex. Doc. 46, 29th Cong, 2nd Sess., Serial No. 499. Senate Ex. Doc. 43, 29th Cong., 1st Sess., Serial No. 472.

18. Gen. Thomas J. Green, *Journal of the Texian Expedition against Mier . . .* (New York, 1845), 87. See also J.

C. Duval, *Early Times In Texas* (Austin, Tex., 1892), 41–42.

19. Donald Jackson and Mary Lee Spence, eds., *The Expeditions of John Charles Fremont* (Urbana, Ill., 1970–73), 1: 40–42.

20. Charles E. Hanson, Jr., *The Hawken Rifle: Its Place in History* (Chadron, Neb., 1979), 75–80.

21. George W. Kendall, *Narrative of an Expedition across the Great South-Western Prairies . . .* (1845; reprint ed., Ann Arbor, Mich., 1966), 1: 247.

22. W. T. Hamilton, *My Sixty Years on the Plains* (Norman, Okla., 1960), 30, 93, 95. John Charles Fremont, *Report of the Exploring Expedition to the Rocky Mountains* (1845; reprint ed., Ann Arbor, Mich., 1966), 24. See also Duval, *Early Times In Texas*, 52–53.

23. Francis Parkman, *The Oregon Trail*, ed. E. N. Feltskog (Madison, Wis., 1969), 11–12, 359.

24. Palliser, *Solitary Rambles*, viii–ix.

25. *American Turf Register*, Dec. 1829: 181–82. [John Deane], *Deane's Manual of the History and Science of Firearms* (1858; reprint ed., Huntington, W.Va., n.d.), 149–51.

26. "Captain Flack," *The Texan Rifle-Hunter* (London, 1866), 34–35.

27. Quotation in Hanson, *The Plains Rifle*, 55. *Oregon Spectator*, 4 May 1848. George Frederick Ruxton, *Adventures in Mexico and the Rocky Mountains* (1847; reprint ed., Glorieta, N.M., 1973), 28.

28. Ewing to Henry, 24 Oct. 1848, Bolton Gun Works Records, microfilm reel 2, J. J. Henry Papers, Eleutherian Mills Historical Library, Wilmington, Del.

CHAPTER 6

1. Geoffrey Boothroyd, *The Handgun* (New York, 1970), 24–55. Norm Flayderman, *Flayderman's Guide to Antique American Firearms*, 2nd ed. (Northfield, Ill., 1980), 294–303, 539–42. [Frank M. Sellers], *The William M. Locke Collection* (East Point, Ga., 1973), 405–20 and *passim*. John A. Atkinson, *Duelling Pistols* (Harrisburg, Pa., 1966). W. Keith Neal, *Collecting Duelling Pistols* (London and Ontario, 1973). Robert Held, *The Age of Firearms* (New York, 1957), 97, 162–63, 165. J. H. Walsh, *The Modern Sportsman's Gun and Rifle* (London, 1882–84), 2: 444. W. Keith Neal and D. H. L. Back, *The Mantons: Gunmakers* (New York, 1966), pls. 23, 24, 27, 80.

2. *Museum of the Fur Trade Quarterly*, Summer 1975: 1–2. Ledgers of Bryan & Morrison, 1809–1810, microfilm reel 27, Pierre Menard Papers, Illinois State Historical Library, Springfield, Ill. H. M. Brackenridge, *Recollections of Persons and Places in the West*, 2nd ed. (Philadelphia, 1868), 263. H. M. Brackenridge, *Views of Louisiana . . .* (1814; reprint ed., Ann Arbor, Mich., 1966), 237, 241.

3. Ross Cox, *The Columbia River*, ed. Edgar I. Stewart and Jane R. Stewart (Norman, Okla., 1957), 116. Clarence Edwin Carter, comp. and ed., *The Territorial Papers of the United States* (Washington, 1934–62), 13: 516. St. Louis *Missouri Gazette*, 25 May and 22 June 1816. Kaskaskia *Il-*

linois Intelligencer, 16 June 1819 and 31 Jan. 1820. Donald Dean Parker, ed., *The Recollections of Philander Prescott, 1819–1862* (Lincoln, Neb., 1966), 30, 53. Charles E. Hanson, Jr., *The Hawken Rifle: Its Place in History* (Chadron, Neb., 1979), 15–16. See also Reuben Gold Thwaites, ed., *Early Western Travels, 1748–1846* (Cleveland, 1904–7), 18: 127. For a reference to an occasional double-barreled pistol in Texas in the 1830s, see Creed Taylor and James T. DeShields, *Tall Men With Long Rifles* (San Antonio, Tex., 1971), 12.

4. Quotation in Dale L. Morgan, *Jedidiah Smith and the Opening of the West* (New York, 1953), 93. *Western Monthly Review*, July 1829: 15–18.

5. Washington Irving, *A Tour on the Prairies*, ed. John Francis McDermott (Norman, Okla., 1956), 145, 173, 177–78. Osborne Russell, *Journal of a Trapper*, ed. Aubrey L. Haines (Lincoln, Neb., 1965), 17. See also Dale L. Morgan, ed., *The Rocky Mountain Journals of William Marshall Anderson* (San Marino, Cal., 1967), 93, 168, 175, and Russell, *Guns on the Early Frontiers*, 88–89.

6. Milo Milton Quaife, ed., *Kit Carson's Autobiography* (Chicago, 1935), 43.

7. Hanson, *The Hawken Rifle*, 73, 75. New Orleans *Picayune*, 1 March 1838.

8. John E. Parsons, *Henry Deringer's Pocket Pistol* (New York, 1952), 25–26. Maurice S. Sullivan, *The Travels of Jedediah Smith* (Santa Ana, Cal., 1934), 153–54. *Arkansas Gazette & Democrat*, 21 Dec. 1831.

9. Randolph B. Marcy, *Thirty Years of Army Life on the Border* (1866; reprint ed., Philadelphia and New York, 1963), 396. Hanson, *The Hawken Rifle*, 74–76.

10. N. Bosworth, *A Treatise on the Rifle, Musket, Pistol, and Fowling-Piece* (1846; reprint ed., Huntington, W.Va., n.d.), 84, 103–5. Quotation in Held, *The Age of Firearms*, 166. Bosworth noted that "the properties of a ten-inch rifle pistol are known to but few. With accurate aim, it would never miss a turkey at the distance of a hundred yards. With such a pistol, using both hands, I have never thought it a great matter to take a chicken at the distance of seventy or eighty yards, and have frequently done it at a hundred."

11. Marcy, *Thirty Years of Army Life*, 396–97.

12. Quotation in Russell, *Guns on the Early Frontiers*, 309. John E. Parsons, "Gunmakers for the American Fur Company," *New York Historical Society Quarterly*, April 1952: 192.

13. Philip F. Van Cleave, "The Arms of Ethan Allen and Associates," in James E. Serven, ed., *The Collecting of Guns* (Harrisburg, Pa., 1964), 127–28. Harold R. Mouillesseaux, *Ethan Allen, Gunmaker: His Partners, Patents, and Firearms* (Ottawa, 1973), 20, 31–33.

14. St. Louis *Missouri Republican*, 29 Sept. and 20 Oct. 1835. Herschel C. Logan, *The Pictorial History of the Underhammer Gun* (New York, 1960), 88–89, 124–25, 134–35. Quotation in Hanson, *The Hawken Rifle*, 76.

15. G. W. Tysen order of Jan. 1836, Bolton Gun Works Records, microfilm reel 9, J. J. Henry Papers, Eleutherian Mills Historical Library, Wilmington, Del.

16. Mouillesseaux, *Ethan Allen, Gunmaker*, 20, 22–23,

46. Van Cleave, "The Arms of Ethan Allen," 125–27. U.S. pat. 461, of 11 Nov. 1837.

17. Quotation in Hanson, *The Hawken Rifle*, 76. Logan, *The Underhammer Gun*, 128–31. See also *American Turf Register*, Jan. 1837: 225.

18. Photostat and quotation in Hanson, *The Hawken Rifle*, 77–78.

19. Ibid. 79. U.S. pat. 254, of 5 July 1837. Lewis Winant, *Firearms Curiosa* (New York, 1955), 27–32.

20. James Wilson Nichols, *Now You Hear My Horn*, ed. Catherine W. McDowell (Austin, 1967), 62–64.

21. J. C. Duval, *Early Times In Texas* (Austin, Tex., 1892), 12, 51–54.

22. Hanson, *The Hawken Rifle*, 22, 50–51. Charles E. Hanson, Jr., *The Plains Rifle* (Harrisburg, Pa., 1960), 155, 158–59. Jackson Arms (Dallas, Tex.) Catalog 16, item 190. For typical loading rods, see Logan, *The Underhammer Gun*, 102, 146.

23. George W. Kendall, *Narrative of an Expedition across the Great South-Western Prairies . . .* (1845; reprint ed., Ann Arbor, Mich., 1966), 1: 83. John Charles Fremont, *Narratives of Exploration and Adventure*, ed. Allan Nevins (New York, 1956), 442. Donald Jackson and Mary Lee Spence, eds., *The Expeditions of John Charles Fremont* (Urbana, Ill., 1970–73), 1: 142. See also François des Montaignes, *The Plains*, ed. Nancy Alpert Mower and Don Russell (Norman, Okla., 1972), 23, 42. Hanson, *The Hawken Rifle*, 71. Consignment book, microfilm reel 9, Henry Papers.

24. W. T. Hamilton, *My Sixty Years on the Plains* (Norman, Okla., 1960), 7. Senate Ex. Doc. 43, 29th Cong., 1st Sess., Serial No. 472. Lewis H. Garrard, *Wah-To-Yah and the Taos Trail* (Norman, Okla., 1955), 22. Francis Parkman, *The Oregon Trail*, ed. E. N. Feltskog (Madison, Wis., 1969), 78–81, 109, 394–95.

25. Frederick Merk, ed., *Fur Trade and Empire: George Simpson's Journal* (Cambridge, Mass., 1931), 173. *American Turf Register*, June 1830: 495–97. *Missouri Republican*, 12 May 1835. St. Louis *Reveille*, 14 May 1845.

26. William B. Edwards, *The Story of Colt's Revolver* (Harrisburg, Pa., 1953), 33, 60, 62, 67, 85–89. *Spirit of the Times*, 23 June and 7 July 1838. Charles T. Haven and Frank A. Belden, *A History of the Colt Revolver* (New York, 1940), 41, 543, 545.

27. U.S. pat. 1304, of 29 Aug. 1839.

28. U.S. pat. 3998, of 16 April 1845. *Spirit of the Times*, 5 Feb. 1842.

29. Jack Dunlap, *American, British, and Continental Pepperbox Firearms* (Palo Alto, Cal., 1967), 70–76. A. W. F. Taylerson, R. A. N. Andrews, and J. Frith, *The Revolver, 1818–1865* (New York, 1968), 52–54. Longworth's *American Almanac, New York Register, and City Directory*, 1838. Logan, *The Underhammer Gun*, 71.

30. Quotation in Hanson, *The Hawken Rifle*, 78.

31. *Spirit of the Times*, 7 July 1838. Josiah Gregg, *Commerce of the Prairies*, ed. Max L. Moorhead (Norman, Okla., 1954), 229, 245.

32. Edwards, *Colt's Revolver*, 93–101. Nelson Lee, *Three Years among the Comanches* (Norman, Okla., 1957), 14, 23–

25. See also John H. Jenkins, ed., *The Papers of the Texas Revolution, 1835–36* (Austin, 1973), 6: 514–15.

33. Frederic Remington, *Frederic Remington's Own West* (New York, 1960), 122.

34. Kendall, *Narrative of an Expedition*, 1: 249, 253–55.

35. Edwin L. Sabin, *Kit Carson Days, 1809–1868* (Chicago, 1914), 199–200.

36. Hamilton, *Sixty Years*, 71–72.

37. *Missouri Republican*, 15 Feb. and 1 March 1841. Edwards, *Colt's Revolver*, 127–36. Edwin Bryant, *What I Saw in California . . . 1846–47* (Santa Ana, Cal., 1936), 93.

38. Mouillesseaux, *Ethan Allen, Gunmaker*, 47–49, 63–65, 71. Van Cleave, "The Arms of Ethan Allen," 129–31. Letter from Philip Van Cleave to the authors, 24 Mar. 1973. U.S. pat. 3998, of 16 April 1845.

39. Dunlap, *Pepperbox Firearms*, 57, 62–63. Mouillesseaux, *Ethan Allen, Gunmaker*, 66–69, 160.

40. Maria R. Audubon, ed., *Audubon and His Journals* (New York, 1899), 2: 27–28. Hanson, *The Hawken Rifle*, 80. *Missouri Republican*, 1 March 1841. St. Louis *Reveille*, 8 Oct. 1844 and 14 May 1845. Quotation in Hanson, *The Plains Rifle*, 54–55. George Simpson's letter of 1845, in *American Historical Review*, July 1924: 691. Russell, *Guns on the Early Frontiers*, 92–93.

41. Quotation in Russell, *Guns on the Early Frontiers*, 217–18.

42. Edwards, *Colt's Revolver*, 229, 233. Heinrich Leinhard, *From St. Louis to Sutter's Fort, 1846*, trans. and ed. Erwin G. Gudde and Elizabeth K. Gudde (Norman, Okla., 1961), 28. Allen & Thurber daybooks, Oct. 1846–March 1848, in the possession of Philip F. Van Cleave, Carlsbad, N.M. Mouillesseaux, *Ethan Allen, Gunmaker*, 75.

CHAPTER 7

1. Col. Berkeley R. Lewis, *Small Arms and Ammunition in the United States Service* (Washington, 1956), 108–11, 115, pls. 23–25. Senate Doc. 15, 25th Cong., 1st Sess., Serial No. 309; cited hereafter as Serial No. 309. Annual *Reports of the Chief of Ordnance, 1835–1840*; cited hereafter as RCO. Specific locations for the reports of the chief of ordnance from 1822 to 1865 are given in the bibliography.

2. Quotation in Maj. James E. Hicks, *U.S. Military Firearms, 1776–1956* (1940; reprint ed., La Canada, Cal., 1962), 53. Ed Bearss and Arrell M. Gibson, *Fort Smith, Little Gibraltar on the Arkansas* (Norman, Okla., 1969), 79–80.

3. Col. Arcadi Gluckman, *Identifying Old U.S. Muskets, Rifles & Carbines*, rev. ed. (Harrisburg, Pa., 1965), 117–18. Hicks, *Military Firearms*, 53–57. *American State Papers, Military Affairs* (Washington, 1832–61), 1: 855; 2: 531; hereafter cited as ASP, MA. Lewis, *Small Arms and Ammunition*, 48. The correct model/year designation for this musket has been the subject of controversy since the 1930s. Because all Ordnance documents postdating 1822 refer to the arm as the Model 1822, and because we liberally quote such documents later in the text, we have chosen to follow the 1822 designation.

4. Col. George Croghan, *Army Life on the Western Fron-*

tier, ed. Francis Paul Prucha (Norman, Okla., 1958), 95–96, 99.

5. Gluckman, *Muskets, Rifles & Carbines*, 118, 124–31. RCO, 1823–39. *War Department Contracts*, 1823, 1828–31; cited hereafter as *WDC*. Specific locations for the annual summaries of contracts made by the War Department between 1828 and 1861 are given in the bibliography.

6. House Doc. 94, 27th Cong., 1st Sess., Serial No. 404. Quotations in Hicks, *Military Firearms*, 63–65. *National Armories Expenditures Statement*, 1835–36 and 1840; cited hereafter as *NAES*. Specific locations for the annual statement of operations and expenditures at the National Armories from 1822 to 1860 are given in the bibliography. RCO, 1840.

7. Gluckman, *Muskets, Rifles & Carbines*, 159–61. Albert N. Hardin, Jr., *The American Bayonet, 1776–1964* (Philadelphia, 1964), 11–29. House Doc. 44, 24th Cong., 1st Sess., Serial No. 287. Arthur Woodward, ed., *Journal of Lt. Thomas W. Sweeny, 1849–1853* (Los Angeles, 1956), 172–73.

8. Lewis, *Small Arms and Ammunition*, 95.

9. *NAES*, 1844. Statements from Springfield and Harper's Ferry Armories, in *RCO*, 1845. Quotation in *RCO*, 1845.

10. *RCO*, 1845–50.

11. Gluckman, *Muskets, Rifles & Carbines*, 141–43. Statements from Harper's Ferry Armory, in *RCO*, 1847.

12. Quotation in Harold L. Peterson, *Arms and Armor in Colonial America, 1526–1783* (Harrisburg, Pa., 1956), 163. Jac Weller, "Shooting Confederate Infantry Arms," *American Rifleman*, April 1954: 42–44. See also quotation in Sir Ralph Payne-Gallwey, *The Crossbow* (1903; reprint ed., London, 1958), 26.

13. Lewis, *Small Arms and Ammunition*, 92, 114–15. Statement from Fort Monroe Arsenal, in *RCO*, 1845.

14. N. Bosworth, *A Treatise on the Rifle, Musket, Pistol, and Fowling-Piece . . .* (1846; reprint ed., Huntington, W. Va., n.d.), 80–81.

15. Statement from Washington Arsenal, in *RCO*, 1846. House Com. Rpt. 86, 28th Cong., 2nd Sess., Serial No. 468.

16. Statement from Harper's Ferry Armory, in *RCO*, 1852.

17. Bosworth, *Treatise on the Rifle*, 100, 102.

18. *ASP, MA*, 2: 491, 499.

19. Leavenworth's official correspondence, in *South Dakota Historical Collections*, 1902, 207, 209–10.

20. Philip St. George Cooke, *Scenes and Adventures in the Army* (Philadelphia, 1859), 52.

21. Quotation in Marvin F. Kivett, "Excavations at Fort Atkinson, Nebraska—A Preliminary Report," *Fort Atkinson on the Council Bluffs* (Lincoln, Neb., 1972), 56. House Ex. Doc. 44, Serial No. 287. Croghan, *Army Life*, 98.

22. RCO, 1839–40. *Spirit of the Times*, 10 Sept. 1842. Cooke, *Scenes and Adventures*, 53.

23. William E. Connelley, *Doniphan's Expedition and the Conquest of New Mexico and California* (Kansas City, 1907), 379, 413. Donald Jackson and Mary Lee Spence, eds., *The Expeditions of John Charles Fremont* (Urbana, Ill., 1970–73), 2: 348. Gen. Dabney H. Maury, *Recollections of a Virginian in the Mexican, Indian, and Civil Wars* (New York, 1894), 88.

24. Philip St. George Cooke, *The Conquest of New Mexico and California* (1878; reprint ed., Chicago, 1964), 145–46.

25. Lt. James W. Abert, *Report of Lieut. J. W. Abert, of His Examination of New Mexico* (House Ex. Doc. 41, 30th Cong., 1st Sess., Serial No. 517; reprint ed., Albuquerque, N.M., 1962), 171.

26. Samuel C. Reid, Jr., *The Scouting Expeditions of McCulloch's Texas Rangers . . . 1846* (1847; reprint ed., Austin, 1935), 157.

27. Lewis H. Garrard, *Wah-To-Yah and the Taos Trail* (1850; reprint ed., Norman, Okla., 1955), 258, 275. George Douglas Brewerton, *Overland with Kit Carson* (New York, 1930), 97.

28. Col. George A. McCall, *New Mexico in 1850: A Military View*, ed. Robert W. Frazer (Norman, Okla., 1968). Col. Joseph K. F. Mansfield, *Mansfield on the Condition of the Western Forts, 1853–54*, ed. Robert W. Frazer (Norman, Okla., 1963), 224, 231. RCO, 1848–55.

29. Mansfield, *Western Forts*, 67.

30. John Russell Bartlett, *Personal Narrative of Exploration and Incidents . . .* (New York, 1854), 2: 143–44.

31. U.S. pat. 4208, of 22 Sept. 1845. *WDC*, 1845.

32. *WDC*, 1848. RCO, 1849–50.

33. "Report of Inspection of Eighth Military Department [Texas] Made by Bvt. Lt. Col. W. G. Freeman . . . 1853," Record Group 94 (Records of the Adjutant General's Office), National Archives, Washington, D.C.; cited hereafter as "Freeman's Report on Texas." This report, minus the appendix on Maynard-primer muskets, is reprinted in the *Southwestern Historical Quarterly*, July 1947–Oct. 1950.

34. "Freeman's Report on Texas."

CHAPTER 8

1. *American State Papers, Military Affairs* (Washington, 1832–61), 6: 107. R. T. Huntington, *Hall's Breechloaders*, ed. Nancy Bagby (York, Pa., 1972), 305, 316, 318.

2. Col. Berkeley R. Lewis, *Small Arms and Ammunition in the United States Service* (Washington, 1956), 108–11, pl. 27. Col. Arcadi Gluckman, *Identifying Old U.S. Muskets, Rifles & Carbines*, rev. ed. (Harrisburg, Pa., 1965), 164. Huntington, *Hall's Breechloaders*, 314, 317.

3. Huntington, *Hall's Breechloaders*, 318.

4. *National Armories Expenditures Statements*, 1823–27; cited hereafter as *NAES*. Specific locations for the annual statements of operations and expenditures at the National Armories from 1822 to 1860 are given in the bibliography. *War Department Contracts*, 1828; cited hereafter as *WDC*. Specific locations for the annual summaries of contracts made by the War Department from 1828 to 1861 are given in the bibliography. Huntington, *Hall's Breechloaders*, 28–32, 41–44.

5. Huntington, *Hall's Breechloaders*, 44, 109–12, 278–

79. *Report of the Chief of Ordnance*, 1830; cited hereafter as *RCO*. Specific locations for the annual reports of the chief of ordnance from 1822 to 1865 are given in the bibliography.

6. Huntington, *Hall's Breechloaders*, 120, 189–95, 341. *NAES*, 1824–40. *RCO*, 1830–36.

7. *RCO*, 1836–45. Huntington, *Hall's Breechloaders*, 237, 241–49. Gluckman, *Muskets, Rifles & Carbines*, 173.

8. *ASP, MA*, 2: 491, 499. Quotation in Marvin F. Kivett, "Excavations at Fort Atkinson, Nebraska—A Preliminary Report," *Fort Atkinson on the Council Bluffs* (Lincoln, Neb., 1972), 56.

9. Kivett, "Excavations at Fort Atkinson," 54.

10. Quotation in Carl P. Russell, *Guns on the Early Frontiers* (Berkeley and Los Angeles, 1957), 331–32.

11. Otis Young, *The First Military Escort on the Santa Fe Trail, 1829* (Glendale, Cal., 1952), 64. Philip St. George Cooke, *Scenes and Adventures in the Army* (Philadelphia, 1859), 52.

12. House Doc. 44, 24th Cong., 1st Sess., Serial No. 287.

13. Ibid.

14. Ibid.

15. *RCO*, 1830–40. *ASP, MA*, 2: 599–609. *WDC*, 1840. House Doc. 44, Serial No. 287. *RCO*, 1835. Senate Ex. Doc. 54, 30th Cong., 1st Sess., Serial No. 509.

17. House Doc. 3, 27th Cong., 2nd Sess., Serial No. 401. See also House Doc. 3, 27th Cong., 3rd Sess., Serial No. 418. *RCO*, 1840 and 1842.

18. *RCO*, 1841.

19. Gluckman, *Muskets, Rifles & Carbines*, 179–82. *NAES*, 1841–46. *WDC*, 1842–45. *RCO*, 1844–46.

20. *NAES*, 1841–44. Huntington, *Hall's Breechloaders*, 86–87, 89, 137–39, 195–98.

21. Huntington, *Hall's Breechloaders*, 137, 191, 196–97, 305, 354–56. Quotations in Claude E. Fuller, *The Breech-Loader in the Service, 1816–1917* (1933; reprint ed., New Milford, Conn., 1965), 41, 66. Lewis, *Small Arms and Ammunition*, 95. All military Halls, from the first Harper's Ferry production models, had a U-shaped sheet-iron gas deflector or "apron" inside the stock recess around the sides and bottom of the breechblock-barrel joint. This deflector helped prevent the direct lateral and downward escape of gas, but did not actually seal off gas leakage.

22. Quotation in George W. Smith and Charles Judah, *Chronicles of the Gringos* (Albuquerque, N.M., 1968), 120. Samuel E. Chamberlain, *My Confession* (New York, 1956), 119, 157, 261. George Rutledge Gibson, *Over the Chihuahua and Santa Fe Trails, 1847–1848*, ed. Robert W. Frazer (Albuquerque, 1981), 66.

23. *RCO*, 1836–48. Marcellus Ball Edwards, A. R. Johnson, and Philip Ferguson, *Marching with the Army of the West, 1846–1848*, ed. Ralph B. Bieber (Glendale, Cal., 1936), 133.

24. Daniel Tyler, *A Concise History of the Mormon Battalion* (1881; reprint ed., Waynesboro, Va., 1964), 136. Smith and Judah, *Chronicles of the Gringos*, 138.

25. *RCO*, 1849; *WDC*, 1849. See also Harold L. Peterson, *American Knives* (New York, 1958).

26. *RCO*, 1848–55. *NAES*, 1848–55. *WDC*, 1848–55.

27. John J. Batten, "Major Hagner's Wurfflein Rifle," *The Arms Gazette*, Nov. 1975: 38–44.

28. Statements from Washington, Watervliet, Watertown, Allegheny, and St. Louis Arsenals, 1849–53, in *RCO*, 1853.

29. Col. Joseph K. F. Mansfield, *Mansfield on the Condition of the Western Forts, 1853–54*, ed. Robert W. Frazer (Norman, Okla., 1963), 224, 231.

CHAPTER 9

1. R. T. Huntington, *Hall's Breechloaders*, ed. Nancy Bagby (York, Pa., 1972), 75, 123, 178, 199, 203, 217.

2. Ibid. 123–25. Quotation from Maj. James E. Hicks, *U.S. Military Firearms, 1776–1956* (1940; reprint ed., La Canada, Cal., 1962), 62.

3. Huntington, *Hall's Breechloaders*, 125–27, 140, 216–19, 261–63. *Report of the Chief of Ordnance*, 1833–34; cited hereafter as *RCO*. Specific locations for the annual reports of the chief of ordnance from 1822 to 1865 are given in the bibliography.

4. Huntington, *Hall's Breechloaders*, 74, 128, 199, 218. *National Armories Expenditures Statements*, 1836; cited hereafter as *NAES*. Specific locations for the annual statements of operations and expenditures at the National Armories from 1822 to 1860 are given in the bibliography.

5. Huntington, *Hall's Breechloaders*, 173, 199–204, 342. *NAES*, 1836–40. *RCO*, 1836–40.

6. Huntington, *Hall's Breechloaders*, 220–26, 343.

7. Ibid. 205–7, *NAES*, 1842–43.

8. Huntington, *Hall's Breechloaders*, 142, 227–29, 339–40.

9. *RCO*, 1834–39. Huntington, *Hall's Breechloaders*, 238–40.

10. Huntington, *Hall's Breechloaders*, 127–28, 137, 281. *RCO*, 1834. House Doc. 44, 24th Cong., 1st Sess., Serial No. 287.

11. Col. George Croghan, *Army Life on the Western Frontier*, ed. Francis Paul Prucha (Norman, Okla., 1958), 97–100.

12. Quotation in Huntington, *Hall's Breechloaders*, 169, 173. Senate Misc. Doc. 9, 30th Cong., 2nd Sess., Serial No. 533.

13. Quotations in Claud E. Fuller, *The Breech-Loader in the Service, 1816–1917* (1933; reprint ed., New Milford, Conn., 1965), 39, 65–66. Croghan, *Army Life*, 99–100. Apparently a few of the carbines were issued which, through oversight, did not even have the chocks installed. See the quotations in Huntington, *Hall's Breechloaders*, 284, and in Carl P. Russell, *Guns on the Early Frontiers* (Berkeley and Los Angeles, 1957), 327.

14. U.S. pat. 747, of 25 May 1838. Fuller, *Breech-Loader in the Service*, 63–71. Robert M. Reilly, *United States Military Small Arms, 1816–1865* (Baton Rouge, La., 1970), 136–

39. Andrew F. Lustyik, "Jenks Carbine—Gun with a Jinx," *American Rifleman*, April 1969: 18–20.

15. Senate Misc. Doc. 9, Serial No. 533. *RCO*, 1841–44. Senate Ex. Doc. 54, 30th Cong., 1st Sess., Serial No. 509.

16. Senate Doc. 29, 25th Cong., 1st Sess., Serial No. 309.

17. Senate Doc. 503, 26th Cong., 1st Sess., Serial No. 360. William B. Edwards, *The Story of Colt's Revolver* (Harrisburg, Pa., 1953), 65–71. Senate Doc. 14, 26th Cong., 2nd Sess., Serial No. 376.

18. *WDC*, 1841 and 1845. Quotation in Charles T. Haven and Frank A. Belden, *The History of the Colt Revolver* (New York, 1940), 310.

19. Senate Ex. Doc. 54, Serial No. 509.

20. *RCO*, 1834–46. Donald Jackson and Mary Lee Spence, eds., *The Expeditions of John Charles Fremont* (Urbana, Ill., 1970–73), 1: 343, 428. Lt. James W. Abert, *Report of Lieut. J. W. Abert, of His Examination of New Mexico, 1846–47* (House Ex. Doc. 41, 30th Cong., 1st Sess., Serial No. 517; reprint ed., Albuquerque, N.M., 1962), 122.

21. Samuel E. Chamberlain, *My Confession* (New York, 1956), 188–89.

22. Philip St. George Cooke, *Scenes and Adventures in the Army* (Philadelphia, 1859), 156.

23. Col. Arcadi Gluckman, *Identifying Old U.S. Muskets, Rifles & Carbines*, rev. ed. (Harrisburg, Pa., 1965), 306–7. *RCO*, 1839. *NAES*, 1844–47. Statements from Springfield Armory, in *RCO*, 1846–47. At Ft. Leavenworth in 1840 Col. George Croghan had presented his idea of a "proper carbine . . . one to load at the muzzle and large enough to chamber three buck shot." Croghan, *Army Life*, 100.

24. House Doc. 44, Serial No. 287. Quotation in George W. Smith and Charles Judah, *Chronicles of the Gringos* (Albuquerque, N.M., 1968), 382.

25. Gluckman, *Muskets, Rifles & Carbines*, 307–9. Reilly, *Military Small Arms*, 114–16. *RCO*, 1847–51.

26. Huntington, *Hall's Breechloaders*, 295–96, 344. *WDC*, 1850. *RCO*, 1848–55.

27. Col. George A. McCall, *New Mexico in 1850: A Military View*, ed. Robert W. Frazer (Norman, Okla., 1968).

28. McCall, *New Mexico in 1850*, 121.

29. Col. Joseph K. F. Mansfield, *Mansfield on the Condition of the Western Forts 1853–54*, ed. Robert W. Frazer (Norman, Okla., 1963), 65–67. "Report of Inspection of Eighth Military Department [Texas] Made by Bvt. Lt. Col. W. G. Freeman . . . 1853." Record Group 94 (Records of the Adjutant General's Office), National Archives, Washington, D.C.; cited hereafter as "Freeman's Report on Texas."

30. Statement from St. Louis Arsenal, in *RCO*, 1855. Percival G. Lowe, *Five Years a Dragoon* (Norman, Okla., 1965), 93.

31. Quotation from Fuller, *Breech-Loader in the Service*, 42.

32. U.S. pat. 5763, of 12 Sept. 1848. Frank M. Sellers, *Sharps Firearms* (N. Hollywood, Cal., 1978), 2–4.

33. Ibid. 4–5, 15–18. *Scientific American*, 9 March 1850.

34. Sellers, *Sharps Firearms*, 16, 18–20, 40.

35. Ibid. 11, 18–20, 67–68. Quotation in Martin Rywell, *The Gun That Shaped American Destiny* (Harriman, Tenn., 1957), 32. *RCO*, 1852.

36. Sellers, *Sharps Firearms*, 8–11, 27–30, 39–40.

37. Marius B. Peladeau, "The Boxlock Sharps," *American Rifleman*, June 1967: 49–50. Sellers, *Sharps Firearms*, 44. *RCO*, 1852–53. Craig to commanding officer, Ninth Military Dept., 19 Feb. 1853, Arrott Collection, card 00010, Fort Union Natl. Monument, Watrous, N.M. "Freeman's Report on Texas." See also the quotations in Fuller, *Breech-Loader in the Service*, 76.

38. Mansfield, *Western Forts*, 224, 231.

39. Ibid. 66.

40. *RCO*, 1847–56.

41. Sellers, *Sharps Firearms*, 30, 40–41, 45–47.

42. Sellers, *Sharps Firearms*, 41–43, 54–58. *WDC*, 1854–55. *Reports of Experiments with Small Arms for the Military Service . . .* (Washington, 1856), 25, 118.

43. "Freeman's Report on Texas." Quotation in Rywell, *American Destiny*, 37.

CHAPTER 10

1. *American State Papers, Military Affairs* (Washington, 1832–61), 2: 327, 329, 532–33; cited hereafter as *ASP, MA*.

2. Samuel E. Smith, "The Single Shot Martial Pistols of the U.S.," in James E. Serven, ed., *The Collecting of Guns* (Harrisburg, Pa., 1964), 111–12. Robert M. Reilly, *United States Military Small Arms, 1816–1865* (Baton Rouge, La., 1970), 176–78. See also Carl P. Russell, *Guns on the Early Frontiers* (Berkeley and Los Angeles, 1957), 88–89.

3. Philip St. George Cooke, *Scenes and Adventures in the Army* (Philadelphia, 1859), 38.

4. *Report of the Chief of Ordnance, 1834*; cited hereafter as *RCO*. Specific locations for the annual reports of the chief of ordnance from 1822 to 1865 are given in the bibliography. Cooke, *Scenes and Adventures*, 224. House Ex. Doc. 44, 24th Cong., 1st Sess., Serial No. 287.

5. *War Department Contracts, 1836* and *1840*; cited hereafter as *WDC*. Specific locations for the annual summaries of contracts made by the War Department between 1828 and 1861 are given in the bibliography. Reilly, *Military Small Arms*, 178–80. Senate Ex. Doc. 54, 30th Cong., 1st Sess., Serial No. 509. The list of War Department contracts for 1835 shows that Johnson also had a contract that year (dated 11 Nov. 1835) for 2,400 pistols.

6. Col. George Croghan, *Army Life on the Western Frontier*, ed. Francis Paul Prucha (Norman, Okla., 1958), 98, 100.

7. House Doc. 3, 27th Cong., 2nd Sess., Serial No. 401. See also House Doc. 3, 27th Cong., 3rd Sess., Serial No. 418.

8. *WDC*, 1845. Smith, "Single Shot Martial Pistols," 113. Reilly *Military Small Arms*, 183–85.

9. *National Armories Expenditures Statements*, 1842 and 1845; cited hereafter as *NAES*. Specific locations for the annual statements of operations and expenditures at the National Armories from 1822 to 1860 are given in the bibliography. *WDC*, 1845 and 1851. *RCO*, 1845–47. Reilly, *Military Small Arms*, 181–82.

10. Cooke, *Scenes and Adventures*, 301.

11. *WDC*, 1845. Senate Ex. Doc. 54, Serial No. 509. U.S. pat. 9430X, of 25 Feb. 1836; reproduced in Charles T. Haven and Frank A. Belden, *A History of the Colt Revolver* (New York, 1940), 539–48. Senate Doc. 14, 26th Cong., 2nd Sess., Serial No. 376. Quotation in Russell, *Guns on the Early Frontiers*, 338–39.

12. Quotations in Haven and Belden, *The Colt Revolver*, 273–75. See also William B. Edwards, *The Story of Colt's Revolver* (Harrisburg, Pa., 1953), 216–17.

13. Haven and Belden, *The Colt Revolver*, 273–75, 280–85. James E. Serven, *Colt Firearms from 1836* (Harrisburg, Pa., 1979), 56–57, 73–80. Col. Berkeley R. Lewis, *Small Arms and Ammunition in the United States Service* (Washington, 1956), 100.

14. *WDC*, 1847. Quotations in Haven and Belden, *The Colt Revolver*, 275–79, 286. Serven, *Colt Firearms*, 56, 78.

15. Quotations in Haven and Belden, *The Colt Revolver*, 271, 286–87, 292–93, 308–9.

16. Maj. Gen. Ethan Allen Hitchcock, *Fifty Years in Camp and Field*, ed. W. A. Croffut (New York, 1909), 310.

17. *RCO*, 1848.

18. Samuel E. Chamberlain, *My Confession* (New York, 1956), 172, 208, 221.

19. John Salmon Ford, *Rip Ford's Texas*, ed. Stephen B. Oates (Austin, Tex., 1963), 105.

20. Quotation in Lewis, *Small Arms and Ammunition*, 100.

21. *WDC*, 1847. Serven, *Colt Firearms*, 42–43, 58–61.

22. *RCO*, 1848–49. Serven, *Colt Firearms*, 43, 48. Edward F. Beale, "A Ride Across Mexico," Washington *National Intelligencer*, 28 September 1848.

23. *RCO*, 1849–56. Quotation in Maj. B. R. Lewis, "Sam Colt's Repeating Pistol," *American Rifleman*, June 1947: 25.

24. Statements from Watertown, Allegheny, and St. Louis arsenals, in *RCO*, 1849–55.

25. Senate Com. Rpt. 257, 31st Cong., 2nd Sess., Serial No. 593.

26. *RCO*, 1849–51. *WDC*, 1849–60. St. Louis *Missouri Republican*, 21 Mar. 1850.

27. William Woods Averell, *Ten Years in the Saddle*, ed. Edward K. Eckert and Nicholas J. Amato (San Rafael, Cal., 1978), 88–89.

28. Senate Com. Rpt. 257, Serial No. 593.

29. McCall, *New Mexico in 1850*. "Report of Inspection of Eighth Military Department [Texas] Made by Bvt. Lt. Col. W. G. Freeman . . . 1853," Record Group 94 (Records of the Adjutant General's Office), National Archives, Washington, D.C. This report, minus the appendix on Maynard-primer muskets, is reprinted in the *Southwestern Historical Quarterly*, July 1947–Oct. 1950.

30. Senate Ex. Doc. 35, 32nd Cong., 1st Sess., Serial No. 618.

31. Percival G. Lowe, *Five Years a Dragoon* (Norman, Okla., 1965), 83–84, 115–16.

CHAPTER 11

1. Report of the Chief of Ordnance, 1849; cited hereafter as *RCO*. Specific locations for the annual reports of the chief of ordnance from 1822 to 1865 are given in the bibliography.

2. *RCO*, 1849–50.

3. *RCO*, 1849. Senate Doc. 229, 26th Cong., 2nd Sess., Serial No. 378. Senate Doc. 60, 36th Cong., 1st Sess., Serial No. 1037.

4. Senate Ex. Doc. 60, Serial No. 1037. *RCO*, 1849–50. *Reports of Experiments with Small Arms . . .* (Washington, D.C., 1856), 11, 18.

5. *RCO*, 1852.

6. *Reports of Experiments*, Appendix, 20.

7. Senate Ex. Doc. 60, Serial No. 1037.

8. *Reports of Experiments*, 14–15.

9. *RCO*, 1854.

10. Statements from Allegheny Arsenal and Harper's Ferry Armory, in *RCO*, 1855.

11. Augustus Meyers, *Ten Years in the Ranks of the U.S. Army* (New York, 1914), 39–40. John Todd's Journal is in *Nebraska History*, June 1962, 113–14.

12. Senate Ex. Doc. 1, 34th Cong., 1st Sess., Serial No. 811.

13. *RCO*, 1854. *Reports of Experiments*, 53–55, 75–78.

14. *RCO*, 1855.

15. Statement from Springfield Armory, in *RCO*, 1855. Senate Ex. Doc. 1, Serial No. 811.

16. *Reports of Experiments*, 94. *RCO*, 1856–57.

17. Statements from Springfield and Harper's Ferry Armories, in *RCO*, 1855–56.

18. Statement from Frankford Arsenal, in *RCO*, 1856. *War Department Contracts*, 1854; cited hereafter as *WDC*. Specific locations for the annual summaries of contracts made by the War Department between 1828 and 1861 are given in the bibliography.

19. Statement from Frankford Arsenal, in *RCO*, 1856.

20. Statements from Springfield and Harper's Ferry armories, in *RCO*, 1856.

21. *RCO*, 1856, and statement from Frankford Arsenal, in *RCO*, 1858.

22. Inspection of the Department of Texas, 1856, misc. file 282, Record Group 94 (Records of the Adjutant General's Office), National Archives, Washington, D.C.; cited hereafter as Mansfield's report on Texas. This report is reprinted in *Southwestern Historical Quarterly*, Oct. 1938–April 1939.

23. Eugene Bandel, *Frontier Life in the Army 1854–1861*, ed. Ralph P. Bieber (Glendale, Cal., 1932), 102–4.

24. Statement from Harper's Ferry Armory, in *RCO*, 1856.

25. Gen. Dabney H. Maury, *Recollections of a Virginian*

in the Mexican, Indian and Civil Wars (New York, 1894), 111.

26. Statements from Frankford, St. Louis, and Benecia arsenals, in *RCO*, 1857.

27. *RCO*, 1856–57.

28. *Report of Experiments*, 87–94. *RCO*, 1857–60.

29. George Crook, *General George Crook, His Autobiography*, ed. Martin F. Schmitt (Norman, Okla., 1960), 46, 58.

30. Senate Ex. Doc. 1, 35th Cong., 2nd Sess., Serial No. 975. Statement from St. Louis Arsenal, in *RCO*, 1859.

31. *RCO*, 1858. John Salmon Ford, *Rip Ford's Texas*, ed. Stephen B. Oates (Austin, Tex., 1963), 243.

32. *RCO*, 1856–60.

33. *RCO*, 1860. See also House Report 85, 36th Cong., 2nd Sess., Serial No. 1105.

34. *The War of the Rebellion: A Compilation of the Official Records of the Union and Confederate Armies* (Washington, D.C., 1880–1900); series 3, 1: 1; cited hereafter as *OR*.

35. *Reports of Experiments*, 73–74, 80, 109, 114–17.

36. William Woods Averell, *Ten Years in the Saddle*, ed. Edward K. Eckert and Nicholas J. Amato (San Rafael, Cal., 1978), 188. *RCO*, 1856. *Reports of Experiments*, 111–13.

37. Statement from New York Arsenal, in *RCO*, 1858. *WDC*, 1859.

38. *Ordnance Manual for the Use of the Officers of the United States Army*, 1861, 179, 183.

39. Claud E. Fuller and Richard D. Steuart, *Firearms of the Confederacy* (Huntington, W.Va., 1944), 25–27.

40. *RCO*, 1859.

41. *OR*, series 1, 4: 78, 154. Card No. 00062, Arrott Collection, Fort Union Natl. Monument, Watrous, N.M.

42. Reilly, *Military Small Arms*, 27.

43. House Ex. Doc. 67, 37th Cong., 2nd Sess. Serial No. 1131. House Report 2, 37th Cong., 2nd Sess., Serial No. 1142. Senate Com. Rpt. 108, 37th Cong., 3rd Sess., Serial No. 1154. House Ex. Doc. 99, 40th Cong., 2nd Sess., Serial No. 1338. Herschel C. Logan, "H. E. Dimick of St. Louis," *American Rifleman*, April 1958, 31–32.

44. [Lorenzo] "Ren" Barker, *Military History [of] Company "D," 66th Illinois, Birge's Western Sharpshooters . . .* (Reed City, Mich., 1905).

45. *RCO*, 1862.

46. Senate Ex. Doc. 60, Serial No. 1037. C. M. Wilcox, *Rifles and Rifle Practice* (New York, 1861), 178.

47. Senate Ex. Doc. 60, Serial No. 1037. "The Rifle—Its Probable Influence on Modern Warfare," *Journal of the Royal United Service Institution*, 26 June 1857. House Ex. Doc. 67, Serial No. 1131.

48. Senate Ex. Doc. 72, 37th Cong., 2nd Sess., Serial No. 1123. House Ex. Doc. 99, Serial No. 1338. *Instructions for Making Quarterly Returns of Ordnance and Ordnance Stores . . .*, 1865; reprinted in Col. Berkeley R. Lewis, *Small Arms and Ammunition in the United States Service* (Washington, D.C., 1956), 287–88.

49. *Reports of Experiments*.

50. *OR*, series 3, 1: 418, 538–39. House Rpt. 2, Serial No. 1142.

51. Senate Ex. Doc. 60, Serial No. 1037. Wilcox, *Rifles and Rifle Practice*, 181–82. Senate Ex. Doc. 72, Serial No. 1123. Frederick P. Todd et al., *American Military Equipage, 1851–1872* (New York, 1980), 131–37.

52. House Rpt. 2, Serial No. 1142. Senate Rpt. 108, Serial No. 1154.

53. *OR*, series 1, 3: 612.

54. Senate Ex. Doc. 72, Serial No. 1123. House Ex. Doc. 99, Serial No. 1338.

55. Senate Ex. Doc. 60, Serial No. 1037, Senate Ex. Doc. 72, Serial No. 1123. Wilcox, *Rifles and Rifle Practice*, 181–82. Todd, *American Military Equipage*, 135–36.

56. Senate Ex. Doc. 72, Serial No. 1123.

57. *OR*, series 1, 13: 687–88.

58. *Minnesota in the Civil and Indian Wars* (St. Paul, Minn., 1890–93), 1: 3; 2: 165. "Ledger of Issues of Ordnance and Ordnance Stores to the Loyal States under the President's Calls of 1862," Entry 118, Record Group 156 (Records of the Office of the Chief of Ordnance), National Archives, Washington, D.C. Cited hereafter as "Ledger of Issues, 1862."

59. "Ledger of Issues, 1862."

60. *Minnesota in the Wars*, 2: 43, 188–89.

61. Quotation from Agnes Wright Spring, ed., *Casper Collins: The Life and Exploits of an Indian Fighter of the Sixties* (New York, 1927), 121.

62. Senate Ex. Doc. 72, Serial No. 1123. *OR*, series 1, 8: 557.

63. "Ledger of Issues, 1862."

64. Accession nos. A6/1, A6/7, A2/10.

65. *OR*, series 1, 15: 649.

66. *Minnesota in the Wars*, 1: 386. *OR*, series 1, 22: pt. 1, 311; pt. 2, 360.

67. Fuller and Steuart, *Firearms of the Confederacy*, 139–43. William A. Albaugh III, "The Confederate Firearms," in James E. Serven, ed., *The Collecting of Guns* (New York, 1964), 160.

68. William A. Albaugh III, ed., *Tyler, Texas, C. S. A.* (Harrisburg, Pa., 1958). Albaugh, "The Confederate Firearms," 160.

69. William A. Albaugh III and Edward N. Simmons, *Confederate Arms* (Harrisburg, Pa., 1957), 61–62. *Confederate Field Manual*, 1862, reprinted in Lewis, *Small Arms and Ammunition*, 64–67.

70. "Quarterly Summary Statement of Ordnance and Ordnance Stores on Hand in the Infantry Regiments in the Service of the United States during the Fourth Quarter Ending Dec. 31, 1863 [and] the First Quarter Ending March 31, 1865," Entry 111, Record Group 156 (Records of the Office of the Chief of Ordnance), National Archives, Washington, D.C.; cited hereafter as *SSOI*. House Ex. Doc. 99, Serial No. 1338.

71. "Quarterly Summary Statement of Ordnance and Ordnance Stores on Hand at the Forts, Batteries, and Garrisons of the United States during the First Quarter Ending March 31, 1863 [and] March 31, 1864," Record Group 156 (Records of the Office of the Chief of Ordnance), National Archives, Washington, D.C.; cited hereafter as *SSOF*.

72. *SSOF*, 31 March 1864.

73. Ibid.

74. Ibid. Senate Ex. Doc. 72, Serial No. 1123.

75. William B. Edwards, *Civil War Guns* (Harrisburg, Pa., 1962), 60–64. *SSOF*, 31 March 1864.

76. *SSOF*, 31 March 1864.

77. *SSOF*, 31 March 1864.

78. *OR*, series 1, 41: pt. 1, 366. *SSOF*, 31 March 1864.

79. Senate Ex. Doc. 72, Serial No. 1123. House Ex. Doc. 99, Serial No. 1338.

80. Senate Doc. 229, Serial No. 378. Senate Ex. Doc. 60, Serial No. 1037. Lt. John Gibbon, *The Artillerist's Manual* (1860; reprint ed., New York, 1970), 139. Letter from H. Michael Madaus, Milwaukee Public Museum, to authors, 5 July 1974. Todd, *American Military Equipage*, 145–51.

81. *RCO*, 1849. Madaus to authors, 5 July 1974.

82. *RCO*, 1849. *Reports of Experiments*, Appendix, 6–7, 14. Senate Ex. Doc. 60, Serial No. 1037. *OR*, series 3, vol. 1, 484. Madaus to authors, 5 July 1974.

83. *SSOF*, 31 March 1863.

84. *SSOF*, 31 March 1864. Madaus to authors, 5 July 1974.

85. *SSOF*, 31 March 1864. Madaus to authors, 5 July 1974.

86. *SSOF*, 31 March 1863, and 31 March 1864. Senate Ex. Doc. 72, Serial No. 1123. Madaus to authors, 5 July 1974.

87. *SSOF*, 31 March 1864. Madaus to authors, 5 July and 16 Oct. 1974. Claude Blair, *European and American Arms* (New York, 1962), fig. 538. Senate Ex. Doc. 60, Serial No. 1037. House Ex. Doc. 67, Serial No. 1131. House Ex. Doc. 99, Serial No. 1338.

88. Madaus to authors, 5 July 1974. Senate Ex. Doc. 60, Serial No. 1037. *Instructions for Making Quarterly Returns*, 287. See also *OR*, series 3, 1: 594, 656. As late as 1867, 850 Dresden rifle-muskets (and 257 light French rifles) were listed as "in the hands of troops"; see House Misc. Doc. 152, 40th Cong., 2nd Sess., Serial No. 1350.

89. *Minnesota in the Wars*, 2: 217.

90. *SSOI*, 31 Dec. 1864, and 31 March 1865. Quotation in Grace Raymond Hebard and E. A. Brininstool, *The Bozeman Trail* (Cleveland, 1922), 1: 179–81. House Ex. Doc. 53, 39th Cong., 2nd Sess., Serial No. 1290.

CHAPTER 12

1. U.S. pats. 14554, of 1 April 1856, and 26504, of 20 Dec. 1859. Frank M. Sellers, *Sharps Firearms* (N. Hollywood, Cal., 1978), 39, 41, 43, 57.

2. Report of the Chief of Ordnance, 1855–1856; cited hereafter as *RCO*. Specific locations for the annual reports of the chief of ordnance from 1822 to 1865 are given in the bibliography. Col. Arcadi Gluckman, *Identifying Old U.S. Muskets, Rifles & Carbines*, rev. ed. (Harrisburg, Pa., 1965), 310–11. Robert M. Reilly, *United States Military Small Arms, 1816–1865* (Baton Rouge, La., 1970), 116–18, 185–86.

3. *Reports of Experiments with Small Arms . . .* (Washington, D.C., 1856), 74–78, 85–86, 94. *RCO*, 1855–57.

4. R. T. Huntington, *Hall's Breechloaders*, ed. Nancy Bagby (York, Pa., 1972), 295–96. Statement from Harper's Ferry Armory, in *RCO*, 1856.

5. *RCO*, 1855. *War Department Contracts, 1855*; cited hereafter as *WDC*. Specific locations for the annual summaries of contracts made by the War Department between 1828 and 1861 are given in the bibliography.

6. War Department General Order No. 13, 15 Aug. 1855, in Capt. George F. Price, *Across the Continent with the Fifth Cavalry* (1883; reprint ed., New York, 1959), 29–30.

7. U.S. pats. 6945, of 11 Dec. 1849, and 12244, of 16 Jan. 1855. *Scientific American*, 16 Sept. 1854. The Perry was somewhat more successful commercially than it was with the military. Statement from Harper's Ferry Armory, in *RCO*, 1850.

8. U.S. pat. 14077, of 8 Jan. 1856.

9. Col. Eben Swift, *The Pistol, the Mellay, and the Fight at Devil's River* (Leavenworth, Kan., 1914), 6–7.

10. "Inspection of the Department of Texas, 1856," Misc. File 282, Record Group 94 (Records of the Adjutant General's Office), National Archives, Washington, D.C.; cited hereafter as "Mansfield's Report on Texas." This report is reprinted in *Southwestern Historical Quarterly*, Oct. 1938–April 1939.

11. U.S. pat. 8210, of 8 July 1851. Lewis Winant, *Early Percussion Firearms* (New York, 1859), 202–3. Norman E. Flayderman, *Flayderman's Guide to Antique American Firearms*, 2nd ed. (Northfield, Ill., 1980), 576–77. Statement from New York Arsenal, in *RCO*, 1854.

12. "Mansfield's Report on Texas."

13. Ibid.

14. Ibid.

15. Ibid. Sellers, *Sharps Firearms*, 35–37, 61–63. See also House Misc. Doc. 152, 40th Cong., 2nd Sess., Serial No. 1350.

16. U.S. pat. 11157, of 27 June 1854. *RCO*, 1857. Senate Ex. Doc. 60, Serial No. 1037. Lt. Eli Long's Journal, May–Sept. 1857, United States Army Military History Institute, Carlisle Barracks, Pa. Andrew F. Lustyik, *Civil War Carbines* (Aledo, Ill., 1962), 11–12.

17. U.S. pats. 13999, of 25 Dec. 1855, 18678, of 24 Nov. 1857, and 20144, of 4 May 1858. The rifle in its early production version is shown in British pat. 908, of 16 April 1856.

18. *WDC*, 1857. *RCO*, 1857. James E. Serven, *Colt Firearms from 1836* (Harrisburg, Pa., 1979), 331–47.

19. Marcy to Colt, 4 Oct. 1857, Colt Patent Fire Arms Manufacturing Co. correspondence, Connecticut State Library, Hartford, Conn.; cited hereafter as Colt Letters.

20. Quotation in Otis E. Young, *The West of Philip St. George Cooke* (Glendale, Cal., 1955), 286–87.

21. U.S. pat. 14491, of 25 March 1856. British pat. 2581, of 15 Nov. 1855. Lt. John Gibbon, *The Artillerist's Manual* (1860; reprint ed., New York, 1970), 123–24.

22. *WDC*, 1856. Lustyik, *Civil War Carbines*, 6–8. Wil-

liam B. Edwards, *Civil War Guns* (Harrisburg, Pa., 1962), 114–15. Quotation in Claud E. Fuller, *The Breech-Loader in the Service, 1816–1917* (1933; reprint ed., New Milford, Conn., 1965), 102.

23. *Scientific American*, 12 Sept. 1857. C. M. Wilcox, *Rifles and Rifle Practice* (New York, 1861), 217.

24. Quotation in Fuller, *The Breech-Loader in the Service*, 76–77. *Synopsis of the Military Career of Brevet Maj. Gen. Eli Long, U.S.V.* (n.p., n.d.); one copy is located at the United States Army Military History Institute, Carlisle Barracks, Pa.

25. RCO, 1855–58. Quotation in Fuller, *The Breech-Loader in the Service*, 76–77. Senate Ex. Doc. 60, Serial No. 1037. Wilcox, *Rifles and Rifle Practice*, 218.

26. RCO, 1855–60.

27. Quotations in Martin Rywell, *The Gun That Shaped American Destiny* (Harriman, Tenn., 1957), 34–36.

28. Senate Ex. Doc. 1, 35th Cong., 2nd Sess., Serial No. 975.

29. Statement from Frankford Arsenal, in RCO, 1859.

30. U.S. pats. 8126, of 27 May 1851, 15141, of 17 June 1856, and 26364, of 6 Dec. 1859. British pat. 725, of 22 March 1859. Herschel C. Logan, *Cartridges* (Harrisburg, Pa., 1959), 31, 33–36.

31. *Scientific American*, 19 Sept. 1857. WDC, 1857.

32. RCO, 1859–60. Reilly, *Military Small Arms*, 143–45. House Ex. Doc. 99, 40th Cong., 2nd Sess., Serial No. 1338.

33. RCO, 1857–59. WDC, 1857–59. Serven, *Colt Firearms*, 343–47.

34. Quotation in R. Q. Sutherland and R. L. Wilson, *The Book of Colt Firearms* (Kansas City, 1971), 197. Stuart to Colt, 2 Dec. 1859, Colt Letters.

35. RCO, 1859–60. House Rpt. 85, 36th Cong., 2nd Sess., Serial No. 1105. John Kirwin's account is in *Kansas Historical Quarterly*, Winter 1955, 583.

36. *Ordnance Manual for the Use of the Officers of the United States Army*, 1861, 177.

37. *The War of the Rebellion: A Compilation of the Official Records of the Union and Confederate Armies* (Washington, D.C., 1880–1900), series 1, 4: 78; cited hereafter as OR.

38. *Westerners' Brand Book* (Denver, 1951), 421, 429.

39. OR, series 3, 1: 539. Senate Ex. Doc. 72, 37th Cong., 2nd Sess., Serial No. 1123. House Rpt. 2, 37th Cong., 2nd Sess., Serial No. 1142. Senate Rpt. 108, 37th Cong., 3rd Sess., Serial No. 1154. See also Edwards, *Civil War Guns*, 135–41.

40. OR, series 1, 8: 617, 654.

41. OR, series 1, 8: 278, 316. Jackson Arms (Dallas, Tex.) Catalog 18, item 409.

42. Nolie Mumey, ed., *Bloody Trails along the Rio Grande* (Denver, 1958), 33, 80.

43. Claud E. Fuller and Richard D. Steuart, *Firearms of the Confederacy* (Huntington, W.Va., 1944), 209–11. Edwards, *Civil War Guns*, 383–84, 388–92. Jac Weller, "Shooting Confederate Infantry Arms," *American Rifleman*, May 1954, 22–24. The Enfield "Artillery" carbine had the 24 in. barrel with conventional rifling; the "Sapper's" car-

bine had the 21 in. barrel with swivel ramrod and Lancaster oval-bore rifling; see the *Journal of the Royal United Service Institution*, 26 June 1857, and Senate Ex. Doc. 60, Serial No. 1037.

44. House Ex. Doc. 99, Serial No. 1338.

45. Sellers, *Sharps Firearms*, 75–82. OR, series 1, 50: pt. 1, 775, 971. "Quarterly Summary Statement of Ordnance and Ordnance Stores on Hand in the Cavalry Regiments in the Service of the United States during the Third Quarter Ending Sept. 30, 1863," Entry 110, Record Group 156 (Records of the Office of the Chief of Ordnance), National Archives, Washington, D.C.; cited hereafter as SSOC.

46. RCO, 1862. House Ex. Doc. 67, 37th Cong., 2nd Sess., Serial No. 1131. U.S. pats 20954, of 20 July 1858, and 32032, of 9 April 1861. SSOC, 31 Dec. 1862, 31 Dec. 1863, and 30 June 1864. See also the 1864 Merrill catalog, in L. D. Satterlee, comp., *Ten Old Gun Catalogs for the Collector* (1940; reprint ed., Chicago, 1962).

47. House Ex. Doc. 67, Serial No. 1131. RCO, 1862. *Instructions for Making Quarterly Returns of Ordnance and Ordnance Stores . . . 1865*; reprinted in Col. Berkeley R. Lewis, *Small Arms and Ammunition in the United States Service* (Washington, 1956), 287. Vincent Osborne's account is in *Kansas Historical Quarterly*, May 1952, 127, 129.

48. "Ledger of Issues of Ordnance and Ordnance Stores to the Loyal States under the President's Calls of 1862," Entry 118, Record Group 156 (Records of the Office of the Chief of Ordnance), National Archives, Washington, D.C. SSOC, 30 Sept. and 31 Dec. 1863, 31 March 1864. Maj. Fred B. Rogers, *Soldiers of the Overland* (San Francisco, 1938), 589.

49. George Bird Grinnell, *Two Great Scouts and the Pawnee Battalion* (Cleveland, 1928), 65. Donald F. Danker, ed., *Man of the Plains . . .* (Lincoln, Neb., 1961), 13. SSOC, 30 Sept. and 31 Dec. 1863. The Wiseman musket, made by Whitney in 1839, is now with the Nebraska State Historical Society.

50. SSOC, 31 Dec. 1863 and 31 March 1864.

51. "Abstracts of Army Officers' Reports on Small Arms and on Accoutrements and Horse Equipment," 1863–64, Entry 215, Record Group 156 (Records of the Office of the Chief of Ordnance), National Archives, Washington, D.C.; cited hereafter as "Army Officers' Reports."

52. WDC, 1860. U.S. pats. 15496, of 5 Aug. 1856, and 17644, of 23 June 1857. The production version of Smith's carbine is shown in British pat. 372, of 9 Feb 1859. See also J. H. Walsh, *The Shot-Gun and Sporting Rifle* (London, 1859), 343–44. House Misc. Doc. 20, pt. 1, 47th Cong., 2nd Sess., Serial No. 2119. Logan, *Cartridges*, 33–34. Lustyik, *Civil War Carbines*, 39–40. Senate Ex. Doc. 72, Serial No. 1123. House Ex. Doc. 99, Serial No. 1338.

53. U.S. pat. 29157, of 17 July 1860. House Misc. Doc. 20, Serial No. 2119. Logan, *Cartridges*, 36. Lustyik, *Civil War Carbines*, 11, 47. House Ex. Doc. 99, Serial No. 1338.

54. U.S. pat. 21523, of 14 Sept. 1858. Andrew F. Lustyik, "The Starr Carbine," *American Rifleman*, March 1966, 30–32. House Ex. Doc. 99, Serial No. 1338.

55. House Ex. Doc. 99, Serial No. 1338. Sellers, *Sharps*

Firearms, 75–76, 84–85. J. Ross Browne, *Adventures in the Apache Country* (New York, 1871), 125.

56. "Summary Statement of Ordnance and Ordnance Stores on Hand at the Forts, Batteries, and Garrisons of the United States during the First Quarter Ending March 31, 1864," Record Group 156 (Records of the Office of the Chief of Ordnance), National Archives, Washington, D.C.; cited hereafter as SSOF.

57. SSOC, 31 Dec. 1863 and 31 March 1864. SSOF, 31 Dec. 1863 and 31 March 1864.

58. OR, series 1, 41: pt. 1, 238–39; pt. 4, 23. Mrs. Ellen Williams, *History of the Second Colorados* (New York, 1885), 45–46. Senate Rpt. 142, 38th Cong., 2nd Sess., Serial No. 1214. Irving W. Stanton, *Sixty Years in Colorado* (Denver, 1922), 106.

59. "Army Officers' Reports." Senate Ex. Doc. 26, 39th Cong., 2nd Sess., Serial No. 1277. Irving Howbert, *Memories of a Lifetime in the Pike's Peak Region* (New York and London, 1925), 119. Morse H. Coffin, *The Battle of Sand Creek*, ed. Alan W. Farley (Waco, Tex., 1965), 23.

60. Coffin, *Sand Creek*, 9, 24. U.S. pats. 25926, of 25 Oct. 1859, and 36925, of 11 Nov. 1862. *Scientific American*, 6 July 1861. *Leslie's Weekly*, 23 Nov. and 28 Dec. 1861. *Frank Leslie's Illustrated Newspaper*, 4 Jan. 1862.

61. Capt. Eugene F. Ware, *The Indian War of 1864*, ed. Clyde C. Walton (N.Y., 1960), 6. OR, series 1, 48: 323.

62. Senate Ex. Doc. 72, Serial No. 1123. Edwards, *Civil War Guns*, 144–57. House Ex. Doc. 99, Serial No. 1338. See also House Ex. Doc. 53, 39th Cong., 2nd Sess., Serial No. 1290.

63. U.S. pats. 27393, of 6 March 1860, and 36062, of 29 July 1862. A Spencer ring-lever rifle is shown in British pat. 843, of 5 April 1861. *Scientific American*, 25 Jan. 1862. H. W. S. Cleveland, *Hints to Riflemen* (New York, 1864), 164–68.

64. Cleveland, *Hints to Riflemen*, 168. Edwards, *Civil War guns*, 144–57, passim. Col. Berkeley R. Lewis, *Notes on Cavalry Weapons of the American Civil War, 1816–1865* (Washington, D.C., 1961), 7–8. See also the cartridges illustrated in the Schuyler, Hartley, & Graham 1864 catalog.

65. Quotation in Spencer Repeating Rifle Co. 1866 Catalog, in Satterlee, *Ten Old Gun Catalogs*.

66. J. W. Vaughn, *The Battle of Platte Bridge* (Norman, Okla., 1963), 50, 116.

67. Charles H. Springer, "Campaign against the Sioux Indians . . . ," unpublished manuscript, United States Army Military History Institute, Carlisle Barracks, Pa.

CHAPTER 13

1. *War Department Contracts*, 1855; cited hereafter as WDC. Specific locations for the annual summaries of contracts made by the War Department between 1828 and 1861 are given in the bibliography.

2. "Inspection of the Department of Texas, 1856," Miscellaneous File 282, Record Group 94 (Records of the Adjutant General's Office), National Archives, Washington, D.C.; cited hereafter as "Mansfield's Report on Texas." This report is reprinted in the *Southwestern Historical Quarterly*, Oct. 1938–April 1939. Several M1842 pistols from the collection of the late Joseph W. Dessrich are rifled with wide, shallow grooves; this was probably done in the 1850s.

3. "Mansfield's Report on Texas." John Van Deusen DuBois, *Campaigns in the West, 1856–61*, ed. George P. Hammond (Tucson, Ariz., 1949), 114.

4. Otis E. Young, *The West of Philip St. George Cooke* (Glendale, Cal., 1955), 286—87.

5. Quotation in Robert M. Utley, *Frontiersmen in Blue* (New York, 1967), 26–27.

6. J. B. Hood, *Advance and Retreat*, ed. Richard N. Current (Bloomington, Ind., 1959), 11. Senate Ex. Doc. 11, 35th Cong., 1st Sess., Serial No. 920. Ferguson's account is in *Kansas Historical Collections*, 1911–12, 305–8.

7. Capt. Randolph B. Marcy, *The Prairie Traveller* (New York, 1859), 165–66.

8. Waldo E. Rosebush, *Frontier Steel* (Appleton, Wis., 1958), frontispiece, 278–79.

9. George Crook, *General George Crook, His Autobiography*, ed. Martin F. Schmitt (Norman, Okla., 1960), 46.

10. William B. Edwards, *The Story of Colt's Revolver* (Harrisburg, Pa., 1953), 322–23, 343–46. *Report of the Chief of Ordnance*, 1857; cited hereafter as RCO. Specific locations for the annual reports of the chief of ordnance from 1822 to 1865 are given in the bibliography. WDC, 1857.

11. A. W. F. Taylerson, R. A. N. Andrews, and J. Frith, *The Revolver, 1818–1865* (New York, 1968), 71–120, passim.

12. Frank M. Sellers and Samuel E. Smith, *American Percussion Revolvers* (Ottawa, 1971), 1, 14, 80, 96–97.

13. Lt. Eli Long's Journal, May–Sept. 1857, United States Army Military History Institute, Carlisle Barracks, Pa. RCO, 1858–60. See also House Report 85, 36th Cong., 2nd Sess., Serial No. 1105.

14. RCO, 1858. U.S. pats. 8982, of 1 June 1852, and 15144, of 17 June 1856. Sellers and Smith, *American Percussion Revolvers*, 113–17.

15. RCO, 1855–60. U.S. pat. 28331, of 15 May 1860. Sellers and Smith, *American Percussion Revolvers*, 152–55. House Ex. Doc. 99, 40th Cong., 2nd Sess., Serial No. 1338.

16. RCO, 1855–60. Senate Ex. Doc. 35, 35th Cong., 2nd Sess., Serial No. 984. Quotation in Claud E. Fuller, *The Breech-Loader in the Service, 1816–1917* (1933; reprint ed., New Milford, Conn., 1965), 76.

17. House Report 85, Serial No. 1105. RCO, 1856–60.

18. RCO, 1855–60.

19. *The War of the Rebellion: A Compilation of the Official Records of the Union and Confederate Armies* (Washington, D.C., 1880–1900), series 1, 4: 78. Card No. 00062, Arrott Collection, Ft. Union National Monument, Watrous, N.M.

20. Photostat in Charles T. Haven and Frank A. Belden, *The History of the Colt Revolver* (New York, 1940), 388. Edwards, *The Story of Colt's Revolver*, 356–62. House Ex. Doc. 99, Serial No. 1338.

21. OR, series 1, 8: 557, 617.

22. *RCO,* 1862.

23. House Ex. Doc. 67, 37th Cong., 2nd Sess., Serial No. 1131. House Ex. Doc. 99, Serial No. 1338. Kerr held two British patents: 2896, of 17 Dec. 1858, and 242, of 26 Jan. 1859. He also held U.S. pat. 39409, of 4 Aug. 1863. See Taylerson, Andrews, and Frith, *The Revolver, 1818– 1865,* 140–42. The Great Western Gun Works catalog of 1871 offered .44 cal. Kerrs for eight dollars; see L. D. Satterlee, comp., *Ten Old Gun Catalogs for the Collector* (1940; reprint ed., Chicago, 1962). The Perrin was the subject of British pat. 2263, of 5 Oct. 1859. An undated Ordnance document in the National Archives, probably compiled in the spring of 1865, lists 99 Perrins at Fort Leavenworth. Another undated Ordnance document, compiled about 1867 (House Misc. Doc. 152, 40th Cong., 2nd Sess., Serial No. 1350), shows 495 Perrins in government storage. The "Raphael" revolver and its rimless metallic cartridge were patented in France and Belgium in 1860 by Pidault & Cordier and were, in all probability, manufactured by them; letter from A. W. F. Taylerson to authors, 14 May 1975.

24. On 24 April 1862, Eliphalet Remington testified that "our revolvers . . . heretofore delivered are upon Beal's patent; those we propose to make in future are in accordance with Elliott's patent. The patented part, in both cases, is the mode of releasing the cylinder from its position . . ."; see Senate Ex. Doc. 72, Serial No. 1123. House Ex. Doc. 99, Serial No. 1338. William B. Edwards, *Civil War Guns* (Harrisburg, Pa., 1962), 192–95. U.S. pats 21478, of 14 Sept. 1858, 33932, of 17 Dec. 1861, 37329, of 6 Jan. 1863, and 37921, of 17 March 1863.

25. Senate Ex. Doc. 72, Serial No. 1123. Gardner's account is in *Kansas Historical Collections,* 1915–18, 240, 269.

26. U.S. pats. 14118, of 15 Jan. 1856, and 30843, of 4 Dec. 1860. British pat. 880, of 7 April 1860. *WDC,* 1858.

27. Sellers and Smith, *American Percussion Revolvers,* 168– 70. U.S. pat. 42435, of 19 April 1864. House Ex. Doc. 99, Serial No. 1338.

28. British pat. 955, of 27 April 1854. Taylerson, Andrews, and Frith, *The Revolver, 1818–1865,* 303. *OR,* series 3, vol. 1, 485, 594. House Ex. Doc. 67, Serial No. 1131. House Ex. Doc. 99, Serial No. 1338. Schuyler, Hartley, & Graham were selling LeFaucheux revolvers as early as 1859; see *Spirit of the Times,* 9 April 1859.

29. Osborne's account is in the *Kansas Historical Quarterly,* May 1952, 129. "Summary Statement of Ordnance and Ordnance Stores on Hand in the Cavalry Regiments in the Service of the United States during the Fourth Quarter Ending Dec. 31, 1862 . . . the Second Quarter Ending June 30, 1863 . . . the Third Quarter Ending Sept. 30, 1863, [and] the Fourth Quarter Ending Dec. 31, 1863," Entry 110, Record Group 156 (Records of the Office of the Chief of Ordnance), National Archives, Washington, D.C.; cited hereafter as *SSOC.*

30. *SSOC,* 30 June and 30 Sept. 1863.

31. Edwards, *Civil War Guns,* 357. William A. Albaugh III, Hugh Benet, Jr., and Edward N. Simmons, *Confederate Handguns* (Philadelphia, 1963).

32. "Summary Statement of Ordnance and Ordnance Stores on Hand at the Forts, Batteries, and Garrisons of the United States during the First Quarter Ending March 31, 1864," Record Group 156 (Records of the Office of the Chief of Ordnance), National Archives, Washington, D.C.; cited hereafter as *SSOF. SSOC,* 30 Sept. and 31 Dec. 1863, 31 March 1864.

33. Mrs. Ellen Williams, *History of the Second Colorados* (New York, 1885), 45–46. "Abstracts of Army Officers' Reports on Small Arms and on Accoutrements and Horse Equipment," 1863–64, Entry 215, Record Group 156 (Records of the Office of the Chief of Ordnance), National Archives, Washington, D.C.

34. *SSOC,* 31 Dec. 1863. Sellers and Smith, *American Percussion Revolvers,* 152–55.

35. U.S. pat 21054, of 27 July 1858. Senate Ex. Doc. 72, Serial No. 1123. Sellers and Smith, *American Percussion Revolvers,* 126–30, 142–47.

36. House Ex. Doc. 99, Serial No. 1338.

37. *SSOC,* 30 Sept. and 31 Dec. 1863. *SSOF,* 31 March 1864. An undated Ordnance document in the National Archives, probably compiled in the spring of 1865, shows 539 LeFaucheux revolvers at San Antonio Arsenal, 622 at Vancouver, 36 at Leavenworth, and 29 at Ft. Union.

38. *SSOF,* 31 March 1864.

39. John Biringer Daybooks, June–November, 1864, in the possession of J. Biringer Miller, Leavenworth, Kansas.

40. J. W. Vaughn, *The Battle of Platte Bridge* (Norman, Okla., 1963), 63.

CHAPTER 14

1. Benjamin Butler Harris, *The Gila Trail,* ed. Richard H. Dillon (Norman, Okla., 1960), 97, 101.

2. Charles E. Hanson, Jr., *The Hawken Rifle: Its Place in History* (Chadron, Neb., 1979), 87. Clipping from the St. Louis *Globe-Democrat,* c. 1882, Jacob and Samuel Hawken Papers, Missouri Historical Society, St. Louis, Mo.

3. St. Louis *Missouri Democrat,* 26 July 1853 and 2 April 1856. Hanson, *The Hawken Rifle,* 41–43, 49. John D. Baird, *Hawken Rifles, the Mountain Man's Choice* (Franklin, Ind., 1968).

4. Charles E. Hanson, Jr., *The Plains Rifle* (Harrisburg, Pa., 1960), 28, 43. [Frank M. Sellers], *The William M. Locke Collection* (East Point, Ga., 1973), 493.

5. Herschel C. Logan, "H. E. Dimick of St. Louis," *American Rifleman,* April 1958, 29–33. St. Louis *Missouri Republican,* 15 May 1850.

6. Logan, "H. E. Dimick," 31. Hanson, *The Plains Rifle,* 66. Jackson Arms (Dallas, Tex.) Catalog 24, item 408A.

7. *Missouri Republican,* 5 March 1850. *Missouri Democrat,* 8 May 1854. *Western Journal and Civilian,* Dec. 1854. Albright orders of Feb. 1849, April–Sept. 1850, and Aug. 1853, Bolton Gun Works Records, microfilm reels 9 and 10, J. J. Henry Papers, Eleutherian Mills Historical Library, Wilmington, Del.

8. Child, Pratt, & Co.–P. S. Justice order of April 1854, microfilm reel 10, Henry Papers.

9. Justice to Henry, 16 May 1855, microfilm reel 2; Albright-Justice order of Feb. 1856; H. E. D.–Justice order of May 1857; and R. B.–Justice order of Aug. 1857, microfilm reel 10, Henry Papers. Hanson, *The Plains Rifle*, 58–59. Hanson, *The Hawken Rifle*, 71.

10. Hanson, *The Plains Rifle*, 35, 66.

11. Freide-Justice orders of April 1858, and Feb. 1859, microfilm reel 10, Henry Papers. Hanson, *The Plains Rifle*, 41, 67.

12. Albright order of Feb. 1858, microfilm reel 10, Henry Papers.

13. Logan, "H. E. Dimick," 30–31. Topeka *Tribune*, 31 March 1859.

14. George Jackson's Journal, in *Colorado Magazine*, Nov. 1935, 208–9. David Kellogg's Diary, in *The Trail*, Jan. 1913, 9.

15. John E. Parsons, *Henry Deringer's Pocket Pistol* (New York, 1952), 153, 172. Portland *Oregonian*, 28 Aug. 1852. Oregon *Spectator*, 29 Oct. 1853. The *Columbian*, 10 Sept. 1853.

16. Lawrence P. Shelton, *California Gunsmiths, 1846–1900* (Fair Oaks, Cal., 1977), 10. Sacramento *Union*, 21 Sept. 1855 and 30 Sept. 1856.

17. San Francisco *Alta California*, 15 Nov. 1853 and 13 Oct. 1856. Parsons, *Deringer's Pocket Pistol*, 184.

18. Alonzo Delano, *Life on the Plains and Among the Diggings* (1854; reprint ed., Ann Arbor, Mich., 1966), 65, 112, 145–46. David Morris Potter, ed., *The Trail to California . . .* (New Haven, 1945), 57–60. LeRoy R. Hafen, ed., *Pike's Peak Gold Rush Guidebooks of 1859* (Glendale, Cal., 1941), 133.

19. Gammell order of Feb. 1851, microfilm reel 9; Gammell to Henry, 15 Aug. 1853 and 9 May 1854, microfilm reel 2, Henry Papers.

20. Ewing to Henry, 12 and 20 Aug. 1851, microfilm reel 2, Henry Papers. Photostat in Parsons, *Deringer's Pocket Pistol*, 73. Galveston *News*, 16 Feb. 1858.

21. Little Rock *Arkansas Gazette*, 17 Aug. 1851 and 19 Aug. 1853.

22. *Missouri Democrat*, 1 Sept. 1854, 27 July 1855, and 6 March 1856. *Forest & Stream*, 2 Aug. 1877. Photostat in Parsons, *Deringer's Pocket Pistol*, 73. *Alta California*, 25 Aug. 1860.

23. Enterprise Gun Works 1876 Catalog, in L. D. Satterlee, comp., *Ten Old Gun Catalogs for the Collector* (1940; reprint ed., Chicago, 1962). Hanson, *The Plains Rifle*, 58, 78.

24. Hanson, *The Hawken Rifle*, 71. Lawrence P. Shelton, "A California Gunmaker: Joseph Allen Craig," *The Gun Report*, Jan. 1976, 60–61.

25. John C. Cremony, *Life among the Apaches, 1850–1868* (1868; reprint ed., Glorieta, N.M., 1969), 83. Galveston *News*, 30 March and 13 July 1852. Sacramento *Union*, 20 Sept. 1856. Photostats in Parsons, *Deringer's Pocket Pistol*, 43, 73.

26. *Alta California*, 17 Sept. 1855. Col. Robert E. Gardner, *Small Arms Makers* (New York, 1963), 79. *Spirit of the Times*, 31 July 1852 and 21 June 1856.

27. Galveston *News*, 2 May and 5 Sept. 1854. Wolfe & Gillespie orders of April and Nov. 1853, microfilm reel 10, Henry Papers. Sacramento *Union*, 20 Nov. 1856. Gardner, *Small Arms Makers*, 49.

28. Hanson, *The Plains Rifle*, 87–90. N. Flayderman & Co. (New Milford, Conn.) Catalog 89, item 978. Jackson Arms Catalog 18, item 391.

29. Granville Stuart, *Forty Years on the Frontier*, ed. Paul C. Phillips (Glendale, Cal.), 135–36. Lord George C. F. Berkeley, *The English Sportsman in the Western Prairies* (London, 1861), 9, 255.

30. George Douglas Brewerton, *Overland with Kit Carson* (New York, 1930), 49. New Orleans *Picayune*, 10 March 1849.

31. Grant Foreman, *Marcy and the Gold Seekers . . .* (Norman, Okla., 1939), 117.

32. *Missouri Republican*, 11 Aug. 1849 and 21 March 1850. Ralph P. Bieber, ed., *Southern Trails to California in 1849* (Glendale, Cal., 1937), 169. Enos Christman, *One Man's Gold . . .*, ed. Florence Morrow Christman (New York, 1930), 12, 137, 141. See also Irene D. Paden, ed., *The Journal of Madison Berryman Moorman, 1850–1851* (San Francisco, 1948), 3–4. *Southwestern Historical Quarterly*, April 1932, 298.

33. *Missouri Democrat*, 7 April 1853. Portland *Oregonian*, 3 May 1856.

34. House Ex. Doc. 5, 31st Cong., 1st Sess., Serial No. 569.

35. Senate Ex. Doc. 60, 36th Cong., 1st Sess., Serial No. 1037. J. H. Walsh, *The Shot-Gun and Sporting Rifle* (London, 1859), 315–19, 324, 354–55. "Rifled Guns," *Atlantic Monthly*, Oct. 1859, 444–55. *Journal of the Royal United Service Institution*, 26 June 1857; 26 March, 9 April, and 14 June 1858; 4 June 1860; 1 Feb. 1864. *Scientific American*, 22 April 1854. U.S. pat. 11174, of 27 June 1854. British pat. 1959/1859. Col. Berkeley R. Lewis, *Small Arms and Ammunition in the United States Service* (Washington, D.C., 1956), pl. 32.

36. *Missouri Democrat*, 16 March and 27 July 1855. Photostat in Parsons, *Deringer's Pocket Pistol*, 43. Memphis *Appeal*, 6 Jan. 1858.

37. U.S. pat 5763, of 12 Sept. 1848. Frank M. Sellers, *Sharps Firearms* (N. Hollywood, Cal., 1978), 4–7, 15–21.

38. *Scientific American*, 9 March 1850. Sellers, *Sharps Firearms*, 21–23.

39. *Missouri Republican*, 21 April 1850. John Russell Bartlett, *Personal Narrative of Exploration and Incidents . . .* (New York, 1854), 1: 48.

40. Sellers, *Sharps Firearms*, 40, 43–44.

41. Ibid., 40–42, 45–56.

42. Ibid., 40, 45–46, 49.

43. Quotation in Martin Rywell, *The Gun That Shaped American Destiny* (Harriman, Tenn., 1957), 37. *Alta California*, 3 May 1854.

44. Frederick Law Olmsted, *A Journey through Texas . . .* (New York and London, 1857), 74, 286–87. W. T. Hamilton, *My Sixty Years on the Plains* (Norman, Okla., 1960), 162. Quotation in Rywell, *American Destiny*, 38.

45. *Missouri Democrat*, 8 May 1854. *Alta California*, 6 and 24 Feb. 1854.

46. Sellers, *Sharps Firearms*, 92–94.

47. Sellers, *Sharps Firearms*, 92–94. George Douglas Brewerton, *The War in Kansas* (New York, 1856), 188.

48. William Phillips, *The Conquest of Kansas* (Boston, 1856), 163, 180.

49. Sellers, *Sharps Firearms*, 34–37, 61–64, 100–102. House Ex. Doc. 1, 34th Cong., 3rd Sess., Serial No. 894.

50. Phillips, *The Conquest of Kansas*, 285. *Kansas Historical Quarterly*, May 1947, 211–13. House Ex. Doc. 1, Serial No. 894.

51. Phillips, *The Conquest of Kansas*, 355, 387.

52. Charles De Long's Journal, in the *California Historical Society Quarterly*, March 1930, 57. Memphis *Appeal*, 22 Oct. 1856 and 6 Jan. 1858. John C. Reid, *Reid's Tramp* (1858; reprint ed., Austin, Tex., 1935), 15.

53. *Missouri Democrat*, 4 Oct. 1858. Hafen, *Gold Rush Guidebooks*, 62. Horace Greeley, *An Overland Journey . . .* (1860; reprint ed., Ann Arbor, Mich., 1966), 82, 92. See also Francis P. Farquhar, ed., *Up and Down California in 1860–1864* (Berkeley and Los Angeles, 1949), 107, 109, and the quotation in Ralph Moody, *Stagecoach West* (New York, 1967), 85.

54. Bill Hickman, *Brigham's Destroying Angel . . .* (New York, 1873), 66–67, 74–75. *Alta California*, 2 and 3 April, 1850. William Manly, *Death Valley in '49* (1894; reprint ed., Ann Arbor, Mich., 1966), 152, 199.

55. Frank M. Sellers and Samuel E. Smith, *American Percussion Revolvers* (Ottawa, 1971), 15. William G. Renwick, "The Revolving Cylinder Shoulder Arms," in James E. Serven, ed., *The Collecting of Guns* (Harrisburg, Pa., 1964), 88–90. See also R. R. Olmsted, *Scenes of Wonder and Curiosity from Hutchings California Magazine, 1856–1861* (Berkeley, 1962), 364.

56. Galveston *News*, 13 July 1852 and 31 Oct. 1854. Sellers and Smith, *American Percussion Revolvers*, 67–68, 114–16, 180–84. Renwick, "Revolving Cylinder Shoulder Arms," 90–93.

57. R. L. Wilson, *The Colt Heritage* (New York, n.d.), 84, 86, 88. British pat. 908, of 16 April 1856. Photostat in Charles J. Haven and Frank A. Belden, *A History of the Colt Revolver* (New York, 1940), 374.

58. Capt. Randolph B. Marcy, *The Prairie Traveler* (New York, 1859), 42–43. Wilson, *The Colt Heritage*, 30, 148. H. W. S. Cleveland, *Hints to Riflemen* (New York, 1864), 157–64, 213–16.

59. Quotation in Rywell, *American Destiny*, 38–39. U.S. pat 18678, of 24 Nov. 1857. David Edwards had patented this idea as early as 1839; see his U.S. pat 1134, of 25 April 1839. See also U.S. pats. 15110, of 10 June 1856, and 15202, of 24 June 1856.

60. U.S. pat. 13507, of 28 Aug. 1855. Andrew F. Lustyik, "Joslyn: The Man and His Carbines," *American Rifleman*, July 1968, 32–34. *Scientific American*, 12 Sept. 1857.

61. *Missouri Democrat*, 28 March 1859. U.S. pat. 33435, of 8 Oct. 1861.

62. U.S. pat 14491, of 25 March 1856. Tubac *Arizonian*, 2 June 1859. William B. Edwards, *Civil War Guns* (Harrisburg, Pa., 1962), 115.

63. *Arizonian*, 2 June 1859. Quotation in William B. Edwards, *The Story of Colt's Revolver* (Harrisburg, Pa., 1953), 349.

64. U.S. pat 27874, of 10 April 1860. *Scientific American*, 20 Dec. 1862. U.S. pat. 38042, of 31 March 1863.

65. U.S. pats 8126, of 27 May 1851, 15141, of 17 June 1856, and 26364, of 6 Dec. 1859. *Scientific American*, 19 Sept. 1857.

66. Cleveland, *Hints to Riflemen*, 137–48, 251–52. Galveston *News*, 22 Nov. 1859. Sir Richard Francis Burton, *The City of the Saints*, ed. Fawn M. Brodie (New York, 1963), 13, 505. Stuart, *Forty Years on the Frontier*, 168, 190–2.

67. British pat. 386, of 21 Feb. 1855. [John Deane], *Deane's Manual of the History and Science of Fire-Arms* (1858; reprint ed., Huntington, W.Va., n.d.), 181–86. J. H. Walsh, *The Shot-Gun and Sporting Rifle* (London, 1859), 329–32.

68. Berkeley, *The English Sportsman*, 9.

69. Hafen, *Gold Rush Guidebooks*, 167–69. Quotation in A. C. Gould, *Modern American Rifles* (1892; reprint ed., Plantersville, S.C., 1946), 40–41.

70. Letter from Lt. Col. C. F. Smith to the assistant adjutant general, City of New York, 18 July 1860, supplied by James E. Serven.

71. *Missouri Democrat*, 12 Sept. 1859. Denver *Rocky Mountain News*, 25 Jan. 1860 and 4 April 1862. Hanson, *The Hawken Rifle*, 46.

72. Hanson, *The Hawken Rifle*, 46.

73. Tobin's account in *Colorado Magazine*, March 1932, 64.

74. Hanson, *The Plains Rifle*, 34, 65, 124, 139–41. Folsom Bros. 1869 catalog, in Satterlee, *Ten Old Gun Catalogs*. Logan, "H. E. Dimick," 31. N. Flayderman & Co. catalogs 48, item 517, and 51, item 83.

75. William Gallaher's Journal, in the *Missouri Historical Review*, Oct. 1962–July 1963, 165, 280.

76. W. B. Vickers, *History of the City of Denver, Arapahoe County, and Colorado* (Chicago, 1880). Council Bluffs *Bugle*, 28 April 1857. Frank Sellers, "Carlos Gove," *The Colorado Gun Collectors 1974 Annual*.

77. Sellers, "Carlos Gove." *Rocky Mountain News*, 10 May and 5 Sept. 1865.

78. R. Glison, *Journal of Army Life* (San Francisco, 1874), 59. *Missouri Republican*, 21 March 1850. *Omaha Times*, 18 June 1857.

79. Gammell order of March 1853, microfilm reel 10, Henry Papers. *Arkansas Gazette*, 17 Feb. 1854. Galveston *News*, 19 Jan. 1858.

80. Quotation in Gould, *Modern American Rifles*, 41. Berkeley, *The English Sportsman*, 9, 253–54.

81. Gardner, *Small Arms Makers*, 165. *Rocky Mountain News*, 22 May 1863. Maurice O'Connor Morris, *Rambles in the Rocky Mountains* (London, 1864), 159. Nolie Mumey, *The Life of Jim Baker* (Denver, 1931), 79.

82. A. K. McClure, *Three Thousand Miles through the Rocky Mountains* (Philadelphia, 1869), 70–71.

83. Memphis *Appeal*, 11 June 1851. *Missouri Democrat*, 19 Sept. 1855. Westport, Kansas, *Border Star*, 31 Dec. 1858. Quotation in Hanson, *The Hawken Rifle*, 57. Helen McCann White, ed., *Ho! For the Gold Fields* (St. Paul, Minn., 1966), 54.

84. House Ex. Doc. 99, 40th Cong., 2nd Sess., Serial No. 1338. U.S. pats. 25926, of 25 Oct. 1859, and 36925, of 11 Nov. 1862. *Scientific American*, 6 July 1861. Cleveland, *Hints to Riflemen*, 149–54, 266.

85. *Leslie's Weekly*, 23 Nov. and 28 Dec. 1861. *Frank Leslie's Illustrated Newspaper*, 4 Jan. 1862. Senate Ex. Doc. 17, 37th Cong., 3rd Sess., Serial No. 1149. Frank A. Root and William Elsey Connelley, eds., *The Overland Stage to California* (1901; reprint ed., Columbus, Ohio, 1950), 190, 583.

86. *Missouri Democrat*, 22 July 1863. Andrew F. Rolle, ed., *The Road to Virginia City* (Norman, Okla., 1960), 43. Alexander Toponce, *Reminiscences of Alexander Toponce, Pioneer, 1839–1923* (Ogden, Utah, 1923), 114–17. Daybooks of John Biringer, Leavenworth, 1859–1881, in the possession of J. Biringer Miller, Leavenworth, Kansas.

87. *Missouri Republican*, 8 Feb. 1865. U.S. pat. 33631, of 5 Nov. 1861. *American Artisan*, 7 Nov. 1866.

88. Frank de Haas, *Single Shot Rifles and Actions* (Chicago, 1969), 9–12. *Frank Leslie's Illustrated Newspaper*, 29 March 1862. House Ex. Doc. 99, Serial No. 1338. Edward C. Barber, *The Crack Shot* (New York, 1868), 121–23.

89. U.S. pat 41166, of 5 Jan. 1864. Robert B. David, *Finn Burnett, Frontiersman* (Glendale, Cal., 1937), 32. Omaha *Nebraska Republican*, 10 Oct. and 3 Nov. 1865. Atchison *Champion*, 6 Oct. 1865. Raymond W. Settle and Mary Lund Settle, *Overland Days to Montana in 1865* (Glendale, Cal., 1971), 190.

90. U.S. pat 8317, of 26 Aug. 1851. *Alta California*, 11 Aug. 1851. U.S. pat. 10535, of 14 Feb. 1854.

91. John E. Parsons, *The First Winchester* (New York, 1955), 4–7. *New York Times*, 1 Sept. 1859. *Harper's Weekly*, 10 March 1860. Shelton, *California Gunsmiths*, 4.

92. U.S. pat. 30446, of 16 Oct. 1860.

93. Parsons, *The First Winchester*, xx–xxi, 8–10, 16, 24. House Ex. Doc. 99, Serial No. 1338.

94. Parsons, *The First Winchester*, 13–14. *Missouri Democrat*, 30 March and 10 Oct. 1863. *Alta California*, 29 Sept. 1863.

95. New Haven Arms Co., 1865 catalog, in Satterlee, *Ten Old Gun Catalogs*.

96. Parsons, *The First Winchester*, xxii, 8. Toponce, *Reminiscences*, 114–17.

97. Parsons, *The First Winchester*, 38–40, 42, 46–49.

98. U.S. pat. 27393, of 6 March 1860. British pat. 843, of 5 April 1861. House Ex. Doc. 99, Serial No. 1338. *Scientific American*, 25 Jan. 1862. Cleveland, *Hints to Riflemen*, 173, 184–92, 264. Spencer Repeating Rifle Co. 1866 catalog, in Satterlee, *Ten Old Gun Catalogs*.

99. *Alta California*, 26 Aug. 1864. Photostat in Parsons, *Deringer's Pocket Pistol*, 57. Demas Barnes, *From the Atlantic to the Pacific, Overland* (New York, 1866), 44.

CHAPTER 15

1. New Orleans *Picayune*, 12 May 1849. St. Louis *Missouri Republican*, 7 and 21 March 1850. Quotation in Charles E. Hanson, Jr., *The Plains Rifle* (Harrisburg, Pa., 1960), 121. See also Wm. G. Johnston, *Experiences of a Forty-Niner* (1892; reprint ed., New York, 1973), 38–39.

2. Albright orders of April 1850 and May 1852, Bolton Gun Works Records, microfilm reel 9; J. J. Henry Papers, Eleutherian Mills Historical Library, Wilmington, Del.

3. David Morris Potter, ed., *The Trail to California* (New Haven, 1945), 9, 27. Cape Girardeau, Mo., *Eagle*, 19 Jan. 1849. New Orleans *Picayune*, 14 March and 1 May 1849. *Alta California*, 18 April 1850. Quotations in Hanson, *The Plains Rifle*, 149–50.

4. Solomon Carvalho, *Incidents of Travel and Adventure in the Far West* (1857; reprint ed., New York, 1973), 90, 152. "Captain Flack," *The Texan Rifle Hunter* (London, 1866), 139.

5. *Missouri Republican*, 11 Aug. 1849. *Missouri Democrat*, 17 May 1854, 19 Sept. 1855, and 2 Aug. 1860.

6. William Phillips, *The Conquest of Kansas* (Boston, 1856), 194, 286, 318, 386. House Ex. Doc. 1, 34th Cong., 3rd Sess., Serial No. 894. Samuel Reader's account in the *Kansas Historical Quarterly*, Nov. 1931, 32. Alexander Toponce, *Reminiscences of Alexander Toponce, Pioneer, 1839–1923* (Ogden, Utah, 1923), 24.

7. Capt. George F. Price, *Across the Continent with the Fifth Cavalry* (1883; reprint ed., New York, 1959), 52. Frederick Law Olmsted, *A Journey Through Texas . . .* (New York and London, 1857), 74. David Meriwether, *My Life in the Mountains and on the Plains*, ed. Robert A. Griffen (Norman, Okla., 1965), 262.

8. William B. Napton, *Over the Santa Fe Trail, 1857* (1905; reprint ed., Santa Fe, N.M., 1964), 45. Ray H. Mattison, ed., *Henry A. Boller, Missouri River Fur Trader* (Bismarck, N.D., 1966), 17, 29, 70, 93. *Scientific American*, 14 April 1855. U.S. pats. 17886, of 28 July 1857, and 25967, of 1 Nov. 1859.

9. Galveston *News*, 19 Jan. 1858. Memphis *Appeal*, 6 Jan. 1858.

10. Lord George C. F. Berkeley, *The English Sportsman in the Western Prairies* (London, 1861), 29, 328, 335–36.

11. *Alta California*, 25 Aug. 1860.

12. Sir Richard Francis Burton, *The City of the Saints*, ed. Fawn M. Brodie (New York, 1963), 504.

13. Helen Fitzgerald Sanders, *X Biedler, Vigilante* (Norman, Okla., 1957), 9. John Young Nelson, *Fifty Years on the Trail* (Norman, Okla., 1963), 188.

14. Maurice O'Connor Morris, *Rambles in the Rocky Mountains* (London, 1864), 247–48, 254–55.

15. Granville Stuart, *Forty Years on the Frontier*, ed. Paul C. Phillips (Glendale, Cal., 1957), 188. Thomas J. Dimsdale, *The Vigilantes of Montana* (Norman, Okla., 1953), 22–23. Sanders, *X Biedler, Vigilante*, 36, 90.

16. Daniel Ellis Conner, *Joseph Reddeford Walker and the Arizona Adventure*, ed. Donald J. Berthrong and Odessa Davenport (Norman, Okla., 1956), 211.

17. *Missouri Democrat*, 20 Feb. and 26 May 1864. Photostat in Parsons, *Deringer's Pocket Pistol*, front endpaper.

18. Photostat in Parsons, *Deringer's Pocket Pistol*, 57. W. W. Greener, *The Gun and Its Development* (1910; reprint ed., New York, n.d.), 288.

19. Lewis Winant, *Early Percussion Firearms* (New York, 1959), 116–17.

20. W. W. Greener, *Modern Breech-Loaders: Sporting and Military* (1871; reprint ed., Pueblo, Colo., n.d.), 1–5. A. W. F. Taylerson, R. A. N. Andrews, and J. Frith, *The Revolver 1818–1865* (New York, 1968), 58–59. Marius B. Peladeau, "Crimean War's End Also Ended American Arms Firm," *American Rifleman*, Jan. 1970, 42–44.

21. J. H. Walsh, *The Shot-Gun and Sporting Rifle* (London, 1859), 254–56, 276–80, 296–304. J. H. Walsh, *The Modern Sportsman's Gun and Rifle* (London, 1882), vol. 1, 144.

22. Frank M. Sellers, *Sharps Firearms* (N. Hollywood, Cal., 1978), 48, 59. *Missouri Democrat*, 1 July 1859.

23. Walsh, *The Shot-Gun and Sporting Rifle*, 267–70. Greener, *Modern Breech-Loaders*, 25. Walsh, *Gun and Rifle*, 145–49. Photostat in Taylerson, Andrews, and Frith, *The Revolver, 1818–1865*, 133.

CHAPTER 16

1. House Ex. Doc. 1, 30th Cong., 2nd Sess., Serial No. 537. William B. Edwards, *The Story of Colt's Revolver* (Harrisburg, Pa., 1953), 229–47. James E. Serven, *Colt Firearms from 1836* (Harrisburg, Pa., 1979), 44–66, 73–79, 110–13. [Frank M. Sellers], *The William M. Locke Collection* (East Point, Ga., 1973), 45–66.

2. Edwards, *Colt's Revolver*, 259–64. Serven, *Colt Firearms*, 114–17, 153–54. Sellers, *The Locke Collection*, 67–87.

3. Senate Rpt. 257, 31st Cong., 2nd Sess., Serial No. 593. Edwards, *Colt's Revolver*, 276–80, 286. Serven, *Colt Firearms*, 118–23. Sellers, *The Locke Collection*, 88–112.

4. Allen and Thurber Daybooks, Oct. 1846–March 1848, in the possession of Philip F. Van Cleave, Carlsbad, N.M. Philip F. Van Cleave, "The Arms of Ethan Allen and Associates," in James E. Serven, ed., *The Collecting of Guns* (Harrisburg, Pa., 1964), 129–31. Harold R. Mouillesseaux, *Ethan Allen, Gunmaker: His Partners, Patents, and Firearms* (Ottawa, 1973), 75–79, 96–103. Jack Dunlap, *American, British and Continental Pepperbox Firearms* (Palo Alto, Cal., 1967), 49–53, 55–56.

5. Frank M. Sellers and Samuel E. Smith, *American Percussion Revolvers* (Ottawa, 1971), 83, 90–91, 185–86. U.S. pat. 182, of 29 April 1837.

6. U.S. pat. 6669, of 28 Aug. 1849. Sellers and Smith, *American Percussion Revolvers*, 91, 186.

7. *Samuel Colt vs. the Massachusetts Arms Company. Report of the Trial, etc. . . .* (Boston, 1851). Edwards, *Colt's Revolver*, 269–74.

8. William Kelly, Jr., *An Excursion to California . . .* (London, 1851), 1: 34, 44.

9. Quotations in Charles T. Haven and Frank A. Belden, *A History of the Colt Revolver* (New York, 1940), 310–11. See also Walker J. Wyman, *California Emigrant Letters* (New York, 1952), 161.

10. New Orleans *Picayune*, 14 March 1849. Galveston *News*, 27 Aug. 1849. Austin *Tri-Weekly Gazette*, 3 Dec. 1849. *Missouri Republican*, 28 Sept. and 22 Oct. 1849. Quotation in Frank A. Root and William Elsey Connelley, *The Overland Stage to California* (1901; reprint ed., Columbus, O., 1950), 4.

11. Enos Christman, *One Man's Gold . . .*, ed. Florence Morrow Christman (New York, 1930), 203–4.

12. *Alta California*, 12 March, 7 Aug. and 8 Aug. 1851. John E. Parsons, "Colt's Pistols in the Gold Rush," *The Gun Collector*, June 1951, 558, 560, 562. Helen Giffen, ed., *The Diaries of Peter Decker* (Georgetown, Cal., 1966), 248, 255.

13. Mass. Arms Co. revolver, serial no. 431; accession no. 5128. *Oregon Spectator*, 4 May 1848, and 15 Nov. 1849. Jessie Gould Hannon, *The Boston-Newton Company Venture . . .* (Lincoln, Neb., 1969), 30.

14. New Orleans *Picayune*, 12 May and 30 Oct. 1849, and 1 May 1850. *Missouri Republican*, 28 Sept. and 22 Oct. 1849.

15. Parsons, "Colt's Pistols," 557. Marguerite Eyer Wilbur, ed. and trans., *A Pioneer at Sutter's Fort, 1846–1850* (Los Angeles, 1941), 209. Chauncey L. Canfield, *Diary of a Forty-Niner* (1906; reprint ed., Stanford, Cal., 1947), 22. See also Charles D. Ferguson, *The Experiences of a Forty-Niner* (Cleveland, 1888), 95.

16. Kenneth M. Johnson, ed., *San Francisco as It Is, Being Gleanings from the Picayune, 1850–1852* (Georgetown, Cal., 1964), 198–99.

17. Data on the Scuder pepperbox is on Card 2952, Sutter's Fort files, Sacramento, Cal. The other three pepperboxes are now in the Sutter's Fort Collection.

18. *Missouri Republican*, 14 Nov. and 13 Dec. 1849, 14 March 1850. Letters from Philip F. Van Cleave to authors, 24 March and 10 June 1973. Mouillesseaux, *Ethan Allen, Gunmaker*, 108. Dunlap, *Pepperbox Firearms*, 94–95. The "late improved Thumb Revolvers" offered by T. J. Albright in the *Republican* on 22 Oct. 1849 may also have been Stockings.

19. S. C. Jett's advertisement in the *Missouri Republican* for 28 Sept. 1849 specifically lists Allen "single barrel, self cocking" pistols. Norm Flayderman, *Flayderman's Guide to Antique American Firearms*, 2nd ed. (Northfield, Ill., 1980), 114, 334, 339. Van Cleave, "The Arms of Ethan Allen," 130. Allen and Thurber Daybooks. Mouillesseaux, *Ethan Allen, Gunmaker*, 96, 108–16. Card 206, Sutter's Fort Files. Bill Gary, "Ogden, Utah, or Lancaster, Texas?" *The Gun Report*, July 1980, 19. Herschel C. Logan, *The Pictorial History of the Underhammer Gun* (New York, 1960), 220–21. Burlington, Iowa, *Hawk Eye*, 22 Nov. 1849.

20. Flayderman, *Antique American Firearms*, 334, 348. Albright orders of June and Sept. 1850, Bolton Gun Works Records, microfilm reel 9, J. J. Henry Papers, Eleutherian Mills Historical Library, Wilmington, Del.

21. Mahlon Fairchild's Journal, in the *California Historical Society Quarterly*, March 1934, 21.

22. Quotation in Carl P. Russell, *Guns on the Early Frontiers* (Berkeley and Los Angeles, 1957), 309. John E. Parsons, *Henry Deringer's Pocket Pistol* (New York, 1952), 45, 132, 160. Jackson Arms (Dallas, Tex.) catalog 21A, item 791.

23. George Douglas Brewerton, *Overland with Kit Carson* (New York, 1930), 188. See also Samuel Chamberlain, *My Confession* (New York, 1956), 28. New Orleans *Picayune*, 14 March 1849. *Missouri Republican*, 28 Sept. 1849.

24. Parsons, *Deringer's Pocket Pistol*, 70–78, 155. The pistols were reaching other parts of the West at about the same time; see the Sutton, Griffith, & Co. advertisement for twelve pairs of "Genuine Derringer Pistols" in the Fort Smith, Arkansas, *Herald*, 21 March 1851.

25. Sacramento *Union*, 20 March 1852. G. C. Pearson, *Overland in 1849*, ed. Jessie H. Goodman (Los Angeles, 1961), 41. James S. Brown, *Life of a Pioneer* (Salt Lake City, 1900), 149. Christman, *One Man's Gold*, 182.

26. J. D. Borthwich, *The Gold Hunters* (New York, 1917), 84.

27. Wilbur, *A Pioneer at Sutter's Fort*, 135. J. D. Borthwich, *Three Years in California* (Edinburgh, 1857), 119.

28. New Orleans *Picayune*, 23 May 1851. Memphis *Appeal*, 11 June 1851.

29. Galveston *News*, 1 April and 13 July 1852.

30. Galveston *News*, 25 March 1851. *Alta California*, 18 Dec. 1851. Marius B. Peladeau, "Springfield Arms Co. Revolvers," *American Rifleman*, Feb. 1967, 26–29. Sellers and Smith, *American Percussion Revolvers*, 161–68, 180–3.

31. *Missouri Democrat*, 7 April 1853. *Western Journal and Civilian*, Nov. 1853, 90.

32. *Missouri Democrat*, 8 May, 1 Sept., and 25 Nov. 1854. Memphis *Appeal*, 12 May 1852.

33. Gammell orders of Feb. 1851, microfilm reel 9; Sept. 1852 and March 1853, microfilm reel 10, Henry Papers.

34. *Missouri Democrat*, 24 June 1854.

35. U.S. pats. 6723, of 18 Sept. 1849, and 7493, of 9 July 1850. Marius B. Peladeau, "The Leonard Pepperbox," *American Rifleman*, Dec. 1964, 42–45. Dunlap, *Pepperbox Firearms*, 79–83. Charles Edward Chapel, *Guns of the Old West* (New York, 1961), 90. Sellers, *The Locke Collection*, 481–82.

36. George Yale to ?, 18 Dec. 1854, Robbins & Lawrence Letterbooks, 1854–56, Robbins & Lawrence Papers, Connecticut Historical Society, Hartford, Conn.

37. Sellers and Smith, *American Percussion Revolvers*, 92–94. Granville Stuart, *Forty Years on the Frontier*, ed. Paul C. Phillips (Glendale, Cal., 1957), 40. Sacramento *Union*, 11 Dec. 1854.

38. Sellers and Smith, *American Percussion Revolvers*, 94–97. San Diego *Herald*, 19 May 1855.

39. C. C. Holloway, "San Antonio Letters of 1854–56," *Texas Gun Collector*, Dec. 1954, 12–14. *Scientific American*, 14 May 1853. Galveston *News*, 17 April 1855. San Antonio *Herald*, 5 June 1855 and 26 Nov. 1858.

40. Solomon N. Carvalho, *Incidents of Travel and Adventure in the Far West* (1857; reprint ed., New York, 1973), 97–98. Frederick Law Olmsted, *A Journey through Texas . . .* (New York and London, 1857), 75.

41. *Missouri Democrat*, 19 Sept. 1855.

42. Parsons, *Deringer's Pocket Pistol*, 38–45.

43. Elizabeth Margo, *Taming the Forty-Niner* (New York, 1955), 135–37. Frank Soule et al., *The Annals of San Francisco* (New York, 1855), 397–400. Sacramento *Union*, 28 Feb. 1855. Parsons, *Deringer's Pocket Pistol*, 43. Daniel K. Stern, "California's Duelling Decade," *American Rifleman*, Aug. 1952, 31. See also John A. Atkinson, *Duelling Pistols* (Harrisburg, Pa., 1966), 125–37.

44. Memphis *Appeal*, 11 June 1851. *Arkansas Gazette*, 15 June 1855. *Missouri Democrat*, 19 Sept. 1855. Herschel C. Logan, "H. E. Dimick of St. Louis," *American Rifleman*, April 1958, 32–33. William A. Albaugh III, Hugh Benet, Jr., and Edward N. Simmons, *Confederate Handguns* (Philadelphia, 1963), 218. It is interesting to note that John G. Syms of New York was selling dueling pistols as late as 1859; see his advertisement for "Duelling, Target, and Deringer Pistols" in *Spirit of the Times*, 14 May 1859.

45. Ferguson, *Experiences of a Forty-Niner*, 190–91.

46. Mouillesseaux, *Ethan Allen, Gunmaker*, 79, 81. Waldo E. Nutter, *Manhattan Firearms* (Harrisburg, Pa., 1958), 5–8. *Missouri Democrat*, 19 Sept. 1855.

47. Letters from Philip F. Van Cleave to the authors, 24 March and 10 June, 1973. *Spirit of the Times*, 15 June 1850. The 1850 federal census for Norwich lists Bacon as a "pistol manufacturer."

48. Flayderman, *Antique American Firearms*, 328, 355. Dunlap, *Pepbbox Firearms*, 92–93. Galveston *News*, 13 July 1852. Photostat in Parsons, *Deringer's Pocket Pistol*, 43. The Bacon found in Kansas is now with the Kansas State Historical Society.

49. *Kansas Historical Quarterly*, Nov. 1931, 31. William Phillips, *The Conquest of Kansas* (Boston, 1856), 192. Dunlap, *Pepperbox Firearms*, 148–52.

50. Phillips, *The Conquest of Kansas*, 214. Senate Rpt. 278, 36th Cong., 1st Sess., Serial No. 1040. William B. Edwards, *Civil War Guns* (Harrisburg, Pa., 1962), 3–4.

51. R. L. Wilson, *The Colt Heritage* (New York, n.d.), 84, 86, 88. Edwards, *Colt's Revolver*, 325–33. *Arkansas Gazette*, 6 Dec. 1856. See also Colt's British pat. 908, of 16 April 1856. The sidehammer Colts in the Sutter's Fort collection bear the serial numbers 5275 and 18253.

52. *Alta California*, 10 Nov. 1857. Atchison *Freedom's Champion*, 26 Feb. 1859. Tubac *Arizonian*, 2 June 1859. William B. Napton, *Over the Santa Fe Trail, 1857* (1905; reprint ed., Santa Fe, N.M., 1964), 20, 67. Stuart, *Forty Years on the Frontier*, 122. Hamilton's account is in *Contributions to the Historical Society of Montana*, 1900, 40, 47, 110. A Navy Colt with original 12 in. barrel is shown in Serven, *Colt Firearms*, 221; a Dragoon with 12 in. barrel is in Jackson Arms catalog 17, item 270. See also Senate Ex. Doc. 35, 35th Cong., 2nd Sess., Serial No. 984.

53. Omaha *Times*, 18 June 1857. Sellers and Smith, *American Percussion Revolvers*, 55–60. U.S. pats. 11419, of 1 Aug. 1854, and 17143, of 28 April 1857.

54. Eugene Bandel, *Frontier Life in the Army*, ed. Ralph P. Bieber (Glendale, Cal., 1932), 130, 150.

55. A. W. F. Taylerson, R. A. N. Andrews, and J. Frith, *The Revolver, 1818–1865* (New York, 1968), 71–120, *passim*.

56. Ibid. See also [John Deane], *Deane's Manual of the History and Science of Fire-Arms* (1858; reprint ed., Huntington, W. Va., n.d.), 209–16.

57. Taylerson, Andrews, and Frith, *The Revolver, 1818–1865*, 84–87, 159, 167.

58. Ibid., 116–18, 180.

59. William Chandless, *A Visit to Salt Lake . . .* (London, 1857), 57, 255. *Missouri Democrat*, 11 March 1856. Taylerson, Andrews, and Frith, *The Revolver 1818–1865*, 118–20.

60. Memphis *Appeal*, 6 Jan. and 22 Sept. 1858. Galveston *News*, 19 Jan. 1858, and 29 March 1859. New Orleans *Picayune*, 21 June 1859. Leavenworth *Kansas Herald*, 19 Feb. 1859. Photostat in Parsons, *Deringer's Pocket Pistol*, 57.

61. Taylerson, Andrews, and Frith, *The Revolver, 1818–1865*, 272–82.

62. Ibid. Memphis *Appeal*, 22 Sept. 1858. *Kansas Herald*, 19 Feb. 1859. *Missouri Democrat*, 12 Oct. 1859. See also the advertisements in *Spirit of the Times*, 9 April and 10 Sept. 1859, and 26 May 1860. The Tranter in the Sutter's Fort collection bears serial no. 16852T.

63. Edwards, *Colt's Revolver*, 322–23, 343–46. Sellers and Smith, *American Percussion Revolvers*, 12–13. Albaugh, Benet, and Simmons, *Confederate Handguns*, 81–123.

64. Mouillesseaux, *Ethan Allen, Gunmaker*, 119–20. Sellers and Smith, *American Percussion Revolvers*, 1–3, 95–97.

65. Sellers and Smith, *American Percussion Revolvers*, 191–94. *Scientific American*, 1 Sept. 1855.

66. Sellers and Smith, *American Percussion Revolvers*, 194–98. Flayderman, *Antique American Firearms*, 259–60. Paul S. Lederer, "Whitney Revolvers for the Navy," *American Rifleman*, April 1966, 66–67.

67. Sellers and Smith, *American Percussion Revolvers*, 158.

68. Ibid., 3–4. Mouillesseaux, *Ethan Allen, Gunmaker*, 120–24. U.S. pats. 16367, of 13 Jan., and 18836, of 15 Dec. 1857.

69. Memphis *Appeal*, 6 Jan. and 22 Sept. 1858. *Arkansas Gazette*, 30 April 1859. *Missouri Democrat*, 12 Oct. 1859.

70. John Biringer Daybooks, 1859–81, in the possession of J. Biringer Miller, Leavenworth, Kansas.

71. Ibid. U.S. pat. 17904, of 28 July 1857. Sellers and Smith, *American Percussion Revolvers*, 184–85. Galveston *News*, 29 March 1859. *Arkansas Gazette*, 30 April 1861.

72. U.S. pats. 15167, of 24 June 1856, and 17359, of 26 May 1857. Sellers, *The Locke Collection*, 293. Photostat in Charles Lee Karr, Jr., and Caroll Robbins Karr, *Remington Handguns*, 2nd ed. (Harrisburg, Pa., 1951), 11. *Harper's Weekly*, 6 Aug. 1859.

73. U.S. pat. 23861, of 3 May 1859. New Orleans *Picayune*, 21 April 1861.

74. The .36 caliber Allen and the Beckwith are now with the Colorado State Historical Society in Denver. The smaller bar-hammer Allen is at Ft. Kearny National Monument, Kearny, Neb. The Patrick pistols are in the Pioneer Museum, Colorado Springs, Colo.

75. Parsons, *Deringer's Pocket Pistol*, 68, 79–89. *Alta California*, 2 Sept. 1859. Langley's *San Francisco City Directory*, 1861.

76. Parsons, *Deringer's Pocket Pistol*, 96–97. Flayderman, *Antique American Firearms*, 345–52. Dallas *Herald*, 6 April 1859. Galveston *News*, 25 Jan. 1859. Memphis *Appeal*, 6 Aug. 1856 and 6 Jan. 1858.

77. Jackson Arms catalog 17, items 408, 411, 412, 419. Galveston *News*, 2 May 1854. New Orleans *Picayune*, 12 Oct. 1858 and 28 June 1860. *Spirit of the Times*, 4 Oct. 1856.

78. Jackson Arms catalog 17, item 403. Parsons, *Deringer's Pocket Pistol*, 34–36. James E. Serven, "The Derringer Pistols," in Serven, ed., *The Collecting of Guns* (New York, 1964), 1963–65. Galveston *News*, 19 Jan. 1858. New Orleans *Picayune*, 21 June 1859.

79. J. Ross Browne, *Adventures in the Apache Country* (New York, 1871), 36. Asbury Harpending, *The Great Diamond Hoax*, ed. James H. Wilkins (Norman, Okla., 1958), 53.

80. Mouillesseaux, *Ethan Allen, Gunmaker*, 104–5, 168. Van Cleave, "The Arms of Ethan Allen," 130.

81. LeRoy R. Hafen, ed., *Colorado Gold Rush: Contemporary Letters and Reports, 1858–1859* (Glendale, Cal., 1941), 281. Mark Twain, *Roughing It* (New York and London, 1913), 1: 5–6.

82. The Russell's Gulch and the Lewis & Tomes pepperboxes are now with the Colorado State Historical Society. The smaller pepperbox found on the Upper Missouri (near Radersberg, Montana) is with the Montana Historical Society, accession no. P.111. Photostat in Parsons, *Deringer's Pocket Pistol*, 96. Tryon price lists of Jan. and Sept. 1864, in the possession of Raymond J. Riling, Philadelphia, Pa.

83. Libeus Barney, *Letters of the Pike's Peak Gold Rush* (San Jose, Cal., 1959), 58–59. Sir Richard Francis Burton, *The City of the Saints*, ed. Fawn M. Brodie (New York, 1963), 12–13.

84. Quotation in Hafen, *Colorado Gold Rush*, 309.

85. Burton, *City of the Saints*, 518. Kate B. Carter, *Utah and the Pony Express* (Salt Lake City, 1960). Alexander Majors, *Seventy Years on the Frontier*, ed. Col. Prentiss Ingraham (Minneapolis, 1965), 179.

86. Raymond W. and Mary Lund Settle, *Saddles and Spurs: The Pony Express Saga* (Harrisburg, Pa., 1955), 154. Letter from Lt. Col. C. F. Smith to the assistant adjutant general, City of New York, 18 July 1860, supplied by James E. Serven.

87. John C. Cremony, *Life among the Apaches, 1850–1868* (1868; reprint ed., Glorieta, N.M., 1969), 23, 46, 203.

88. Photostat in Haven and Belden, *The Colt Revolver*, 388. Edwards, *Colt's Revolver*, 356–70, 464. *Arkansas Gazette*, 29 Sept. 1860.

89. Helen Fitzgerald Sanders, ed., *X. Biedler, Vigilante* (Norman, Okla., 1957), 98.

90. Ibid., 73. John S. duMont, "Early Snub-Nosed Colts," *American Rifleman*, Aug. 1956, 22–23. The Colt found in Eldorado County, its barrel cut to 2¹/₁₆ in., is now in the Sutter's Fort collection. Other cut-down Colts are in the collection of the Nevada State Historical Society, Reno.

91. House Ex. Doc. 99, 40th Cong., 2nd Sess., Serial No. 1338. *Missouri Democrat*, 16 July and 8 Oct. 1863 and 7 June 1864. *Alta California*, 26 Aug. 1864. According to a Colt factory letter, a Model 1861 Navy, serial no. 6502 (examined by the authors), was one of fifty guns shipped to Neosfield and Mitchell on 6 July 1863.

92. Nutter, *Manhattan Firearms*. Edwards, *Colt's Revolver*, 461.

93. *Missouri Democrat*, 8 Oct. 1863. John Biringer Daybooks, June–November 1864.

94. William E. Florence and Karl F. Moldenhauer, "The Firearms of Remington," in Serven, *The Collecting of Guns*, 148–50. Flayderman, *Antique American Firearms*, 138–45. Karr and Karr, *Remington Handguns*, 12–19, 28–31, 36–43. Senate Ex. Doc. 72, 37th Con., 2nd Sess., Serial No. 1123. House Ex. Doc. 67, 37th Cong., 2nd Sess., Serial No. 1131.

95. U.S. pats. 33932, of 17 Dec. 1861, 37329, of 6 Jan. 1863, and 37921, of 17 March 1863. Senate Ex. Doc. 72, Serial No. 1123. Flayderman, *Antique American Firearms*, 142–45. *Harper's Weekly*, 1 and 15 Aug. 1863.

96. *Missouri Democrat*, 10 Dec. 1862, 16 July and 2 Sept. 1863. The cut-down Remington is now with the Colorado State Historical Society.

97. Mouillesseaux, *Ethan Allen, Gunmaker*, 138–40. House Ex. Doc. 99, Serial No. 1338. Photostat in H. H. Thomas, *The Story of Allen and Wheelock Firearms* (Cincinnati, O., 1965), frontispiece.

98. New Orleans *Picayune*, 16 Feb. 1861.

99. John E. Parsons, *Smith & Wesson Revolvers* (New York, 1957), 3–11, 26–27.

100. Parsons, *Smith & Wesson Revolvers*, 11–25. U.S. pat. 20607, of 15 June 1858.

101. Roy G. Jinks and Robert J. Neal, *Smith & Wesson, 1857–1945*, rev. ed. (New York, 1975), 19. Parsons, *Smith & Wesson Revolvers*, 14–16.

102. Jinks and Neal, *Smith & Wesson*, 22. Mouillesseaux, *Ethan Allen, Gunmaker*, 122–28. Van Cleave, "The Arms of Ethan Allen," 130. Parsons, *Smith & Wesson Revolvers*, 10–13, 26, 44.

103. Jinks and Neal, *Smith & Wesson*, 23–25. Parsons, *Smith & Wesson Revolvers*, 19–20, 26, 44–46; 219 gives citations for the various lawsuits.

104. Jinks and Neal, *Smith & Wesson*, 62–65, 258–59. Parsons, *Smith & Wesson Revolvers*, 27–29, 44–46.

105. San Francisco *Alta California*, 25 Aug. 1860. Little Rock *Arkansas Gazette*, 29 Sept. 1860. Mark Twain, *Roughing It*, 1: 5. John Young Nelson, *Fifty Years on the Trail* (Norman, Okla., 1963), 170.

106. Parsons, *Smith & Wesson Revolvers*, 29. *Missouri Democrat*, 30 March, 16 July, and 30 Sept. 1863. Andrew

F. Rolle, ed., *The Road to Virginia City* (Norman, Okla., 1960), 38. In the summer and fall of 1864, John Biringer of Leavenworth was selling an occasional S & W #1 for fifteen dollars and a #2 for twenty dollars; Biringer Daybooks.

107. Jinks and Neal, *Smith & Wesson*, 258–59. Parsons, *Smith & Wesson Revolvers*, 44–46, 55–56.

108. Photostat in Parsons, *Smith & Wesson Revolvers*, 57. *Alta California*, 26 Aug. 1864.

109. U.S. pat. 28951, of 3 July 1860. Mouillesseaux, *Ethan Allen, Gunmaker*, 131–34.

110. U.S. pat. 30109, of 25 Sept. 1860.

111. Mouillesseaux, *Ethan Allen, Gunmaker*, 135–38, 167. U.S. pat. 33328, of 24 Sept. 1861.

112. Tryon price lists of Jan. and Sept. 1864; and letter from Philip F. Van Cleave to the authors, 24 March 1973.

113. U.S. pat. 29126, of 10 July 1860. Herschel C. Logan, "The L. W. Pond Revolvers," *American Rifleman*, Jan. 1961, 26–28.

114. Jinks and Neal, *Smith & Wesson*, 258–59. Logan, "The Pond Revolvers," 27–28. Pond separate-chamber arms are shown in Schuyler, Hartley, & Graham's 1864 catalog. Data on the number of revolvers turned over to Smith & Wesson is based on the Smith & Wesson Archives, Smith & Wesson, Springfield, Mass. Robert M. Reilly, *United States Military Small Arms, 1816–1865* (Baton Rouge, La., 1970), 231–32.

115. U.S. pat. 30079, of 18 Sept. 1860.

116. Parsons, *Smith & Wesson Revolvers*, 55. Jinks and Neal, *Smith & Wesson*, 258. Information on shipments to dealers is in the Daniel B. Wesson Papers, 1852–1906, in the possession of Roy G. Jinks, Springfield, Mass.

117. Nutter, *Manhattan Firearms*, 41–44. *Harper's Weekly*, 14 Dec. 1861.

118. Sellers, *The Locke Collection*, 375–77. U.S. pat. 35419, of 27 May 1862. Jinks and Neal, *Smith & Wesson*, 259. Parsons, *Smith & Wesson Revolvers*, 56.

119. Campbell & Richardson's *St. Louis Business Directory*, 1863. *Missouri Democrat*, 25 April 1863.

120. *Missouri Democrat*, 16 July 1863, et seq. Jinks and Neal, *Smith & Wesson*, 259.

121. Parsons, *Smith & Wesson Revolvers*, 56. U.S. pat. 41117, of 5 Jan. 1864. Nutter, *Manhattan Firearms*, 44. U.S. pat. 28461, of 29 May 1860.

122. Daniel B. Wesson Papers. Jinks and Neal, *Smith & Wesson*, 258 (the total on this page should read 1,395 instead of 1,437). The serial numbers of Warner cartridge revolvers examined by the authors extend very nearly to the 4,000 range. Parsons, *Smith & Wesson Revolvers*, 56. House Ex. Doc. 99, Serial No. 1338.

123. Sellers and Smith, *American Percussion Revolvers*, 132–33. Sellers, *The Locke Collection*, 388–91.

124. *Harper's Weekly*, 18 Jan. 1862. *Frank Leslie's Illustrated Newspaper*, 15 March 1862. *Missouri Democrat*, 31 Aug. 1863. See also the *Army and Navy Journal*, 12 Sept. 1863.

125. House Ex. Doc. 99, Serial No. 1338. *Spirit of the*

Times, 9 April 1859 and 26 May 1860. Schuyler, Hartley, & Graham 1864 catalog.

126. U.S. pats. 6960, of 18 Dec. 1849, and 22753, of 25 Jan. 1859.

127. Frank Sellers, *Sharps Firearms* (N. Hollywood, Cal., 1978), 106–8, 125–29, 133–49.

128. Lord George C. G. Berkeley, *The English Sportsman in the Western Prairies* (London, 1861), 370.

129. Sellers, *Sharps Firearms*, 106–8. Paul S. Lederer, "Sharps & Hankins Weapons," *American Rifleman*, Sept. 1966, 101–4. U.S. pat. 32790, of 9 July 1861.

130. This is based in part on actual firing tests with a Sharps .22 and a Sharps & Hankins .32 using .32 Long blackpowder cartridges.

131. *Alta California*, 25 Aug. 1860. The Sharps & Hankins found in Ponca Park is now in the Municipal Museum in Canon City, Colorado.

132. U.S. pats. 28460 and 28461, both of 29 May 1860. See also Elliot's U.S. pat. 21188, of 17 Aug. 1858, which shows this pistol in a percussion version. Karr and Karr, *Remington Handguns*, 60–61.

133. *Leslie's Weekly*, 14 Sept. 1861 and 29 Aug. 1863. *Harper's Weekly*, 14 Dec. 1861 and 17 Oct. 1863. See also the *Army and Navy Journal*, 30 Jan. 1864. The .22 found in Sacramento is now in the Sutter's Fort collection, file card 5024. The .22 found near Cripple Creek is in a private collection in Colorado Springs, Colo.

134. A number of these pistols are illustrated in Flayderman, *Antique American Firearms*.

135. U.S. pat. 31473, of 19 Feb. 1861. Parsons, *Deringer's Pocket Pistol*, 103–5, 208–9.

136. Quotations in Parsons, *Deringer's Pocket Pistol*, 91–92.

137. U.S. pat. 44798, of 25 Oct. 1864. Flayderman, *Antique American Firearms*, 374. Sellers, *The Locke Collection*, 510.

138. U.S. pats. 40887, of 8 Dec. 1863, and 45123 of 15 Nov. 1864. Parsons, *Deringer's Pocket Pistol*, 122–23, 220–21. Olympia, Washington, *Standard*, 4 May 1867; Dallas *Herald*, 31 Aug. 1867.

139. House Ex. Doc. 99, Serial No. 1338. House Ex. Doc. 53, 39th Cong., 2nd Sess., Serial No. 1290. Claud E. Fuller, *The Breech-Loader in the Service, 1816–1917* (1933; reprint ed., New Millford, Conn., 1965), frontispiece, 233, 235, 239. See also *American Artisan*, 12 June 1867.

140. U.S. pat. 46617, of 7 March 1865. Parsons, *Deringer's Pocket Pistol*, 121, 123–24. Mouillesseaux, *Ethan Allen, Gunmaker*, 143–47.

141. U.S. pat. 24726, of 12 July 1859. Sellers, *The Locke Collection*, 382–85.

142. U.S. pat. 39318, of 21 July 1863. *Harper's Weekly*, 20 Feb. and 19 March 1864, 11 Feb. 1865.

143. Sellers and Smith *American Percussion Revolvers*, 131. *American Artisan*, 11 May 1864. Jackson W. Moore, Jr., *Bent's Old Fort: An Archeological Study* (Boulder, Colo., 1973), 95, 98. Atchison *Champion*, 6 Oct. 1865.

144. *Army and Navy Journal*, 30 April 1864. U.S. pat. 38321, of 28 April 1863.

145. Sellers, *The Locke Collection*, 280–81. *Missouri Democrat*, 19 May 1865.

146. U.S. pat. 38204, of 14 April 1863. Flayderman, *Antique American Firearms*, 372. Schuyler, Hartley, & Graham 1864 catalog. *Harper's Weekly*, 21 Jan. 1865.

147. *Missouri Democrat*, 21 Jan. and 19 May 1865. *Harper's Weekly*, 30 July 1864. Parsons, *Deringer's Pocket Pistol*, 104–5. Fuller, *The Breech-loader in the Service*, frontispiece, 237. See also *American Artisan*, 31 Oct. 1866.

148. Sellers and Smith, *American Percussion Revolvers*, 98–100. Logan, "H. E. Dimick," 30, 33.

149. Berkeley, *The English Sportsman*, 370.

150. Prof. Thomas Dimsdale, *The Vigilantes of Montana* (Norman, Okla., 1953), 25. Nathaniel Pitt Langford, *Vigilante Days and Ways* (Chicago, 1912), 161.

151. Dimsdale, *The Vigilantes of Montana*, 138–39.

152. Parsons, *Deringer's Pocket Pistol*, 57, 59. *Alta California*, 26 Aug. 1864. *Missouri Democrat*, 19 May 1865. *Rocky Mountain News*, 10 May 1865.

153. Samuel Bowles, *Across the Continent* (New York and Springfield, Mass., 1865), 23.

CHAPTER 17

1. Reuben Gold Thwaites, ed., *Early Western Travels, 1748–1846* (Cleveland, 1904–7), 21: 76.

2. Otis E. Young, *The West of Philip St. George Cooke* (Glendale, Cal., 1955), 48.

3. George Catlin, *North American Indians, Being Letters and Notes on Their Manners, Customs, and Conditions . . .* (Edinburgh, 1926), 1: 38, 266.

4. Josiah Gregg, *Commerce of the Prairies*, ed. Max L. Moorhead (Norman, Okla., 1954), 416–17.

5. Gregg, *Commerce of the Prairies*, 371.

6. Lt. J. Henry Carleton, *The Prairie Logbooks . . .*, ed. Louis Pelzer (Chicago, 1943), 271–72.

7. Thwaites, *Early Western Travels*, 28: 85–86.

8. Eugene Bandel, *Frontier Life in the Army*, ed. Ralph P. Bieber (Glendale, Cal., 1932), 95.

9. Quotation in Charles E. Hanson, Jr., "The Deadly Arrow," *Museum of the Fur Trade Quarterly*, Winter 1967, 4.

10. T. D. Bonner, *The Life and Adventures of James P. Beckwourth* (New York, 1856), 65. W. T. Hamilton, *My Sixty Years on the Plains* (Norman, Okla., 1960), 7.

11. Kenneth A. Spaulding, ed., *On the Oregon Trail: Robert Stuart's Journal of Discovery* (Norman, Okla., 1953), 36–37.

12. John Canfield Ewers, *The Horse in Blackfoot Indian Culture* (Washington, D.C., 1955), 13. George E. Hyde, *The Pawnee Indians* (Denver, 1951), 80–81. Carl P. Russell, *Guns on the Early Frontiers* (Berkeley and Los Angeles, 1957), 296. Bernard DeVoto, *Across the Wide Missouri* (Boston, 1947), 43, 50.

13. Ewers, *The Horse in Blackfoot Culture*, 13. Antonio Comaduran, "Diario de operaciones y novedades ocuridos . . .," Legajo 225, Casa Amarilla, Indiferente, Archiva Géneral y Pública de la Nación, Mexico City.

14. Reuben Gold Thwaites, ed., *Original Journals of the Lewis and Clark Expedition* (New York, 1904), 1: 231; 4: 159–60; 6: 45. George Hyde, *Red Cloud's Folk* (Norman, Okla., 1937), 5.

15. Francis Haines, *Red Eagles of the Northwest . . .* (Portland, Ore., 1939), 52. Thwaites, *Lewis and Clark Journals,* 4: 159–60.

16. Milo M. Quaife, ed., *The Journals of Captain Meriwether Lewis and Sergeant John Ordway . . .* (Madison, Wis., 1916), 305–6.

17. Donald Jackson, ed., *The Journals of Zebulon Montgomery Pike, with Letters and Related Documents* (Norman, Okla., 1966), 1: 218–23. Charles E. Hanson, Jr., *The Northwest Gun* (Lincoln, Neb., 1955), 2, 15.

18. Hanson, *The Northwest Gun,* 7. Russell, *Guns on the Early Frontiers,* 110–11, 114–15, 128–29, 317. Carl P. Russell, *Firearms, Traps, and Tools of the Mountain Men* (New York, 1967), 66–70.

19. Hanson, *The Northwest Gun,* 7. Letters from the American Fur Company to J. J. Henry, 1 and 20 Dec. 1826, Bolton Gun Works Records, microfilm reel 1, J. J. Henry Papers, Eleutherian Mills Historical Library, Wilmington, Del. *Museum of the Fur Trade Quarterly,* Winter 1969, 5–6.

20. Hanson, *The Northwest Gun,* 25–26. Office of Indian Affairs to James Henry, 12 Jan. 1844, microfilm reel 2, Henry Papers.

21. Charles J. Keim, "Beaver Pelts and Trade Muskets," *American Rifleman,* Feb. 1958, 27. Russell, *Firearms, Traps, and Tools,* 93.

22. Letter from Charles E. Hanson, Jr., to the authors, 12 Aug. 1982.

23. John E. Parsons, "Gunmakers for the American Fur Company," *New York Historical Society Quarterly,* April 1952, 184. Russell, *Guns on the Early Frontiers,* 105–7.

24. A great deal of primary-source information about the government's factory system is in the *American State Papers, Indian Affairs* (Washington, 1832–34), vols. 1 and 2.

25. Maj. James E. Hicks, *American Military Firearms, 1776–1956* (1940; reprint ed., La Canada, Cal., 1962), 26–27. *American State Papers, Military Affairs* (Washington, 1832–61), 1: 302, 680; 2: 478. Quotation in Russell, *Guns on the Early Frontiers,* 106.

26. Parsons, "American Fur Company," 182–83. J. J. Astor to J. J. Henry, 17 Aug. 1827; American Fur Co. order of 5 Nov. 1828; and Ramsay Crooks to Henry, 14 July 1829, microfilm reel 1, Henry Papers.

27. E. E. Rich, ed., *Snake Country Journals, 1824–26* (London, 1950), 43, 146. Quotation in Russell, *Guns on the Early Frontiers,* 124.

28. M. Catherine White, ed., *David Thompson's Journals Relating to Montana . . .* (Missoula, Mont., 1950). The price was still the same in the mid-1820s. At Hudson's Bay posts such as Fort George and Spokane House, a "Com. N. W. Gun" brought from 18 to 20 prime beaver pelts, while a "fine half stocked Gun" brought 30 pelts; see Frederick Merk, ed., *Fur Trade and Empire: George Simpson's Journal* (Cambridge, Mass., 1931), 173. Hiram Martin Chittenden, *History of the American Fur Trade of the Far West* (1902; reprint ed., Stanford, Cal., 1954), 1: 4–5.

29. Spaulding, *On the Oregon Trail,* 36–37.

30. Dale L. Morgan, ed., *The West of William H. Ashley* (Denver, 1964), 27. Hamilton, *Sixty Years on the Plains,* 52–53.

31. Warren Angus Ferris, *Life in the Rocky Mountains 1830–1835,* ed. Paul C. Phillips (Denver, 1940), 192. See also E. Willard Smith's Journal, in *Colorado Magazine,* July 1950.

32. Russell, *Firearms, Traps, and Tools,* 70. Russell, *Guns on the Early Frontiers,* 132–33. Hanson, *The Northwest Gun,* 45–46. Hicks, *Military Firearms,* 89–90. Capt. John G. W. Dillin, *The Kentucky Rifle* (1924; reprint ed., York, Pa., 1959), 92–93. See also *American State Papers, Indian Affairs,* 2: 290–93, 301–2, 332–34, 340.

33. Quotation in Russell, *Guns on the Early Frontiers,* 131.

34. Russell, *Guns on the Early Frontiers,* 132. Hanson, *The Northwest Gun,* 45–46. Hicks, *Military Firearms,* 89–90.

35. Menard & Valle Ledgers, 1825, microfilm reel 19, and Menard Business Papers, 1825–34, microfilm reel 12, Pierre Menard Papers, Illinois State Historical Library, Springfield, Ill. Hanson, *The Northwest Gun,* 47. Henry Putman Beers, *Western Military Frontiers, 1815–1846* (Philadelphia, 1935), 97.

36. Office of Indian Affairs to J. J. Henry, 10 Jan. 1829, microfilm reel 1, Henry Papers. Senate Doc. 512, 23rd Cong., 1st Sess., Serial Nos. 244, 248. Grant Foreman, *The Five Civilized Tribes* (Norman, Okla., 1934), 28.

37. Quotation in *Museum of the Fur Trade Quarterly,* Fall 1966, 2. House Doc. 174, 25th Cong., 2nd Sess., Serial No. 327.

38. Parsons, "American Fur Company," 186. American Fur Co. order of Dec. 1840, microfilm reel 2, Henry Papers; the order is marked "To be delivered 20 February 1841."

39. Crooks to Henry, 19 June 1837, microfilm reel 2, Henry Papers.

40. Order from the Office of Indian Affairs, 12 Jan. 1844, and Ewing to Henry, 11 April 1853, microfilm reel 2, Henry Papers.

41. Quotation in Russell, *Guns on the Early Frontiers,* 320.

42. W. G. and G. W. Ewing to James Henry, 18 Jan. 1843, and Ewing order of 28 Dec. 1844, microfilm reel 2, Henry Papers.

43. Col. Robert E. Gardner, *Small Arms Makers* (New York, 1963), 115. Galveston *News,* 16 Feb. 1858. Photostat in John E. Parsons, *Henry Deringer's Pocket Pistol* (New York, 1952), 73.

44. John Francis McDermott, *Tixier's Travels on the Osage Prairies* (Norman, Okla., 1940), 112, 254.

45. George Bird Grinnell, *The Fighting Cheyenne* (Norman, Okla., 1956), 95–96.

46. Quotation in Russell, *Guns on the Early Frontiers,* 135, and in Parsons, "American Fur Company," 190.

47. *War Department Contracts 1839–48;* cited hereafter

as *WDC*. Specific locations for the annual summaries of contracts made by the War Department between 1828 and 1861 are given in the bibliography. One of these 1839 Deringer trade muskets is in the Museum of the Fur Trade in Chadron, Neb. James E. Serven, "Tryon Gunmaking Firm Grew with the Nation," *American Rifleman,* Dec. 1970, 39–40.

48. Rich, *Snake Country Journals,* 252. Parsons, "American Fur Company," 192–93. Solomon N. Carvalho, *Incidents of Travel and Adventure in the Far West* (1857; reprint ed., New York, 1973), 199–200.

49. Grinnell, *The Fighting Cheyennes,* 103–4.

50. J. N. B. Hewitt, ed., *Journal of Rudolph Friederich Kurz . . . 1846–1852,* trans. Myrtis Jarrell (Lincoln, Neb., 1970), 194–95.

51. Thwaites, *Early Western Travels,* 2: 223.

52. Francis Parkman, *The Oregon Trail,* ed. E. N. Feltskog (Madison, Wis., 1969), 362–65.

53. Parkman, *The Oregon Trail,* 357.

54. *Minnesota in the Civil and Indian Wars, 1861–1865* (St. Paul, Minn., 1890–93), 2: 168. Clyde and Mae Reed Porter, comps., *Ruxton of the Rockies,* ed. LeRoy R. Hafen (Norman, Okla., 1950), 82. Daniel Ellis Conner, *Joseph Reddeford Walker and the Arizona Adventure,* ed. Donald J. Berthrong and Odessa Davenport (Norman, Okla., 1956), 153.

BIBLIOGRAPHY

PRIMARY SOURCES: BOOKS

Abert, Lt. James W. *Report of Lieut. J. W. Abert, of His Examination of New Mexico.* 1848. Reprint ed., Albuquerque, N.M., 1962.

Albaugh, William A., III. *Tyler, Texas, C.S.A.* Harrisburg, Pa., 1958.

Audubon, Maria R., ed. *Audubon and His Journals.* 2 vols. New York, 1899.

Averell, William Woods, *Ten Years In the Saddle.* Edited by Edward J. Eckert and Nicholas J. Amato. San Raphael Cal., 1978.

Bandel, Eugene. *Frontier Life in the Army.* Edited by Ralph P. Bieber. Glendale, Cal., 1932.

Barber, Edward C. *The Crack Shot.* New York, 1868.

Barker, [Lorenzo] "Ren." *Military History [of] Company "D," 66th Illinois, Birge's Western Sharpshooters . . .* Reed City, Mich., 1905.

Barnes, Demas. *From the Atlantic to the Pacific, Overland.* New York, 1866.

Barney, Libeus. *Letters of the Pike's Peak Gold Rush.* San Jose, Cal., 1959.

Bartlett, John Russell. *Personal Narrative of Exploration and Incidents . . .* 2 vols. New York, 1854.

Bell, Capt. John R. *The Journal of Captain John R. Bell, Official Journalist for the Stephen H. Long Expedition . . .* Edited by Harlin M. Fuller and LeRoy R. Hafen. Glendale, Cal., 1957.

Berenger, Baron de. *Helps and Hints How to Protect Life and Property.* London, 1835.

Berkeley, Lord George C. F. *The English Sportsman in the Western Prairies.* London, 1861.

Bieber, Ralph P., ed. *Southern Trails to California in 1849.* Glendale, Cal., 1937.

Borthwich, J. D. *Three Years in California.* Edinburgh, 1857.

Brown, James S., *Life of a Pioneer.* Salt Lake City, 1900.

Browne, J. Ross. *Adventures in the Apache Country.* New York, 1871.

Bonner, T. D. *The Life and Adventures of James P. Beckwourth.* New York, 1858.

Bosworth, N. *A Treatise on the Rifle, Musket, Pistol, and Fowling-Piece.* 1846. Reprint ed., Huntington, W.Va., n.d.

Bowles, Samuel. *Across the Continent. . . .* New York and Springfield, Mass., 1865.

Brackenridge, H. M. *Recollections of Persons and Places in the West.* 2nd ed. Philadelphia, 1868.

———. *Views of Louisiana.* 1814. Reprint ed., Ann Arbor, Mich., 1966.

Bradbury, John. *Travels in the Interior of America.* 1817. Reprint ed., Ann Arbor, Mich., 1966.

Brewerton, George Douglas. *Overland with Kit Carson.* New York, 1930.

———. *The War in Kansas.* New York, 1856.

Bryant, Edwin. *What I Saw in California . . . 1846–1847.* Santa Ana, Cal., 1936.

Burton, Sir Richard Francis. *The City of the Saints.* Edited by Fawn M. Brodie. New York, 1963.

Carleton, Lt. James H. *The Prairie Logbooks. . . .* Edited by Louis Pelzer. Chicago, 1943.

Carvalho, Solomon N. *Incidents of Travel and Adventure in the Far West.* 1857. Reprint ed., New York, 1973.

Catlin, George. *North American Indians, Being Letters and Notes on Their Manners, Customs, and Conditions. . . .* Edinburgh, 1926.

Chamberlain, Samuel. *My Confession.* New York, 1956.

Chandless, William. *A Visit To Salt Lake . . .* London, 1857.

Chapman, John Ratcliffe. *Instructions to Young Marksmen.* 1848. Reprint ed., N. Hollywood, Cal., 1976.

Christman, Enos. *One Man's Gold.* Edited by Florence Morrow Christman. New York, 1930.

Clayton, William. *William Clayton's Journal.* 1921. Reprint ed., New York, 1973.

Cleveland, H. W. S. *Hints to Riflemen.* New York, 1864.

Connelley, William E. *Doniphan's Expedition and the Conquest of New Mexico and California.* Kansas City, 1907.

Conner, Daniel Ellis. *Joseph Reddeford Walker and the Arizona Adventure.* Edited by Donald J. Berthrong and Odessa Davenport. Norman, Okla., 1956.

Cooke, Philip St. George. *The Conquest of New Mexico and California.* 1878. Reprint ed., Chicago, 1964.

———. *Scenes and Adventures in the Army.* Philadelphia, 1859.

Cox, Ross. *The Columbia River.* Edited by Edgar I. Stewart and Jane R. Stewart. Norman, Okla., 1957.

Coyner, David H. *The Lost Trappers.* Cincinnati, 1859.

Cremony, John C. *Life among the Apaches, 1850–1868.* 1868. Reprint ed., Glorieta, N.M., 1969.

Croghan, Col. George. *Army Life on the Western Frontier.* Edited by Francis Paul Prucha. Norman, Okla., 1958.

Crook, George. *General George Crook, His Autobiography.* Edited by Martin F. Schmitt. Norman, Okla., 1960.

David, Robert B., ed. *Finn Burnett, Frontiersman.* Glendale, Cal., 1937.

[Deane, John]. *Deane's Manual of the History and Science of Fire-Arms.* 1858. Reprint ed., Huntington, W.Va., n.d.

Dimsdale, Prof. Thomas. *The Vigilantes of Montana.* Norman, Okla., 1953.

Duval, J. C. *Early Times In Texas.* Austin, Tex., 1892.

Edwards, Marcellus Ball; Johnson, A. R.; and Ferguson, Philip. *Marching with the Army of the West.* Edited by Ralph P. Bieber. Glendale, Cal., 1936.

Ferguson, Charles D. *The Experiences of a Forty-Niner.* Cleveland, 1888.

Field, Matthew C. *Prairie and Mountain Sketches.* Norman, Okla., 1957.

"Flack, Captain." *The Texan Rifle-Hunter.* London, 1866.

Ford, John Salmon. *Rip Ford's Texas.* Edited by Stephen B. Oates. Austin, Tex., 1963.

Fremont, John Charles. *Narratives of Exploration and Adventure.* Edited by Allan Nevins. New York, 1956.

———. *Report of the Exploring Expedition to the Rocky Mountains.* 1845. Reprint ed., Ann Arbor, Mich., 1966.

Gale, Surgeon John. *The Missouri Expedition, 1818–1820.* Edited by Roger L. Nichols. Norman, Okla., 1969.

Garrard, Lewis H. *Wah-To-Yah and the Taos Trail.* Norman, Okla., 1966.

Gerstaecker, Frederick. *Wild Sports in the Far West.* Boston, 1866.

Gibbon, Lt. John. *The Artillerist's Manual.* 1860. Reprint ed., New York, 1970.

Gibson, George Rutledge. *Over the Chihuahua and Santa Fe Trails.* Edited by Robert W. Frazer. Albuquerque, 1981.

Giffen, Helen, ed. *The Diaries of Peter Decker.* Georgetown, Cal., 1966.

Glison, R. *Journal of Army Life.* San Francisco, 1874.

Gould, A. C. *Modern American Rifles.* 1892. Reprint ed., Plantersville, S.C., 1946.

Greeley, Horace. *An Overland Journey . . .* 1860. Reprint ed., Ann Arbor, Mich., 1966.

Green, Gen. Thomas J. *Journal of the Texian Expedition against Mier . . .* New York, 1845.

Greener, W. W. *Modern Breech Loaders: Sporting and Military.* 1871. Reprint ed., Pueblo, Colo., n.d.

Gregg, Josiah. *Commerce of the Prairies.* Edited by Max L. Moorhead. Norman, Okla., 1954.

Hafen, LeRoy R., ed. *Rufus Sage: His Letters and Papers, 1836–1847.* 2 vols. Glendale, Cal., 1956.

———. *Colorado Gold Rush: Contemporary Letters and Reports, 1858–1859.* Glendale, Cal., 1941.

———. *Pike's Peak Gold Rush Guidebooks of 1859.* Glendale, Cal., 1941.

——— and Hafen, Ann W., eds. *Fremont's Fourth Expedition.* Glendale, Cal., 1960.

Haines, Francis. *Red Eagles of the Northwest.* Portland, Ore., 1939.

Hamilton, W. T. *My Sixty Years on the Plains.* Norman, Okla., 1960.

Harpending, Asbury. *The Great Diamond Hoax.* Edited by James H. Wilkins. Norman, Okla., 1958.

Harris, Benjamin Butler. *The Gila Trail.* Edited by Richard H. Dillon. Norman, Okla., 1960.

Hawker, Lt. Col. Peter. *Instructions to Young Sportsmen . . .* Philadelphia, 1846.

Hewitt, J. N. B., ed. *Journal of Rudolph Friederich Kurz . . . 1846–1852.* Translated by Myrtis Jarrell. Lincoln, Neb., 1970.

Hickman, Bill. *Brigham's Destroying Angel . . .* New York, 1873.

Hittell, Theodore H., ed. *The Adventures of James Capen Adams.* New York, 1911.

Hobbs, Capt. James. *Wild Life in the Far West.* 1872. Reprint ed., Glorieta, N.M., 1969.

Howbert, Irving. *Memories of a Lifetime in the Pike's Peak Region.* New York and London, 1925.

Irving, Washington. *The Adventures of Captain Bonneville.* Norman, Okla., 1961.

———. *A Tour on the Prairies.* Edited by John Francis McDermott. Norman, Okla., 1956.

Jackson, Donald, ed. *The Journals of Zebulon Montgomery Pike, with Letters and Related Documents.* 2 vols. Norman, Okla., 1966.

———. *Letters of the Lewis and Clark Expedition, with Related Documents, 1789–1854.* Urbana, Ill., 1962.

——— and Spence, Mary Lee, eds. *The Expeditions of John Charles Fremont.* 3 vols. Urbana, Ill., 1970–73.

James, Edwin, comp. *Account of an Expedition from Pittsburgh to the Rocky Mountains.* 2 vols. 1823. Reprint ed., Ann Arbor, Mich., 1966.

Jenkins, John H., ed. *Papers of the Texas Revolution, 1835–1836.* 10 vols. Austin, Tex., 1973.

Johnson, Kenneth M., ed. *San Francisco as It Is, Being Gleanings from the Picayune, 1850–1852.* Georgetown, Cal., 1964.

Johnston, Wm. G. *Experiences of a Forty-Niner.* 1892. Reprint ed., New York, 1973.

Kelly, William, Jr. *An Excursion to California . . .* 2 vols. London, 1851.

Kendall, George Wilkins. *Narrative of an Expedition across the Great South Western Prairies . . .* 2 vols. 1845. Reprint ed., Ann Arbor, Mich., 1966.

Larpenteur, Charles. *Forty Years a Fur Trader on the Upper Missouri.* Chicago, 1933.

Lee, Nelson. *Three Years among the Comanches.* Norman, Okla., 1957.

Leinhard, Heinrich. *From St. Louis to Sutter's Fort 1846.* Translated and edited by Erwin G. and Elizabeth K. Gudde. Norman, Okla., 1961.

Leonard, Zenas. *Narrative of the Adventures of Zenas Leonard.* 1839. Reprint ed., Ann Arbor, Mich., 1966.

Lewis, Meriwether. *The Lewis and Clark Expedition.* 3 vols. 1814. Reprint ed., Philadelphia and New York, 1961.

Lowe, Percival G. *Five Years a Dragoon.* Norman, Okla., 1965.

Majors, Alexander. *Seventy Years on the Frontier*. Edited by Col. Prentiss Ingraham. Minneapolis, 1965.

Manly, William. *Death Valley in '49*. 1894. Reprint ed., Ann Arbor, Mich., 1966.

Mansfield, Col. Joseph K. F. *Mansfield on the Condition of the Western Forts, 1853–54*. Edited by Robert W. Frazer. Norman, Okla., 1963.

Marcy, Randolph B. *The Prairie Traveller*. New York, 1859.

——. *Thirty Years of Army Life on the Border*. 1866. Reprint ed., Philadelphia and New York, 1963.

Marsh, James B. *Four Years in the Rockies*. Newcastle, Pa., 1884.

Mattison, Ray H., ed. *Henry Boller, Missouri River Fur Trader*. Bismarck, N.D., 1966.

Maury, Gen. Dabney H. *Recollections of a Virginian in the Mexican, Indian, and Civil Wars*. New York, 1894.

McCall, Col. George A. *New Mexico in 1850: A Military View*. Edited by Robert W. Frazer. Norman, Okla., 1968.

McClure, A. K. *Three Thousand Miles through the Rocky Mountains*. Philadelphia, 1869.

Meriwether, David. *My Life in the Mountains and on the Plains*. Edited by Robert A. Griffen. Norman, Okla., 1965.

Merk, Frederick, ed. *Fur Trade and Empire: George Simpson's Journal*. Cambridge, Mass., 1931.

Meyers, Augustus. *Ten Years in the Ranks of the U.S. Army*. New York, 1914.

Minnesota in the Civil and Indian Wars. 2 vols. St. Paul, 1890–93.

Montaignes, François des. *The Plains*. Edited by Nancy Alpert Mower and Don Russell. Norman, Okla., 1972.

Morgan, Dale L., ed. *The West of William H. Ashley*. Denver, 1964.

——. *The Rocky Mountain Journals of William Marshall Anderson*. San Marino, Cal., 1967.

Morris, Maurice O'Conner. *Rambles in the Rocky Mountains*. London, 1864.

Napton, William B., *Over the Santa Fe Trail, 1857*. 1905. Reprint ed., Santa Fe, N.M., 1964.

Nelson, John, *Fifty Years on the Trail*. Norman, Okla., 1963.

Nichols, James Wilson. *Now You Hear My Horn*. Edited by Catherine W. McDowell. Austin, Tex., 1967.

Olmsted, Frederick Law. *A Journey Through Texas . . .* New York and London, 1857.

Palliser, John. *Solitary Rambles and Adventures of a Hunter in the Prairies*. London, 1853.

Patents for Inventions. Abridgements of Specifications, Class 119, Small-Arms, 1855–1866. London, 1905.

Parker, Donald Dean, ed. *The Recollections of Philander Prescott, 1819–1862*. Lincoln, Neb., 1966.

Parkman, Francis. *The Oregon Trail*. Edited by E. N. Feltskog. Madison, Wis., 1969.

Pearson, G. C. *Overland in 1849*. Edited by Jessie H. Goodman. Los Angeles, 1961.

Phillips, William. *The Conquest of Kansas*. Boston, 1856.

Pike, Albert. *Prose Sketches and Poems Written in the Western Country*. Edited by David J. Weber. Albuquerque, N.M., 1967.

Pike, Maj. Z[ebulon] M. *An Account of Expeditions to the Sources of the Mississippi, and through the Western Parts of Louisiana 1810*. Reprint ed., Ann Arbor, Mich., 1966.

Porter, Clyde and Mae Reed, comps. *Matt Field on the Santa Fe Trail*. Edited by John E. Sunder. Norman, Okla., 1960.

——. *Ruxton of the Rockies*. Edited by LeRoy R. Hafen. Norman, Okla., 1950.

Potter, David Morris, ed. *The Trail to California: The Overland Journal of Vincent Geiger and Wakefield Bryarly*. New Haven, Conn., 1945.

Price, Capt. George F. *Across the Continent with the Fifth Cavalry*. 1883. Reprint ed., New York, 1959.

Quaife, Milo M., ed. *The Journals of Captain Meriwether Lewis and Sergeant John Ordway . . .* Madison, Wis., 1916.

——. *Kit Carson's Autobiography*. Chicago, 1935.

Reid, John C. *Reid's Tramp*. 1858. Reprint ed., Austin, Tex., 1935.

Reid, Samuel C., Jr. *The Scouting Expeditions of McCullough's Texas Rangers . . . 1846*. 1847. Reprint ed., Austin, Tex., 1935.

Reports of Experiments with Small Arms for the Military Service. . . . Washington, D.C., 1856.

Rolle, Andrew F., ed. *The Road to Virginia City: The Diary of James Knox Polk Miller*. Norman, Okla., 1960.

Root, Frank A., and Connelley, William E. *The Overland Stage to California*. 1901. Reprint ed., Columbus, O., 1950.

Ross, Alexander. *Adventures of the First Settlers on the Oregon or Columbia Rivers*. 1849. Reprint ed., Ann Arbor, Mich., 1966.

——. *The Fur Hunters of the Far West*. Norman, Okla., 1956.

Rowland, Mrs. Dunbar, ed. *Life, Letters and Papers of William Dunbar*. Jackson, Miss., 1930.

Russell, Osborne. *Journal of a Trapper*. Edited by Aubrey L. Haines. Lincoln, Neb., 1965.

Ruxton, George Frederick. *Adventures in Mexico and the Rocky Mountains*. 1847. Reprint ed., Glorieta, N.M., 1973.

——. *Life in the Far West*. Edited by LeRoy R. Hafen. Norman, Okla., 1951.

Samuel Colt vs. the Massachusetts Arms Company: Report of the Trial, etc. . . . Boston, 1851.

Sanders, Helen Fitzgerald, ed. *X. Biedler. Vigilante*. Norman, Okla., 1957.

Satterlee, L. D., comp. *Ten Old Gun Catalogs for the Collector*. 1940. Reprint ed., Chicago, 1962.

Schuyler, Hartley & Graham Catalog, 1864.

Settle, Raymond W., and Mary Lund, eds. *Overland Days to Montana in 1865*. Glendale, Cal., 1971.

Smith, George W., and Judah, Charles, eds. *Chronicles of the Gringos*. Albuquerque, N.M., 1968.

Soule, Frank, et al. *The Annals of San Francisco.* New York, 1855.

Spaulding, Kenneth A., ed. *On the Oregon Trail: Robert Stuart's Journal of Discovery.* Norman, Okla., 1953.

Spring, Agnes Wright, ed. *Casper Collins: The Life and Exploits of an Indian Fighter of the Sixties.* New York, 1927.

Stockbridge, V. D., comp. *Digest of Patents Relating to Breech-Loading and Magazine Small Arms, 1836–1873.* 1874. Reprint ed., Greenwich, Conn., 1963.

Stuart, Granville. *Forty Years on the Frontier.* Edited by Paul C. Phillips. Glendale, Cal., 1957.

Sullivan, Maurice S., ed. *The Travels of Jedediah Smith.* Santa Ana, Cal., 1934.

Thwaites, Reuben Gold, ed. *Early Western Travels 1748–1846.* 31 vols. Cleveland, 1904–7.

———. *Original Journals of the Lewis and Clark Expedition.* 7 vols. New York, 1904.

Toponce, Alexander. *Reminiscences of Alexander Toponce, Pioneer, 1839–1923.* Ogden, Utah, 1923.

Twain, Mark. *Roughing It.* 2 vols. New York and London, 1913.

Tyler, Daniel. *A Concise History of the Mormon Battalion.* 1881. Reprint ed., Waynesboro, Va., 1964.

Walsh, J. H. *The Shot-Gun and Sporting Rifle.* London, 1859.

Webb, James J. *Adventures in the Santa Fe Trade.* Edited by Ralph P. Bieber. Glendale, Cal., 1931.

White, Helen McCann, ed. *Ho! For the Gold Fields.* St. Paul, Minn., 1966.

White, M. Catherine, ed. *David Thompsons's Journals Relating to Montana.* Missoula, Mont., 1950.

Wilbur, Marguerite Eyer, ed. and trans. *A Pioneer at Sutter's Fort, 1846–1850.* Los Angeles, 1941.

Wilcox, C. M. *Rifles and Rifle Practice.* New York, 1861.

Woodward, Arthur, ed. *Journal of Lt. Thomas J. Sweeney, 1849–1853.* Los Angeles, 1956.

Wyman, Walker D., ed. *California Emigrant Letters.* New York, 1952.

Young, F. G., ed. *The Correspondence and Journals of Captain Nathaniel Wyeth.* 1899. Reprint ed., New York, 1973.

Young, Frank C. *Across the Plains in '65.* Denver, 1905.

MANUSCRIPTS

Wherever possible, we tried to rely on published sources. In some cases, however, only manuscripts supplied the information we needed. The most important of these are listed below.

Records of the Office of the Chief of Ordnance, Record Group No. 156. National Archives, Washington, D.C.

Records of the Adjutant General's Office, Record Group No. 94. National Archives, Washington, D.C.

Allen & Thurber daybooks, 1846–48. Collection of Philip F. Van Cleave, Carlsbad, N.M.

John Biringer daybooks, 1859–81. Collection of J. Biringer Miller, Leavenworth, Kansas.

Bolton Gun Works Records, 1817–60. J. J. Henry Papers, Eleutherian Mills Historical Library, Wilmington, Del.

Colt's Patent Fire Arms Mfg. Co. correspondence. Connecticut State Library, Hartford, Conn.

Jacob and Samuel Hawken Papers. Missouri Historical Society, St. Louis, Mo.

Hudson's Bay Company Archives. Hudson's Bay Company, Beaver House, London.

Pierre Menard Papers, 1803–40. Illinois State Historical Library, Springfield, Ill.

Robbins and Lawrence Papers, 1854–56. Connecticut Historical Society, Hartford, Conn.

Sharps factory records. Collection of Dr. R. L. Moore, Philadelphia, Mississippi.

Smith & Wesson Archives. Smith & Wesson, Springfield, Mass.

Daniel B. Wesson Papers, 1852–1906. Collection of Roy G. Jinks, Springfield, Mass.

Edwin Wesson Papers, 1839–49. Connecticut Historical Society, Hartford, Conn.

GOVERNMENT DOCUMENTS

The two most valuable published sources of information on U.S. military arms are the seven volumes of *American State Papers, Military Affairs*, and the dozens of pertinent volumes in the U.S. Congressional Serial Set. Both series are available at the Government Documents section in some of the larger municipal and college libraries.

ANNUAL REPORTS OF THE CHIEF OF ORDNANCE

The annual Ordnance reports from 1822 to 1836 are in the *American State Papers, Military Affairs*, vols. 2–7. We used the *State Papers* only for the reports from 1822 to 1829, and used the Serial Set for the reports from 1830 to 1861. The reports for 1862 to 1865 are in the *Official Records of the Union and Confederate Armies*. Prior to 1861, an Ordnance report (or a national armory expenditures statement) published in the Senate documents for a given congressional session was often duplicated in the House documents for the same session. We have listed below only the documents we actually used.

1822–29: *American State Papers, Military Affairs*, vols. 2–4.
1830: House Doc. No. 2, 21st Cong. 2d sess., Serial No. 206.
1831: House Doc. No. 2, 22nd Cong. 1st sess., Serial No. 216.
1832: House Doc. No. 2, 22d Cong. 2d sess., Serial No. 233.
1833: Senate Doc. No. 1, 23d Cong. 1st sess., Serial No. 238.
1834: House Doc. No. 2, 23d Cong. 2d sess., Serial No. 271.
1835: House Doc. No. 2, 24th Cong. 1st sess., Serial No. 286.
1836: Senate Doc. No. 1, 24th Cong. 2d sess., Serial No. 297.
1837: House Doc. No. 3, 25th Cong. 2d sess., Serial No. 321.

1838: House Doc. No. 2, 25th Cong. 3d sess., Serial No. 344.

1839: Senate Doc. No. 1, 26th Cong. 1st sess., Serial No. 354.

1840: Senate Doc. No. 1, 26th Cong. 2d sess., Serial No. 375.

1841: Senate Doc. No. 1, 27th Cong. 2d sess., Serial No. 395.

1842: Senate Doc. No. 1, 27th Cong. 3d sess., Serial No. 413.

1843: Senate Doc. No. 1, 28th Cong. 1st sess., Serial No. 431.

1844: Senate Doc. No. 1, 28th Cong. 2d sess., Serial No. 449.

1845: Senate Doc. No. 1, 29th Cong., 1st sess., Serial No. 470.

1846: Senate Doc. No. 1, 29th Cong., 2d sess., Serial No. 493.

1847: Senate Ex. Doc. No. 1, 30th Cong. 1st sess., Serial No. 503.

1848: House Ex. Doc. No. 1, 30th Cong. 2d sess., Serial No. 537.

1849: House Ex. Doc. No. 5, 31st Cong. 1st sess., Serial No. 569.

1850: Senate Ex. Doc. No. 1, 31st Cong. 2d sess., Serial No. 587.

1851: Senate Ex. Doc. No. 1, 32d Cong. 1st sess., Serial No. 611.

1852: Senate Ex. Doc. No. 1, 32d Cong. 2d sess., Serial No. 659.

1853: Senate Ex. Doc. No. 1, 33d Cong. 1st sess., Serial No. 692.

1854: Senate Ex. Doc. No. 1, 33d Cong. 2d sess., Serial No. 747.

1855: Senate Ex. Doc. No. 1, 34th Cong. 1st sess., Serial No. 811.

1856: Senate Ex. Doc. No. 5, 34th Cong. 3d sess., Serial No. 876.

1857: House Ex. Doc. No. 2, 35th Cong. 1st sess., Serial No. 943.

1858: Senate Ex. Doc. No. 1, 35th Cong. 2d sess., Serial No. 976.

1859: Senate Ex. Doc. No. 2, 36th Cong. 1st sess., Serial No. 1025.

1860: Senate Ex. Doc. No. 1, 36th Cong. 2d sess., Serial No. 1079.

1861: Senate Ex. Doc. No. 1, 37th Cong. 2d sess., Serial No. 1118.

1862: *The War of the Rebellion: A Compilation of the Official Records of the Union and Confederate Armies*, Series 3, vol. 2, pp. 849–59.

1863: *Official Records*, Series 3, vol. 3, pp. 930–37.

1864: *Official Records*, Series 3, vol. 4, pp. 799–806.

1865: *Official Records*, Series 3, vol. 5, pp. 140–45.

NATIONAL ARMORIES EXPENDITURES STATEMENTS

1822–29: *American State Papers, Military Affairs*, vols. 2–4.

1830: House Doc. No. 125, 21st Cong. 2d sess., Serial No. 209.

1831: House Doc. No. 170, 22d Cong. 1st sess., Serial No. 219.

1832: House Doc. No. 121, 22d Cong. 2d sess., Serial No. 235.

1833: House Doc. No. 322, 23d Cong. 1st sess., Serial No. 257.

1834: House Doc. No. 188, 23d Cong. 2d sess., Serial No. 275.

1835: House Doc. No. 294, 24th Cong. 1st sess., Serial No. 292.

1836: Senate Doc. No. 221, 24th Cong. 2d sess., Serial No. 299.

1837: House Doc. No. 428, 25th Cong. 2d sess., Serial No. 331.

1838: Senate Doc. No. 292, 25th Cong. 3d sess., Serial No. 342.

1839: House Doc. No. 100, 26th Cong. 1st sess., Serial No. 365.

1840: Senate Doc. No. 175, 26th Cong. 2d sess., Serial No. 378.

1841: House Doc. No. 157, 27th Cong. 2d sess., Serial No. 403.

1842: House Doc. No. 113, 27th Cong. 3d sess., Serial No. 421.

1843: House Doc. No. 23, 28th Cong. 1st sess., Serial No. 441.

1844: House Doc. No. 43, 28th Cong. 2d sess., Serial No. 464.

1845: House Doc. No. 96, 29th Cong. 1st sess., Serial No. 483.

1846: House Doc. No. 41, 29th Cong. 2d sess., Serial No. 499.

1847: House Ex. Doc. No. 22, 30th Cong. 1st sess., Serial No. 516.

1848: House Ex. Doc. No. 25, 30th Cong. 2d sess., Serial No. 540.

1849: Senate Ex. Doc. No. 27, 31st Cong. 1st sess., Serial No. 554.

1850: House Ex. Doc. No. 20, 31st Cong. 2d sess., Serial No. 598.

1851: Senate Ex. Doc. No. 17, 32d Cong. 1st sess., Serial No. 614.

1852: House Ex. Doc. No. 26, 32d Cong. 2d sess., Serial No. 677.

1853: Senate Ex. Doc. No. 15, 33d Cong. 1st sess., Serial No. 694.

1854: House Ex. Doc. No. 33, 33d Cong. 2d sess., Serial No. 783.

1855: House Ex. Doc. No. 21, 34th Cong. 1st sess., Serial No. 851.

1856: Senate Ex. Doc. No. 19, 34th Cong. 3d sess., Serial No. 878.

1857: House Ex. Doc. No. 55, 35th Cong. 1st sess., Serial No. 955.

1858: House Ex. Doc. No. 32, 35th Cong. 2d sess., Serial No. 1004.

1859: House Ex. Doc. No. 27, 36th Cong. 1st sess., Serial No. 1048.

1860:: House Ex. Doc. No. 35, 36th Cong. 2d sess., Serial No. 1097.

ANNUAL WAR DEPARTMENT CONTRACTS

1818: *American State Papers, Military Affairs,* vol. 1, pp. 851–55.

1819: House Doc. No. 47, 16th Cong. 1st sess., Serial No. 33.

1821–23: *American State Papers, Military Affairs,* vol. 2, pp. 599–609.

1823: House Doc. No. 59, 18th Cong. 1st sess., Serial No. 96.

1828: House Doc. No. 105, 20th Cong. 2d sess., Serial No. 186.

1829: House Doc. No. 86, 21st Cong. 1st sess., Serial No. 197.

1830: House Doc. No. 73, 21st Cong. 2d sess., Serial No. 208.

1831: House Doc. No. 89, 22d Cong. 1st sess., Serial No. 218.

1832: House Doc. No. 118, 22d Cong. 2d sess., Serial No. 235.

1833: House Doc. No. 99, 23d Cong. 1st sess., Serial No. 256.

1834: House Doc. No. 142, 23d Cong. 2d sess., Serial No. 274.

1835: House Doc. No. 248, 24th Cong. 1st sess., Serial No. 291.

1836: House Doc. No. 99, 24th Cong. 2d sess., Serial No. 303.

1837: House Doc. No. 174, 25th Cong. 2d sess., Serial No. 327.

1838: House Doc. No. 94, 25th Cong. 3d sess., Serial No. 346.

1839: House Doc. No. 89, 26th Cong. 1st sess., Serial No. 365.

1840: House Doc. No. 72, 26th Cong. 2d sess., Serial No. 383.

1841: House Doc. No. 34, 27th Cong. 2d sess., Serial No. 402.

1842: House Doc. No. 68, 27th Cong. 3d sess., Serial No. 420.

1843: House Doc. No. 42, 28th Cong. 1st sess., Serial No. 441.

1844: House Doc. No. 44, 28th Cong. 2d sess., Serial No. 464.

1845: House Doc. No. 51, 29th Cong. 1st sess., Serial No. 482.

1846: House Doc. No. 46, 29th Cong. 2d sess., Serial No. 499.

1847: House Ex. Doc. No. 29, 30th Cong. 1st sess., Serial No. 516.

1848: House Ex. Doc. No. 44, 30th Cong. 2d sess., Serial No. 541.

1849: House Ex. Doc. No. 38, 31st Cong. 1st sess., Serial No. 576.

1850: House Ex. Doc. No. 23, 31st Cong. 2d sess., Serial No. 599.

1851: Senate Ex. Doc. No. 12, 32d Cong. 1st sess., Serial No. 614.

1852: Senate Ex. Doc. No. 18, 32d Cong. 2d sess., Serial No. 660.

1853: House Ex. Doc. No. 63, 33d Cong. 1st sess., Serial No. 721.

1854: House Ex. Doc. No. 68, 33d Cong. 2d sess., Serial No. 788.

1855: House Ex. Doc. No. 17, 34th Cong. 1st sess., Serial No. 851.

1856: House Ex. Doc. No. 59, 34th Cong. 3d sess., Serial No. 900.

1857: House Ex. Doc. No. 58, 35th Cong. 1st sess., Serial No. 955.

1858: House Ex. Doc. No. 50, 35th Cong. 2d sess., Serial No. 1006.

1859: House Ex. Doc. No. 22, 36th Cong. 1st sess., Serial No. 1047.

1860: House Ex. Doc. No. 47, 36th Cong. 2d sess., Serial No. 1099.

1861: House Ex. Doc. No. 101, 37th Cong. 2d sess., Serial No. 1136.

MISCELLANEOUS ORDNANCE DOCUMENTS

House Doc. No. 44, 24th Cong. 1st sess., Serial No. 287 (Ordnance returns from armories, arsenals, posts, and troop units, 1834; also in *American State Papers, Military Affairs,* vol. 5, p. 737).

House Report No. 375, 24th Cong. 1st sess., Serial No. 294 (Documents concerning the Hall rifle, 1819–1836; also in *American State Papers, Military Affairs,* vol. 6, p. 104).

Senate Doc. Nos. 15 and 29, 25th Cong. 1st sess., Serial No. 309 (Small arms trials at West Point, 1837; also in *American State Papers, Military Affairs,* vol. 7, p. 466).

House Report No. 453, 26th Cong. 1st sess., Serial No. 371 (Documents concerning the Hall rifle, 1840).

Senate Doc. No. 14, 26th Cong. 2d sess., Serial No. 376 (Army trials of the Colt revolving carbine, 1840).

Senate Doc. No. 196, 26th Cong. 2d sess., Serial No. 378 (Navy trials of the Hall, Colt, and Nutting rifles, 1840).

Senate Doc. No. 229, 26th Cong. 2d sess., Serial No. 378 (U.S. military commission to Europe, 1840).

House Doc. No. 3, 27th Cong. 2d sess., Serial No. 401 (Ordnance returns from armories, arsenals, and depots, 1841).

House Doc. No. 194, 27th Cong. 2d sess., Serial No. 404 (U.S. military commissions to Europe, 1825–40).

House Doc. No. 207, 27th Cong. 2d sess., Serial No. 404 (Operations at Springfield Armory, 1841).

House Doc. No. 3, 27th Cong. 3d sess., Serial No. 418 (Ordnance returns from armories, arsenals, and depots, 1842).

House Report No. 53, 28th Cong. 2d sess., Serial No. 468 (Development of the percussion cap).

House Report No. 86, 28th Cong. 2d sess., Serial No. 468 (Colt tinfoil cartridges).

Senate Doc. No. 43, 29th Cong. 1st sess., Serial No. 472 (Arms taken from Texans by Philip St. George Cooke, 1843).

Senate Ex. Doc. No. 54, 30th Cong. 1st sess., Serial No. 509 (Arms manufacture and purchases, 1820–48).

Senate Misc. Doc. No. 9, 30th Cong. 2d sess., Serial No. 533 (Reports on the Jenks carbine, 1841–48).

Senate Report No. 296, 30th Cong. 2d sess., Serial No. 535 (Reports on Colt firearms, 1846–48).

Senate Report No. 257, 31st Cong. 2d sess., Serial No. 593 (Ordnance trials of, and reports on, Colt and other handguns, 1850).

Senate Ex. Doc. No. 35, 32d Cong. 1st sess., Serial No. 618 (Arms owned by the U.S., 1851).

Senate Ex. Doc. No. 65, 33d Cong. 1st sess., Serial No. 700. (Nippes and Pomeroy contracts for the Model 1840 musket).

Senate Ex. Doc. No. 75, 33d Cong. 2d sess., Serial No. 756 (Arms issued to states and territories, 1854).

Senate Ex. Doc. No. 35, 35th Cong. 2d sess., Serial No. 984 (Army trials of stocked Colt Dragoons, 1858).

Senate Ex. Doc. No. 60, 36th Cong. 1st sess., Serial No. 1037 (U.S. military commission to Europe, 1855–56).

House Report No. 85, 36th Cong. 2d sess., Serial No. 1105 (Arms issued to states and territories, 1860).

Senate Ex. Doc. No. 72, 37th Cong. 2d sess., Serial No. 1123 (Ordnance contracts and purchases, 1861–62).

House Ex. Doc. No. 67, 37th Cong. 2d sess., Serial No. 1131 (Ordnance contracts and purchases, 1861–62).

House Report No. 2, 37th Cong. 2d sess., Serial No. 1142 (John C. Fremont's Civil War arms purchases).

Senate Report No. 108, 37th Cong. 3d sess., Serial No. 1154 (John C. Fremont's Civil War arms purchases).

House Ex. Doc. No. 16, 39th Cong. 2d sess., Serial No. 1288 (Naval ordnance returns, 1866).

House Ex. Doc. No. 53, 39th Cong. 2d sess., Serial No. 1290 (Ordnance contracts, 1864–65).

House Ex. Doc. No. 99, 40th Cong. 2d sess., Serial No. 1338 (Ordnance contracts and purchases, 1861–66).

House Misc. Doc. No. 152, 40th Cong. 2d sess., Serial No. 1350 (Arms owned by the U.S., ca. 1867).

ARMS SUPPLIED TO INDIANS

American State Papers, Indian Affairs, 2 vols. Washington, D.C., 1832–34

Senate Doc. No. 512, 23d Cong. 1st sess., Serial Nos. 244, 248.

House Doc. No. 174, 25th Cong. 2d sess., Serial No. 327.

ANNUAL COMMISSIONER OF PATENTS REPORTS

A List of Patents Granted by the United States from April 10, 1790, to December 31, 1836 . . . Executed Under the Direction of the Commissioner of Patents. Washington, D.C., 1872.

1801–29: House Doc. No. 50, 21st Cong. 2d sess., Serial No. 207.

1830: House Doc. No. 49, 21st Cong. 2d sess., Serial No. 207.

1831: House Doc. No. 39, 22d Cong. 1st sess., Serial No. 217.

1832: House Doc. No. 130, 22d Cong. 2d sess., Serial No. 235.

1833: House Doc. No. 58, 23d Cong. 1st sess., Serial No. 255.

1834: House Doc. No. 55, 23d Cong. 2d sess., Serial No. 272.

1835: House Doc. No. 64, 24th Cong. 1st sess., Serial No. 288.

1836: House Doc. No. 174, 24th Cong. 2d sess., Serial No. 304.

1837: House Doc. No. 112, 25th Cong. 2d sess., Serial No. 325.

1838: House Doc. No. 80, 25th Cong. 3d sess., Serial No. 346.

1839: Senate Doc. No. 111, 26th Cong. 1st sess., Serial No. 356.

1840: Senate Doc. No. 152, 26th Cong. 2d sess., Serial No. 378.

1841: House Doc. No. 74, 27th Cong. 2d sess., Serial No. 402.

1842: House Doc. No. 109, 27th Cong. 3d sess., Serial No. 420.

1843: Senate Doc. No. 150, 28th Cong. 1st sess., Serial No. 433.

1844: Senate Doc. No. 75, 28th Cong. 2d sess., Serial No. 451.

1845: House Doc. No. 140, 29th Cong. 1st sess., Serial No. 484.

1846: House Doc. No. 52, 29th Cong. 2d sess., Serial No. 499.

1847: House Ex. Doc. No. 54, 30th Cong. 1st sess., Serial No. 519.

1848: House Ex. Doc. No. 59, 30th Cong. 2d sess., Serial No. 542.

1849: House Ex. Doc. No. 20, 31st Cong. 1st sess., Serial No. 574.

1850: House Ex. Doc. No. 32, 31st Cong. 2d sess., Serial No. 600.

1851: House Ex. Doc. No. 102, 32d Cong. 1st sess., Serial No. 645.

1852: House Ex. Doc. No. 65, 32d Cong. 2d sess., Serial No. 682.

1853: House Ex. Doc. No. 39, 33d Cong. 1st sess., Serial No. 719.

1854: House Ex. Doc. No. 59, 33d Cong. 2d sess., Serial Nos. 785–86.

1855: House Ex. Doc. No. 12, 34th Cong. 1st sess., Serial Nos. 848–49.

1856: House Ex. Doc. No. 65, 34th Cong. 3d sess., Serial Nos. 902–4.

1857: House Ex. Doc. No. 32, 35th Cong. 1st sess., Serial Nos. 951–53.

1858: House Ex. Doc. No. 105, 35th Cong. 2d sess., Serial Nos. 1009–11.

1859: Senate Ex. Doc. No. 12, 36th Cong. 1st sess., Serial Nos. 1029–30.

1860: Senate Ex. Doc. No. 7, 36th Cong. 2d sess., Serial Nos. 1083–84.

1861: House Ex. Doc. No. 53, 37th Cong. 2d sess., Serial Nos. 1131–33.

1862: House Ex. Doc. No. 52, 37th Cong. 3d sess., Serial Nos. 1166–67.

1863: House Ex. Doc. No. 60, 38th Cong. 1st sess., Serial No. 1191–92.

1864: House Ex. Doc. No. 51, 38th Cong. 2d sess., Serial Nos. 1225–26.

1865: House Ex. Doc. No. 52, 39th Cong. 1st sess., Serial Nos. 1257–59.

PERIODICALS (TO 1865)

American Artisan, 1864–65.

American Repertory of the Arts, Sciences, and Useful Manufactures, 1840.

American Turf Register and Sporting News, 1829–44.

Army and Navy Journal, 1863–65.

Atlantic Monthly, 1859.

Harper's Weekly, 1859–65.

Journal of the Royal United Service Institution, 1857–65.

Leslie's Weekly, 1860–65.

Mechanic's Magazine (New York), 1834–37.

Niles' Register, 1814–22.

Scientific American, 1845–65.

Spirit of the Times, 1832–60.

Western Journal and Civilian, 1848–54.

Western Monthly Review, 1827–30.

CITY DIRECTORIES

Denver, 1859, 1861.

Kansas City, 1859–60; 1865–66.

Leavenworth, Kan., 1859–60; 1860–61; 1862–63; 1863–64; 1865–66.

New Orleans, 1822.

New York–Philadelphia, 1832.

New York, 1838.

Placerville, Cal., 1862.

St. Joseph, Mo., 1859–60; 1860.

St. Louis, 1821; 1863; 1864.

San Francisco, 1861–65.

STATE DIRECTORIES

Illinois–Missouri, 1854–55.

Iowa, 1865.

Missouri, 1860.

NEWSPAPERS

Alton (Ill.) *Courier*, 1853.

Alton (Ill.) *Spectator*, 1837–39.

Alton (Ill.) *Telegraph*, 1836–42; 1854.

Atchison (Kan.) *Champion*, 1858–65.

Austin (Tex.) *Gazette* and *State Gazette*, 1849–57.

Boise (Idaho) *Statesman*, 1864–65.

Burlington (Iowa) *Hawk Eye*, 1839–59.

Cape Girardeau (Mo.) *Eagle*, 1848–49.

Council Bluffs (Iowa) *Bugle*, 1857–59.

Dallas *Herald*, 1855–59.

Denver *Rocky Mountain News*, 1859–65.

Fort Smith (Ark.) *Herald*, 1849–51; 1857.

Frank Leslie's Illustrated Newspaper (New York), 1861–65.

Galveston (Tex.) *News*, 1848–59.

Gold Hill (Nev.) *Morning Message*, 1864.

Gold Hill (Nev.) *News*, 1864–65.

Independence (Mo.) *Occidental Messenger*, 1854.

Independence (Mo.) *Western Missourian*, 1842.

Kansas City *Western Journal of Commerce*, 1861; 1863; 1865.

Kaskaskia (Ill.) *Western Intelligencer* and *Illinois Intelligencer*, 1816–21.

Lawrence (Kan.) *Herald of Freedom*, 1855–59.

Leavenworth *Kansas Herald*, 1859.

Leavenworth *Times*, 1857–59; 1862–65.

Little Rock *Arkansas Gazette* and *Arkansas State Gazette*, 1819–23; 1826–29; 1832–40; 1842–46; 1853–62.

Memphis (Tenn.) *Appeal*, 1851–60.

Mesilla (Ariz.) *Times*, 1860.

Natchez *Mississippi Free Trader* and *Natchez Gazette*, 1845.

Nebraska City *News*, 1857–60.

New Orleans *Picayune*, 1837–61.

Olympia (Wash.) *Columbian*, 1853.

Omaha *Nebraska Republican* and *Republican*, 1859; 1864–65.

Omaha *Times*, 1857–59.

Oregon City *Spectator*, 1846–55.

Portland *Oregonian*, 1852–56; 1865.

Quincy (Ill.) *Whig*, 1839–40.

Sacramento (Cal.) *Placer Times*, 1849–50.

Sacramento *Union*, 1851–56.

St. Charles *Missourian*, 1820–21.

St. Louis *Enquirer*, 1819–24.

St. Louis *Missouri Argus*, 1835.

St. Louis *Missouri Democrat*, 1853–65.

St. Louis *Missouri Gazette*, 1812–18.

St. Louis *Missouri Republican*, 1835; 1840–41; 1849–50.

St. Louis *Missouri Sentinel*, 1852.

St. Louis *Reveille*, 1844–47.

San Antonio (Tex.) *Herald*, 1855–62.

San Diego (Cal.) *Herald*, 1855–60.

San Francisco *Alta California*, 1849–65.

San Francisco *Mining & Scientific Press*, 1860–65.

Santa Fe *Gazette*, 1856–60; 1864.

Santa Fe *New Mexican*, 1864–65.

Santa Fe *Republican*, 1847–48.

Topeka (Kan.) *Tribune*, 1859–60.

Westport (Kan.) *Border Star*, 1858–60.

SECONDARY SOURCES: BOOKS

Albaugh, William A., III, and Edward N. Simmons. *Confederate Arms*. Harrisburg, Pa., 1957.

Albaugh, William A., III, Hugh Benet, Jr., and Edward N. Simmons. *Confederate Handguns*. Philadelphia, 1963.

Atkinson, John A. *Duelling Pistols*. Harrisburg, Pa., 1966.

Baird, John D. *Hawken Rifles, The Mountain Man's Choice.* Franklin, Ind., 1968.

Bearss, Ed, and Arrell M. Gibson. *Fort Smith: Little Gibraltar on the Arkansas.* Norman, Okla., 1969.

Billon, Frederic L. *Annals of St. Louis in Its Territorial Days.* St. Louis, 1888.

Blackmore, Howard L. *Guns and Rifles of the World.* New York, 1965.

———. *Hunting Weapons.* New York, 1971.

Brinckerhoff, Sidney B., and Pierce A. Chamberlain. *Spanish Military Weapons in Colonial America, 1700–1821.* Harrisburg, Pa., 1972.

Brown, Dee Alexander. *The Galvanized Yankees.* Urbana, Ill., 1963.

Brown, Stuart E., Jr. *The Guns of Harper's Ferry.* Berryville, Va., 1968.

Browning, John, and Curt Gentry. *John M. Browning: American Gunmaker.* Garden City, N.Y., 1964.

Carter, Kate B. *Utah and the Pony Express.* Salt Lake City, 1960.

Chittenden, Hiram Martin. *History of the American Fur Trade of the Far West.* 1902. Reprint ed., Stanford, Cal., 1954.

Dellenbaugh, Frederick S. *Fremont and '49.* New York, 1914.

DeVoto, Bernard. *Across the Wide Missouri.* Boston, 1947.

Dillin, Capt. John G. W. *The Kentucky Rifle.* 1924. Reprint ed., York, Pa., 1959.

Dunlap, Jack. *American, British, and Continental Pepperbox Firearms.* Palo Alto, Cal., 1967.

Edwards, William B. *Civil War Guns.* Harrisburg, Pa., 1962.

———. *The Story of Colt's Revolver.* Harrisburg, Pa., 1953.

Ewers, John Canfield. *The Horse in Blackfoot Indian Culture.* Washington, D.C., 1955.

Flayderman, Norm. *Flayderman's Guide to Antique American Firearms.* 2nd ed. Northfield, Ill., 1980.

Foreman, Grant. *The Five Civilized Tribes.* Norman, Okla., 1934.

———. *Marcy and the Gold Seekers . . .* Norman, Okla., 1939.

Fuller, Claud E. *The Breech-Loader in the Service, 1816–1917.* 1933. Reprint ed., New Milford, Conn., 1965.

Fuller, Claud E. and Richard D. Steuart. *Firearms of the Confederacy.* Huntington, W.Va., 1944.

Gardner, Col. Robert E. *Small Arms Makers.* New York, 1963.

George, John Nigel. *English Guns and Rifles.* Plantersville, S.C., 1947.

———. *English Pistols and Revolvers.* London, 1961.

Gluckman, Col. Arcadi. *Identifying Old U.S. Muskets, Rifles, and Carbines.* Rev. ed., Harrisburg, Pa., 1965.

———. *United States Martial Pistols and Revolvers.* Buffalo, N.Y., 1944.

Grant, James J. *Single Shot Rifles.* New York, 1947.

———. *More Single Shot Rifles.* New York, 1959.

Grinnell, George Bird. *The Fighting Cheyennes.* Norman, Okla., 1956.

———. *Two Great Scouts and the Pawnee Battalion.* Cleveland, Oh., 1928.

de Haas, Frank. *Single Shot Rifles and Actions.* Chicago, 1969.

Hannon, Jessie Gould. *The Boston-Newton Company Venture. . . .* Lincoln, Neb., 1969.

Hanson, Charles E., Jr. *The Hawken Rifle: Its Place in History.* Chadron, Neb., 1979.

———. *The Plains Rifle.* Harrisburg, Pa., 1960.

———. *The Northwest Gun.* Lincoln, Neb., 1955.

Hanson, James Austin, and Kathryn J. Wilson. *The Mountain Man's Sketch Book.* Canyon, Tex., 1976.

Hardin, Albert N., Jr. *The American Bayonet.* Philadelphia, 1964.

Hartzler, Daniel E. *Arms Makers of Maryland.* York, Pa., 1977.

Haven, Charles T., and Frank A. Belden. *The History of the Colt Revolver.* New York, 1940.

Hebard, Grace Raymond, and E. A. Brininstool. *The Bozeman Trail.* Cleveland, Oh., 1922.

Held, Robert. *The Age of Firearms.* New York, 1957.

Hicks, Maj. James E. *U.S. Military Firearms, 1776–1956.* 1940. Reprint ed., La Canada, Cal., 1962.

Houck, Louis. *The History of Missouri.* Chicago, 1908.

Huntington, R. T. *Hall's Breechloaders.* Edited by Nancy Bagby. York, Pa., 1972.

Hyde, George E. *The Pawnee Indians.* Denver, 1951.

———. *Red Cloud's Folk.* Norman, Okla., 1937.

Kauffman, Henry J. *The Pennsylvania-Kentucky Rifle.* Harrisburg, Pa., 1960.

Jacobs, James Ripley. *The Beginning of the U.S. Army, 1783–1812.* Princeton, N.J., 1947.

Jinks, Roy G., and Robert J. Neal. *Smith & Wesson, 1857–1945.* Rev. ed., New York, 1975.

Karr, Charles Lee, Jr., and Caroll Robbins Karr. *Remington Handguns.* 2nd ed., Harrisburg Pa., 1951.

Kindig, Joe, Jr. *Thoughts on the Kentucky Rifle in Its Golden Age.* York, Pa., 1960.

Kivett, Marvin J. *Fort Atkinson on the Council Bluffs.* Lincoln, Neb., 1972.

Koury, Michael J. *Arms for Texas.* Ft. Collins, Co., 1973.

Langford, Nathaniel Pitt. *Vigilante Days and Ways.* Chicago, 1912.

Lavender, David. *Bent's Fort.* New York, 1954.

Lewis, Col. Berkeley R. *Notes on Cavalry Weapons of the American Civil War.* Washington, D.C., 1961.

———. *Small Arms and Ammunition in the United States Service.* Washington, D.C., 1956.

Logan, Herschel C. *Cartridges.* Harrisburg, Pa., 1959.

———. *The Pictorial History of the Underhammer Gun.* New York, 1960.

Lustyik, Andrew F. *Civil War Carbines.* Aldeo, Ill., 1962.

McDermott, John Francis. *Tixier's Travels on the Osage Prairies.* Norman, Okla., 1940.

Margo, Elizabeth. *Taming the Forty-Niner.* New York, 1955.

Moody, Ralph. *Stagecoach West.* New York, 1967.

Moore, Jackson W., Jr. *Bent's Old Fort—An Archeological Study.* Boulder, Co., 1973.

Morgan, Dale L. *Jedediah Smith and the Opening of the West.* New York, 1953.

———. *The West of William H. Ashley.* Denver, 1964.

Mouillesseaux, Harold R. *Ethan Allen, Gunmaker: His Partners, Patents, and Firearms.* Ottawa, 1973.

Mumey, Nolie. *Bloody Trails Along the Rio Grande.* Denver, 1958.

———. *The Life of Jim Baker.* Denver, 1931.

Nance, Joseph Milton. *After San Jacinto: The Texas-Mexican Frontier, 1836–1841.* Austin, Tex., 1963.

———. *Attack and Counterattack.* Austin, 1964.

Neal, W. Keith. *Collecting Duelling Pistols.* London and Ontario, 1973.

Neal, W. Keith, and D. H. L. Back. *The Mantons: Gunmakers.* New York, 1966.

Nutter, Waldo E. *Manhattan Firearms.* Harrisburg, Pa., 1958.

Olmsted, R. R. *Scenes of Wonder and Curiosity from Hutchings' California Magazine.* Berkeley, Cal., 1962.

Parsons, John E. *The First Winchester.* New York, 1955.

———. *Henry Deringer's Pocket Pistol.* New York, 1952.

———. *Smith & Wesson Revolvers.* New York, 1957.

Peterson, Harold L. *Arms and Armor in Colonial America, 1526–1783.* Harrisburg, Pa., 1956.

Prucha, Francis Paul. *The Sword of the Republic.* New York, 1969.

Reilly, Robert M. *United States Military Small Arms, 1816–1865.* Baton Rouge, La., 1970.

Remington, Frederic. *Frederic Remington's Own West.* New York, 1960.

Roberts, Ned H. *The Muzzle Loading Cap Lock Rifle.* 1944. Reprint ed., Harrisburg, Pa., 1958.

Rogers, Maj. Fred B. *Soldiers of the Overland.* San Francisco, 1938.

Rosebush, Waldo E. *Frontier Steel.* Appleton, Wis., 1958.

Russell, Carl P. *Firearms, Traps, and Tools of the Mountain Men.* New York, 1967.

———. *Guns on the Early Frontiers.* Berkeley and Los Angeles, 1957.

Rywell, Martin. *The Gun That Shaped American Destiny.* Harriman, Tenn., 1957.

Sabin, Edwin L. *Kit Carson Days.* Chicago, 1914.

Sellers, Frank M. *Sharps Firearms.* N. Hollywood, Cal., 1978.

———. *The William M. Locke Collection.* East Point, Ga., 1973.

Sellers, Frank M., and Samuel E. Smith. *American Percussion Revolvers.* Ottawa, 1971.

Serven, James E. *Colt Firearms From 1836.* Harrisburg, Pa., 1979.

———, ed. *The Collecting of Guns.* New York, 1964.

Settle, Raymond W., and Mary Lund. *Saddles and Spurs: The Pony Express Saga.* Harrisburg, Pa., 1953.

Shelton, Lawrence P. *California Gunsmiths, 1846–1900.* Fair Oaks, Cal., 1977.

Sutherland, R. Q., and R. L. Wilson. *The Book of Colt Firearms.* Kansas City, 1971.

Swift, Col. Eben. *The Pistol, the Mellay, and the Fight at Devil's River.* Leavenworth, Kan., 1914.

Taylerson, A. W. F., R. A. N. Andrews, and J. Frith. *The Revolver, 1818–1865.* New York, 1968.

Thomas, H. H. *The Story of Allen & Wheelock Firearms.* Cincinnati, Oh., 1965.

Todd, Frederick P., et al. *American Military Equipage, 1851–1872.* New York, 1980.

Utley, Robert M. *Frontiersmen in Blue.* New York, 1967.

Vaughn, J. W. *The Battle of Platte Bridge.* Norman, Okla., 1963.

Westerners' Brand Book. Denver Posse, 1946–70.

Williams, Mrs. Ellen. *History of the Second Colorados.* New York, 1885.

Wilson, L. R. *The Colt Heritage.* New York, n.d.

Winant, Lewis. *Early Percussion Firearms.* New York, 1959.

———. *Firearms Curiosa.* New York, 1955.

Young, Otis E. *The First Military Escort on the Santa Fe Trail, 1829.* Glendale, Cal., 1952.

———. *The West of Philip St. George Cooke.* Glendale, Cal., 1955.

PERIODICALS (CURRENT AND RECENT HISTORICAL)

California Historical Society Quarterly
Colorado Magazine
Kansas Historical Collections
Kansas Historical Quarterly
Mississippi Valley Historical Review
Missouri Historical Review
Missouri Historical Society Collections
Montana Historical Society Contributions
Museum of the Fur Trade Quarterly
Nebraska History
New Mexico Historical Review
New York Historical Society Quarterly
North Dakota Historical Quarterly
Oregon Historical Quarterly
South Dakota Historical Collections
Southwestern Historical Quarterly
The Trail
Washington Historical Quarterly

PERIODICALS (CURRENT AND RECENT FIREARMS)

The American Rifleman
The Arms Gazette
The Gun Collector
The Gun Report
Men-At-Arms
The Texas Gun Collector

INDEX